The Author

Thomas D. Burleigh first became interested in preparing a reliable book on the birds of Georgia when, as professor of forestry in the University of Georgia at Athens, he had difficulty in finding out just what was known about the birds in the state. For the past twenty-eight years he has been a biologist with the U. S. Fish and Wildlife Service, having turned his avocation into his vocation. Currently stationed at Moscow, Idaho, he has to date published more than 150 articles on birds and is co-author (with Harold S. Peters) of *The Birds of Newfoundland* (Cambridge, Mass., 1951).

The Artist

George Miksch Sutton, whose thirty-five magnificent water-color paintings complement the author's excellent and thorough text, is one of America's foremost ornithologists and bird artists. He is the author of five books, including *Mexican Birds* (Norman, 1951), and is now professor of zoology in the University of Oklahoma and curator of birds in the University Museum.

Georgia Birds

Georgia Birds

BY THOMAS D. BURLEIGH

with Reproductions of Original Paintings

BY GEORGE MIKSCH SUTTON

Norman : University of Oklahoma Press

Library of Congress Catalog Card Number 58–6850
Copyright 1958 by the University of Oklahoma Press
Publishing Division of the University
Composed and printed at Norman, Oklahoma, U.S.A.
by the University of Oklahoma Press
First Edition

GEORGIA BIRDS

HAS BEEN PUBLISHED

IN CO-OPERATION WITH

THE U.S. DEPARTMENT OF THE INTERIOR,

FISH AND WILDLIFE SERVICE,

WASHINGTON, D.C.,

THE GEORGIA ORNITHOLOGICAL SOCIETY,

AND THE GARDEN CLUB OF GEORGIA, INC.

TO HERBERT L. STODDARD, SR.

WITHOUT WHOSE UNFAILING ENCOURAGEMENT

AND SUPPORT

THIS BOOK WOULD

NEVER HAVE BECOME A REALITY

PREFACE

It was in September, 1920, that I first went to Georgia to join the Division of Forestry (now the School of Forestry) of the College of Agriculture of the University of Georgia at Athens. Interested in birds since childhood, and never having been in any of the Southern states before, I took advantage of the leisure that Sundays offered to explore the near-by fields and woods for the new birds I was sure that I would see. I had preconceived ideas of what the bird life of Georgia would be like, but as the weeks went by, it became apparent that those ideas would have to be discarded. For example, instead of towhees with white eyes, there were birds with red eyes; Mourning Doves were common, but the Ground Dove was conspicuous by its absence; and careful scrutiny of the woodpeckers failed to reveal a single Red-cockaded one. Available literature was not very helpful in answering the question of just where one would look for such unfamiliar species, and it was this temporary disillusionment which eventually resulted in the conviction that a thorough and reliable book on the bird life of Georgia was needed.

The possibility of writing such a book was not given serious thought at the time, and a few years later was definitely abandoned when the late Arthur H. Howell, then Senior Biologist of the United States Biological Survey, came to Georgia for preliminary field work in connection with a proposed report on the birds of the state. The Georgia Game and Fish Commission had expressed an interest in such a publication, but a conflict in ideas about the nature of the work made it impracticable for Howell to devote further time or thought to the project. As a result, it was officially dropped, but Mr. Howell and I agreed, as opportunity offered, to compile all available distributional records and a bibliography of all ornithological writings that pertained to the state, with the thought that the time might come when a Georgia bird book would be a reality. This was the situation up to the time of Mr. Howell's death in 1940.

In 1930, I left Georgia, and until 1945 my contacts with the state were brief. In June of that year, Charles N. Elliott, then director of the Georgia Department of Natural Resources, entered into an arrangement with the United States Fish and Wildlife Service to have the project on the survey of the birds of Georgia restored, with the understanding that the results should be published as a state bird book. The outcome of this agreement was my transfer to Georgia from Louisiana, where I had been working on another assignment for the Fish and Wildlife Service. And so once again I found myself at work on the birds of Georgia. Two years were required to complete essential field work in Georgia and several more to compile the data and write the manuscript. Such, in brief, is the history of the present volume dealing with the interesting and varied bird life of the state of Georgia. Twenty-five years is a long time to wait for a personal ambition to be realized, but in spite of the many ups and downs and the intervals when there seemed little probability that the book would ever be written, it finally has been completed. May it serve the purpose for which it is intended, and show not only the people of Georgia, but those of the country as a whole, the wealth of bird life the state possesses.

Without a thorough knowledge of the state, the task of preparing such a book as this would have been not only difficult but far from satisfactory. Fortunately, I have not been handicapped in this respect. During my ten years' residence at Athens, from 1920 to 1930, I was frequently in the field in various parts of the state and kept detailed notes of the birds I saw. From 1930 until 1945 a year rarely went by that did not see at least a little additional field work carried on in Georgia, and from 1945 until October, 1947, those parts of the state that were least known were carefully studied. Field notes kept during this period have been utilized to good advantage, and have frequently been a source of information which would otherwise have been lacking. The manuscript of *Georgia Birds* was finished in 1956, and the information included may be considered complete up to that time. Since then only minor changes have been possible.

Arthur H. Howell's contribution to the distributional records and to the bibliography were not only extremely important but essential to the writing of the book, for he was in a position to extract from the unsurpassed distributional files of the Fish and Wildlife Service (originally the Biological Survey) in Washington, D. C., all information pertinent to the bird life of Georgia. As opportunity offered, I worked with him on this exacting task, and it is doubtful that many records of value were overlooked. The notes of W. W. Worthington, W. J. Hoxie, and A. H. Helme, later often quoted, are largely from this source.

There has been an interest in Georgia's birds from early colonial days, but this interest has fluctuated, and only since the turn of the century has it developed to the point where consistent and careful studies have been made. The publication of a quarterly journal, *The Oriole,* beginning in January, 1936, and the adoption of that periodical as the organ of the Georgia Ornithological Society, organized in December of the same year, have resulted in the accumulation of a large store of published knowledge concerning the bird life of the state, and this has been freely drawn upon in the writing of this book. Much additional information has been obtained from the steadily growing number of competent amateur ornithologists in Georgia, information that might well have been published, but for one reason or another has remained in temporary obscurity.

Finally, all current periodicals dealing with ornithology have been scrutinized, and many references in them to the birds of Georgia utilized in this work.

Statements of ranges as well as both common and scientific names have been to a large extent taken from the fourth edition of the American Ornithologists' Union's *Check-List of North American Birds,* published in 1931, and from the supplements subsequently published in *The Auk.* Modifications have been made only in those cases where additional knowledge of the range or geographical variation of a species has been ascertained through publications or personal investigations.

The primary objective of Georgia Birds has been to make available all that is known directly about the bird life of Georgia. The account of each species was written to accord with its actual status in the state, and no attempt has been made to discuss any phase of its activities not directly applicable to its occurrence in the state. There is no description of the breeding habits of those species that do not nest in Georgia. There are good reference books available to readers desiring further information about the life history of any bird. It has seemed unnecessary to give detailed descriptions of the species included in this book, as various reliable and well-written guides are already available for this purpose. Hence, only outstanding field characteristics, those most readily apparent to the observer, are mentioned.

The treatment of the distributional records follows a definite pattern that should make it easy to refer to these data regardless of degree of familiarity with the state. In the case of migration records, spring dates are cited from the Florida line to the mountains, whereas fall records are in the reverse of that order. This seemed the obvious method to use, and in many instances it shows clearly the time interval involved in the seasonal movement of birds across the state. Years in parentheses indicate that more than one year is involved, and that the date given is a summarization of two or more records. If no parentheses are used, only a single record is available.

Attempts to identify subspecies have frequently been the source of much confusion to bird students, and much thought was given to the advisability of including subspecies here. There is little question that information pertaining to the subspecies or races occurring in the state is indispensable for a thorough knowledge of distribution and migration, and consequently could not be omitted. Only the active field collector, however, is in a position to supply such information, for almost without exception specimens are necessary for satisfactory identification. It is only the more advanced student of ornithology who is concerned with this phase of bird study. His efforts produce information as to where Georgia's transients and winter residents spend the summer months and in what relative numbers they appear each year. He is also able to tell us what effect Georgia's environmental factors have on those species influenced by changes in climate or altitude. Such studies have resulted in the description of local races, as Wayne's Clapper Rail, Worthington's Marsh Wren, and the Athens Yellowthroat. Knowledge of subspecies is important in a detailed account of the bird life of the state, but to persons afield with binoculars and notebook it is suggested that speculation concerning subspecies be largely avoided. Without the actual specimen in hand, a Yellowthroat can only be a Yellowthroat, and it is not only impracticable but usually impossible to identify it as a Maryland Yellowthroat or an Athens Yellowthroat. In the case of those species with only one subspecies breeding within the state, the Mississippi Song Sparrow and the Carolina Junco for instance, it would seem safe to use the subspecific designation during the breeding season, but even that practice involving sight records, serves no useful purpose and should be discouraged. In general, it seems best for the field observer to use only the species name in referring to the birds he sees.

It is indeed a happy circumstance that George Miksch Sutton enthusiastically agreed to paint the most characteristic and distinctive birds found in Georgia for the color plates in this volume. Mr. Sutton is one of the outstanding bird artists of the country, and the excellence of the plates shows clearly that his reputation is well deserved. While he was painting the birds of Georgia, he spent the spring months of 1952 on Sherwood Plantation, near Thomasville, hence his portraits are of birds native to the state. Mr. Sutton and I have been close friends for many years, and as far back as 1921 it was suggested that he be the artist if circumstances ever made it possible to publish a book on the birds of Georgia. The plans made then have now been carried out, and it is with considerable satisfaction that the author sees realized another ambition of many years' standing.

Thomas D. Burleigh

Moscow, Idaho
January, 1958

ACKNOWLEDGMENTS

First, I wish to acknowledge my indebtedness to Charles N. Elliott, who, as director of the Georgia Department of Natural Resources in 1945, made the preparation of this book possible. Without his interest, manifest over a period of years, and his efforts in my behalf, it is doubtful that this book would yet be written.

Special thanks are also due Herbert L. Stoddard, Sr., for his generous support and unfailing co-operation throughout the preparation of the manuscript. Difficulties that developed from time to time prompted immediate action on his part, and I gratefully acknowledge my indebtedness to a man who, with no direct interests of his own involved, never failed to respond when his services were needed. It is doubtful that this book could have been made available to those interested in the ornithology of Georgia without his continued encouragement and support.

To my colleagues, John W. Aldrich and Allen J. Duvall of the U. S. Fish and Wildlife Service, thanks are due for their counsel and advice in the preparation of the manuscript, and for their help in solving difficult problems involving the identification of recently described races.

Without the full co-operation of the many competent field observers in Georgia and the use of their field notes, which in many instances had not been published, much information concerning the bird life of the state would not have been available. The following have contributed materially in making the book as complete as possible, and sincere thanks are given them for their assistance: J. Fred Denton, George A. Dorsey, Walter J. Erichsen, William W. Griffin, Mrs. R. F. Hamilton, Frederick V. Hebard, Milton Hopkins, Jr., David W. Johnston, Robert A. Norris, Eugene P. Odum, Gilbert R. Rossignol, and Ivan R. Tomkins. In addition to supplying field notes of value, Robert A. Norris was especially helpful in pointing out obscure references that could easily have been overlooked, and in contributing the account of the physiographic regions of Georgia. William W. Griffin, with a wide knowledge of Georgia ornithology, willingly accepted the responsibility of writing the ornithological history of the state. To both of these contributors I feel deeply indebted. The entire manuscript has been edited by W. L. McAtee.

Thomas D. Burleigh

TO THE SUBSCRIBERS

Through the interest and generosity of a number of individuals and organizations, the publication of this book has been made possible and with it the establishment of the Herbert L. Stoddard, Sr., and George Miksch Sutton Ornithological Scholarships at the University of Georgia and the University of Oklahoma, respectively. The latter have been founded in recognition of the work that Herbert L. Stoddard, Sr., has done for game conservation in the Southeastern states and of George M. Sutton's very special contribution to ornithology through his superb paintings of birds, particularly those in this book. Proceeds from the sale of *Georgia Birds,* after costs, will be added to these scholarship funds. It is the earnest hope of the donors that the scholarships will stimulate interest in and study of ornithology and conservation in both Georgia and Oklahoma. A list of subscribers will be found on pages 733–34.

ABOUT THE COLOR PLATES

Tom Burleigh and I began planning my illustrations for this book almost forty years ago. I was on the staff of the Carnegie Museum in those days. Tom's father and mother lived in Pittsburgh, and our friendship began when Tom, home on a vacation visit, suggested that he and I hike through country he had known as a boy. He had been living in the South. An outdoorsman by nature as well as by profession, he had been teaching forestry in the University of Georgia. Wherever he had gone in this "new country," he had gone right on with his study of birds. Day after day he had recorded notes, collected specimens, and worked out facts about bird distribution in the southeastern United States. The mass of information he had collected was impressive. I was not greatly surprised when he informed me that he was planning to write a book on Georgia birds.

From the very first, Tom seemed to feel that this book of his would not be complete without some illustrations by me. Halftone reproductions of a few of my bird drawings had appeared in *The Oölogist*, a little magazine published by R. Magoon Barnes at Lacon, Illinois. Tom seemed to like especially well my Carolina Wren and Blue-gray Gnatcatcher, species he and I had been seeing much of—he in Georgia, I in West Virginia. I was busy at the moment with my first big illustrating job, the plates for Harold H. Bailey's *Birds of Florida*. These were to be reproduced in full color. I sensed from what Tom said—from the tone of his voice more than from his actual words—that he thought Georgia's birdlife just as wonderful, just as worthy of portrayal, as Florida's.

I told Tom that I wanted to make the drawings for him. Even as I spoke, however, I sensed that I would want to make the drawings on the ground—in Georgia. While painting the Florida plates, I had been sorely handicapped by my ignorance of Florida. I had seen palmettos, but I had never sketched them from life. I had been in swamps, but never in cypress swamps. I had heard of the wonderful green of the Florida Keys water and of the mangroves which grew in it, but, not having experienced either, I had painted them as if copying a picture post card. I had felt especially bad when obliged to use as models stuffed skins of birds I had never seen alive. Yes, I would make the Georgia bird drawings some day, but I would do the job authoritatively.

As the years passed, the friendship between Tom and me became stronger and a practical note came into our correspondence. Painting a series of plates would take time—much time. If the plates were to show all of Georgia's birds, how could we be sure that, by the time the manuscript was ready for press, the plates would show every species discussed? An active field-man myself, I had seen state lists and county lists change radically almost overnight as species were dropped or added. "When are you going to start those paintings?" was part of almost every letter I received from Tom. "How can we be sure which species are to be shown?" was a customary reply.

World War II came. Both Tom and I were in uniform. There was little time for correspondence, but neither the friendship nor the plan died. I remember thinking in those days of confusion and distress: "If ever I have the chance to make those pictures, I'll make them the best, the very best, I'm capable of. When I get at them, I'll have learned what to do and what not to do in making bird pictures. They'll be pictures no one will need be ashamed of." I was discharged from the Air Force in the fall of 1945 and promptly came down with a fever.

During the long illness I came to a full understanding with myself as to what the pictures would be. They would be ecological in nature—each bird in its habitat. They would, in a very real sense, be Georgia—Georgia trees, Georgia flowers, the colors of Georgia, the atmosphere of Georgia. Birds would be central, dominant figures, of course; but no bird would dominate at the expense of the beauty or rightness of its habitat. No plate would be a "composite"—a hodge-podge of sparrows or of warblers thrown together to save engraving costs or to help people identify the several species. There were field guides and composite plates galore, too many of them.

Tom didn't approve at first of my idea of doing only a few of Georgia's birds, one species to a plate. He wanted his book to make clear that Georgia was a wonderful place for birds. He wanted the color plates to advertise, in a dignified way, the wealth and variety of the state's birdlife. I told Tom frankly that a series of composite plates by me was foredoomed to failure. I had no interest in doing such a series. If the plates were to represent me fairly, the painting of the originals would have to rouse my deepest interest.

By this time my subconscious must have been at work, for suddenly I found myself thinking hard about certain of the drawings, especially that of the Red-cockaded Woodpecker. Here was a species which long had interested me. During the war, while based at Orlando, Florida, I had found a nest only a few feet from the ground and I had watched the parent birds eagerly. Would my Georgia painting show only the adult bird and a bit of its pineland home, or might I show the nest and a young bird, too?

The instant I perceived that doing these drawings right would necessitate working with living wild models, I thought of Herbert L. Stoddard, Sr., and his wonderful Sherwood Plantation near Thomasville, Georgia. In my correspondence with Herb I had learned long since that Red-cockaded and Pileated Woodpeckers lived on Sherwood, not to mention the Chuck-will's-widows, Bob-whites, and Wild Turkeys. Back in 1935, when I had first visited Sherwood, I had made turkey sketches on which I had based a cover-painting for a magazine called *The Sportsman*. The thought of making a Bob-white painting at Sherwood, a spot known the world over because of the Bob-white investigation Herb Stoddard had completed there, thrilled me through. Sherwood would be my studio—if Herb would have me. Sherwood, not some room in Herb's house, not some room in Thomasville, thirteen miles away, but the pines and ponds and thickets of the plantation itself.

Herb and Mrs. Stoddard could not have been more cordial had I been the Duke and Duchess of Windsor or the Nizam of Hyderabad. Sherwood was mine. The room at the quiet end of the long, long house was ready for me. The Komareks, who lived at Birdsong, the next plantation to the east, were excited over the possibility that a bird artist might be working in the neighborhood. Indeed, long before I set out for Georgia, I was convinced that both I and what I wanted to do were of considerable significance. A feeling of this sort can be important.

Spring and I arrived arm in arm. The yellow jessamine buds were opening. The swamp maples were decked with bright red seed-wings. Carolina Wrens and Cardinals were singing ebulliently. I was told where, early in the morning, I might hear a turkey gobbling. I was driven all over the place—shown the several ponds, the tung orchards, the open patches in which chufa nuts had been planted for the turkeys, the smilax thickets, some of which were ready for burning off when wind and weather were just right. I was shown gigantic magnolia trees, tall spruce pines, a species new to me, huge longleaf and loblolly pines, shortleaf pines, tulip poplars, sweet gums, cypresses, bays, maples, live oaks. Along the brooks a low-growing buckeye was common. I foresaw that I would be wanting to paint the red flowers when they opened.

Soon I was part of all this. I spent a day or so wandering about—not like a lost soul, but like one who finds one's soul agreeable because everything within seeing, hearing, and feeling distance is agreeable. Herb and I breakfasted early. Mrs. Stoddard's insistence that she fry bacon and scramble eggs for us morning after morning touched me deeply. I shall never forget her flinging of eggshells from the stove to the sink—a field goal each time! And her yarns about the characters of the countryside were so funny that I could hardly eat for laughing. My boon field companion was Rip, a blooded setter who liked me because I liked to take walks. Never did I set out in those early days without Rip at my heels or in front of me quartering the thicket. Once my work was under way, I always had my equipment with me—paints, brushes, water-jar, pencils, erasers, drawing board, paper, an old rug. Mrs. Stoddard had furnished me with a shopper's bag for carrying most of this, and Betty Komarek had given me a nice red cushion on which to sit.

The April mornings were wonderful. Sometimes the early air was so cool that my fingers were stiff, but along toward eight o'clock things warmed up, and pencils, erasers, brushes, and paints flew. I started out on a bird which caught my fancy right off—a white-eyed form of towhee. After studying the bird a while, I decided that jessamine was part of its normal habitat, so I began the picture with a detailed study of some jessamine flowers and buds. While I was at work, a pair of Brown-headed Nuthatches attracted my attention and I glanced about for a likely pine branch on which to depict them. Carolina Wrens and Ground Doves lived near my rug in the brush, and I noticed how pretty were the wrens as they fed about an old pine log, and the doves as they walked with bobbing heads among the dewberry vines and sapling water oaks. By the end of the second week several paintings were under way. I worked at one for an hour or so after breakfast, at another for the rest of the morning, at a third early in the afternoon, at a fourth with what was left of the day. In this way I made certain that the light fell on my subject matter in about the same way during each painting session.

If the paintings mark any sort of step forward (and I sincerely hope they do), let it be borne in mind that I worked under virtually ideal conditions. I was happy because I knew I was at something worth while. I had fine companionship every day. Leon Neel and his wife Julie (Julie laughed gaily when I called her my "dearest friend and severest critic") were always ready to jump in and help, whatever my problem. Ed Komarek gave me the run of Birdsong Plantation and showed me a flock of Wild Turkeys whose burnished elegance I shall never forget. Betty, Ed's wife, served coffee to all of us at ten o'clock Sunday mornings—and to me whenever I stopped by. She was especially helpful in showing me a Summer Tanager's nest and in obtaining for me a fine Yellow-billed Cuckoo. Without her the Wood Duck painting might never have been made, for she it was who saw the duck leaving its nest in the big post oak. She it was, too, who straightened out the many plant names for me. She occasionally brought the children, Eddie and Betsy, to watch me at work, and the whispered comments were so full of respect as to be almost inaudible. "Sonny" Stoddard, Herb's son, brought me a Chuck-will's-widow he had found dead on a road. The Mason children came over from Susina Plantation with a White-eyed Vireo's nest they had found. Willie Lurry, a Negro employee at Sherwood, chopped a great pine down for me so that I could paint a young Red-cockaded Woodpecker directly from life. Oh, they were wonderful days, those spring and summer days of 1952!

Best of all, of course, was Herb Stoddard himself. In Herb I had the perfect mentor, the perfect critic, for his whole life had been devoted to birds, he knew every foot of Sherwood well, and he seemed to like nothing better than talking over ideas, problems, and plans. Each evening he and I had a wonderful bird-skinning session or talked about the day's work. I gloried in his knowledge of conservation, especially in his knowledge of quail and turkey management and of what he called "control burning," for I knew that his knowledge was born of experience, of hard work, of trial and error, of trial and success. Before my painting work was over, he had taken me to many parts of the state. Along the coast near Savannah he and Ivan R. Tomkins showed me Oyster-catchers, Black Skimmers, Thick-billed Plovers, and Seaside Sparrows.

Each picture of the thirty-five reproduced here was something of a project. In the legends I have supplied for them I have told a little about how each came into being.

George Miksch Sutton

Norman, Oklahoma
January 21, 1958

CONTENTS

THE PAINTINGS

THE PHOTOGRAPHS

TABLES

FIGURES

DISTRIBUTION MAPS

Georgia Birds

HISTORY OF ORNITHOLOGY
IN GEORGIA

By William W. Griffin

Pre-Colonial Explorations, 1540–1733

Georgia, of the original thirteen colonies the last to be settled by the British, was actually the first to be visited by Europeans. In March, 1540, Hernando de Soto and his army of six hundred Spaniards entered the present boundaries of the state in the southwestern corner near the modern city of Thomasville. Traveling generally northeasterly, the army by May had reached the Indian village of Cutifachiqui, now generally thought to have lain in the region of Silver Bluff on the Savannah River below Augusta. Changing directions, De Soto then proceeded northwesterly to the Appalachian Mountains of Georgia and then on to the junction of two rivers where lies the present city of Rome. Here his army rested for about a month, fattening their horses and generally recuperating from the rigors of their journey through the wilderness. In July, 1540, De Soto departed from Georgia to the westward and the eventual discovery of the Mississippi River. In none of the several accounts of the journey is there more than casual reference to birds, for these intrepid Spaniards were primarily interested in gold, silver, and gems. Nevertheless, the famous unidentified Gentleman of Elvas, who wrote of the expedition in 1557, gives us the first published reference to Georgia birds. He mentions that upon the Spaniards' entry into an Indian village thought to have been somewhere in the present Laurens County, Georgia, the natives brought gifts of partridges and two turkeys. He also states that turkeys abounded in another region, which he called Chelaque, probably near the present Franklin County. In one village, seven hundred turkeys were given to the army, "and there was no scarcity of them in other localities."

Spanish influence in Georgia continued to be felt for nearly two hundred years after De Soto's march through the state. Missions were established along the coast, and it is thought that gold mines were placed in operation in the mountains of northern Georgia near the present site of Nacoochee. Yet the contribution of these people to our knowledge of birds in the state was negligible. Nor did the early French explorers of our coast

3

in the sixteenth and early seventeenth centuries take occasion to examine the bird life. Jean Ribaut, the French sea captain who sailed the coast from the St. Johns River in Florida to the Port Royal River in South Carolina in 1562, mentions having seen several varieties of birds in both Florida and South Carolina, but he fails to record his observations of them along the inland waterways of Georgia, though he lauds the country as a land of plenty.

In the late seventeenth century, the English first began to take note of the land that is now Georgia. Charleston, in present South Carolina, was founded in 1670, and generally the English considered the colony of Carolina to extend southward to the Altamaha River. What we now regard as Georgia was therefore considered by the British to be a part of Carolina, while the Spaniards claimed it as part of Florida. To the Spaniards, the section now comprising Georgia was known more particularly as "Guale"; and an Englishman, Sir Robert Montgomery, proposed to establish a settlement in the land to be called "Azilia." In Montgomery's prospectus for the projected colony, published in London in 1717, he describes the land as "the most delightful country of the universe." Of birds, the weather and scenery, he says: "The many Lakes, and pretty Rivulets throughout the Province, breed a Multitude of Geese, and other Water Fowl; The Air is found so temperate and the seasons of the Year so very regular, that there is no Excess of Heat or Cold, nor any sudden Alterations in the Weather; the River Banks are cover'd with a strange Variety of lovely Trees, which being always green, present a thousand Landskips to the Eye, so fine, and so diversified; that the Sight is entirely charm'd with them."

Similar enthusiastic but vague statements are characteristic of the accounts of the early English pioneers and explorers. Prior to the founding of the colony of Georgia in 1733, but one person who could be classed an ornithologist had visited the region now comprising the state of Georgia. This was Mark Catesby.

In the summer of 1723, after a year in the coastal country near Charleston in Carolina, the Englishman Mark Catesby arrived in the region of the Savannah River just south of the present city of Augusta. He was primarily concerned with the collection of plants and seeds to send back to his wealthy patrons in England who were financing his exploration. Botany was at that time the most popular of the sciences and all of his patrons but one were botanists. The satisfaction of their demands for botanical specimens thus consumed most of Catesby's time. Nevertheless he developed an abiding interest in the birds, stating: ". . . as there is greater Variety of the feather'd Kind than any other Animals, (at least to be come at) and as they excel in the Beauty of their Colours, and have a nearer relation to the Plants which they feed on and frequent; I was induced chiefly (so far as I could) to compleat an Account of them, rather than to describe promiscously Insects and other Animals."

While the exact itinerary of Catesby's explorations remains unplotted, we know from his letters that he set up a base of operations along the middle Savannah River a few miles below the present city of Augusta at Fort Moore, sometimes referred to as Savannah Garrison, and near the spot De Soto had visited nearly two centuries before. From here he journeyed through the then uninhabited regions of Georgia and South Carolina with an Indian for a bearer. Each day he covered great distances by foot, made sketches, and collected specimens of plants and birds. Concerning this period Catesby later stated: "After my continuance almost three years in Carolina and the adjacent parts (which the Spaniards call Florida, particularly that province lately honoured with the name of Georgia) I went to Providence."

In 1726 he returned to England and began his monumental work, *The Natural History of Carolina, Florida and the Bahama Islands,* the first edition of which was published in two volumes between 1730 and 1748. Altogether, this work contains plates depicting 109 species of American birds, most of which had been found during the period 1722 to 1726 in South Carolina and Georgia. The paintings and the text accompanying them demonstrate a scientific attitude not previously displayed by anyone toward American birds. Upon Catesby's plates and text, Linnaeus, the founder of the present binomial system of scientific nomenclature, based many of the names of North American birds which are in use today.

After publication of the *Natural History,* Catesby was honored by election to fellowship in the Royal Society of London in April, 1733. It must have been a distinct pleasure to Mark Catesby, explorer of the Savannah River, to sponsor General James Oglethorpe, founder of the colony of Georgia and the city of Savannah, in the Royal Society. General Oglethorpe was elected to the organization in 1749, and within the year Catesby was dead.

Ornithology from Colonial Times to Mid-Nineteenth Century, 1733–1860
In 1733, the settlement at Savannah was laid out. A period followed during which Spanish designs and claims upon the land north of the St. Marys River were shattered. Immigrants settled in Georgia and great plantations were established. Yet for the next forty years no scientist visiting or residing in the colony showed more than cursory interest in ornithology. Botany still being the leading science of the day, those few persons of scientific bent who visited Georgia during this period were principally concerned with plant life. Such was the case with the eminent Philadelphian, John Bartram, who with his son, Billy, visited Augusta, Savannah, and the coastal counties in 1765.

In 1773, however, William Bartram, son of John Bartram, returned to Georgia, this time alone, and interested in birds as well as plants. Following the same trails he and his father had traveled eight years before, through the Carolinas into Georgia, up the Savannah-Augusta route which many naturalists were to follow later, and north of Augusta into the Piedmont region of Georgia, then back to Savannah and to the Altamaha River and along the coast southward into Florida, Bartram recorded his observations. Fourteen years after his return to Philadelphia, he published his famous *Travels through North and South Carolina, Georgia, East and West Florida* (1791) in which he listed 215 birds known to him in the eastern part of North America, some of which he specifically mentions as having been recorded in Georgia.

In February, 1776, shortly before the Declaration of Independence was drafted, Georgia's first resident ornithologist, the Englishman John Abbot, moved to Georgia from Virginia. After military service in the American Revolution, he settled on a plantation in Screven County near the old town of Jacksonboro between Augusta and Savannah. Here he resided until about 1806, at which time he moved to Savannah. In 1814 he returned to the plantation, but after 1820 he spent most of his time in Bulloch County. During the years preceding his death about 1840, he lived a rather solitary life, with but a single slave in attendance, on the plantation of his friend, William McElveen, in Bulloch County.

From the time of his entrance into Georgia, Abbot was interested in natural history, having possessed as a young man in England a cabinet of insects which he had collected. Actually it is as an entomologist that Abbot is most famous today, for his only published work is the handsome *Natural History of the Rarer Lepidopterous Insects,* printed in London in 1797. Nevertheless, Abbot, like Catesby and the younger Bartram, was also a careful student of the birds and an artist.

Today several separate sets of paintings of the birds of Georgia by John Abbot are in existence, some are in European collections and some in America. Probably the most important of these sets is that which now reposes in the British Museum Department of Manuscripts. This set, executed in water color between 1790 and 1809, is handsomely bound in two volumes and contains over two hundred drawings. Accompanying the drawings is text, handwritten in a most beautiful script, in which Abbot describes the habits of his birds in Georgia. Although never published, this manuscript represents the first complete work on the birds of a single state in America and, as such, is the forerunner of the modern state bird books.

Abbot corresponded with some of the leading zoologists of the times. Among the more ornithologically inclined of these were Alexander Wilson and George Ord of Philadelphia and John Latham and William Swainson of England. It has recently been disclosed that some of Abbot's specimens, deposited in 1812 in the Zoological Museum of the University of Berlin, were the types from which descriptions of the Bachman's Sparrow, Short-billed Sedge Wren, and Golden-crowned Kinglet were originally published by the German ornithologists Litchenstein and Naumann. It is quite possible that specimens or drawings by Abbot provided the basis for original descriptions of several other species or subspecies of birds, among which may be cited the Leconte's Sparrow, Swamp Sparrow, Vesper Sparrow, and Florida Barred Owl. Descriptions and names of these four forms were first made known to science through publication by John Latham. As additional knowledge of this pioneer is brought to light by such researchers as Mrs. Anna Stowell Bassett, Mrs. Elsa Allen, W. L. McAtee, and Erwin Stresemann, we find conclusive evidence that the little-known and unsung ornithologist, John Abbot of Georgia, was without equal in his time.

In the early spring of 1809, Alexander Wilson visited Savannah, Augusta, the Ogeechee and Altamaha rivers. While in Georgia he visited John Abbot and wrote to William Bartram from Savannah as follows: "I have gained a great mass of information respecting the birds that winter in the southern states, and some that never visit the middle states; and this information I have derived personally, and can therefore the more certainly depend upon it." A part, at least, of this great mass of information was published in his *American Ornithology*, which appeared in nine volumes between 1808 and 1814. In this great work, Wilson, sometimes called the "Father of American Ornithology," alludes to the occurrence in Georgia of nearly one hundred species, including the Savannah Sparrow and the Fish Crow, which he made known to science after first discovering them near Savannah.

In 1815, the distinguished botanist and ornithologist Thomas Nuttall visited Savannah and Augusta, and again in 1830 he crossed central Georgia into Alabama and returned to Savannah by way of the Altamaha River. Nuttall was the author of the first American handbook of birds, the two-volume *Manual of the Ornithology of the United States and Canada,* published from 1832 to 1834.

The celebrated John James Audubon sailed the Georgia coast, stopping at St. Simons Island on his way from Charleston to Florida in 1831. On his return trip in 1832, he stopped at Savannah, and in 1837 he crossed the state in traveling from Charleston to Montgomery. His principal contribution to Georgia ornithology was an indirect one, however, resulting from the influence upon later generations of Georgia ornithologists of his published works on American birds.

John Eatton LeConte (1739–1822) resided in New York, but was accustomed to spending his winters on his plantation, "Woodmanston," in

Liberty County, Georgia. Here on this plantation his four famous naturalist descendants, John Eatton LeConte, Jr. (1784–1860), John Lawrence LeConte (1825–83), John LeConte (1818–91), and Joseph LeConte (1823–1901), studied the bird life at one time or another in their illustrious careers. John Eatton, Jr., and his son John Lawrence LeConte, a famous entomologist, were known to visit the plantation from time to time. The brothers John and Joseph, nephews of John Eatton, Jr., were born at Woodmanston and spent their youth there. During the period from about 1840 until 1860, both brothers were intensely interested in ornithology. Opportunity for travel over the state was afforded during this time and collections were made by both. Joseph contributed his collection to the Smithsonian Institution in 1857. John contributed some, at least, of his specimens to the Philadelphia Academy of Natural Science. To John goes the honor of publication of the first list of Georgia birds. This list of 273 species was included in *Statistics of the State of Georgia* (1849) by George White, but, unfortunately, it contains few notes regarding habits and distribution. Shortly before the War between the States, John and Joseph LeConte resigned their professorships at the University of Georgia for positions at the University of South Carolina, and after the war they were instrumental in the founding and development of the University of California.

A German ornithologist, Alexander Gerhardt, resided in northwestern Georgia, in Whitfield County near the present city of Dalton, in the mid-nineteenth century. He was a careful student of the habits of birds, and today the papers on his observations in Georgia, published in 1855 and 1856 in the German ornithological journal *Naumannia*, give us a most elucidating account of the habits of forty-three species of birds a century ago.

In 1859, John Krider of Philadelphia was on the coast of Georgia. He is known to have collected the first specimen of the Gray Kingbird for the state on St. Simons Island. Also during the period 1853 through 1865, Professor S. W. Wilson, primarily an oölogist, collected on St. Simons Island and in Wayne and McIntosh counties. Certain of the nesting records of this Wilson—those of the Cowbird, Bank Swallow, and Short-billed Marsh Wren breeding in coastal Georgia—became the subject of much discussion and controversy after their publication later in the century.

It may generally be said that ornithology up through this period was still in its formative stages. Modern methods of preservation of skins had not been perfected. There were no American ornithological magazines in which findings could be easily published. The population of the state and nation was still relatively small, travel was slow, and communication difficult. In short, the conveniences of today were unknown. The remarkable thing is that men during this time could record as much information as they did about the bird life of Georgia.

Modern Investigations, 1861–1953

After the fruitful activity of the LeContes, Gerhardt, Krider, and S. W. Wilson, in the 1840's and 1850's, ornithological investigation in Georgia all but ceased for a considerable number of years.

Social and economic conditions in the state, occasioned by the War between the States and its aftermath, were certainly not conducive to leisurely investigation, and until almost the beginning of the twentieth century there were no resident ornithologists in Georgia. This hiatus was bridged to some extent by occasional expeditions into the state by naturalists of the North. While Georgia never attracted the number of collectors who began visiting Florida after the cessation of hostilities, the contributions of these transient ornithologists has been notable.

In 1877 and 1878, William Brewster of Massachusetts visited St. Marys, Georgia. He was very young at the time, but keenly interested in ornithology. He collected a few birds during his short visits, kept a journal of his activities, and published several notes on his observations. His records and collections are now deposited in the Museum of Comparative Zoology, Harvard University.

In the interests of Mr. Brewster, Willis W. Worthington, of New York, collected along the Georgia coast in 1888 and 1890. Among the interesting birds collected by him were the first Georgia specimens of the King Eider, the Ipswich Sparrow, and Krider's Red-tailed Hawk. Worthington's Marsh Wren, a subspecies of the Long-billed Marsh Wren with type locality at Sapelo Island, Georgia, was named in honor of Worthington by William Brewster.

The famous field naturalist, Vernon Bailey, spent ten days in early April, 1892, collecting on the old LeConte plantation near Riceboro in Liberty County. This was the first field work to be carried on in the state of Georgia by the U. S. Biological Survey, now known as the Fish and Wildlife Service.

Outram Bangs, in the interests of the Museum of Comparative Zoology at Harvard, worked in Camden County in 1897, collecting birds and mammals. Edgar A. Mearns, attached at the time to the Reserve Hospital Corps, School of Instruction, was at Camp MacKenzie, Augusta, from January 1 to 24, 1899, and collected several specimens of the commoner species of birds which are now in the National Museum.

Shortly before 1900, there was a marked reawakening of interest in birds in Georgia among the residents. Almost simultaneously in Savannah, Augusta, and Atlanta, groups of ornithologists became active. Troup Douglas Perry was the first of the Savannah group. In the early 1880's, Perry began the study of birds through oölogy. He amassed a considerable egg collection during his lifetime and corresponded and exchanged with the foremost oölogists of the time, among them Spencer F. Baird and Elliott Coues; Charles Bendire, a leading oölogist, even visited him in Savannah. Perry published a number of short notes in the early oölogical magazines on the nesting habits of birds about Savannah, including an account of the first nest of the Swainson's Warbler ever found. Perry was actively interested in birds until his death in 1925.

Walter J. Erichsen became interested in birds shortly after the turn of the century. He was primarily concerned with life histories of the various nesting species of Chatham and Liberty counties and compiled copious notes from his observations. Although he is the author of four valuable papers on coastal birds, much of his work remains unpublished today.

Walter John Hoxie moved to Savannah from Beaufort, South Carolina, in 1901, and retained residence there until about 1925, when he moved to St. Petersburg, Florida. During this period he spent many hours in the field with Perry, Rossignol, Erichsen, and Irving. He published many items of a popular nature in the Savannah newspapers. Among the species recorded in coastal Georgia by Hoxie were the Greater Shearwater, Great Black-backed Gull, and Saw-whet Owl.

Gilbert R. Rossignol was born in Savannah in 1885 and began the serious study of birds in 1904. This he has continued until very recently with but a few brief absences and one of about five years, when he resided in Tampa, Florida. He collected both eggs and skins in the coastal counties, principally Chatham County. Among the interesting sets of eggs collected by him are those of the Royal Tern and Bachman's Warbler; among the rarer specimens, the Man-o'-war Bird, Wilson's Petrel, and Scissor-tailed Flycatcher. His large collection of eggs is still intact and in his possession. His skins have been donated to various museums, a number of them being in the LaPrade Collection at Emory University.

Frank N. Irving, now of Washington, D. C., lived in Savannah from his birth in 1884 until about 1916. He was an associate of Rossignol and Perry in their oölogical pursuits and an enthusiastic photographer of birds, particularly water birds.

While Isaac F. Arnow did not actually reside in Savannah, he was well known to the Savannah group and on occasion visited Chatham County. Arnow spent his life at St. Marys in coastal Camden County, where he was lately postmaster. From about 1900 to 1910 he was an extremely active collector in his home county and published short notes on the more interesting of his birds. Among those species collected by Mr. Arnow during this period were the Holboell's Grebe, American Scoter, Krider's Hawk, Avocet, Bachman's and Kirtland's Warblers, American Crossbill, and the Henslow's and Lark Sparrows. Unfortunately, several of these unusual specimens can no longer be found. Some, however, were deposited in the Emory University Collection.

In Augusta, the late eminent Eugene Edmund Murphey began the study of birds as an avocation about 1890. From then until his death in 1952 he maintained an abiding interest, although in later years he was unable to be active in field work. His ornithological studies in Georgia were limited largely to the middle Savannah River valley, but there he recorded such rarities as the Red-throated Loon, Holboell's Grebe, White-fronted Goose, Sooty Tern, White-rumped Sandpiper, and Yellow-headed Blackbird. His extensive paper on the birds of this region was published in 1937, and contributed immeasurably to our knowledge of distribution in this interesting region. Dr. Murphey prepared beautiful bird skins and exchanged with many ornithologists. He amassed a private collection of considerable size, most of which is now deposited in the Charleston Museum. However, one pair of every species in the collection was given to the Augusta Museum, where they make an imposing display. In 1940, Dr. Murphey was honored by election to the Member class in the American Ornithologists' Union.

Henry Hillyer and George P. Butler were associates of Eugene Murphey in the 1890's in the Augusta area. Both collected birds during this period, but neither published anything on his ornithological findings. Hillyer collected the first specimen of the Snow Bunting for the state, and Butler added the Cabot's Tern and the Philadelphia Vireo to the state list. It was a great loss to ornithology in Georgia when Hillyer died as a result of malaria at an early age and Butler became absorbed in other interests.

M. T. Cleckley, a well-known oölogist, also collected in and about Augusta in the early years of this century, and published several short papers on Swainson's Warbler.

The Atlanta group of resident ornithologists who became interested at about this time consisted of Robert Windsor Smith, Luther R. Smith, William Mills, and William H. LaPrade, Jr. Robert Windsor Smith resided in Kirkwood, Georgia, and began the study and collections of birds about 1893. His active interest continued for about fifteen years, during which time he kept notes on his observations and collected and exchanged specimens. Among the species collected by him were the first specimens for the state of the Lincoln's Sparrow and Red-breasted Nuthatch. For many years Robert Windsor Smith sent migration reports to the U. S. Biological Survey from Kirkwood, now a part of Atlanta. He published a few notes in *The Wilson Bulletin* from 1901 through 1905, and his journals are now deposited in the library of the Georgia Ornithological Society at Athens. Many of his specimens are in the Emory University Collection.

Luther R. Smith collected about Atlanta during the same period, but not so extensively as Robert Windsor Smith. William J. Mills also did some collecting of bird skins and eggs during the early 1900's and published a few notes on his observations at East Point in 1902 and 1905.

William H. LaPrade, Jr. began the study of birds in childhood, and about 1900 he set out to form a collection of bird skins for Emory College, then located at Oxford, Georgia. For the next twenty-five years LaPrade, a Methodist minister, studiously sought out the birds in Fulton and De-Kalb counties, and in Cherokee, Union, Clayton, Newton, and other north Georgia counties. His collection of nearly 2,000 specimens, including many donated by other Georgia ornithologists previously mentioned, is now deposited in the Emory University Museum in Atlanta. A sizable collection of eggs was also donated by Rev. LaPrade to the Emory Museum, and although he published only a few short articles on birds, the collections he assembled remain as evidence of his acumen in the field. Among the interesting specimens collected by him are the Wilson's Warbler and the Cliff Swallow.

Most of these resident ornithologists whose activities began about the turn of the last century were native Georgians. However, between 1900 and 1915, four ornithologists from other parts of the country began work in Georgia which was to continue intermittently for some years. These were Arthur H. Helme, Arthur Holmes Howell, Francis Harper, and S. Prentiss Baldwin. Arthur H. Helme of New York spent the periods from January to April, 1903, and from December, 1903, to April, 1904, collecting birds in Camden County. It was during these trips that he added to the Georgia list the Kirtland's Warbler, Florida Mottled Duck, European Widgeon, Western Meadowlark, and Sprague's Pipit. His collections were originally deposited in the Brooklyn Museum in New York.

Arthur Holmes Howell made an extensive survey of breeding birds in northern Georgia, principally the Mountain Province, in the summer of 1908. His report was published in *The Auk* in 1909. Later, Howell returned to Georgia in 1927 and in 1932, collecting and plotting distribution of species in preparation for a definitive book on the birds of this state which, unfortunately, was never completed. Howell was a friend and correspondent of many resident ornithologists, among them Ivan R. Tomkins, Herbert L. Stoddard, and Thomas D. Burleigh, with whom he collaborated in collecting expeditions. One of his principal contributions was the encouragement of more serious and detailed investigation in the state.

Francis Harper, presently of Mount Holly, New Jersey, made his first trip to the Okefenokee Swamp in May, 1912, with A. H. Wright. Since that memorable experience, he has returned sixteen times over a period of forty years. He has collected approximately 300 specimens in Georgia which are now deposited in collections at the National Museum, Cornell University, and the Academy of Natural Sciences of Philadelphia. In 1934, 1936, 1939, and 1940, he worked along the trail of William Bartram through Georgia and also along the fall line from Augusta to Columbus. He has published several articles on his observations of birds during these trips, but a great many of his notes remain unpublished. During his travels he became acquainted with many Georgia ornithologists, including Hoxie, Perry, Rossignol, Arnow, Murphey, Robert Norris, and Milton Hopkins. Among the species recorded by Harper from Georgia are the White-winged Dove, Limpkin, and Roseate Spoonbill.

S. Prentiss Baldwin pioneered the development of bird-banding in America. A resident of Cleveland, Ohio, he spent a portion of each winter near Thomasville, Georgia, from 1915 until 1924. There he set up his early banding stations and worked out techniques still in use. In collaboration with Baldwin, Samuel E. Perkins, III, T. E. Musselman, Lesley R. Talbot, and John B. May also visited and worked in Thomasville. The results of their investigations are amply documented by published accounts appearing in *The Auk* and *Proceedings of the Linnaean Society of New York*.

In the 1920's the state was fortunate in having three men who were to make important ornithological contributions move within her boundaries and settle in three widely separated localities. Their coming heralded a rebirth in the study of ornithology in Georgia and kindled the flame of interest in a new generation of students.

In 1920, Thomas Dearborn Burleigh, already an experienced and traveled ornithologist, moved to Athens and into a position on the faculty of the University of Georgia. For the next ten years, he lived in Athens and used this city as a base of operations for study of the birdlife of all parts of the state. After his departure from Athens and from Georgia as a place of residence in 1930, he continued to return each year until 1945 for varying periods of from a few days to several months. During these visits his principal purpose was to spend as much time in the field as possible. In 1945, he again established residence in Georgia, this time expressly to carry on intensive field work preparatory to writing this book. For two years he covered all parts of the state, so that now he has the unique distinction of having collected and observed birds in each of the 159 counties of the state. During the last thirty years, he has collected approximately 3,000 specimens in Georgia, more than has any other living ornithologist. These skins, all skillfully prepared, are now deposited in the U. S. Fish and Wildlife Service Collection in the National Museum in Washington. Among the species added to the Georgia list by Thomas D. Burleigh are the Least Flycatcher, Alder Flycatcher, Yellow-bellied Flycatcher, Arkansas Kingbird, Nashville Warbler, and Connecticut Warbler. He is responsible for adding the Song Sparrow, Least Flycatcher, Rose-breasted Grosbeak, Winter Wren, and others to the list of breeding birds in the state. Mr. Burleigh was elected to full Membership in the American Ornithologists' Union in 1932, and, in recognition of his distinctive contribution to ornithology in Georgia and the South, he was made a Fellow of that organization in 1950. The present book bears witness to the contribution of this man, one of the ablest field ornithologists America has known.

Two years after Burleigh migrated to Athens, Ivan Rexford Tomkins moved to Georgia. Originally a resident of Pennsylvania, as was Burleigh, Tomkins settled in Savannah in 1922 and has continued to live there since that date. Soon after his arrival, he became acquainted with the Savannah ornithologists, Rossignol, Perry, and Erichsen, and began the study of birds. As an engineer engaged in dredging operations on the lower Savannah River, Ivan Tomkins was presented with unique opportunity for the study of water birds, and took full advantage of it. From 1928 to the present time he collected extensively, amassing some 750 skins from the region, many of which have been donated to the Charleston Museum. Among the species added to the Georgia list by Tomkins are the European Cormorant, Snow Goose, Glaucous Gull, Iceland Gull, Lapland Longspur, Marbled Godwit, Northern Phalarope, Bridled Tern, Noddy Tern, Purple Sandpiper, Buff-breasted Sandpiper, and Black-necked Stilt. He has contributed to ornithological publications many papers dealing not only with the unusual species recorded, but also with life-history studies of the common coastal birds. Ivan Tomkins was elected to membership in the American Ornithologists' Union in 1939.

The last of the trio to migrate to Georgia in the twenties was Herbert Lee Stoddard, Sr. From the spring of 1924 until the present, with the exception of about a year's absence in Washington, D. C., Stoddard has resided near Thomasville. For nearly twenty years, his principal studies were directed to problems of life history and management of the Bobwhite, first under the U. S. Biological Survey (1924 to 1929) and later as director of the Co-operative Quail Study Association under private auspices (1931 to 1943). The results of this intensive study of a single species have been documented in many short papers and in the monograph, *The Bobwhite Quail,* published in 1931. For his pioneering efforts in this field, Stoddard was awarded the Brewster Medal of the American Ornithologists' Union.

During all the time that Herbert Stoddard was engaged in his exhaustive studies of the Bobwhite, he also was observing other species of birds in Grady and Thomas counties, and since 1943 he has devoted a great deal of time to general ornithology. At present a manuscript on the birds of Grady County is practically completed. About 1,000 specimens have been collected by him in the Thomasville region, and approximately 15,000 birds have been banded by or in collaboration with him during his residence in southwestern Georgia. He has added to the state list the Olive-sided Flycatcher, Bullock's Oriole, Lark Bunting, and American Rough-legged Hawk. Advanced to membership (1924) and to fellowship (1926) in the American Ornithologists' Union, Herbert Stoddard has long been regarded as one of America's most distinguished ornithologists.

The 1920's saw—in addition to the entry into Georgia of Burleigh, Tomkins, and Stoddard—the beginning of a period of enthusiastic study by a group of native Georgians. This reawakening of active and rather widespread interest in ornithology paralleled the previous periods of activity around the turn of the nineteenth century and in the 1850's.

Earle R. Greene was active in field work about his home in Atlanta from about 1921 until 1934, when he left to manage the federal wildlife refuge at Lake Mattamuskeet, North Carolina. In 1933 his bulletin on the birds of the Atlanta area was published; it covered his observations during the period of his residence. In late 1936 he returned to Georgia, this time as manager of the Okefenokee Swamp Refuge. For over two years he studied the birds of the Swamp, making careful notes on his observations. In 1939 he was transferred to Key West, Florida, and since that time has not resided in Georgia, although he still actively corresponds with Georgia ornithologists. He was one of the co-authors—with Griffin, Odum, Stoddard, and Tomkins—of the preliminary check-list and bibliography of the birds of Georgia published in 1945 as *Occasional Publication Number 2* of the Georgia Ornithological Society. Elected a Member of the American Ornithologists' Union in 1942, Earle Greene now lives in California.

Wallace Rogers, long a friend of LaPrade and other north Georgia ornithologists, was particularly active in this period, searching for and photographing the nests of many of the breeding birds of Atlanta, including the Black-billed Cuckoo, Swainson's Warbler, and Baltimore Oriole. He has published few scientific papers, but his photographs and beautiful moving pictures of birds have been viewed with pleasure by many. Rev. Rogers presently spends a great deal of his time in the pursuit of his hobby, photographing the birds, after long service as one of Georgia's most beloved Methodist ministers.

Lucien Harris, Jr., a friend of Rogers, LaPrade, Stoddard, and many others, was also active in the Atlanta region in the 1920's, and during this decade Ray C. Werner began his studies of the birds of this region which he has continued to the present day. Both Harris and Werner have contributed notes on their observations for publication.

In and about Roswell, just north of Atlanta, David V. Hembree and his brother-in-law, Lucius M. Taylor, collected birds, their period of greatest activity being from about 1915 to 1934. Hembree and Taylor collected both eggs and bird skins and were professional taxidermists. Many of the skins in the LaPrade collection were collected and prepared by Hembree, and the mounted collection now in the Georgia State Museum in Atlanta contains much of his work. Together, Hembree and Taylor are responsible for the addition to the Georgia list of several species, including the Snowy Owl, Mourning Warbler, and Brewer's Blackbird. They still reside in Roswell but have done little collecting since 1934.

In 1926, Carter R. Whittaker, George A. Dorsey, and several other bird students founded the Atlanta Bird Club. Whittaker and Dorsey to this day retain their interest in birds, and the club they founded now has more than three hundred members. Among the early members of the Atlanta Bird Club whose names deserve special mention are Mrs. James Connor Oliver, Mrs. Lewis Gordon, Sr., Mrs. Hugh H. Harris, and Mrs. Maurice Abercrombie.

Glenn W. Bell began the study of birds in 1928 in Rome while on the staff of the Berry Schools. For four years he kept notes on his observations, banded several hundred birds, and made a special study of bird song. Bell later moved to Atlanta, where he has continued his observations, publishing notes from time to time in *The Oriole.*

In Macon, Lewis H. and Beryl T. Mounts were active during the decade from 1920 to 1930 and published several notes in *The Wilson Bulletin.* Among the interesting species recorded by them near Macon were the Purple Gallinule, Black Rail, and White-crowned Sparrow. Since 1936, unfortunately, they have published little. In Savannah, the first permanent bird club in the state, the Savannah Audubon Society, had been organized in 1916, and many of its members were active field observers in the twenties. Among them, to name but a few, were Mrs. Victor H. Bassett, Mr. and Mrs. J. E. Wingo, Edna A. Pigman, and Mrs. J. R. Cain. And in Milledgeville, Mabel T. Rogers and Blanche Tait were beginning their observations on birds around the campus of the Georgia State College for Women.

Bird study by 1930 was beginning to become a popular pastime in Georgia, and serious students of ornithology were increasing in number. By 1930 there were active bird clubs in Savannah and Atlanta, and that year one was organized in Milledgeville. To tell of the work of all the students who have participated in observations in the field from 1930 to the present would be to reprint hundreds of pages from the various ornithological journals of America. Suffice it to say that substantial contributions to the ornithology of Georgia have been made by many not mentioned in this account.

Norman H. Giles, Jr., Don E. Eyles, and Nelson T. Spratt, Jr., became intensely interested in birds about 1930, and for the next six or seven years the three were active in the field about Atlanta. Together they compiled a mimeographed list of dates of migration of birds in the Atlanta region, and in 1936, Giles and Eyles founded *The Oriole,* a quarterly journal of Georgia ornithology. The magazine was initially published by the Atlanta Bird Club, of which Spratt was then president. In 1936, Spratt left the state for graduate study, and he was followed by Giles in 1937 and Eyles in 1938. Today none of the three resides in Georgia, but at the time of this writing *The Oriole* was in its eighteenth volume.

About 1930, J. Fred Denton also became interested in ornithology and, except for an absence of three years (1938–41) during which time he was studying for his doctorate, he has been continuously active in field ornithology in Georgia. Among the localities worked by Denton are Macon, Cochran, Athens, Lookout and Tray mountains, Americus, and Augusta. Since 1942 he has lived in Augusta and, in addition to general observations of birds in that area, has made special studies of the Swainson's Warbler and the Dickcissel. He is a past editor of *The Oriole,* a past president of the Georgia Ornithological Society, and a full Member of the American Ornithologists' Union. A few of the nearly five hundred specimens collected by Denton in Georgia have been deposited in the University of Georgia Collection; the rest remain in his possession. Among them are such unusual species for the state as Harris' Sparrow, White-rumped Sandpiper, and Sprague's Pipit.

Frederick V. Hebard of Philadelphia has spent many days afield in the region of the Okefenokee Swamp and Coleraine Plantation in Charlton and Camden counties. Here his family have had until recently extensive holdings since 1901, and he has had ample opportunity to study the birds. In 1941 his bulletin on the winter birds of the region, covering his observations there since about 1932, was published. In addition, many pages of *The Oriole* contain his notes and short articles on birds from this region. He was elected to Membership in the American Ornithologists' Union in 1951.

Frederick S. Barkalow, Jr., made many observations of birds in the field about his home in Marietta, Georgia, during the period from 1929 to 1936. Here he collected about 200 specimens, most of which are now deposited in the Museum of Zoology, University of Michigan. In 1936 he left Georgia to serve as a research assistant on a Mourning Dove project in Alabama, and at the present time he is the head of the Department of Zoology in North Carolina State College in Raleigh.

Harold C. Jones, presently of Greenville, North Carolina, moved to Mt. Berry near Rome in 1934 and began his studies of the birds of that region. He remained at Rome until June, 1947, and contributed several papers on the bird life of the region to *The Oriole.* During these years, Jones banded over 1,500 birds and on several occasions offered a course in ornithology at Berry College. This institution now has a collection of eggs of some 265 species of birds donated in 1937 by Lynds Jones, Harold's father and an ornithologist of note, long-time editor of the *Wilson Bulletin,* who resided in Oberlin, Ohio, but visited his son at Rome during several winters.

In 1936, Harold S. Peters first visited the state in connection with bird-banding activities. As an ornithologist with the U. S. Biological Survey, now the Fish and Wildlife Service, he made frequent trips to Georgia while stationed at Auburn, Alabama, and later at Charleston, South Carolina. In 1949, Peters established residence in Atlanta and has been very

NORTHERN ANHINGAS

Anhinga anhinga leucogaster

A few Anhingas or Water Turkeys regularly visited certain ponds on
Sherwood Plantation. I made sketches of one of them as it dried its plumage
after a long dive. For details I needed a fresh specimen, so shot an adult
female. To my dismay the dead bird lodged on the top of a tall stub and
would not come down. My friend Stoddard got an ax, walked to the
spot with me, and chopped away. Down came the stub with a mighty
splash, the Anhinga with it, and down sat the artist, his hands in perfect
condition for finishing the picture. The flowers in the water
are cow-lilies or spatterdock. The flying bird is a male.

active in affairs of the Georgia Ornithological Society and the Atlanta Bird Club, serving as president of both organizations. Peters was elected to full membership in the American Ornithologists' Union in 1947.

In December, 1936, the Georgia Ornithological Society was founded in Atlanta. It adopted as its official organ *The Oriole*, and as one of its objects the dissemination of ornithological knowledge. About this time, several students were beginning their ornithological pursuits about Atlanta. Among this group were William W. Griffin, George W. Sciple, Ralph L. Ramsey, and Richard A. Parks.

William W. Griffin has contributed frequent notes to *The Oriole* and has written papers on the migration and nesting of birds in the Atlanta region. He has served as editor of *The Oriole* as well as president of both the Atlanta Bird Club and the Georgia Ornithological Society. His recent collection of about 800 bird skins, principally from the Atlanta region, has provided valuable study material for taxonomic data presented in this book. Among the more unusual species collected by him are the Harris', LeConte's, and Henslow's Sparrows, and the Saw-whet Owl. He has added to the list of breeding birds of the state the Horned Lark and the Spotted Sandpiper. George W. Sciple, during the years from 1936 to 1942 and again from 1946 to 1951, collaborated with Griffin in many studies. Notes on his observations are published in both *The Auk* and *The Oriole*. He has collected in Georgia such rare species as the American Brant, Red Crossbill, and Cabot's Tern. Sciple now resides in Denver, Colorado, where he is associated with the U. S. Fish and Wildlife Service. Ralph L. Ramsey, during these same years and up to the present time, has been actively interested in birds. He has been particularly helpful in encouraging interest among the Boy Scouts. Richard A. Parks has been most active since his return from service in World War II in 1946. He is at present the editor of *The Oriole* and has served as president of the Atlanta Bird Club. He has collected several hundred birds in the vicinity of Atlanta, including the Red Crossbill and the Philadelphia Vireo. His objective water color portraits of birds have been exhibited widely in the United States and demonstrate that he is a painstakingly accurate ornithologist as well as an artist of rare ability. Griffin, Ramsey, and Parks are still actively engaged in ornithology in the state, although none has chosen this field as a profession.

In 1938, Robert A. Norris began the study of birds at his home in Fitzgerald. With unparalleled enthusiasm, energy, and ability he amassed a wealth of data on migration and nesting in the region of Fitzgerald and Tifton prior to the outbreak of World War II. His numerous notes during this period are published in *The Oriole*, which he edited for a time. In 1946 he returned from the armed services to renew his studies at the University of Georgia in Athens, where he obtained a master's degree in 1949 under the tutelage of Eugene P. Odum. His thesis on the birds of south-western Georgia, published by the Georgia Ornithological Society in 1951, contributes a wealth of information on such problems as population density and range extension. Most of Norris's specimens collected in Georgia, numbering over 500, are deposited in the collection at the University of Georgia. Among them are such interesting birds as the Gray Kingbird, LeConte's Sparrow, and White-crowned Sparrow. Norris is now engaged in graduate study in the University of California at Berkeley.

Associated with Norris in southern Georgia were two other bird students whose contributions to our knowledge of ornithology in this section has been significant. They are Milton Hopkins of Fitzgerald and Willard Gaulding of Tifton. Both have added much in the fields of distribution and migration. Reports of their activity, found throughout the last twelve volumes of *The Oriole,* record such interesting species as the Vermilion and Scissor-tailed Flycatchers. Hopkins wrote his master's thesis at the University of Georgia on the Mourning Dove. Hopkins and Gaulding still reside in Georgia.

Athos Menaboni came to Georgia from his native Italy and in 1938 began to paint oil portraits of the birds. Almost immediately his paintings were in great demand, and today he is generally recognized as one of the leading bird artists of the country. He and his wife, Sara, live among the birds in their woodland home on the outskirts of Atlanta.

In 1939, Raymond J. Fleetwood of the U. S. Fish and Wildlife Service moved to Round Oak, Georgia, to become manager of the Piedmont National Wildlife Refuge. He remained there in central Georgia through 1946; and from January, 1947, through September, 1948, he was biologist at the Okefenokee Swamp Refuge in southeastern Georgia. During all of this time, Fleetwood was active afield, particularly in the banding of birds. During his nearly ten years of residence he banded over 70,000 birds in the state, becoming the leading Chimney Swift bander in the country in point of numbers of birds banded. Among his contributions to the knowledge of birds in Georgia are valuable population studies in our pine forests as well as general notes on observations.

Also, in the late 1930's, Mr. and Mrs. R. E. Hamilton of Dalton began studies of the birds of the northwestern corner of the state. Accompanying them on many expeditions was Fannie McClellan. Records of some of the observations of these three can be found published in the pages of *The Oriole.* The Hamiltons still continue their observations about Dalton, but Fannie McClellan now lives in North Carolina.

In 1940, Eugene P. Odum accepted an appointment in the Zoology Department of the University of Georgia and established residence in Athens. Here he has worked and taught, and he has become first a Member (1944) and then a Fellow (1951) of the American Ornithologists'

Union. Although he is primarily an ecologist and a physiologist, many of his ornithological papers are studies in ecology or physiology as related to birds. His thought-provoking papers on distribution, range extension, and life history have been of particular interest to the more general ornithologist. The inspiration and direction which he has given to an increasing number of graduate students is not the least of his contributions. Odum has served as president of the Georgia Ornithological Society as well as in various capacities in national ornithological organizations. Generally recognized as one of the more progressive ornithologists of the country, Eugene Odum has heralded in Georgia a new phase of ornithological research, research from the point of view of explanation rather than mere description, research emphasizing study of the usual rather than the unusual.

Among the many students coming under the influence of Odum at Athens, Norris, Hopkins, and Gaulding have already been mentioned. Others have been David Johnston, James Major, Terry McGowan, and James Jenkins. David W. Johnston is now engaged in graduate research and study in ornithology in the University of California at Berkeley. Johnston began bird study in the early 1940's about his home city of Atlanta, and during the early years of World War II, he was an avid field observer. After his return in 1946 from a short tour with the U. S. Navy, his interest did not abate, and he collected and prepared several hundred study skins of birds for the Museum of the Zoology Department of the University of Georgia. Here he studied and received a master's degree in ornithology in 1950, the subject of his thesis being breeding bird population in relation to plant succession in the Piedmont. During this period, Johnston contributed a great deal to our knowledge of distribution, as well as conducting special studies in population. James C. Major was also a native of Atlanta and during the decade from 1940 to 1950 was a close companion of Johnston on many forays into the field, both at Atlanta and at Athens. Major is now studying medicine at Emory University in Atlanta. McGowan, also a member of the Atlanta group of graduate students at Athens, has completed his thesis on Mourning Doves and is now employed by the Kentucky Game Commission. James H. Jenkins is a native Ohioan who came to Georgia as a biologist with the state Game and Fish Commission. Now an assistant professor of wildlife management in the University of Georgia and working toward a doctorate under the guidance of Eugene Odum, Jenkins has contributed notes to *The Oriole* and has made special studies of the Mourning Dove and Barn Owl.

While Johnston and Major were roaming the fields during the early 1940's, Branch Howe, Jr., was an enthusiastic young student of birds about Atlanta. His notes and papers are to be found in *The Oriole*.

During these same years of World War II, ornithologists from other states, called into the service of their country, were sent to army camps in

Georgia. Brooke Meanley was one such soldier given an opportunity to study birds around Macon and in the swamps of southern Georgia. During 1944 and 1945, Meanley contributed a great many observations to *The Oriole*. In addition, he gathered much life-history data on the Swainson's Warbler in the canebrakes of the river swamps below Macon. William C. Grimm was another student of birds in the army. From March, 1942, to September, 1945, he was stationed at Camp Stewart in southeastern Georgia near Hinesville. His paper on the bird life of Camp Stewart is a valuable addition to knowledge of distribution of birds in this section.

Subsequent to World War II, cultural and scientific activity showed a marked increase throughout the country, and Georgia ornithology reflected the trend. Membership in local bird clubs in the state began to increase. The preliminary check-list and bibliography of birds of Georgia, published by the Georgia Ornithological Society in 1945, was out of print within five years. Ornithologists were working in all sections of the state: Thomas D. Burleigh was conducting his intensive field work throughout the state; Tomkins, Hebard, Fleetwood, and others were covering the coast and the southeastern part of Georgia; Stoddard, Norris, Gaulding, and Hopkins were working in southern and southwestern Georgia; Denton, Murphey, and groups in Macon and Milledgeville covered the Fall Line area of middle Georgia; the cities of the Piedmont Province, Atlanta and Athens, had many workers; Harold Jones and the Hamiltons covered the Appalachian Valley Province of northwestern Georgia; and Mrs. Dorothy P. Neal was active in the Mountain Province of northeastern Georgia. For the first time, every major physiographic province counted at least one bird student. While it is impossible to mention each student during the years since World War II, the following cannot be omitted.

Mrs. Dorothy P. Neal began the study of birds in 1946 in Demorest. Here at the northern edge of the Piedmont and at her home on Tray Mountain, one of Georgia's highest peaks, she has added much to our knowledge of the birds of the Mountain Province of northeastern Georgia. In Milledgeville, the club which had been organized earlier continued to thrive in postwar years. Among the students of birds afield in Milledgeville during the period since 1945 are Dr. and Mrs. Samuel Anderson who now reside in Atlanta, Thomas M. Hall, III, Lucille C. Rotchford, Katherine Weaver, and Fern E. Dorris.

In the Macon area, Edmund Farrar, Jr., and Nathaniel R. Whitney, Jr., have been active field ornithologists recently, contributing population studies to *Audubon Field Notes* as well as notes on more general observations to *The Oriole*. Also active in the Macon region since World War II have been Gregor Rohwer and Mr. and Mrs. Thomas Cater. In West Point, Georgia, Mrs. Grace M. Whiteman has recently become an interested student of ornithology. At Rome, an active bird club was organized in 1952.

Here Gordon L. Hight, Jr., and George A. Dorsey are now leaders among the group which, among other activities, is conducting rather extensive bird-banding in co-operation with the U. S. Fish and Wildlife Service.

In Atlanta, many new ornithologists are active. Rufus Godwin is an avid field observer and bird-bander. George Beal and Louis Fink, formerly of Massachusetts and New Jersey, respectively, have recently established residence in the city and are active. Terry McGowan, George Goldman, Wallace Dreyfoos, Robert and Russell Adams, Edward and Thomas Collum, Henry Robert, Jack Carusos, William Calder, and Hugh Moore are younger students of birds in the Atlanta area. At near-by Marietta, Manilla Land and Mary Phillips are interested students.

In Albany, a small group of ornithologists are afield. Among them are Harry Dann, Mrs. Emma J. Giffen, and Charles M. Jones. At Statesboro, Malvina Trussell and Tully Pennington have added to our knowledge of the birds in this region of southeastern Georgia. And in Augusta, Clarence Belger and William Thomas are among the students of bird life in that city who since 1945 have contributed notes on their observations to *The Oriole.* Along the coast of Georgia, observers of recent years have been joined by Herman Cooledge of Savannah and Richard Kuerzi of St. Marys. John Oney has conducted an extensive study of the Clapper Rail in the salt marshes near Brunswick.

Persons mentioned as having entered Georgia ornithology since 1920 have all been, for at least a time, residents of Georgia, and largely through the efforts of those students, living in various sections of the state, has our present knowledge of the distribution of birds been gained. Nevertheless, important contributions have been made by the many ornithologists visiting Georgia for periods of short duration since 1900. Briefly mentioning the more prominent among them, James Lee Peters visited Canton and Toccoa in May and June, 1916, and Waldo L. McAtee spent a week on Jekyll Island in June of 1923. T. Gilbert Pearson visited Cumberland Island in May, 1921, and published a list of species found there. In 1929, he visited the area near Darien at the mouth of the Altamaha River. Alexander Sprunt also visited Cumberland Island in 1935 and the lower Altamaha River in 1945. Lawrence H. Walkinshaw spent a week in April, 1945, studying the Sandhill Cranes of the Okefenokee Swamp. Albert F. Gainer has made frequent short trips to Georgia during the last thirty years. John W. Aldrich made important population studies near Hinesville during the spring of 1946. Herbert Stoddard's Sherwood Plantation, near Thomasville, has proved to be a mecca for prominent ornithologists from all parts of the country. Here George Miksch Sutton, Arthur A. Allen, Waldo L. McAtee, Olin Sewall Pettingill, and many others have visited, studied, and worked.

PHYSIOGRAPHIC & BIOGEOGRAPHIC REGIONS OF GEORGIA

With Special Reference to the Distribution of Breeding Birds

By Robert A. Norris

INTRODUCTION

The state of Georgia, the largest state east of the Mississippi River, has an area exceeding 59,000 square miles. It is situated between the parallels 30° 21′ and 35° north latitude and the meridians 80° 50′ and 85° 36′ west of Greenwich [McCallie, 1925].[1] Bounded by Alabama, Tennessee, and the Carolinas on the west, north, and northeast, respectively, Georgia meets the Atlantic Ocean on the east and Florida on the south and southwest. Within the state, there is a high degree of physiographic diversity; with a forest-clothed highland rising above 4,000 feet in the northeastern portion; with mesa-like mountains in the northwestern corner; with large sections of Appalachian valley land and undulating piedmont plateau; and with a sandy, seaward-sloping coastal plain featuring flatwoods, swamps, marshes, dunes and beaches. Geologically, the state is equally diversified, Pre-Cambrian rocks dominating the highland and the piedmont; Palaeozoic rocks, the northwestern corner; and Cretaceous, Tertiary, and Quaternary formations making up the coastal plain (Fig. 1). The general climate is characterized by long, warm summers and short, comparatively mild winters, with little snow except in the northernmost parts. The vegetation, like the land, is remarkably varied; the climax forests, comprising the final or ultimate vegetation favored by climate, of "Appalachian Georgia" (all the state except the coastal plain) are deciduous, whereas climax associations on the coastal plain show an increase in broadleaf evergreen species as one approaches the coast. Subclimax pineland, maintained by immature, sandy soils, and through the occurrence of periodic fires, is areally widespread over the coastal plain and lower piedmont.

Differences in physiography, climate, and vegetation are abundantly reflected in the distribution of animal life, of which the breeding birds furnish an excellent example. Some bird species are wholly confined to the highland, others to the coastal plain; still others are spread over most

[1] The literature cited in this chapter is included in the Bibliography of Georgia Ornithology at the end of the book.

or all of the state. The total number of breeding species is approximately 160. Although the ranges of these birds are fairly well known, we have yet to learn many lessons about their geographical and particularly their ecological distribution. The acquisition, organization, and synthesis of data on Georgian biota generally, even on such relatively well-worked groups as birds and vascular plants, are still insufficient and cannot, in the immediate future, yield a widely acceptable classification of "natural regions" and subdivisions. Yet there will eventually be such an undertaking, perhaps many undertakings. It is hoped that this chapter will contribute, however slightly, to that store of information requisite to a definitive regional and subregional classificatory scheme.

Apparently it is not so much Georgia's larger physiographic regions as the smaller ones that offer the most puzzling problems. Yet the larger regions and questions revolving about them are important and provocative, and we shall, therefore, attempt to compare these regions with those involved in three well-known systems of biogeographic classification. Subregions are dealt with in later sections of the chapter. The five major physiographic regions of Georgia may be associated, and in part coordinated, with recognized major biogeographic divisions, whether life-zone (as conceived and described by C. Hart Merriam), biome (developed by V. E. Shelford), or biotic-province, systems [Dice, 1943], be employed (Table I). Although Merriam's temperature laws [1894:236], offered as basic explanations of his zones (whose bounds follow temperature isotherms), have now been discarded, these zones retain a certain descriptive value and utility, particularly where they correspond with vegetational types. The biome, as conceived by Shelford, is a major biotic community characterized and given unity by its dominant, or controlling, plants and its major, or "influent," animals. It is a basic community unit, and its limits are defined by the climax formation which characterizes it [Clements and Shelford, 1939:20], although each biome also includes seral, or successional, and other communities subordinate to the climax. Climax formations, such as grassland or eastern deciduous forest, are distinguished by the life-form and spacing of their dominant plants. These characteristics vary in developmental communities, as well as in those resulting from biotic or pyric disturbances (these often called disclimax) and in peculiar edaphic or physiographic conditions. As plants and animals tend strongly to reflect climate, both climate and biota provide the basis for the arrangement of biomes. Dice [1943:3] defines the biotic province as a biogeographic unit which "covers a considerable and continuous geographic area and is characterized by the occurrence of one or more important ecologic associations that differ, at least in proportional area covered, from the associations of adjacent provinces." A subdivision of the biotic province is the biotic district, likewise a continuum; further

TABLE I.

Terminological equivalents (approximate) between physiographic, ecologic, and biotic regions of Georgia

Physiographic Regions (Fenneman; LaForge *et al.*)	Ecologic Regions		Biotic Provinces (Dice)
	Life Zones (Merriam)	*Biomes and Subregions* (Shelford; Braun)	
Highland (Blue Ridge)	Transition	Deciduous Forest: Oak-Chestnut with small areas Hemlock-White Pine-Northern Hardwood	Carolinian: Southern Appalachian Biotic District
Lookout Plateau (Cumberland Plateau)	Transition	Deciduous Forest: Mixed Mesophytic Forest	Carolinian
Appalachian Valley (Ridge and Valley)	Upper Austral	Deciduous Forest: Oak-Hickory with extensive Oak-Pine subclimax	Carolinian
Piedmont Region	Upper Austral	Deciduous Forest: Oak-Hickory with extensive Oak-Pine subclimax	Carolinian: Appalachian Piedmont Biotic District
Coastal Plain	Lower Austral	Deciduous Forest, approaching Subtropical Evergreen Forest on Coast: Pine subclimax very extensive	Austroriparian

subdivisions are called "life belts" and "ecologic associations." For all the seeming discrepancies in these systems, including the principal physiographic units (Table I), they should not be regarded as competing systems but as approaches from somewhat different viewpoints. It is true that all four serve, first, to emphasize the dichotomy between Appalachian Georgia and the coastal plain and, second, to set off the highland from the rest of Appalachian Georgia. Yet we should point out that certain of the classificatory schemes, notably biomes and biotic provinces, are not strictly comparable, the former being ecologic divisions and the latter florofaunal regions. The two systems may, however, be expected to approach one another more closely once their subdivisions will have been fully explored and designated. It seems to the writer that for many regions, including the southeastern United States, the biome system is the most generally acceptable and potentially useful among schemes based on biological characteristics. For more comprehensive discussions of life zones, biomes, and biotic provinces, see, for example, Pitelka [1941], Dice [1943], Odum [1945e], and Shelford [1945].

A few words about the scope of this chapter and certain mechanics relative to its preparation may not be amiss. Because physiography is well correlated with biological features in Georgia, an attempt to relate the distribution of breeding birds directly with physical regions should prove convenient and instructive. Hence particular emphasis is placed on physiography and breeding-bird distribution in the regional characterizations in subsequent paragraphs, with somewhat less emphasis on climate and vegetation, and with bare mention of geology, soil types, land use, and additional aspects of cultural geography. Wildlife areas (refuges, monuments, etc.) are scarcely touched upon; these and other especially attractive bird habitats in Georgia are well treated by Eyles [1938c], Jenkins [1953], and Pettingill [1951]. The present chapter is mainly descriptive, with only occasional reference to dynamics, whether geomorphologic or vegetational. For information on physiography, the work by LaForge *et al.* [1925] has been heavily relied upon, more so than is suggested by the scattered citations; for the work of each of these co-authors the writer is duly appreciative, as he is also to R. M. Harper [1930] especially for his scheme of subdivision of the coastal plain. The treatment of bird distribution, even though analytical in part, is best regarded as only preliminary, more data being needed, as indicated elsewhere, for many of the species and subspecies. It is hoped that in the not too distant future published information on Georgia's avifauna will have warranted a thoroughgoing analysis, on the order of that made by Miller [1951] for California. The information used in this chapter was derived from many sources, including nearly every issue of *The Oriole*, and was subsequently revised and brought into conformity with the Burleigh manuscript for this book. Although it is impossible to cite all papers and notes, an attempt is made to acknowledge some of the more significant contributions; and, with respect to the literature subsequent to 1943 (this not covered by Greene *et al.* [1945]), to cite various reports that yield new information on breeding-bird distribution. With a view to stimulating further field work in Georgia, the writer has devoted some space, at the end of each section on birds, to various ornithological problems and opportunities of both regional and general nature.

The writer is indebted to J. Fred Denton, William W. Griffin, David W. Johnston, Alden H. Miller, and Herbert L. Stoddard, Sr., for their reading the chapter and providing welcome critical comment, especially on the matter of bird distribution. Eugene P. Odum and Frank A. Pitelka offered valuable suggestions relative to the introduction; Mr. Odum assisted further in the organization of Table I and in contributing Figure 2. Thomas D. Burleigh was very helpful by providing me with a copy of his manuscript, *Georgia Birds*, so that this chapter could be checked against his species accounts. My wife, Vivian E. Norris, lent editorial aid and typed the manuscript.

I. THE HIGHLAND

The Georgia Highland, a segment of the Appalachian system, covers almost 2,000 square miles in the northeastern part of the state (Fig. 1) and

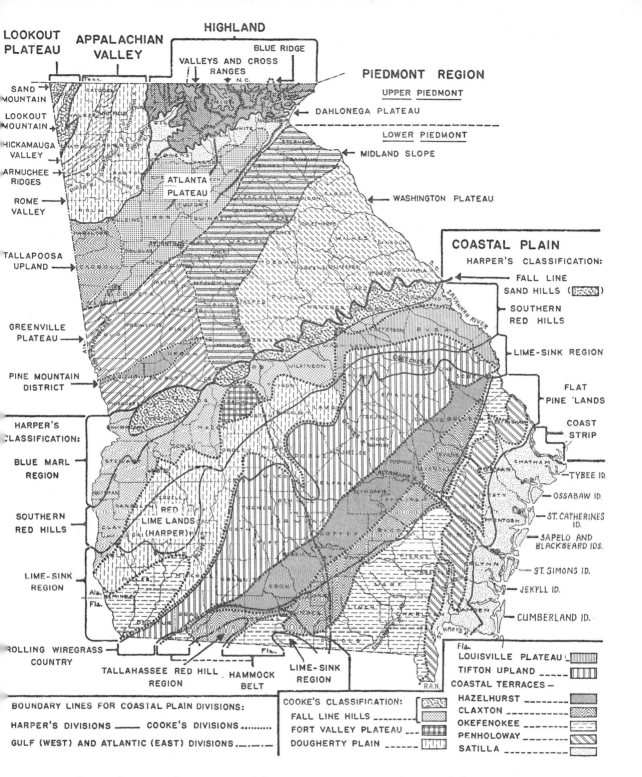

FIG. 1.—Physiographic regions of Georgia. Two systems of regional classification of the coastal plain are superimposed. The map, prepared by Robert A. Norris, is based on figures in LaForge *et al.* (1925) and Harper (1930).

comprises a highly distinctive physiographic and biotic region. It is sharply bounded by the Appalachian Valley on the west and by the Dahlonega Plateau, or "foothill" belt, on the south and southeast. Almost all the area is mountainous, with elevations from about 2,000 to more than 4,000 feet above sea level, the highest peak, Brasstown Bald, or Mount Enotah, rising to 4,768 feet. The ranges in Georgia are continuous with montane country in North Carolina and Tennessee. Headwaters of various rivers, nearly all with Indian names, are found in the Highland, the larger ones heading in the major range, the Blue Ridge, and tending to run off in northwest and southeast directions. Because this range is somewhat cernuous, being tilted toward the above-mentioned hills, its stream grades are particularly steep on the southeast side, where most of them reach the 1,500-foot level in five or six miles. The Blue Ridge itself makes up more than two-thirds of the Highland; its angular course is suggested in Figure 1 (by the heavy dotted line). Viewed from the south, the Ridge "is visible for 50 or 60 miles in clear weather and is always blue from the haze of the atmosphere" [Keith, 1925]. Other features of the Highland include high plateaus, valleys, cross ranges, salients, and outlying mountains. In the following paragraphs, the Blue Ridge and the other main divisions of the Highland are treated separately. The present classification of these divisions is based on that of Keith [*ibid.*:93 ff.].

The *Blue Ridge* forms the crooked backbone of the Georgia Highland and marks the southern boundary of the drainage basin of the Mississippi River. As shown in Figure 1, this ridge extends into Rabun County, in the northeastern corner of the state, then loops northward into North Carolina before doubling back into Georgia. Its course, really a zigzag one on account of alternating positions of headwaters encroaching from either side, may then be traced west-southwestward to an area south of the Toccoa River basin. Here the ridge turns abruptly northwestward, running between the Ellijay and Toccoa rivers and, after another sharp bend, passing northward into Tennessee. Most of the Blue Ridge proper exceeds 3,000 feet in height, although the crest line is irregular and broken into many peaked or rounded summits. There are two major passes, one near the town of Blue Ridge, between the Ellijay and Toccoa rivers, and the other, called Rabun Gap, between the headwaters of the Little Tennessee and Chattooga rivers. The eastern half of this chain is higher than the western; in fact, east of Blood Mountain, near Vogel State Park, twenty-one of Georgia's peaks are 4,000 or more feet in height, whereas there are only six above that height to the westward.

The rocks of the Blue Ridge and neighboring Highland country are crystalline, including marble, slate, schist, quartzite, conglomerate, and gneiss. All these are sedimentary and made their first appearance by or before Cambrian time. There are also large masses of granite and additional igneous types, formed in fluid state under intense heat far below the earth's surface. The rocks vary markedly in their positions relative to surface and to streams and in their resistance to decomposition, these relations having profound effects on relief in the Georgia Highland. The loamy soils are not very fertile except in the bottoms of valleys.

Cross Ranges. In addition to the northwesterly directed arm, or "Western Range," of the Blue Ridge, there are two principal cross ranges. These are connected to the main backbone and extend northwest across the Highland into Tennessee and North Carolina. They are called the Central Range and the Eastern Range, the former passing between the Toccoa and Nottely rivers, which dissect the Ducktown and Hiwassee plateaus, respectively, and the latter passing between the Nottely and Hiwassee rivers, situated, respectively, on western and eastern parts of the Hiwassee Plateau. Near the Tennessee line the Central Range descends to plateau level (roughly 2,000 feet); this notch in the chain, like the one connecting the Ellijay and Toccoa valleys, is due to the solubility of Murphy marble in acidic waters. The Eastern Range is interrupted in similar manner. The heights of the cross ranges, especially in their southeastern sections, compare closely with those of the Blue Ridge proper. On the whole, the Eastern Range is higher than the Central, having, in fact, a length of 6 miles above 4,000 feet. Brasstown Bald forms a conspicuous part of this lofty range, near its junction with the Blue Ridge.

Plateaus. The Ducktown Plateau is an area of broadly rounded summits separated by shallow saddles. It reaches elevations of 1,600 to 1,800 feet. The Hiwassee Plateau, which lies mainly in North Carolina with extensions into the Georgia Highland, has similar topography but averages a few hundred feet higher. In smoother, or less deeply dissected, portions of the latter plateau, the towns of Blairsville, Young Harris, and Hiwassee are located. The streams of these plateaus merge to form the Toccoa and Nottely rivers, as indicated previously, these crossing the state's northern boundary and entering into the Mississippi drainage system. Sprawled in the northeastern corner of Georgia is the Little Tennessee Plateau, about 2,100 feet in height, with its many arms extending into the mountains; one of these stretches through Rabun Gap, across the backbone of the Blue Ridge, into the basin of the Chattooga River, thence into the Tallulah and Chattahoochee basins. Drainages from this plateau diverge greatly, the Little Tennessee moving toward the Mississippi, and others toward the Atlantic and the Gulf. A series of dams built along the Tallulah River has resulted in the formation of several lakes, the largest of these, Lake Burton, having an area in excess of four square miles. There are also large impoundments of waters on the other plateaus.

The *Cohutta Mountains* lie west of the northwesternmost sector of the Blue Ridge, or, in other words, west of that part of the ridge cut off by

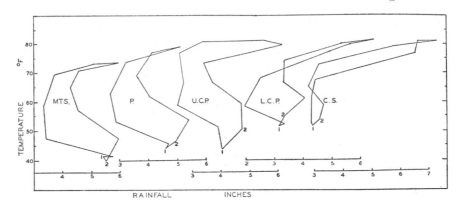

FIG. 2.—Hythergraphs (climographs) for five physiographic divisions of Georgia. Mts.: mountains (Highland); P.: Piedmont Region; U.C.P.: Upper Coastal Plain; L.C.P.: Lower Coastal Plain (exclusive of Coast Strip); C.S.: Coast Strip. 1: January; 2: February; etc. The hythergraphs, based on monthly averages from all available weather stations in Georgia, were prepared by the graduate ecology class, University of Georgia, under the direction of E. P. Odum.

Ellijay Valley and the Ducktown Plateau. The Cohuttas, bounded on their western side by low plains of the Appalachian Valley, are divisible into northern and southern masses, the former range exceeding 3,000 feet, the latter exceeding 2,500 feet. Cowpen Mountain, with an altitude of 4,166 feet, is the highest point, and there are a few other peaks above 4,000 in the northern section. The Cohutta Mountains are drained by tributaries of the Gulfward-flowing Coosawattee River.

Minor divides and peaks appear elsewhere than in the major ranges just mentioned. Most of these are north of the Blue Ridge, although some, as majestic Yonah Mountain (in White County), are south of it. Isolated peaks like Yonah are called monadnocks. From the abrupt bend of the Blue Ridge, south of the head of Toccoa River, there is an extension, or salient, which runs southwestward into Pickens County. Burnt and Oglethorpe mountains, with elevations above 3,000 feet, accentuate this extremity of the Highland. As indicated in Figure 1, this minor divide stretches southwestward beyond the Highland, even though in broken fashion, and includes the bold ridges of Sharp and Pinelog mountains, whose heights are about 2,300 feet. Pinelog, at the boundary of Bartow and Cherokee counties some 20 miles from the Highland margin, is the southernmost high mountain in Georgia.

Climate

The Highland region is the coldest and wettest part of the state, although it is not so extreme in these respects as the adjoining mountain areas of

North Carolina and Tennessee. Generalized weather data for the Georgia mountains, based on combined and averaged figures from available stations [Mindling, 1941: tables] between 2,000 and 4,000 feet in elevation, are as follows: Temperatures (degrees Fahrenheit); January average, 40; July average, 73; annual average, 52–58 (lower for individual mountains); average dates of first and last killing frosts, October 22 and April 18; growing season, 190 days. Annual rainfall, 60–80 inches (average about 70). December and March are the wettest months, each with about seven inches of precipitation, and another peak occurs in July (slightly over six inches). During the summer months, thunderstorms are frequent and often torrential; winter rains last longer and are not so heavy. October and November are the only months averaging less than four inches of rainfall. In both summer and fall, considerable condensation of moisture results from clouds which envelop the higher slopes and summits and from fogs which gather in the valley bottoms. Although nearly all the precipitation is in the form of rain, there is an average annual snowfall of five inches or more, but below 3,000 feet this rarely lies long, even in midwinter. Important climatic differences between the Highland and more southerly regions of the state are shown by hythergraphs (climographs) in Figure 2.

Vegetation

The original climax forest of the Georgia Highland was part of the great Eastern Deciduous Forest Formation and was, in the main, a mixture of hardwoods with a preponderance of chestnut (*Castanea dentata*) and various oaks (*Quercus* spp.). The fungus disease, chestnut blight, as well as lumbering and attendant fires, has had marked effect on the forest physiognomy. The chestnuts have been almost completely eliminated, their many leafless skeletons, still widespread over the mountains, standing bleakly against the green-clad slopes. There remains, however, an abundance of chestnut sprouts, struggling against the disease. Noteworthy deciduous hardwoods of the Highland, some of which have crowded into spaces left by the chestnuts, are northern red oak (*Quercus maxima*), chestnut oak (*Q. montana*), scarlet oak (*Q. coccinea*), white oak (*Q. alba*), red maple (*Acer rubrum*), hickories (*Carya* spp.) tuliptree (*Liriodendron tulipifera*), and mountain magnolia (*Magnolia fraseri*). Shrubs and small trees, some characteristic of the mountain country, include rhododendrons (*Rhododendron catawbiense* and *R. maximum*), mountain laurel (*Kalmia latifolia*), black locust (*Robinia pseudo-acacia*), sassafras (*Sassafras albidum*), smooth shadbush (*Amelanchier laevis*), and, at higher elevations, mountain ash (*Sorbus americana*). Prominent among the coniferous trees are eastern white pine (*Pinus strobus*) and eastern hemlock (*Tsuga canadensis*), species with mainly northward ranges. Where present in quantity, largely in moist coves and on north-facing

Wood Ducks

Aix sponsa

When word reached me that a duck had been seen entering and leaving
a hole in a big post oak near the Komarek house on Birdsong Plantation,
I knew I would have to investigate. The nest cavity was not very high.
With the help of a stepladder, I caught the duck. Herbert Stoddard
held her—gently but firmly, as the saying goes—while I drew her head in
detail, and we set her free. Then, moving all my gear over to
Birdsong, I painted the nest tree. The upper bird, the male, is perched on
what remains of a lightning-struck part of the great trunk.

slopes and generally in remote areas that have escaped lumbering, these handsome conifers in association with broadleaf species make up a transition-type forest with characteristics suggestive of the Boreal Coniferous Forest Formation. This intermediate type, termed the Hemlock-Hardwoods Association [Braun, 1950], is better developed farther north, as in the higher mountains of North Carolina. Several other pines occur in the Highland. The most common are shortleaf (*Pinus echinata*) and scrub pines (*P. virginiana*), often found on lower slopes where the soil is stony and thin. The relative importance of the various hardwoods and conifers is determined by many factors, involving soil, physiography, climate, and biotic agencies (including man), that provide a variety of habitats.

Natural balds, or treeless summits, are not infrequent in the Highland. Some are grassy and some more or less covered with heaths or ericads (rhododendrons, mountain laurel, and several ground-level species). The problem of the origin of the balds, many of which seem of long standing, has been subject to considerable study and debate.

Although the Highland was once heavily forested, much of its better timber has long since been logged away. In valleys and plateaus, the main sections inhabited by largely agrarian residents, the forest remains are mostly woodlots and stands of low-grade timber. But the effects of drastic cutting and fires are less evident now than they were a half-century ago, for the greater portion of the Georgia Highland has come under the aegis of Chattahoochee National Forest (the United States Forest Service having an option on more than 1,500,000 acres, much of which has been purchased). As a consequence, the forest resources are now subject to more conservative methods of exploitation. The same holds true for the wildlife resources.

Birds of the Highland

The Highland stands in clear contrast to other regions of Georgia not only in its topography and vegetation but also in its faunal elements. Differences manifest in the Highland fauna are well illustrated by several vertebrate groups, and birds, as already indicated, are no exception. Nearly twenty species of birds have essentially montane distribution in Georgia during the breeding season. These are mainly limited in their southward distribution by the Highland and its neighboring salients and monadnocks. They include three uncommon but striking species: the Golden Eagle, Peregrine Falcon, and Common Raven; of these, only the raven is known definitely to breed in the Highland. The Peregrine has bred on Lookout Mountain, but for the eagle there are no breeding records anywhere in the state. These birds are met so infrequently that it is probably better not to regard them as characteristic of Georgia mountains. But fully two-thirds of the montane species may be regarded as characteristic and,

35

TABLE II.

Birds characteristic of the Georgia Highland, with approximate minimal breeding elevations (feet above sea level) for this region; breeding-season records of five of these are known from additional regions, as indicated by the abbreviations—DP (Dahlonega Plateau), AP (Atlanta Plateau), and LM (Lookout Mountain)

Canada Warbler	4,000 feet
Winter Wren	4,000 feet
Yellow-bellied Sapsucker	3,800 feet
Veery	3,600 feet
Slate-colored Junco	3,500 feet
Rose-breasted Grosbeak	2,700 feet
Black-throated Blue Warbler	2,700 feet
Chestnut-sided Warbler	2,600 feet
Golden-winged Warbler (LM)	2,500 feet
Blackburnian Warbler	2,200 feet
Least Flycatcher	2,100 feet
Ruffed Grouse (DP)	1,800 feet
Black-throated Green Warbler (LM)	1,800 feet
Worm-eating Warbler (LM,AP)	1,700 feet
Blue-winged Warbler (LM,AP)	1,300 feet

for the larger part, influent members of biotic communities of the Highland region. Their relative prominence naturally varies with altitude, substratum, vegetation and other biotic factors (as insect food, competition, and predation). Such characteristic Highland birds, fifteen in all, are listed in Table II. Three of these, the Yellow-bellied Sapsucker, Least Flycatcher, and Winter Wren, are uncommon or quite limited in distribution, so far as is presently known, and are of less ecologic importance than most of the others.

Table II shows half the characteristic species to be wood warblers (family *Parulidae*), better represented in the Highland than in other regions of Georgia. The Chestnut-sided Warbler is one of the most abundant inhabitants of scrubby disclimax associations that have resulted from blight. Where altitudinal zones and habitats are favorable, the Slate-colored Junco and Black-throated Blue Warbler are common breeders. Most of the characteristic species, including all the warblers, are summer residents, arriving in spring and departing in fall. The Olive-sided Flycatcher, Cerulean Warbler, and Red Crossbill may breed locally or sparingly in the Highland, but their nests remain to be found.

Many other kinds of birds, mostly not characteristic of the Highland, breed in the high country. The total species for this region number ap-

TABLE III.

Occurrence and relative abundance of breeding birds of the Highlands and other physiographic regions of Georgia

Species	HIGH-LAND	LOOKOUT PLATEAU	APPALACHIAN VALLEY	PIEDMONT REGION			COASTAL PLAIN		
				Dahlonega Plateau	Upper (in part)	Lower	NW or W part	S-Central part	E or SE part
Cedar Waxwing	Xx	?	?	Xx					
Whip-poor-will	Xx	Xx	xx[s]	Xx	xx				
Scarlet Tanager	XX	Xx	xx[s]	Xx	(N-1)				
Black-billed Cuckoo	xx	?	(N-1)	?					
Baltimore Oriole	xx		xx	(xx)	xx	?			
Bewick's Wren	Xx	Xx	Xx	(xx)	(N-2)	(N-2)			
Eastern Phoebe	Xx	Xx	XX	xx	XX	xx[se]			
Oven-bird	XX	XX	xx[e]	XX	XX	xx[se]			
Black and White Warbler	XX	XX	Xx	XX	XX	xx			
Yellow Warbler	Xx	?	Xx	XX	Xx	xx			
Grasshopper Sparrow	Xx	?	Xx	(Xx)	Xx	Xx	xx[s]		
American Goldfinch	Xx	Xx	Xx	Xx	Xx	xx	xx[se]		
American Redstart	Xx	?	?	Xx	xx[e]	xx[e]	xx[se]		
Louisiana Waterthrush	Xx	xx	xx	Xx	Xx	xx	xx[e]		
Broad-winged Hawk	XX	Xx	Xx	XX	XX	Xx	xx	xx[e]	
Chipping Sparrow	XX	XX	XX	XX	XX	XX	xx[s]		xx[s]
Field Sparrow	XX	XX	XX	XX	XX	XX	†Xx[e]		xx[s]
Rough-winged Swallow	XX	xx	Xx	Xx	Xx	XX	Xx[s]		Xx[sw]
Prairie Warbler	XX	XX	XX	XX	XX	XX	xx[s]		Xx[w]
Killdeer	xx	?	Xx	(Xx)	Xx	Xx	Xx		xx
Robin	XX	Xx	†XX	†Xx	†Xx	†xx		(N-1?)	(N-1)
Song Sparrow	XX	†xx	†Xx	†Xx	?	†xx			
Solitary Vireo	XX	xx	?	†Xx	†xx	†xx			
Parula Warbler	Xx	xx	xx	Xx	?	(N-1)	XX	XX	XX
Swainson's Warbler	xx			Xx	(N-2)		xx	XX	xx
Turkey	Xx						XX	xx	Xx

Explanation of symbols:
XX: common (to abundant).
Xx: fairly common.
xx: uncommon (to scarce).
( ) enclosing other symbol: the status, as given, only probable or likely and actually based on records from contiguous or surrounding regions.

†: records due to recent southward invasions.

?: suspected or uncertain presence.
e: indicates range boundaries to the east.
w: indicates range boundaries to the west.
n: indicates range boundaries to the north.
s: indicates range boundaries to the south.
N-1, N-2: nests (one or two records), these being the only evidence of breeding within the region.

proximately 110 (69 per cent of the total breeding species in Georgia, which number approximately 160). The noncharacteristic species have wide enough ecologic tolerance, however, so that their ranges extend into two or more of the other major biogeographic regions of Georgia. Practically all are known to breed below 1,500 feet. A preliminary outline of broad distributional patterns embracing the Highland, or considerable parts thereof, and additional regions is contained in Table III and in paragraphs immediately following.

Three of the species listed in Table III, the Robin, Solitary Vireo, and Song Sparrow, are erstwhile "mountain birds" which have invaded or extended their breeding ranges into the Georgia Piedmont and/or the Appalachian Valley in the recent past. Two other invaders from more northerly and westerly regions are the House Wren and Horned Lark (Table V), these having by-passed the mountains and appeared in lower country to the south or west. An account of the Robin's spread during the last three or four decades has been given by Odum and Burleigh [1946]. The others are still more recent in their appearance as breeders in the Piedmont and valley provinces, the story of the Solitary Vireo having been told by Fleetwood [1947c], Odum [1948], and several others; that of the House Wren by Odum and Johnston [1951]; and that of the Song Sparrow by the Hamiltons [1946], in the Appalachian Valley, and by Neal and Denton [1950] and Dorris, Tait, and Weaver [1951] in upper and lower parts of the Piedmont Region. The initial appearance of the Horned Lark as a breeding bird was in the Appalachian Valley, as chronicled by Griffin [1951b]. With respect to all these species (except the Robin), it is remarkable that each invasion was sensed beforehand, on clues from other regions (including Piedmont North Carolina), and, moreover, each of these was formally predicted [Odum, 1943a; Odum and Burleigh, 1946].

Many of the Highland birds have breeding ranges that extend over the entire state. These vary in habitat preference, some with wider selection and others narrower (the latter having similar ecologic niches, whatever the region), but all display wide climatic tolerance and may be common in suitable habitat in any of the regions. These statewide species number forty-two and are as follows: Turkey Vulture, Cooper's Hawk, Red-tailed Hawk, Red-shouldered Hawk, Sparrow Hawk, Bobwhite, Mourning Dove, Yellow-billed Cuckoo, Screech Owl, Chimney Swift, Ruby-throated Hummingbird, Yellow-shafted Flicker, Hairy Woodpecker, Downy Woodpecker, Eastern Kingbird, Great-crested Flycatcher, Acadian Flycatcher, Eastern Wood Pewee, Purple Martin, Blue Jay, Common Crow, Carolina Chickadee, Tufted Titmouse, Carolina Wren, Brown Thrasher, Wood Thrush, Common Bluebird, Blue-gray Gnatcatcher, White-eyed Vireo, Yellow-throated Vireo, Red-eyed Vireo, Pine Warbler, Yellowthroat, Yellow-breasted Chat, Hooded Warbler, House Sparrow,

Common Meadowlark, Redwing, Orchard Oriole, Summer Tanager, Cardinal, and Eastern Towhee.

Other species of the Highland have breeding ranges that are nearly, if not quite, statewide, but they are uncommon or scarce, or even totally wanting, in small or scattered sections. With some of these, such as the King Rail, Belted Kingfisher, Pileated Woodpecker, and Prothonotary Warbler, this is due to the spotty or restricted distribution of favored habitat; with others, as the White-breasted Nuthatch, Yellow-throated Warbler, Blue Grosbeak, and Indigo Bunting, controlling factors are not quite so evident and remain to be elucidated. (For example, along the Georgia coast neither climate nor woody vegetation seems sufficiently different from that of the adjacent interior to explain the extreme rarity or absence of the Indigo Bunting in the coastal counties. Competition afforded by the coast-dwelling Painted Bunting, a bird capable of extreme pugnacity, is perhaps involved in this ecologic barrier.) Twenty-six species approaching statewide status, most of them breeding in the Highland as well as elsewhere, are as follows: Green Heron, Wood Duck, Black Vulture, King Rail, American Woodcock, Barn Owl, Horned Owl, Barred Owl, Chuck-will's-widow, Common Nighthawk, Belted Kingfisher, Pileated Woodpecker, Red-bellied Woodpecker, Red-headed Woodpecker, White-breasted Nuthatch, Mockingbird, Catbird, Loggerhead Shrike, Common Starling, Prothonotary Warbler, Yellow-throated Warbler, Kentucky Warbler, Purple Grackle, Blue Grosbeak, Indigo Bunting, and Bachman's Sparrow. (For available details as to range gaps or areas of scarcity, see the accounts in the main body of the book.)

The mountain region is further distinguished by geographic races, or subspecies, of several of the widespread species. Within Georgia the races listed beyond are peculiar to the Highland, although they have more or less extensive ranges to the northward; they are replaced by different races in lower or more southerly parts of the state. Most of these were shown to occur in the mountains by Burleigh [1947b, 1948a], whereas one, Swainson's Warbler, was first discovered by Denton [1948], whose specimen proved referable to the Appalachian race described by Meanley and Bond [1950]. In another group of species—including the Common Nighthawk, Yellow-shafted Flicker, and Purple Grackle—areas of intergradation are farther south in the Piedmont Region. There may be additional subspecies, as yet undetected, that breed in the Blue Ridge country. The range boundaries and areas of intergradation have not been determined precisely for all these Highland races. In the following list, it suffices to mention only certain specific locations from which specimens of the "mountain races" have been obtained. The adjoining or spatially closest corresponding races occupying lesser elevations or southern parts of Georgia are listed opposite their Highland representatives.

Yellow-shafted Flicker:	*Colaptes auratus luteus* (Fannin County; Brasstown Bald)	*Colaptes auratus auratus*
Hairy Woodpecker:	*Dendrocopos villosus villosus* (Young Harris, Towns County)	*Dendrocopos villosus auduboni*
Blue Jay:	*Cyanocitta cristata bromia* (Rabun and Brasstown balds)	*Cyanocitta cristata cristata*
Swainson's Warbler:	*Limnothlypis swainsonii alta* (Tray Mountain, White County)	*Limnothlypis swainsonii swainsonii*
Yellowthroat:	*Geothlypis trichas brachidactyla* (Blairsville, Union County; Marble Hill, Pickens County)	*Geothlypis trichas typhicola*
Common Meadowlark:	*Sturnella magna magna* (Young Harris, Towns County)	*Sturnella magna argutula*
Eastern Towhee:	*Pipilo erythrophthalmus erythrophthalmus* (Rabun, Habersham, White, and Pickens counties)	*Pipilo erythrophthalmus canaster*

The birds of the Highland thus comprise both indigenous species and races, so far as distribution in Georgia is concerned, and many others whose ranges are less restricted. This avifauna poses many questions for the investigator. For example, the relative importance, in terms of breeding pairs per unit area, of characteristic montane species versus more widespread species in different Highland zones and vegetational types has not been appraised quantitatively. Two other types of problems awaiting the student concern: first, factors that actually limit zonally restricted species and: second, changing distributions that result from habitat modifications. The latter phenomenon is exemplified by the Chestnut-sided Warbler, which, as reported by Odum and Burleigh [1946], has made a spectacular southward invasion into "opened-up" chestnut scrub during the last two decades. Several other warblers have responded similarly in other parts of the Appalachian system [Brooks, 1940]. Interspecific relations of such species as Chuck-will's-widows and Whip-poor-wills, Scarlet and Summer tanagers, and certain congeneric warblers remain almost completely unstudied. Further scientific collecting will, of course, result in the sharpening of race boundaries. And there is still need for general observational work, particularly in less frequented sections like the Cohutta Range, for which, incidentally, the only available lists seem to be those of Anne Hamilton. Transient and winter birds in the Georgia Highland have received little attention. For many of the species almost nothing is known of spans and peaks in song and breeding periods. Thus opportunities for ornithological work are manifold and await inquiry from future "highlanders," whether they be summer vacationists, general collectors, or students with special ecologic or life-history interests.

II. THE LOOKOUT PLATEAU

The northwestern corner of the state (Fig. 1) consists of fairly high plateaus. These represent a small, roughly triangular piece of the extensive Cumberland Plateau, which stretches from Alabama to Kentucky and Virginia and lies northwest of the Appalachian Valley. This broad valley thus separates the plateau area of northwestern Georgia from the northeastern Highland. As Lookout Mountain is, within Georgia, the most prominent ridge of the Cumberland Plateau, we shall refer to this region of the state as the Lookout Plateau [following Campbell, 1925:148]. Covering Dade County and small parts of Walker and Chattooga counties, this region includes the following divisions: (1) the plateau-like ridge of Lookout Mountain, which extends from Gadsden, Alabama, northward and somewhat eastward through Georgia and terminates abruptly near Chattanooga, Tennessee; (2) Pigeon Mountain, a prong of Lookout Mountain on the southeast, extending northeastward in Walker County; and (3) Sand Mountain, which nearly fills the state's corner, on the northwest. Maximal elevations are approximately 2,400, 2,300, and 1,700 feet on Lookout, Pigeon, and Sand mountains, respectively, and their positions are shown in Figure 1. The general surface of the Lookout Plateau descends gradually toward the southwest and west.

This mesa-like region once belonged to a single vast peneplain (nearly a plain) whose surface, because of a long period of quiescence of the earth's crust, had been eroded nearly to sea level. There followed many crustal uplifts, however, and some of the elevations that resulted were fully 2,000 feet above that "datum plain." The rock strata became bent, or folded, rather like the surface of a great washboard, the shallow troughs being termed synclines, now aligned with the mountains themselves, and the alternating, up-folded strata termed anticlines, now replaced by valleys and coves. These strata comprise sandstone and shales of Pennsylvanian (or upper Carboniferous) time. Because of thick beds of resistant sandstone, the surfaces of Lookout and neighboring mountains have been preserved. Hence their topography is immature or, where sufficiently eroded, submature. Since the sandstone beds were sharply folded and weakened along anticlines, they and underlying, less resistant layers were cut down to valley levels, and further deepening of these valleys followed subsequent regional uplifts.

Lookout Valley, formed in the above-described manner, lies between the steep faces of Lookout and Sand mountains. Its elevations are mostly between 700 and 900 feet; its creek, also named from the higher mountain, flows northeastward to the Tennessee River. The towns of Trenton and Rising Fawn are located in this valley, and the valley floor, unlike the nearby mountains, is widely cultivated. Farther south, where Lookout Valley reaches its head near the Alabama line, it meets the head of Wills Valley, which further separates the two mountains. The waters of the latter valley travel southwestward and eventually join the Coosa River, whence they flow to the Gulf. Although Lookout Valley has been regarded as an outlier of the Appalachian Valley, we here follow Campbell [*ibid.*:150] in assigning both valley and mountain, as well as associated areas of the Lookout Plateau, to the Cumberland Province.

Lookout Mountain is the most prominent and conspicuous part of the plateau region of northwestern Georgia. Reared above its steep slopes are nearly vertical cliffs, up to 300 feet in height, and although notched by streams, many of these remain sheer and unscalable. Few roads have found their way across this barrier. Several notable eminences are met along the otherwise flattish, undulating ridge of Lookout Mountain. The southernmost of these is Gulf Peak (also called Gulf Mountain), at the head of McLamore Cove, which lies between Lookout and its spur, Pigeon Mountain. Gulf Peak looms some 1,200 feet above the cove's bottom and its stream, West Chickamauga Creek. Farther north, along the eastern rim of Lookout Mountain, there are three other low peaks rising 200 to 400 feet above the plateau top. One of these, High Point, about six miles south of the state line, reaches a height of 2,392 feet, the greatest in the Lookout region. Its summit is elongate and its east side is a sheer drop of several hundred feet. Between Gulf Peak and scenic Lookout Point, near Chattanooga, Tennessee, the line forming the eastern margin of Lookout Mountain has one notable break, Rock Creek Gorge, and at other places is but slightly offset by minor gulches. Along the western wall, major breaks in the sandstone have occurred at only two locations: Trenton Gulf, a deep ravine not far from Trenton; and Johnson Crook, a massive amphitheater near Rising Fawn, at the juncture of Lookout and Wills valleys. These chasms enhance the imposing westward views to be had from Lookout's higher cliffs.

Pigeon Mountain is, in general, similar to the main ridge. It is flat-topped for nine miles, then tapers off brokenly, and its sides are steep and rugged. One knob near its northeastern end is slightly more than 2,300 feet in height.

Sand Mountain is broader than Lookout, and the portion in Georgia is relatively little dissected. The surface of this "mountain" is flat and sandy, with broad marginal ridges rising above its central area, and its highest elevations, near the Tennessee line, are about 1,700 feet. At the Georgia-Alabama boundary, just west of Rising Fawn, a cleft named Deer Head Cove separates Sand Mountain from its small spur, Fox Mountain, whose terminal half lies in Georgia. In the vicinity of the Tennessee River, Sand Mountain becomes carved into rugged gorges by cascading streams, most of these heading near its eastern border and flowing westward to enter the Tennessee and thus the Mississippi drainage.

Climate

Weather records for the Lookout Plateau are scarce, none appearing in Mindling's tables [1941]. The following figures are based on data from Chattanooga, Tennessee, where the climate approximates that of valleys and lower elevations of the Lookout Plateau in Georgia. Temperatures (degrees Fahrenheit): January average, 42; July average, 79; annual average, 60; average dates of first and last killing frosts, November 11 and March 21; growing season, 235 days. Annual rainfall, 52 inches. December, March, and April are the wettest months; March has nearly six inches of rain. The driest time is early fall. Decidedly cooler conditions prevail at higher elevations on Lookout and neighboring mountains. As in the Highland and elsewhere, microclimatic differences are considerable and are illustrated by the two major types of plant community mentioned below.

Vegetation

Forests of oak, oak-pine, or pine, not as dense as those of the Highland, are scattered over the plateau surfaces, while more mesic associations, displaying a wide variety of broadleaf trees and shrubs, occupy the moister sites of gorges and slopes. Relatively xeric species, characterizing drier sites, include white oak (*Quercus alba*), chestnut oak (*Q. montana*), post oak (*Q. stellata*), hickories (*Carya* spp.), sourwood (*Oxydendrum arboreum*), persimmon (*Diospyros virginiana*), flowering dogwood (*Cornus florida*), shortleaf pine (*Pinus echinata*), and scrub pine (*P. virginiana*), the pines dominating the crests of ridges. Trees partial to gorges and valley slopes include American beech (*Fagus grandifolia*), American elm (*Ulmus americana*), tuliptree (*Liriodendron tulipifera*), sweet-gum (*Liquidambar styraciflua*), American holly (*Ilex opaca*), and some eastern hemlock (*Tsuga canadensis*). The ericads, mountain laurel (*Kalmia latifolia*), and rhododendron (*Rhododendron catawbiense*), along with the hemlock, lend a montane "flavor" to this region. This mixed mesophytic forest, considered climax for the Cumberland Province, would prevail over greater area, at the expense of the oak-pine associations, if the plateaus were more mature [Braun, 1950:114, 115]. The prevalent xeric communities of oaks, pines, and accessory trees represent a physiographic, edaphic, and pyric climax, maintained by topography, sandy soil, and to some degree by fire.

Birds of the Lookout Plateau

There have been few reports on the birds of the Lookout Plateau region, and our knowledge of its avifauna is only partial. As mentioned in the discussion of the Highland, the Peregrine Falcon has been found breeding on Lookout Mountain. The Common Raven and Ruffed Grouse probably nested in the region in earlier days [Fox, 1882], but there is no proof that

43

either does at present, nor even that they occur. As shown in Table II, the Golden-winged, Black-throated, Green, Worm-eating, and Blue-winged warblers are breeding species on Lookout Mountain (the Golden-wing not having been found in recent years). All these warblers might well reach lower elevations here than they do in the Highland. Additional species found on Lookout Mountain are listed in Table III. Some of these, as the Scarlet Tanager and Whip-poor-will, are characteristic only of high country in Georgia, but most of them are more widely distributed. The Dickcissel, whose nesting was reported from Rising Fawn by J. T. Park many years ago [Howell, 1909], breeds in only a few isolated colonies in the state. Thus, the Lookout Plateau shares several breeding species with only two or three other regions. All the subspecies are presumably the same as those occurring in the Appalachian Valley, or, as in the Black-throated Green Warbler, the same as in the Highland. Although the Peregrine Falcon seems to be the only known breeder peculiar to the Lookout region, so far as Georgian distribution is concerned, the extensive cliff formations might harbor nests of the raven, at least occasionally, and of other birds as yet unrecorded as breeding in the state (such as Bank and Cliff swallows).

An account of the general status of summer birds on Lookout Mountain has been prepared by Denton [1953], based on observations from June 18 through August 7, 1936, near Mentone, Alabama, close to the Georgia line. The only other general list is that of Stevenson [1944b], who made an all-day bird count on Lookout, June 10, 1943, between Cloudland, Georgia, and Mentone. Both worked at elevations of 1,500 to 1,800 feet. Considering the findings of Stevenson and others, Denton reckoned that among eighty-one species reported from Lookout in summer, seventy-five were probable breeders (47 per cent of the total breeding species in Georgia). According to Stevenson's list, the five most abundant species were the Red-eyed Vireo, Wood Thrush, Chipping Sparrow, Indigo Bunting, and Oven-bird. Other comparatively numerous birds included the Hooded Warbler, Carolina Chickadee, Tufted Titmouse, Brown Thrasher, Cardinal and Eastern Wood Pewee—to mention but a few of the birds that are widespread in Georgia. The relative abundance of certain others, based on Denton's and Stevenson's records, is indicated in Table III.

The fact that the Lookout area has been little worked by bird students warrants brief comment. Practically nothing has been done on Sand Mountain, Georgia, so far as published evidence indicates, while Pigeon Mountain and some parts of Lookout, including its higher elevations, are apparently ornithologically untouched. It should be stressed that virtually all the types of bird problems referred to in the discussion of the Highland are applicable to the Lookout Plateau.

44

III. THE APPALACHIAN VALLEY

The Appalachian Valley, sometimes called the Ridge and Valley Province, is an extensive, elongate land-formation stretching from north central Alabama to New York. It covers, within Georgia, some nine counties and about 3,000 square miles. Here its general elevation is 600 to 800 feet, roughly 1,000 to 2,000 feet below the adjacent mountain areas, Lookout Mountain and the Cohutta Range, which form its northwestern and northeastern boundaries, respectively. The eastern and southern sides of Georgia's portion of the valley are bounded by the Upper Piedmont, whose hilly terrain is generally more elevated than that of the valley. The line of demarcation between the two, a northwest-facing escarpment, extends from the base of the Cohuttas south to northeastern Bartow County, whence it swings westward via Cartersville and Rockmart and crosses the Alabama line. Along some segments of this boundary the two regions show little contrast, as, for instance, near the last-mentioned town, where the valley becomes hilly and the Piedmont is trenched by streams. The Appalachian Valley is made up of broad valleys and numerous ridges, mostly trending with the valley itself. The ridges, some exceeding 1,500 feet above sea level, are especially prominent in the Armuchee section, shortly to be described, situated north and west of the Oostanaula and Coosa rivers.

As to geologic age, the valley's rocks date from the Cambrian and Ordovician periods and are thus older than those of the Lookout Plateau, although not so ancient as those of the Highland. The surface of the Ridge and Valley Province is underlain chiefly by limestone and shales; these are not very resistant to erosive forces and account for the generally low elevation of the region. Harder rocks, chiefly sandstone, characterize the ridges. Through breakdown and decay, shales, and particularly limestone, give rise to fertile, loamy soils, and the valley has, in consequence, some of the best farmland in the state. In some areas, nodules of chert or flint are so abundant as to discourage tillage, but here fruits and berries are commonly grown.

Three major subdivisions of the valley have been recognized [Campbell, 1925: 139ff.]: Rome Valley, a broad, fertile belt on the south and east; Chickamauga Valley, next to Lookout Plateau; and, running between these two, a strip called Armuchee Ridges, which, like the others, extends from Alabama to Tennessee. The bounds of these divisions are indicated in Figure 1.

Rome Valley, the largest of the three, is drained by the Coosa River and its tributaries and is set off from the Armuchee belt by a line of almost continuous ridges. This valley, in which Rome, Dalton, and Cartersville are located, may well be termed a plain, with elevations from about 700

45

feet, near the Tennessee line, to about 600 feet, where the sluggish Coosa enters Alabama; yet its topography is not unvaried. Its highest point, Indian Mountain (most of which lies in Alabama), rises to nearly 2,000 feet above sea level, and there are a few additional isolated ridges and mountains. Horseleg Mountain, near Rome, is more than 1,500 feet in height, and another ridge in this vicinity reaches 1,200 feet. As the smoother part of the valley has a limy bed, the soil is for the larger part rich, and both farming and stock raising are extensively practiced.

Chickamauga Valley is flanked by Lookout and Pigeon mountains on the west and by Armuchee Ridges on the east. This valley has a fairly smooth surface, with productive, much-tilled soil. It is diversified by a number of low ridges; at its southern end one higher one, Dirtseller Mountain, rises 700 feet above the valley floor. A little north of the town of Lafayette, the Chickamauga Valley is crossed by an inconspicuous divide, north of which streams flow toward the Tennessee River and south of which they find their way to the Coosa River and the Gulf.

Armuchee Ridges lie between these two sections and comprise a series of long ridges whose trend corresponds in a rough way with that of the Valley Province. These mostly rise about 700 feet above the narrow, intervening valleys. The fertile soil of the valley bottoms, like that of other parts of the Appalachian Valley, is largely under cultivation. The ridges, with their steep gradients and porous soils, are ill suited to farming, but have everywhere been cut over for lumber. The hard beds of sandstone, which form the geologic framework for these ridges, and associated strata were long ago folded, through great pressure from the southeast, into arched anticlines and trough-like synclines. A differential wearing away of these, particularly of the anticlines, with the less resistant layers becoming weathered and eroded more deeply than the sandstone, has resulted in the ridge-like formations of harder rock.

Climate

Climatic data for the valley at large, based on records from four counties [Mindling, 1941], are as follows. Temperatures (degrees Fahrenheit): January average, 43; July average 78; annual average, 61; average dates of first and last killing frosts, October 28 and April 9; growing season, 200 days. Annual rainfall, fifty-four inches. As in other parts of northern Georgia, there are two peaks of rainfall, one in midsummer and the other in winter, with lighter rains in late spring and still lighter ones in fall. These data pertain to localities below 800 feet.

Vegetation

The southern extremity of the Appalachian Valley, including the portion in Georgia, was originally covered with an oak-pine forest. The pines, ex-

46

cept on poorer and drier sites, bear a subclimax relation to the oaks. According to Harper [1930], the commonest trees of the general region are loblolly pine (*Pinus taeda*), shortleaf pine (*P. echinata*), post oak (*Quercus stellata*), southern red oak (*Q. falcata*), blackjack oak (*Q. marilandica*), tuliptree (*Liriodendron lulipifera*), and sweet-gum (*Liquidambar styraciflua*). Many other kinds of trees and shrubs are present. There is an increase southward in the abundance of loblolly pine, while longleaf pine (*Pinus palustris*), a species confined principally to the Coastal Plain, extends into Polk, Floyd, and Bartow counties, in the lower part of the Rome Valley [Duncan, 1950]. As is true for most of Georgia, cultivation and lumbering have spared little, if any, of the original forest; the cut-over stands are scattered and are best represented on the rougher ridges. As most of the Armuchee Ridges are now included in an outlying division of Chattahoochee National Forest, the restoration of forests reminiscent of virgin types may be accomplished in time.

Birds of the Appalachian Valley

The sixty-eight species listed as breeding throughout or nearly throughout Georgia occur in varying abundance as breeding species in the Appalachian Valley or parts of it. Additional ones appear in Tables III and V, making a total of about ninety-four species (59 per cent of the total for the state). The valley has no breeding birds which are not found also in one or more other regions of Georgia. Our knowledge of the valley's birds is hardly more than sketchy, however, and information on which the tables and lists are based is derived largely from publications of Gerhardt [1855–56], Pindar [1926], Jones [1947], and correspondence from Anne Hamilton. A certain few species may reach as low a latitude in this region as in the Piedmont lying to the east; among these are the Whip-poor-will, Baltimore Oriole, and Bewick's Wren—the southern limits of whose ranges remain to be accurately determined. The Red-cockaded Woodpecker, characteristic of the Coastal Plain, occurs regularly about Rome and probably in neighboring parts of the Rome Valley, as does another pineland species, the Brown-headed Nuthatch. A few miles north of Rome, the first state record of the Horned Lark's breeding was recently established by Griffin [1951b]; this species was subsequently found as a breeder in the Lower Piedmont [Denton, correspondence].

Apart from the question of precise range boundaries of the above-mentioned species, various other distributional problems present themselves in Georgia's Appalachian Valley. In the Fort Oglethorpe area of the Chickamauga Valley, a few miles south of Chattanooga, Tennessee, Pindar [*op.cit.*] reported as "rare summer habitants" the Ruffed Grouse, Barn Swallow, Solitary Vireo, Worm-eating Warbler, Golden-winged Warbler, Black-throated Blue Warbler, and Chestnut-sided Warbler; he also found the Blackburnian Warbler until mid-June and considered it a probable summer resident. As Pindar was in the area only about seven months (ending June 17, 1919), his findings—all too briefly reported—are as inconclusive as they are interesting, and a reinvestigation of the bird life of the Oglethorpe area is certainly desirable. Some of the other species known from low-montane or Piedmont areas, as the Black-billed Cuckoo, Cedar Waxwing, and Scarlet Tanager, are not recorded as definitely breeding in the Ridge and Valley Province, but might actually do so on such high terrain as is offered by Indian, Horseleg, and Dirtseller mountains. The relative abundance of various breeding birds along lower ridges and intervening valleys is likewise in need of investigation. One sort of study especially pertinent to this widely cultivated region is that of relations between birds and highly modified environments, including effects of vegetational succession on nesting populations. With this type of study Johnston and Odum, working in the Piedmont, have made an impressive beginning. As many species are transient or winter visitants in the Appalachian Valley, these, too, furnish copious material for ecologic and distributional studies, such as those on waterfowl carried out by Jones and associates at Mount Berry [Jones, 1942–44] and by Sciple in Bartow County [Sciple, 1951c].

IV. THE PIEDMONT REGION

The Piedmont Region, or Central Upland [cf. LaForge, 1925:57 ff.], covering the greater part of northern Georgia, is bounded by the Highland and Appalachian Valley on the north and northwest and by the Coastal Plain on the south and southeast. It extends westward into Alabama and northeastward across South Carolina and well beyond. With an area of more than 18,000 square miles (31 per cent of the state), the Piedmont has a general elevation of somewhat less than 2,000 feet where it meets and interdigitates with the Highland, 1,000 to 1,500 feet on the escarpment where it bounds the valley, and 500 to 700 feet along the Fall Line and the border of the Coastal Plain. The Piedmont Region is one of fairly strong relief and is characterized by granite, gneiss, and other crystalline rocks of disordered, or deformed, structure. The rocks are chiefly Pre-Cambrian, with some areas of Carboniferous granite; hence their age is comparable to that of the Highland. The Piedmont, rather diverse in both slope and general surface form, has been divided into several physiographic subregions. A principal dichotomy, shown in Figure 1, recognizes (1) the Upper Piedmont (or "Piedmont Georgia" of LaForge), and (2) the Lower Piedmont (or "Midland Georgia" of LaForge). We here follow Harper [1930] with respect to names for these two sections; and LaForge [*loc. cit.*] with respect to (1) the actual areas involved, and (2) their several subdivisions or districts. Although the biogeographic importance of

48

the districts is probably rather limited, each may be regarded as a physiographic unit and will, accordingly, receive brief consideration.

The Upper Piedmont

The boundary setting off the Upper Piedmont from the Lower, runs northeast and southwest and is formed through most of its course by the divide which separates the Chattahoochee River from the heads of southeastward-flowing streams. It passes from near Toccoa in northeastern Georgia to the vicinity of Newnan, thence westward in an ill-defined way. As stated previously, the northern edge of the Upper Piedmont meets the mountain and valley regions. Whereas the drainage of the Lower Piedmont is dendritic and runs across the main trend of rock structure, southeastward and southward to the Atlantic and the Gulf of Mexico, that of the Upper Piedmont is longitudinal and flows along the trend of rock westward to the Gulf. The Upper Piedmont is, in general, the more elevated and has greater diversity of relief, including numbers of relatively isolated hills and small mountains (monadnocks); the Lower Piedmont, with a lesser elevation, has greater uniformity and few monadnocks. The three subdivisions of the Upper Piedmont are known as the Dahlonega Plateau, the Atlanta Plateau, and the Tallapoosa Upland.

The Dahlonega Plateau, or "foothill" region, situated at the base of the Highland, has a general altitude of 1,400 to 1,800 feet, and on the south grades little by little into the Atlanta Plateau. The belt of separation between the two is suggested by the sinuous line in Figure 1. West to east, the Dahlonega Plateau stretches from the Appalachian Valley to the state's extreme northeastern margin (formed by the Tugaloo and Chattooga rivers, branches of the Savannah). Easterly, a noticeable escarpment separates this plateau from the Midland Slope of the Lower Piedmont (Fig. 1). The Highland salient that includes Sharp and Pinelog mountains, mentioned earlier as the southernmost high mountains in Georgia, bisects the western portion of the plateau. Ellijay Valley, a lobe of this portion, forms a pass across the Blue Ridge onto the Highland's Ducktown Plateau. This area of the Dahlonega Plateau is drained and deeply trenched by the tortuous Coosawattee. The comparatively elongate central part of the plateau, where the city of Dahlonega is located, is aptly called "piedmont" since it grades, often steeply, into the cernuous backbone of the Blue Ridge. Here the boundary is irregular and difficult of delineation. East of Dahlonega, in White County, Mount Yonah and other outliers represent an interrupted salient, and their heights offer panoramic views of the country. This central section has broad, fertile valleys and is generally more thickly settled than the plateau country on the west and east. The easternmost section embraces the towns of Cornelia and Demorest, has bounds that include the Tallulah Mountains on the north and the above-mentioned escarpment on the south, and displays one monadnock, Griffin Mountain, which, although its summit reaches only 1,800 feet, affords fine views to the southward. Most of the Dahlonega Plateau is drained to the Chattahoochee River, directly or through various tributaries, and the course of drainage is generally southwesterly.

The Atlanta Plateau is a broadly rolling upland which abuts on several surrounding regions (Fig. 1) and comprises two rather distinct plateaus or "platforms"—the northern and northeastern Gainesville Platform, generally 1,300 feet or more in elevation, and the more extensive Fairburn Platform, about 1,000 to 1,100 feet in height; the latter encompasses more northerly and westerly parts of the region about Atlanta west to the Tallapoosa Upland. The small part of the Atlanta Plateau north of the Etowah River is hilly and deeply dissected and has lost its plateau-like aspect. Here the most conspicuous landmark is Pinelog Mountain, from which there extends southward a chain of small mountains and hills, with elevations up to 1,800 feet, to a point slightly below the Etowah. North of Atlanta, along the broad upland divide that runs between the Etowah and Chattahoochee rivers are several mountains of fair size, including historic Mount Kennesaw (elevation 1,800 feet). The greater part of this inter-riparian band of the Atlanta Plateau is cultivated and is more generally settled than the hilly, stream-cut country to the north. A third sub-district of this plateau is likewise widely farmed and, like each of the above-mentioned sections, lies athwart the higher Gainesville Platform as well as the Fairburn Platform. This strip includes Atlanta and Gainesville (Fig. 3) and is bounded on the southeast by the Lower Piedmont. One of its most notable features is Stone Mountain, a granitic monadnock, with little soil and sparse vegetation, whose gray dome, rounded and exfoliating, rises 650 feet above the surrounding upland. The line separating the Upper and Lower Piedmont regions represents a former divide between the Chattahoochee basin and various southeastward-flowing rivers, but the latter have now cut through this as the result of headward extension. The Chattahoochee, a fairly straight river, has a narrow drainage basin in relation to its length. This majestic stream, trending with the main rock structure, extends northeast-southwest across practically the full breadth of the Piedmont and has a fringe of flood plain along the greater part of its course.

The Tallapoosa Upland, receiving its name from a town in Haralson County, is the southwestern district of the Upper Piedmont. Its terrain is diverse, partly plateau and partly hilly and rough; it is about 1,300 feet in height, well above surrounding regions. The upland is marked off from the Appalachian Valley by an escarpment, from the Atlanta Plateau by a gradual descent, and from the Lower Piedmont by a strong slope. Westward it extends into Alabama. It is mostly drained by the Tallapoosa and Little Tallapoosa rivers. Between these streams a few prominent knobs

Photograph by Ivan Tomkins

Clapper Rail habitat.

Wilson's Plover habitat at the north end of Tybee Island.

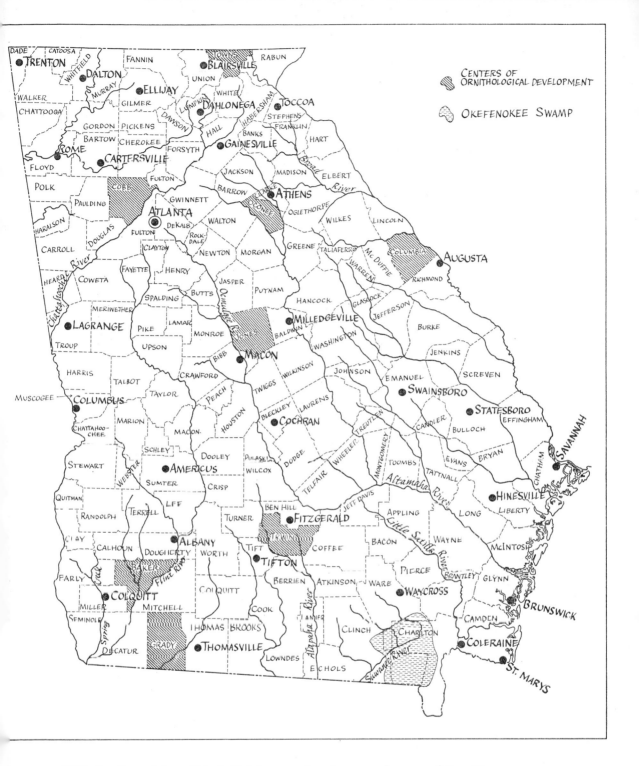

FIG. 3.—Georgia's political divisions, major rivers, and some of its cities and towns. In addition to the shaded counties, most of the localities shown are, or have been, centers of ornithological activity.

51

contribute to the relief; one of these is Tally Mountain, whose elevation approaches 1,500 feet. As is also true of the Atlanta Plateau, settlements and agricultural areas of the Tallapoosa district are mainly on uplands away from the river valleys.

The Lower Piedmont

Specific broad differences between the Upper and Lower Piedmont have already been pointed out. The area covered by the lower region, also called Midland Georgia, is shown in Figure 1, together with its physiographic subdivisions. Each of these units is treated separately in the following paragraphs.

The Greenville Plateau is the highest district and occupies approximately the western third of the Lower Piedmont. A generally uniform upland area, this plateau is 800 to 900 feet above sea level in its northern portion, dropping to 700 feet or less in the vicinity of the Fall Line. Except along the valleys of the Flint and Chattahoochee rivers, it is little dissected; its drainage, unlike that of the rest of the Lower Piedmont, is to the Gulf of Mexico. The south central part of the Greenville Plateau is occupied by the Pine Mountain District. North of this mountain ridge the plateau is highly populated, including the cities of LaGrange and Griffin, and farmland is almost everywhere; the territory south of the ridge is not so extensively cleared and settled. The geologic structure of the Greenville Plateau is similar to that of the Upper Piedmont, although the kinds of rock are not so disordered, diverse, or spottily distributed as they are in the region to the north.

The Pine Mountain District (Fig. 1) is, as the name suggests, the most elevated part of the Greenville region. It extends sixty-five miles, from the Chattahoochee River to Barnesville, and its greatest width is ten miles. Its ridges are linear, steep, and rough, and some are tortuous. Only one ridge, Pine Mountain, is apparent at the eastern and western ends. Nearly unbroken, it traverses the full length of the district. Its maximal elevation, near the resort town of Warm Springs, is between 1,200 and 1,300 feet, about 500 feet above the plateau surface. Where crossed by the Flint River, the ridge is so looped that the river has cut three narrow gorges, with sheer precipices and drops exceeding 400 feet. A few miles south of Pine Mountain there is a line of lesser ridges, collectively called Oak Mountain, which extends interruptedly between Harris and Pike counties. Thick beds of coarsely granular quartzite, with high resistance to erosion, are responsible for the small mountains of this district.

The Midland Slope is a broadly sloping belt, twenty to thirty miles wide, shaped somewhat like a tilted "L" and occupying central and northeastern parts of the Lower Piedmont. Its exact position is shown in Figure 1. On the east and south this district is bordered, respectively, by the

TABLE IV.

Weather data for the Piedmont Region of Georgia

Divisions	Districts	Temperatures (F.)			Average Dates, First and Last Killing Frosts	Growing Season (days)	Annual Rainfall (inches)
		Jan. Average	July Average	Annual Average*			
UPPER PIEDMONT	Dahlonega Plateau	42	77	59	Nov. 2 and Apr. 6	210	60
	Atlanta Plateau and Tallapoosa Upland	43	78	61	Nov. 2 and Apr. 2	214	50
LOWER PIEDMONT	(all combined)	46	80	63	Nov. 5 and Mar. 29	222	50

* Based on Harper [1930:63].

Washington Plateau and the Coastal Plain, both lower than the Greenville and Atlanta plateaus on the west and northwest. The Midland Slope ranges, accordingly, from about 1,000 feet along the upper edges to 700 feet or less along the lower. This area is generally wanting in strong topographic features, having only a few monadnocks, such as Currahee Mountain, southwest of Toccoa, and Alcovy Mountain, south of Monroe, with altitudes of 1,700 and 1,100 feet, respectively. As is apparent in Figure 1, southeastward-flowing branches of several major rivers cross the slope's northern arm, while the Ocmulgee, on its west side, provides most of the drainage for the southern arm. This district is one of the most densely settled in the state, having abundant waterpower, fairly fertile soils, and a generally healthful climate.

The Washington Plateau, named from the seat of Wilkes County, has an indefinite northwestern margin where it grades into the Midland Slope and a sinuous southern boundary formed by the Fall Line Sand Hills. This plateau extends westward to the Ocmulgee River and northeastward to, and beyond, the Savannah River. It is nearly smooth upland, almost a plain, with a gentle southeastward descent from about 800 to 500 feet. There are scarcely any knobs or ridges of consequence. One, Graves Mountain, in Lincoln County, has an elevation of 900 feet and stands 350 feet above its surroundings. The Washington Plateau is crossed by a dendritic pattern of streams. Some of these, especially the Ocmulgee and Oconee rivers and their branches, have cut deep trenches toward the Fall Line. Settlement of the northwestern part of the plateau is comparable to that of the Midland Slope and is greater than that of the eastern and southeastern portions. The cities of Macon, Milledgeville, and Augusta, situated on the Fall Line, may, however, be regarded as occupying the Washington Plateau, in part, as well as the Coastal Plain.

Climate

Weather data for the Piedmont Region averaged for two stations from the Dahlonega Plateau, four from other sections of the Upper Piedmont, and fifteen from the Lower Piedmont [from tables compiled by Mindling, 1941:819 ff.], are presented in Table IV. As for other regions, the averages are rounded off to the nearest whole number.

A large portion of the Piedmont, like the Highland, is comparatively free from oppressive heat, and summer temperatures are remarkably constant, in contrast to variations experienced from year to year at other seasons [Mindling, 1941:828]. For the Dahlonega Plateau, the months with greatest rainfall are December (nearly 7 inches), January, March, and July (these with 5.4 to nearly 6 inches), with dryer conditions in late spring and especially in fall; for the rest of the Piedmont, Harper [1930: 14] states that March is generally the wettest month, with July or August ranking second, and late spring and fall are again rather dry. Thus, the Dahlonega Plateau resembles the Highland in its heavy winter rains, whereas lower parts of the Piedmont are somewhat intermediate toward the Coastal Plain, where the winter peak is much reduced and the summer peak becomes increasingly prominent [Mindling, *loc. cit.*]. In more northerly parts of the Piedmont Region, snowfall amounts to less than five inches, and in more southerly parts it is slight or none.

Vegetation

Although no virgin forest remains in the Georgia Piedmont, there are scattered forests of second-growth oak, hickory, and associated trees. Some are young growths and others old. These forests, together with cleared fields, early seral stages, culled stands of hardwood, and less modified vegetation in places unsuited to cultivation, make up a mosaic or patchwork throughout the Piedmont Region. From these restricted forest areas, particularly the older stands, a fair picture of the original climax forest may be obtained. This oak-hickory forest is part of the Eastern Deciduous Forest Formation. Nearly all of Georgia was wooded in presettlement times; there were, however, "a number of glades and meadows, . . . mostly in the Piedmont, mentioned by Bartram and other early explorers, but apparently no longer distinguishable from areas artificially deforested" [Harper, 1930:79]. Important trees of present climax and near-climax communities in the Piedmont are white oak (*Quercus alba*), hickories (*Carya* spp.), post oak (*Q. stellata*), black oak (*Q. velutina*), scarlet oak (*Q. coccinea*), southern red oak (*Q. falcata*), and northern red oak (*Q. maxima*), with understory species including flowering dogwood (*Cornus florida*), sourwood (*Oxydendrum arboreum*), red maple (*Acer rubrum*), black gum (*Nyssa sylvatica*), red cedar (*Juniperus virginiana*), and sweet-

TABLE V.

Occurrence and relative abundance of certain breeding birds of the Piedmont and other physiographic regions of Georgia

Species	HIGH-LAND	LOOKOUT PLATEAU	APPALACHIAN VALLEY	Dahlonega Plateau	PIEDMONT REGION		COASTAL PLAIN		
					Upper (in part)	Lower	NW or W part	S-Central part	E or SE part
Cerulean Warbler	(N'·?)				(N)?				
Dickcissel		(N-1)	(N-1)		xx	xx	?		
Horned Lark			†(N-1)			†(N-1)			
Sharp-shinned Hawk	?		?	?	(N-1)				
Spotted Sandpiper			?		(N-1)				
House Wren						†xx[s]			
Brown-headed Cowbird			xx		xx	xx			
Least Bittern			?		xx	xx	?	xx	xx
Brown-headed Nuthatch			xx[ne]		xx[n]	Xx	XX	XX	XX
Red-cockaded Woodpecker			xx[ne]		(xx[e])	xx[e]	xx	xx	xx
Fish Crow						xx[nw]	Xx	Xx	Xx

Explanation of symbols:

XX: common (to abundant).

Xx: fairly common.

xx: uncommon (to scarce).

( ) enclosing other symbol: the status, as given, only probable or likely and actually based on records from contiguous or surrounding regions.

†: records due to recent southward invasions.

?: suspected or uncertain presence.

e: indicates range boundaries to the east.

w: indicates range boundaries to the west.

n: indicates range boundaries to the north.

s: indicates range boundaries to the south.

N-1, N-2: nests (one or two records), these being the only evidence of breeding within the region.

gum (*Liquidambar styraciflua*). On drier or poorer soils, post oak may be more abundant than white oak. Pines (*Pinus taeda* and *P. echinata*), although present, are far more prevalent in subclimax stands and, with the addition of scrub pines (*P. virginiana*) in the northern Piedmont, are the first trees to invade abandoned, once-cultivated, upland clearings, commonly called "old fields." Pine forests usually develop on such sites, acquire a deciduous understory, and are eventually replaced, with oak or oak-hickory forming the more stable, self-perpetuating climax associations. Because pines occupy large areas of Piedmont Georgia, the region's general vegetation may appropriately be regarded as an "oak-pine association" if developmental as well as climax forests be taken into account. In lowlands, including riparian strips, noteworthy successional trees are sweet-gum, tuliptree (*Liriodendron tulipifera*), sycamore (*Platanus occidentalis*), river birch (*Betula nigra*), red maple, elms (*Ulmus* spp.), ash (*Fraxinus* spp.), and hackberry (*Celtis* spp.). The preceding lists are based in considerable part on Oosting [1942, 1948]. On higher salients and monadnocks, largely on the Dahlonega Plateau, are vegetational ecotones, intermediate in varying degree between Highland conditions and those characteristic of the Piedmont [cf. Duncan, 1950:maps]. In general, the flora of this region is "like that of the Piedmont Region of the Central Atlantic States, with, however, a strong infusion of other forms from the Mississippi Valley" [Fox, 1926:423].

Birds of the Piedmont Region
The avifauna of the Piedmont is rich in breeding species, about ninety being known from the Atlanta area [Greene, 1933; Griffin, 1940a]; and about eighty-two from the Athens, Clarke County, region [Burleigh, 1938]. These are far and away the best-studied localities of Piedmont Georgia. For the Piedmont Region generally, approximately 105 bird species are known to breed (66 per cent of the total breeding species in Georgia). In the treatment of the Highland (Table III and text), many of the birds that nest on the Piedmont are taken into account, both the widespread ones and others of more limited distribution. As stated previously, all these breed in the Highland to some extent. There remain a few species which either are seemingly confined to parts of the Piedmont Region, so far as Georgian distribution is concerned, or are shared between the Piedmont and one or more additional regions, exclusive of the Highland. The eleven species falling in these categories are listed in Table V, and further comment on some of these is made shortly.

First, let us consider briefly some of the birds which nest both in the Highland and in portions of the Piedmont. The Cedar Waxwing apparently breeds no farther south than the Dahlonega Plateau, and Bewick's Wren and the Scarlet Tanager have not been found regularly as summer residents much farther south than this foothill belt. Species whose ranges are limited on the south by the Upper Piedmont, or parts thereof, are the Black-billed Cuckoo, Whip-poor-will, and Baltimore Oriole; others, as the Yellow Warbler, Black and White Warbler, Eastern Phoebe, and Robin breed south to the Fall Line, or approximately so, but are not known regularly to breed anywhere on the Coastal Plain. That several species (Robin, Song Sparrow, House Wren, and Solitary Vireo) have recently invaded the Piedmont is brought out in the discussion of the Highland. In addition to these newcomers, most of which are spottily distributed in the Piedmont, there are several breeding species that are relative rarities, notably the Spotted Sandpiper [Griffin, 1952a] and Horned Lark [Denton, correspondence], both having been found breeding in the state only since mid-century. Brown-headed Cowbirds have been known to lay eggs in the Piedmont within the last decade [Denton, 1946a; Parks, 1950a; and others], although this was suspected earlier [Burleigh, 1938]. Other birds have breeding grounds that involve both northern Georgia and greater or lesser portions of the Coastal Plain (Tables III and V). The last three species in Table V are more or less limited in their northward distribution by the Piedmont Region; of these, the woodpecker and nuthatch are mentioned in the Appalachian Valley section. Although the Fish Crow's breeding range, as presently known, barely touches the Piedmont, this corvid appears to be invading, as a breeder, many interior parts of the Coastal Plain [Denton, 1950d] and may eventually become established throughout much of middle Georgia. Certain large species occur regularly or irregularly, and some only casually, as summer visitants in the Piedmont. These include herons, ibises, kites, and from time to time coastal birds (often after storms), but as these are not known to breed north of the Fall Line, none is acknowledged among "Piedmont species" in tables or text.

As to the abundance of breeding birds in the Piedmont, Johnston and Odum, working near Athens, found the Common Meadowlark and Grasshopper Sparrow to be the common "grassland species" in early seral vegetation. Odum [1947e] reported the Pine Warbler as the most abundant denizen of immature loblolly-shortleaf pineland, where the Summer Tanaager, Eastern Towhee, and Field Sparrow were also well represented. In climax oak-hickory forest the Red-eyed Vireo was the most numerous among the nesting species [Odum, 1947f]; ranking next were the Wood Thrush, Cardinal, Summer Tanager, and Tufted Titmouse, in descending order of abundance.

A small group of species shows racial intergradation within the Georgia Piedmont. These include the Common Nighthawk (*Chordeiles m. minor* and *C. m. chapmani*) and Purple Grackle (*Quiscalus q. stonei* and *Q. q. quiscula*). Although each of these may tend to intergrade along the Upper and Lower Piedmont boundary, the correlation is at best only a rough one because of the breadth of intergrading areas. The races of Sparrow Hawk (*Falco s. sparverius* and *F. s. paulus*) and Downy Woodpecker (*Dendrocopos pubescens medianus* and *D. p. pubescens*) apparently intergrade farther south, nearer the Fall Line.

Like other provinces, the Piedmont has plenty of ornithological problems. Purely observational work is yet to be done in many parts, as the Tallapoosa Upland, the Pine Mountain District, and other territory near the Alabama line. Also little known are broad areas between Atlanta and Athens and certain of the regional boundaries. Until students assemble lists of breeding birds from various habitats in many of Georgia's counties (of which only about one-fourth have been explored appreciably), it will be difficult to make even reasonably accurate distribution maps for many of the breeding species such as the Black-billed Cuckoo, Eastern Phoebe, and American Redstart. Even in well-worked areas, the status of certain species remains questionable. For example, does either the Black Rail or the Short-billed Sedge Wren nest about Athens? [Cf. Burleigh, 1938.] As to other phases of study, the Piedmont is in a favorable position, so to speak, for it is in this region and on its borders that most of the larger cities and educational institutions are located. A fair share of future college and university-connected work in Georgia ought, and doubtless will, embrace such areas of endeavor as avian life history, population ecology, and physiology, as well as migration and distribution. With a view to carrying on studies of these kinds, Odum and students at the University of Georgia have already made a significant start. The larger institutions are often indispensable for work involving costly laboratory equipment needed for certain investigations in avian biology. A number of specific problems, relative to Georgia birds generally, were outlined by Odum [1944a,b.] Most of these are applicable to the Piedmont; most still await scientific inquiry; and most, it should be stressed, can eventually be solved by serious amateurs as readily as by trained biologists or "professionals."

V. THE COASTAL PLAIN

The Coastal Plain of Georgia, mostly sandy and relatively flat, covers about 35,600 square miles, or three-fifths of the state. This is part of that extensive province which borders the Atlantic and Gulf coasts of North and Middle America. Within Georgia, it is bounded on the north by the Piedmont Region and on the south by the Florida line; its remaining boundaries are the Chattahoochee River on the west, the Savannah River on the northeast, and the Atlantic Ocean on the east. Its northern edge, next to the Piedmont, is a ridge of sand hills, the "Fall Line," whose crooked, southwest-to-northeast course is marked by the cities of Columbus, Macon, Milledgeville, and Augusta. This line formed an ancient ocean margin during the long period in which the Coastal Plain lay beneath the sea. In con-

TABLE VI.

*Comparison of two systems of classification of regions
within the Coastal Plain of Georgia*

Broad Divisions	Cooke	Harper
	Fall Line Hills	Fall Line Sand Hills Blue Marl Region Southern Red Hills (part)
	Fort Valley Plateau	Southern Red Hills (part)
UPPER COASTAL PLAIN	Dougherty Plain	Southern Red Hills (part) Red Lime Lands Lime Sink Region (part)
	Louisville Plateau	Southern Red Hills (part) Lime Sink Region (part)
	Tifton Upland	Rolling Wiregrass Country (part)
	Hazelhurst Terrace	Rolling Wiregrass Country (part)
	Claxton Terrace	Rolling Wiregrass Country (part) Flat Pine Lands (part) Hammock Belt (part)
LOWER COASTAL PLAIN (COASTAL TERRACES)	Okefenokee Terrace	Tallahassee Red Hill Region Flat Pine Lands (part) Hammock Belt (part)
	Penholoway Terrace	Lime Sink Region (part) Flat Pine Lands (part)
	Satilla Terrace	Flat Pine Lands (part) Coast Strip

trast to the Piedmont, which is built of crystalline rocks of Pre-Cambrian times, the Coastal Plain consists of water deposited sand, clay, and lime stone of more recent origin, with crystalline rocks bedded far below. The region is not a plain in its entirety. Its upper terraces, presenting an elevated, rolling, and sometimes broken topography, have been above ocean level since the late Pliocene. Its lower, or coastal, terraces are characterized by flatness and gentle relief and are overlain by Pleistocene sands. The Coastal Plain is much dissected by rivers and lesser streams. Six of the rivers are through-flowing, arising farther north, while others are indigenous, arising on the plain itself. It is particularly in riparian situations that one may readily distinguish areas of Lower Piedmont from areas of Coastal Plain. In the former region, hard crystalline rocks occur as outcrops along beds and banks of streams and create falls and rapids, whereas the sediments of the latter region, being softer and often unconsolidated, do not so obstruct the streams [Cooke, 1925:19]. Naturally occurring ponds, lakes, lime-sinks, all nonexistent in the Piedmont, accentuate the distinctiveness of the region below the Fall Line. Swamps are commonly found in poorly drained areas, both upland and riparian; by far the largest and best known of these is the Okefenokee. Along the coast, sea beaches, sand dunes, and salt marshes provide other scenery peculiar to the region.

The surface features of the Coastal Plain show considerable diversity, and the region, accordingly, has been subdivided in several ways. We shall here consider the classification of subregions made by Cooke [1925: 17, 21 ff.], based on physiographic studies, and by Harper [1930:6 ff.], based on geology, vegetation, and other natural resources. A comparison of the two systems is made in Figure 1 and in Table VI, which, together with descriptions in the following paragraphs (based largely on Cooke's classification and information), ought to enable one better to visualize both physiographic regions and "natural regions" of southern Georgia. The two schemes of classification need not coincide, of course, but, as we learn more about the land, and particularly about the native flora and fauna, they may be found to approach coincidence more nearly than is indicated in Figure 1. The Coastal Plain has also been separated into Gulf and Atlantic portions (Fig. 1); this division, based on drainage, is of less concern to us than the others, for it seems to bear little relation to the distribution of breeding birds.

The Upper Coastal Plain

The geologically older, more elevated, interior half of the Coastal Plain, conveniently termed the Upper Coastal Plain, is flanked by the Piedmont along the Fall Line and by the Hazelhurst Terrace along its coastward margin. Its several divisions are considered in the following paragraphs.

The Fall Line Hills lie just south of the Piedmont Region, their boundaries being shown in Figure 1. It should be stressed that the Fall Line itself is extremely sinuous, even jagged, in its course and is not everywhere easily distinguished. Along streams the crystalline rocks of the Piedmont are exposed, with younger sediments remaining on intervening hills or ridges; hence the irregularity of the line in Figure 1, shown in very generalized fashion, which marks the sand hills' northern boundary and which may, for the present purpose, be regarded as the Fall Line itself. Several sorts of terrain characterize the Fall Line Hills. There are, in general, more rolling elevations, gentler slopes, and lighter soils toward the Piedmont border, and deeper, V-shaped valleys, more frequent gullies, and redder soils on the south. That red soils prevail on both sides of Cooke's southern boundary for the Fall Line Hills is evidenced in Harper's classification (Fig. 1). Subdivision of Cooke's region does indeed seem justified, with the recognition of a Red Hills Belt, but whether we should follow Harper with respect to boundaries or merely modify Cooke's regions [cf. Norris, 1951c:Fig. 1] is still a moot point.

As Harper [1930:18–20] has pointed out, the Red Hills area differs from the Blue Marl and Fall Line Sand Hill regions in its surface appearance and in its calcareous, widely cultivated soils. The hilliest part of the Fall Line Hills lies in Stewart County along the divide between the Flint and Chattahoochee river systems; this divide forms part of the boundary between the Blue Marl and Southern Red Hills regions of Harper. The underlying rocks in the former area are of Cretaceous age; in the latter, of Eocene age. On the Chattahoochee slope of the Fall Line Hills, one frequently encounters deep gullies and ravines, even amphitheaters, with streams rushing toward the great river. Altitudes range from 600 to 700 feet on the divide to less than 200 at Columbus, thence to about 75 feet at the mouth of Cohelee Creek in Early County. On the wider Flint River slope the hill country is less varied, having broad valleys and many orchards and groves. East of the Ocmulgee River the land is mostly cut to valley levels, with many flat-topped ridges and steep-sided remnants of hills and with maximum relief, as furnished by the deep-cutting Ocmulgee and Oconee rivers, in excess of 300 feet. Still farther east, beyond the divide between the Oconee and Ogeechee rivers, gentler slopes again become prevalent.

The Fort Valley Plateau, a small section of the Upper Coastal Plain, lies between the Flint and Ocmulgee rivers and is included in Harper's Southern Red Hills area. It is a nearly flat valley, with an elevation of about 520 feet at Fort Valley and with a gentle southeastward slope. The soil is characterized by a thin layer of bright red sand overlying light-colored sands and clays. The peach is the most important product in this region, and extensive orchards, some of the largest in the world, dominate the landscape.

The Dougherty Plain, named from Dougherty County, is a calcareous region, its limestone beds dating back to the Oligocene. It extends from extreme southwestern Georgia northeast to the Oconee River, adjoining the Fall Line Hills on the north and west and other divisions as shown in Figure 1. The plain encompasses the greater part of the basin of the lower Flint River, including Spring and Ichawaynochaway creeks, as well as a considerable area to the northeast. Although nearly level over most of its area, the region is still complex topographically and may be subdivided, as indicated by Harper's Red Lime Lands and by the embayment of the Okefenokee Terrace; it slopes from almost 600 feet above sea level, along the northwestern margin, to about 160 feet, where it meets the Tifton Upland and the Okefenokee Terrace (the latter here considered part of the Dougherty Plain), and reaches its lowest level, of about 50 feet, at the junction of the Flint and Chattahoochee rivers in the state's southwestern corner. Where limestone forms the underlying rock, particularly in the large area situated west of the Flint River, the flatness of the land is broken by numbers of depressions or "lime-sinks," saucer-like in shape, some many acres in extent. Some sinks may owe their origin to underground solution, cavern-formation, and subsequent collapse of the soft limestone, although Fenneman [1938:76] maintains that this mode of formation is more often assumed than proved. Some of the lime-sinks hold water permanently; others make wet-weather pools and ponds. Throughout this part of the Dougherty Plain, drainage is mostly subterranean; the rain water sinks rapidly through sandy or loamy surfaces, makes its way through limestone pores and passages, and usually reappears as blue springs along banks of rivers and larger creeks. The region's limestone, laid down in the Oligocene, has become silicified near the surface and covered by clay and sand. Darker clay loams, of limy derivation, are among the important soils of the plain. With such level surfaces and generally fertile soils, the Dougherty Plain has been widely cultivated, its largest city, Albany, being a well-known pecan and peanut market. Soils are particularly rich in the Red Lime Lands, where probably half the land is cultivated, as was also true a quarter century ago [Harper, 1930:21].

The Louisville Plateau extends from the Oconee River to the Savannah River. As Harper's classification suggests (Fig. 1), this is a section of deep red sand, its wide, flat areas having elevations from about 500 to 320 feet. Near the plateau's northern edge the land becomes dissected and merges gradually into the Fall Line Hills. Cotton and corn rank among the principal crops.

The Tifton Upland, a non-calcareous region, forms a broad belt across the middle of the Coastal Plain, some 240 miles long with an average width of about 45 miles. As indicated in Figure 1, its northwestern boundary is the more irregular one; between Chattahoochee, Florida, and Cordele, in Crisp County, this boundary is marked by an inland-facing escarpment which, in Decatur County, rises about 150 feet through a horizontal distance of three miles. Elsewhere in the upland, elevations may exceed 350 feet above sea level, as in Jenkins and Tift counties, and they descend to 260 feet, or less, along the edge of the Hazelhurst Terrace. Where crossed by the Ocmulgee River, the upland belt is deeply notched by the Dougherty Plain, or Lime-sink Region, Harper's delineation of this irregularity (Fig. 1) probably being the more accurate. The Tifton Upland is, in general, an area of smoothly rolling hills and plains, with few gullies, and with ridges showing only slight parallelism. Near the larger rivers steeper slopes are found. Cypress ponds are not infrequent, and there are many streams of all sizes. Deep sand beds on east and northeast sides of creeks and rivers, some of the beds more than a mile in width, are especially prominent in this region of the state. The Tifton Upland, corresponding roughly with the northwestern half of Harper's Rolling Wiregrass Country, formerly supported a magnificent growth of longleaf pine forest, of which virgin remnants remain in Grady and Thomas counties. Beneath the cut-over pines are extensive carpets of wiregrass. For many decades the region has been under cultivation, the main crops being cotton, corn, tobacco, sweet potatoes, peanuts, and sugar cane. Stock raising has long been carried on, this being the principal sheep region of the state [Harper, 1930:25]. Some of the towns of the Tifton Upland are Cairo, Moultrie, Tifton, Fitzgerald, McRae, and Swainsboro.

The Lower Coastal Plain

The Lower Coastal Plain consists of several terraces less elevated and more recently exposed than those of the Upper Coastal Plain. The arrangement of the lower ones, as given by Cooke [1925:pl. 5], is indicated by generalized lines in Figure 1. These terraces were once part of the ocean bottom and all were submerged in the late Miocene; they became uncovered and were made into land by the sea's recession from one level to the next. The terrace boundaries thus represent primordial shore lines. As the Hazelhurst was being formed, all of southeastern Georgia, a portion of southwestern Georgia, and probably all the Florida Peninsula were beneath the sea and were then part of the continental shelf. Whereas the Coastal Terraces had their genesis in the Pliocene and Pleistocene periods, the sea beaches and sand dunes, as well as most of the alluvial and swamp deposits, are of still more recent origin.

The Hazelhurst and Claxton Terraces. Adjoining the Tifton Upland at an elevation of 260 feet, the Hazelhurst Terrace gradually slopes toward the southeast, about one and one-half feet per mile, and meets the Claxton along a low scarp, the base of which is about 215 feet above sea level. The latter region, its gradient similar to that of the Hazelhurst, descends to about 160 feet at its coastward margin. Except where trenched by streams, both regions are relatively level, and the strip between the Hazelhurst belt and the rolling hills of the Tifton Upland is one of rather clear contrast. Yet the Hazelhurst Terrace falls within Harper's division, the Rolling Wiregrass Country, as does the northeastern part of the Claxton strip. Near the Florida line, the Claxton Terrace and the still lower Okefenokee Terrace include, but show no correlation with, intrusive parts of Harper's three divisions: the Hammock Belt, the Tallahassee Red Hill Region, and the Lime-sink Region. In Georgia, the last-mentioned is a disjunct region; the other two have centers of development in Florida. The rocks of the Hammock Belt are mostly impure limestone, the topography and soils are varied, and the land is generally more fertile than that of the neighboring wiregrass region [Harper, 1930:26]. In the Tallahassee Red Hill Region, phosphatic rocks are characteristic, and there are many lakes and ponds [*ibid.*:28]. The small tongue of lime-sink country occupying parts of Brooks and Lowndes counties is essentially like that already treated. There can be little doubt that these three regions, as presented by Harper, warrant recognition as both biotic and physiographic units of the Coastal Plain.

The Okefenokee Terrace of southeastern and extreme south central Georgia forms a narrow strip northeast of the Oconee River, from 110 to 120 feet above sea level, and a much wider, subtriangular area to the southward, where its elevation ranges from 160 feet, or less, along its western border and from 150 to 120 feet along its eastern one. The latter boundary, from the Florida line north to beyond Little Satilla River, is manifested by Trail Ridge, an inconspicuous divide whose crest, a few miles north of the St. Marys River, is 170 feet above sea level (55 and 95 feet, respectively, above the Okefenokee and Penholoway terraces). Farther north, in the vicinity of Folkston, Charlton County, its height above the flatwoods on the west and east is less (25 and 70 feet, respectively), and still farther north the ridge becomes even less evident. Although the slopes of this escarpment are gentle, there has been considerable erosion on its broader eastern side. The Okefenokee Terrace is the flattest of the subdivisions of the Lower Coastal Plain, mainly falling within the ambit of Harper's Flat Pine Lands (Fig. 1). As a consequence, it is incompletely drained and swampy, having one well-known wilderness area, Okefenokee Swamp, the second largest swamp in the United States. Further mention of this is made in the section on vegetation. There are two intrusive portions, or embayments, of the Okefenokee Terrace in southwestern Georgia. As indicated in Figure 1, one of these involves parts of five counties and, as aforementioned, is here lumped with the Dougherty Plain. The largest city of the Okefenokee Terrace is the railroad center, Waycross, located in Ware County just north of the great swamp.

The Penholoway Terrace, also included within Harper's Flat Pine Lands, is similarly flat, poorly drained, and swampy. It is of somewhat irregular shape, being indented in riparian areas by embayments of the Satilla Terrace, and itself forming indentations into the higher, neighboring terraces on the west. North of the Satilla River, the Penholoway varies from 60 to 70 feet along its western border to 16 or 18 feet above sea level where it adjoins the Satilla Terrace. The southern part is higher, from 70 to 95 feet, with the maximum height reached along the Satilla River. The area's swamps are often delimited by narrow sand ridges. Some of these stand as much as 20 feet above the swamps, but are inconspicuous because of their gentle slopes.

The Flat Pine Lands of Harper's system involve four terraces: the Penholoway, most of the Okefenokee, and parts of the Claxton and Satilla. All this region may be considered as essentially non-calcareous. [Harper, 1930:28]. Sands and sandy loams are the main types of soil. Like the Rolling Wiregrass Country, the Flat Pine Lands have a rather low fertility, although on farms the soil has been greatly improved.

64

The Satilla Terrace, the lowest of all, averages about 30 miles wide and includes three subdivisions; the mainland, the marshes, and the sea islands. This terrace, as shown in Figure 1, corresponds fairly closely with Harper's Coast Strip.

The mainland is mostly between 15 and 25 feet above sea level, with many shallow depressions and poor drainage in interstream areas; it is divided into broad peninsulas by tidal rivers and associated salt marshes. As pointed out by Cooke [1925:22] and as suggested in Figure 1, the boundary between the mainland of the Satilla Terrace and the adjacent region on the west is irregular because of re-entrants (formerly lagoon-like bodies of water) along a number of the rivers. Harper's boundary, which runs somewhat nearer the coastline, particularly as it approaches the St. Marys River, is based chiefly on edaphic features—specifically, on a transition from nearly pure sand of the Flat Pine Lands to a "more silty or marly soil" of the Coast Strip [Harper, 1930:29]. The soil of this strip is moderately fertile, and its cultivated land is proportionally greater than that of the Flat Pine Lands. Flowing artesian wells are characteristic of the mainland as well as other parts of the coastal terrace. The two main cities of this region are the ports, Savannah and Brunswick.

Along the entire coastline, extensive marshes border the mainland and portions of the islands. They are interrupted by sounds and rivers and by open beaches on the seaward sides of most of the islands. The higher areas of marsh are several feet above sea level and are water covered only during storms or unusually high tides. These picturesque grassy expanses, with patches of brown rush, are chiefly "salt marsh," but where this vegetation extends far enough inland, it becomes brackish or even fresh water in nature.

The Sea Islands, often called "The Golden Isles of Georgia," lie close alongside the state's coast from the Savannah River to the Florida line. From north to south, the most important of these are Tybee, Ossabaw, St. Catherines, Sapelo, St. Simons, Jekyll, and Cumberland (Fig. 1). Between the Ogeechee and Savannah rivers there is a complex system of islands including Tybee, Wassaw, Skidaway, Isle of Hope, and Whitemarsh. Tybee Island, on which Savannah Beach is located, fronts the Atlantic for more than three miles and the Savannah River for more than two miles. Farther south, although still along the northern half of the Georgia coast, are Ossabaw, St. Catherines, Sapelo, and Blackbeard islands (the last two, closely linked, forming one roughly rectangular mass); each island or island mass is approximately eight or nine miles long and, except for the wider Ossabaw, is less than three miles across. About half of St. Catherines is marshland, while Ossabaw consists of strips of sand alternating with marshy lagoons [Cooke, 1925:24]. As is specified in the section on vegetation, all the major islands are to some extent forested, with live oak predominating.

Between the mouth of the Altamaha River and St. Simons Island is a close-set group of islands and islets. St. Simons, the largest among these, is separated from Sea Island and Little St. Simons by rivers and is cut off from the mainland by Frederica River and a network of other channels, large and small. A historic area much frequented by sightseers and vacationists, St. Simons Island has long been connected to the mainland by a causeway. The island's backbone is a sand ridge eleven miles long, extending from the northern end to the southern, with a lesser ridge running along the ocean front, reappearing on Sea Island. Tidal marshes and meandering creeks are sprawled on either side of the larger ridge, and dunes reach thirty feet in height just behind the smaller one. Along the eastern borders of these islands, among others, sandy beaches, smooth and white, add an important feature to the coastline and, indeed, seem to bind landscape with seascape. South of St. Simons lies Jekyll Island, now state-owned and open to the public. It is about seven miles long by one mile wide and, like the other major islands, is characterized by beaches, dunes, and marshes as well as forest. The southernmost of the sea islands are Cumberland and Little Cumberland which together stretch for more than 18 miles in a roughly north-south direction, having a maximum width of three miles. The seaward border is sinuous and mostly sandy beach, with dunes piled up to forty feet above the line of breakers. Its wooded interior resembles the mainland in that it averages twenty feet in elevation, but it rises to fifty feet in a few places. Its landward side is largely fringed by salt marsh. Cumberland is one of the least accessible of the larger Sea Islands and can be reached only by boat.

Climate

Because of its large area, topographic diversity, and proximity to the Atlantic and Gulf coasts, the Coastal Plain has a fairly varied climate. (See Fig. 2 and Table VII.) It is apparent that normal summer temperatures are about the same in all sections. Along the Coast Strip, frost-free seasons are a full month longer than near the Fall Line (where conditions are about the same as in the Lower Piedmont). As is evident in Table VII and in data given for other physiographic regions, the average midwinter temperature in the Coastal Plain and other parts of Georgia is only about thirty degrees lower than that for midsummer; in some of the northern states this annual range is as much as sixty degrees [Mindling, 1941:827]. Unseasonably cold or unseasonably warm weather in winter is frequent in the Coastal Plain, as elsewhere in the state [*loc. cit.*]. Similarly, variations in rainfall from year to year are marked, the wettest years at many stations having twice as much rainfall as the driest years. Although annual rainfall averages about the same throughout the Coastal Plain, there is a southward and coastward shift toward warmer and drier winters, the maritime

Photograph by Ivan Tomkins

Typical winter habitat of the Purple Sandpiper,
on Tybee Island, at the mouth of the Savannah River.

Photograph by Ivan Tomkins

A Black-necked Stilt near Savannah.

TABLE VII.

Weather data for the Coastal Plain of Georgia

Division	Harper's Subdivisions	Temperatures (F.)* Jan. Aver.	July Aver.	Annual Aver.	Average Dates, First and Last Killing Frosts	Growing Season (days)	Annual Rainfall (in.)*
UPPER COASTAL PLAIN	Sand Hills, Blue Marl, and Southern Red Hills	48	81	65	Nov. 11–Mar. 18	238	49
	Red Lime Lands and Lime-sink Region	49	81	66	Nov. 12–Mar. 13	244	49
LOWER COASTAL PLAIN	Rolling Wire-grass Country	51	82	67	Nov. 16–Mar. 10	251	48
	Hammock Belt	53	81	68	Nov. 17–Mar. 10	252	52
	Flat Pine Lands	53	82	67	Nov. 17–Mar. 8	254	51
	Coast Strip	53	81	67	Nov. 26–Mar. 3	268	49

* Based on Harper [1930:63]. Averages otherwise derived from Mindling [1941: tables].

effects being greater and those of northwest winds less. There is a con-comitant shift toward wetter summers; the Lime-sink Region, in contrast to the regions north and west of it, has more than 40 per cent of its rain-fall in the four warmest months, and the Flat Pine Lands has more than half falling in the same period, with two-thirds of the annual rainfall com-ing in the six warmest months [Harper, 1930:28]. For the greater part of the Coastal Plain, the wettest month is July, with August next; the driest are October and November. Along the coast, and less often in the interior, there are hurricanes every few years, generally in late summer or fall. The incidence of other violent weather (lightning, hailstorms, and tornadoes) is no greater than that of other states with moderate to abundant rainfall [Mindling, 1941:827].

Vegetation

The forest vegetation of the Coastal Plain belongs, in general, to the oak-hickory division of the Eastern Deciduous Forest. Near the coast it approaches the Subtropical Broadleaf Evergreen Forest which charac-terizes southern Florida. However, it is a narrowleaf evergreen forest— a subclimax pineland—that makes up the most widespread vegetational type. Single-species dominance is manifest in the open stands of longleaf pine (*Pinus palustris*) which, indeed, tend to monopolize the landscape, especially over the Rolling Wiregrass Country and the Lower Coastal Plain. The evergreen component of forested land is further accentuated by live oaks (*Quercus virginiana*) and evergreen magnolias (*Magnolia grandiflora*), as well as by various undershrubs, with gallberry (*Ilex glabra*) prominent among these. All the above-mentioned plants and many others are characteristic of Coastal Plain communities; the plain is thus readily distinguishable from the Piedmont and other regions vegetationally as well as physiographically. Further evidence of a natural division of habitats along the Fall Line has been provided by the Muskogian Indians, of which there were two major dialect groups, one in Piedmont Georgia and the other on the Coastal Plain [Kroeber, 1939:66]. But the vegetation of the Coastal Plain is varied in life-form and is extremely diverse floristically, and a certain resemblance to the Piedmont is shown by its many kinds of deciduous trees and shrubs, some of which have a statewide distribution. Some of the principal habitat types of the plain and their more prevalent plants are listed below; these are based on Robert F. Thorne, and also on Harper [1930], Grimm [1946], and Duncan [1950], with additional information from Small [1933]. As is true of other regions of the state, the Coastal Plain has been cleared and farmed extensively.

A. HABITAT TYPES FOUND ESSENTIALLY
THROUGHOUT THE GEORGIA COASTAL PLAIN

(1) *Old fields and fence-rows,* on account of the abandonment of cultivated areas, are seral communities, often replaced by pineland, with growths of small trees and shrubs as persimmon (*Diospyros virginiana*), sassafras (*Sassafras albidum*), wild cherry (*Prunus serotina*), old-field, or loblolly, pine (*Pinus taeda*), and at lower levels broomsedge (*Andropogon* spp.), dogfennel (*Eupatorium* spp.), and other grasses and forbs.

(2) *Cypress ponds* support pond cypress (*Taxodium distichum imbricarium*), which is generally dominant; there is frequently an admixture of swamp black gum (*Nyssa sylvatica biflora*) and lower vegetation, including button-bush (*Cephalanthus occidentalis*), red maple (*Acer rubrum*), and myrtle-leaved holly (*Ilex myrtifolia*); often bordering thickets are present, with sweet pepperbush (*Clethra alnifolia*), titi (*Cyrilla racemiflora*), fetter-bush (*Lyonia nitida*), blueberries (*Vaccinium* spp.) and other species; floating aquatics, including *Nymphaea, Brasenia,* and *Nelumbo,* are commonly represented.

(3) *Alluvial bottoms; non-alluvial swamps and bogs:* on river flood plains, trees frequently comprise water oak (*Quercus nigra*), sweet-gum (*Liquidambar styraciflua*), winged elm (*Ulmus alata*), hackberries (*Celtis* spp.) and ash (*Fraxinus* spp.); non-alluvial swamps and bogs have most of these "alluvial species," as well as red maple, swamp black gum, sweet bay (*Magnolia virginiana*), red bay (*Persea pubescens*), and pond pine (*Pinus rigida serotina*).

(4) *Stream banks*, drier than swampy habitats, support many trees, including river cypress (*Taxodium distichum*), black willow (*Salix nigra*), poplar (*Populus deltoides*), river birch (*Betula nigra*), sycamore (*Platanus occidentalis*), and, in southeastern Georgia, Ogeechee lime (*Nyssa ogeche*).

(5) *Pinelands:* the moist type is dominated by slash pine (*Pinus caribaea*) or by pond cypress in wet areas; gallberry (*Ilex glabra*), St. John's-wort (*Hypericum galioides*), and other shrubs may be present (see habitat 2), as well as numerous wild flowers. Dry pineland comprises open stands of longleaf pine (*Pinus palustris*); this is the chief vegetational type of uplands throughout the Coastal Plain; periodic fires are necessary to the perpetuation of this forest type; gallberry is a common shrub in the understory, and wiregrass (*Aristida stricta*) provides main ground cover throughout the Rolling Wiregrass Country and beyond, with saw palmetto (*Serenoa serrulata*) and running oak (*Quercus pumila*) frequent undergrowth on lower terraces.

(6) *Oaklands* are of two types, dry oakland and sandy oak-barrens; the former, which captures sites following the removal of longleaf pine, includes southern red oak (*Quercus falcata*), blackjack oak (*Q. marilandica*), small post oak (*Q. stellata Margaretta*), and mockernut hickory (*Carya alba*) among dominants; oak-barrens, frequent on northeast sides of streams, support turkey oak (*Q. laevis*), bluejack oak (*Q. cinerea*), small post oak, and scattered longleaf pine.

B. HABITAT TYPES OF THE UPPER COASTAL PLAIN

(1) *Rich woods*, of ravines and bluffs along larger rivers, have mainly deciduous trees, including American beech (*Fagus grandifolia*), white oak (*Quercus alba*), southern sugar maple (*Acer saccharum*), and others, together with smaller trees or shrubs (the genera *Cornus*, *Viburnum*, *Calycanthus*, *Hydrangea*, and *Kalmia* are usually represented).

(2) *Beech-magnolia sandy hammocks*, evidently climax on prevailing sandy soil, are notable for their broadleaf evergreen as well as deciduous trees; prominent species are American beech, evergreen magnolia (*Magnolia grandiflora*), pignut hickory (*Carya glabra*), laurel oak (*Quercus phellos laurifolia*), hop-hornbeam (*Ostrya virginiana*), spruce pine (*Pinus glabra*), and flowering dogwood (*Cornus florida*); characteristic shrubs are, in part, American holly (*Ilex opaca*), wild-olive (*Osmanthus americana*), and witch-hazel (*Hamamelis virginiana*).

(3) (*Interior*) *Live-oak hammocks* generally border lime-sinks; live oak may be the sole dominant, although it is often associated with laurel oak, water oak, evergreen magnolia, hickories, and other trees and shrubs; as with the beech-magnolia type, the ground cover is usually sparse.

69

C. HABITAT TYPES OF THE LOWER COASTAL PLAIN

(1) *Beaches and dunes* are present on ocean-fronting islands, the dunes having growths of sea-oats (*Uniola paniculata*); on more stable sands, Spanish bayonet (*Yucca aloifolia*), wax myrtle (*Myrica cerifera*), and yaupon (*Ilex cassine*) are frequent.

(2) *Marshes:* extensive salt marshes, at or near tidal level, comprise switchgrass (*Spartina* spp.) and brown-rush (*Juncus roemerianus*); shoots are mostly two to three feet high, but may exceed six feet along tidal sloughs; *Salicornia* and other halophytic plants are less prevalent; brackish marshes appear where salinity decreases. Various fresh-water marshes, not so extensive as tidal ones, occupy shallower parts of cypress ponds, lakes, or lime-sinks; these often support maiden-cane (*Panicum hemitomon*) or cattail (*Typha latifolia*) and, while present on the Upper Coastal Plain, are generally better developed on the lower terraces.

(3) (*Coastal*) *Live-oak hammocks* are characteristic of the Satilla Terrace but are present farther inland; live oak is dominant, with cabbage-palmetto (*Sabal palmetto*), water oak, evergreen magnolia, American holly, and small trees or shrubs as wax myrtle, yaupon, sparkleberry (*Vaccinium arboreum*), and saw-palmetto present in various combinations.

The Okefenokee Swamp, more than 600 square miles in extent, occupies a large southerly portion of the Okefenokee Terrace, with limited drainage by the Suwannee River toward the Gulf and by the St. Marys River toward the Atlantic. This scenic wilderness consists of several major vegetational associations; these, together with a few of their more prominent plants, are as follows: (1) shallow marshes or "prairies" display growths of white water lily (*Nymphaea odorata*), arrowhead (*Sagittaria* spp.), pickerel-weed (*Pontederia cordata*), and never-wet (*Orontium aquaticum*); (2) open watercourses or "runs", sometimes choked by yellow water lilies (*Nuphar advena*), merge with prairies, with open-centered cypress ponds, or with marginal bogs of sphagnum or fern; (3) wooded swamps or "bays" support stands of pond cypress (river cypress is less frequent), swamp black gum, loblolly bay (*Gordonia lasianthus*), sweet bay, and red bay; the stately cypresses and other trees are draped with Spanish moss (*Tillandsia usneioides*); (4) hammocks have loblolly pine, water oak, evergreen magnolia, and sweet gum, these characterizing smaller islands especially; (5) barrens include moist and dry pineland, with slash and longleaf pines, respectively; present on larger islands and about swamp margins, these barrens are further characterized by saw-palmetto and a mixture of heaths and allies including huckleberries (*Gaylussacia*), blueberries (*Vaccinium*), stagger-bush (*Xolisma ferruginea*), and gallberry. More detailed descriptions of the swamp are given by Wright and Harper [1913] and by Hebard [1941].

70

TABLE VIII.

Occurrence and relative abundance of certain breeding birds of the Coastal Plain of Georgia

Species	COASTAL PLAIN		
	NW or W Part	S-Central Part	E or SE Part
Ground Dove	Xx	Xx	Xx
Great Blue Heron	Xx	Xx	Xx
Little Blue Heron	Xx	Xx	XX
Purple Gallinule	Xx	xx	Xx
Anhinga	xx^n	Xx	Xx
Common Gallinule	xx	xx	xx
Mississippi Kite	xx	xx	xx
Common Egret	Xx	?	XX
Yellow-crowned Night Heron	Xx	?	Xx
Pied-billed Grebe	Xx^n	?	xx^{nw}
Snowy Egret	?	?	XX
Black-crowned Night Heron	?	?	Xx
American Coot	xx^{ne}		xx^{swn}
Osprey	xx		Xx^n
Tricolored Heron			XX
White Ibis			Xx
Painted Bunting			XX^w
Boat-tailed Grackle			XX^w
Swallow-tailed Kite			xx^w
Bald Eagle			Xx^n
Gray Kingbird			xx^{nw}
Sandhill Crane			(O)*
Black-necked Stilt			(N-1)**

* Okefenokee Swamp only.

** Ten other coastal species are listed on page 72.

Explanation of symbols:
XX: common (to abundant).
Xx: fairly common.
xx: uncommon (to scarce).
( ) enclosing other symbol: the status, as given, only probable or likely and actually based on records from contiguous or surrounding regions.
†: records due to recent southward invasions.
?: suspected or uncertain presence.
e: indicates range boundaries to the east.
w: indicates range boundaries to the west.
n: indicates range boundaries to the north.
s: indicates range boundaries to the south.
N-1, N-2: nests (one or two records), these being the only evidence of breeding within the region.

Birds of the Coastal Plain

As the Georgia Coastal Plain occupies a larger area than the other four major physiographic regions combined, it is not surprising that this younger region, together with its coastal fringe, has a greater number of breeding species than any one of the others. Species breeding south of the Fall Line number 120, or 75 per cent of the total (approximately 160 species) known to breed in the state. Among the local or regional studies, all more or less complete with respect to breeding birds, that have been made in various parts of the Coastal Plain are the following: Wright and Harper [1913], F. Harper [1929], Murphey [1937b], Denton [1942–43], Sprunt [1945], Grimm [1946], Woodward [1949], Norris [1951c], Norris and Hopkins [1953], and Stoddard. Aside from the essentially statewide birds listed for the Highland, various forms that breed on the Coastal Plain are named in Tables III, V, and VIII, the last including those whose Georgian ranges are limited to the present region. Ten additional species dwell and breed only in salt marsh or sandy coastal habitats: Clapper Rail, American Oyster-catcher, Thick-billed Plover, Willet, Gull-billed Tern, Least Tern, Royal Tern, Black Skimmer, Marsh Wren, and Seaside Sparrow. Still another, the Black-necked Stilt, has recently attempted to breed in Georgia [Tomkins, 1950b]. Of this group, the salt-marsh breeders are the rail and the two passerines, the rest breeding on sand flats, oyster beds, or beaches and dunes.

Before the turn of the century, the Carolina Parakeet and the Ivory-billed Woodpecker bred on the Coastal Plain. Other former breeding species are the Barn Swallow and Bachman's Warbler. The Chachalaca, introduced on Sapelo Island in 1923, has persisted and reproduced but has shown no permanent spread [Jenkins, 1949a]; other birds introduced on Sapelo, including the Ocellated Turkey and other potential game birds, did not long survive [Phillips, 1928]. Several native species, the Brown Pelican, Double-crested Cormorant, American Bittern, Wood Ibis, Limpkin, and Laughing Gull, have been reported in summer from southern and coastal Georgia (the pelican being common) but are not certainly known to lay eggs [Greene *et al.*, 1945]. Still others that may be found eventually to breed on the plain, or perhaps elsewhere in Georgia, are the Old World Cattle Egret (*Bubulcus ibis*), Hooded Merganser, Black Duck, and Mottled Duck.

Some birds that are relatively abundant or ecologically important over extensive areas of Coastal Plain are as follows: (1) in early seral vegetation (old fields, fence-rows, and young pineland), Common Meadowlark, Mourning Dove, Common Bluebird, Bobwhite, and Mockingbird; (2) in longleaf pine forests (mature or submature), Pine Warbler, Bachman's Sparrow, Brown-headed Nuthatch, Eastern Wood Pewee, Blue Jay, Summer Tanager, Great-crested Flycatcher, and Red-cockaded Woodpecker (the last not common, but characteristic), with others, like Eastern Towhees and Yellowthroats, present in suitable understory vegetation; and (3) sandy hammock (with beech, magnolia, oaks and other broadleaf trees), Cardinal, White-eyed Vireo, Hooded Warbler, Red-eyed Vireo, Yellow-billed Cuckoo, and Carolina Wren; Yellow-throated and Parula warblers are abundant species in live-oak hammocks of southeastern Georgia.

In general, the more numerous species appear first in the preceding

TABLE IX.

Approximate correlation of breeding ranges of eight passerine species with physiographic subregions of the Coastal Plain; the southern boundary of each range, except as otherwise indicated, approaches or coincides with the southern boundary of the region in question

Species	Subregions	
	GULF COASTAL PLAIN*	ATLANTIC COASTAL PLAIN
Grasshopper Sparrow	Fall Line Hills (except southern extremity)	Fall Line Hills (?)
American Goldfinch	Fall Line Hills	Fall Line Hills (?)
Chipping Sparrow	Southern Red Hills	Apparently no correlation; breeds south to northern Liberty County
Prairie Warbler	Southern Red Hills	Apparently no correlation; abundant breeder in Emanuel County and present along coast
Field Sparrow	Southern Red Hills and Red Lime Lands (southward into Seminole County)	Louisville Plateau
Louisiana Waterthrush	Southern Red Hills (scarce south of Sumter County)	"Upper Coastal Plain"
Kentucky Warbler	"Upper Coastal Plain"	"Upper Coastal Plain"
Indigo Bunting	Rolling Wiregrass Country, Hammock Belt, and Tallahassee Red Hill Region	Rolling Wiregrass Country; northern portion of Flat Pinelands (?)

* The Prairie Warbler, Field Sparrow, and Louisiana Waterthrush occur also in the Tallahassee Red Hill Region as known or probable breeders and thus appear to have broken ranges in southwestern Georgia.

lists. This appraisal, both abbreviated and tentative, is based on observations by Grimm [1946] and on counts by Fleetwood [1947d,e; 1948b], Aldrich and Burleigh [1946], Norris [1951c, 1952d], and Whitney and Whitney [1952], in addition to impressions from general field work in southern Georgia. Among the commonest species in deciduous flood-plain forests, as censused by Farrar and Whitney [1952] in Bibb County, are the Red-eyed Vireo, Acadian Flycatcher, Prothonotary Warbler, and Carolina Wren. The writer suspects that in dry, sandy oak-barrens of the Coastal Plain, the ecologically versatile Blue-gray Gnatcatcher is the most abundant species, but only a census will tell. In well-managed timberlands of the Thomasville region, Bobwhite, Turkeys, and Mourning Doves are plentiful, the story of their increase, ways of life, and management, particularly of the Bobwhite, having been well told by Stoddard [1931, 1936, and other publications].

TABLE X.

Approximate or apparent areas of intergradation of adjoining races of twelve widespread, breeding species in relation to physiographic sub-regions of the Coastal Plain; the first-listed race for each species has the more northerly or inland distribution.

Species	RACES	AREA(S) OF INTERGRADATION
Red-bellied Woodpecker	*Centurus carolinus zebra* and *C. c. carolinus*	Fall Line vicinity and Southern Red Hills
Eastern Towhee	*Pipilo erythrophthalmus canaster* and *P. e. rileyi*	Southern Red Hills
Carolina Chickadee	*Parus c. carolinensis* and *P. c. impiger*	"Upper Coastal Plain" (north of Rolling Wiregrass Country)
Great-crested Flycatcher	*Myiarchus crinitus boreus* and *M. c. crinitus*	Rolling Wiregrass Country (Gulf Coastal Plain); Fall Line vicinity (Atlantic Coastal Plain)
Bachman's Sparrow	*Aimophila aestivalis bachmani* and *A. ae. aestivalis*	Rolling Wiregrass Country
White-eyed Vireo	*Vireo griseus noveboracensis* and *V. g. griseus*	Hazelhurst and Claxton terraces; Southern Red Hills (eastern part of Atlantic Coastal Plain)
Redwing	*Agelaius p. phoeniceus* and *A. p. mearnsi*	"Lower Coastal Plain" (inland terraces)
Yellowthroat	*Geothlypis trichas typhicola* and *G. t. ignota*	Hazelhurst and Claxton terraces
Screech Owl	*Otus a. asio* and *Otus a. floridanus*	Okefenokee and adjacent terraces (southern portions)
Brown-headed Nuthatch	*Sitta p. pusilla* and *S. p. caniceps*	Okefenokee and adjacent terraces (southern portions)
Carolina Wren	*Thryothorus l. ludovicianus* and *T. l. miamensis*	Okefenokee and adjacent terraces (southern portions)
Cardinal	*Richmondena c. cardinalis* and *R. c. floridanus*	Okefenokee and adjacent terraces (southern portions)

There is a rough correspondence among the ranges of several breeding species more or less limited in their southward distribution by portions of the Coastal Plain. Eight species showing this are entered in Table IX. Most of these range farther south (several into Florida), and their boundaries show better regional correlation on the Gulf, or western, side of the plain than on the Atlantic side; this is due to relatively abrupt changes in topography and vegetation on the Gulf side [cf. Thorne, 1949; Norris, 1951c]. Additional species with range limits are the Broad-winged Hawk and American Coot, largely but not wholly confined in the breeding season to the Gulf Coastal Plain; the Boat-tailed Grackle and Painted Bunting, occupying the Satilla Terrace; and the Gray Kingbird, sparsely distributed in summer on certain of the islands and neighboring mainland areas (its status reviewed by Eyles [1941]). Most of the other species whose distribution on the plain is shown in a generalized way in Tables III, V, and VIII cannot readily be associated with physiographic regions or subregions.

The breeding distribution of subspecies, or races, of widespread Coastal Plain species is shown in Table X; the areas of intergradation are linked with physiographic subdivisions in approximate fashion. Table X is, in the main, based on specimens reported by Burleigh [1947b, 1948a] and older records compiled by Greene *et al.* [1945]. Tables IX and X ought both to be regarded as only preliminary and will be modified considerably after more field work is done and more specimens are collected and critically compared. One generalization may be made, however, from evidence in these and other tables: On older, more elevated parts of the Upper Coastal Plain, northern and inland affinities are manifest, at both specific and subspecific levels, whereas southern or Floridian influences are more evident on the lower terraces.

An excellent setting for field studies is presented by the state's Coastal Plain. Some questions relative to breeding-season distribution have already been raised in preceding paragraphs and various tables. As in the Piedmont, an eye ought to be kept open for invaders. Southward-pushing Solitary Vireos and Song Sparrows might well be expected in Coastal Plain localities before many more years; other passerines, notably Field Sparrows and Indigo Buntings, already established on parts of the plain, apparently have invaded or reinvaded some areas comparatively recently (Norris [1951c:35]). In coming years, these and others should be carefully looked for in areas beyond their currently outlined ranges. The Fish Crow, as mentioned earlier, seems to be moving northward and interiorward as a breeding species. Interspecific relations, as between this crow and the Common Crow, Indigo and Painted buntings, and Solitary and Yellow-throated vireos, offer challenging opportunities for the field student. And birds of more westerly distribution, as the Lark Sparrow, should be watched for; as stated previously, nests of one invading, grassland species, the Horned Lark, have already been found in Georgia.

Aside from range extensions and related problems, there are other questions to be faced. The influence of the Fall Line on the distribution of breeding species, as described by Murphey [1937a] for the Augusta region, merits further investigation, as does the question of whether this ancient shore line still affects migratory movements of small land birds (Stoddard, oral communication). Bird students with access to telescopes are urged to participate in the co-operative study of nocturnal migration directed by Lowery and Newman in Baton Rouge [see Lowery, 1951; also *The Oriole*, 17:20, 1952]. As for population studies, we still need more bird censuses, in both breeding and winter seasons, particularly in little-worked habitats like sandy-oak barrens, bottomland hardwoods, large cypress ponds, salt and fresh-water marshes, and live-oak hammocks. Ecologic life-history studies, such as those of Tomkins [1933d, 1944c] on the Black Skimmer and Thick-billed Plover and Hopkins on the Mourning Dove, are ever welcome and, in many instances, provide valuable results that may be comparable to those from other populations, subspecies, or allied species. Useful outlines for such life-history studies are given by Odum [1941] and Skutch [1950]. A greater volume of bird-banding, including color-banding, should be carried out in Georgia; remember that one of the myriads of Chimney Swifts banded by Fleetwood in middle Georgia was among the few that turned up in Peru! The collector can still shed important light on problems relating to racial characteristics of Coastal Plain populations and, with more collecting, can better pinpoint areas of intergradation crudely shown in Table X. Further attempts to correlate distribution of areally restricted species with physiographic sub-regions will likewise hinge upon field observation and collecting. And what is more important, insights into causal relations between racial attributes or range boundaries and environmental factors will, through such endeavor, eventually be gained.

In short, well-conceived regional studies in various disciplines, including life history, taxonomy, and distribution, may and often do yield results which, although worthy in themselves, have far-reaching ecologic and evolutionary implications. Consider, for example, the many sources drawn upon in a recent monograph on the evolution of parental care in birds [Kendeigh, 1952]. Thus, observers in Georgia, from the Highland to the Coastal Plain, can contribute materially to broad biological fields as well as to more restricted ones. As to Georgia's future role in ornithology, we have fervent hopes that her corps of bird students will grow apace and that each will employ any and all species, seasons, surroundings, and study approaches that he can in his efforts to further ornithological knowledge.

ORDER GAVIIFORMES

Loons: *Family Gaviidae*

Common Loon
Gavia immer (Brunnich)

GENERAL DISTRIBUTION: Breeds from northwestern Alaska east across the continent to Labrador and Newfoundland, and south to northern Illinois, northern Indiana, northern Pennsylvania, and Connecticut. Winters almost entirely within the United States, from northern New England and the Great Lakes south to Florida and the Gulf Coast; also to Lower California.

STATUS IN GEORGIA: Occurs as a transient in the spring and in the fall in the interior of the state and as a winter resident on the coast. It is possibly not uncommon, but actual records are not numerous.

Norris reports a bird seen at Tifton May 5 and 6, 1933 [Norris and Hopkins, 1953].[1] About Atlanta it occurs regularly in the spring and in the fall, extreme dates as given by Griffin [MS] being March 22 (1949) and June 3 (1946), and September 30 (1928) and November 28 (1929). Apparently late April sees the height of the spring migration, for Greene [1933] has noted twenty birds on April 25 (1932) in this vicinity. At Athens there are no bodies of water of any size, and the loon is consequently extremely scarce there. There are but two records for the spring migration, May 6, 1926, and April 10, 1927; it was observed in the fall only on November 1, 1925. At Demorest, in Habersham County, Neal [1948] saw a flock of twelve loons on April 11 and 12, 1947. All except two were in full breeding plumage. Jones [1942] considers this species a rare transient at Mt. Berry, in Floyd County, dates of occurrence being October 8, 1934, May 21–22, and October 29, 1939, and December 27, 1941. On the coast A. H. Helme has reported it from Cumberland Island on March 26, and April 16, 1902, and Mrs. V. H. Bassett has recorded it at Savannah on February 11, and March 11, 1928. A rather unusual record is that of a bird in full breeding plumage seen by W. L. McAtee, E. V. Komarek, and H. L. Stoddard on June 11, 1937, on Highway 38, about seven miles west of Hinesville, in Liberty County. It was in a roadside ditch, and while apparently in good physical condition, proved unable to fly because of the limited extent of water available for a take-off. F. V. Hebard observed a

[1] Names and dates in brackets refer to the bibliography or to manuscripts; dates in parentheses are years of observation.

single bird on the St. Marys River, a short distance above the mouth of Mill Creek, on December 31, 1940, and four on Cumberland Sound on February 25, 1949. Specimens have been taken at East Lake, DeKalb County, by Robert W. Smith; at Lakewood, Fulton County, on October 29, 1905, by G. W. Hall; in Newton County on November 13, 1911, by W. H. LaPrade; and on the St. Marys River, in western Camden County, on November 20, 1948, by F. V. Hebard.

HABITS AND RECOGNITION: Because of its extreme wariness, the loon is found in migration mostly on the larger bodies of water, and away from the coast is only infrequently seen. Water-power developments in recent years in the northern part of the state have resulted in the creation of large lakes, and here the loon should be found regularly each spring and fall. In Georgia single birds are usually seen, although on occasion small groups have been observed. Wherever found, the common loon should be easily recognized. In the spring the spotted black and white back and flanks, white breast, and greenish-black head with its long, stout, sharp-pointed bill are unmistakable. The fall plumage is less conspicuous, the top of the head and back being more or less uniformly grayish-black, and the throat white. However, its size (that of a small goose) and distinctive bill should readily identify it. This is one bird that will rarely be seen at close range. Because its food is largely fish, it has acquired a bad reputation with sportsmen, and has been so consistently shot at that it has learned the necessity of keeping well out of gun range.

Red-throated Loon
Gavia stellata (Pontoppidan)

GENERAL DISTRIBUTION: Breeds in the northern part of the Northern Hemisphere, in North America from northern Alaska, northern Canada, and Greenland south to northern British Columbia, northern Manitoba, southeastern Quebec, and Newfoundland. Winters on the Atlantic Coast from the Gulf of St. Lawrence to Florida, and on the Pacific Coast from the Aleutian Islands to Lower California, and on the Great Lakes.

STATUS IN GEORGIA: Occurs as a rare winter visitant on the coast and casually in the interior in migration.

There are comparatively few records for the occurrence of this species in the state. W. W. Worthington records one seen on February 12 and two on February 21, 1890, in the mouth of the Altamaha River. Walter Hoxie secured a specimen at Savannah on February 18, 1908, and this is probably the one that is now in the collection of the University of Georgia, at Athens, without any data. He also identified one picked up by Mrs. V. H. Bassett on the beach at Tybee Island, March 4, 1925. Eugene E. Murphey had a specimen in his collection taken on the Savannah River in Screven County on December 19, 1930. Three birds were seen by William Cordes and Thomas Paxton in Glynn County on December 21, 1940, and F. V. Hebard noted five beyond the St. Marys jetties on February 25, 1949.

HABITS AND RECOGNITION: It is not always possible at a distance to identify this species satisfactorily, so it may be commoner than the few records indicate. It is smaller than the Common Loon, and the bill is less stout and slightly upturned, but often a direct comparison is necessary to determine these points. Possibly the best character for identification is the fact that in winter plumage the back is spotted with white, in contrast to the unspotted back of the larger loon at that season. Its habits are much the same, and when seen, it will be at a distance, on open water of sufficient area to afford suitable protection from any danger that threatens. It readily dives if approached too closely, but is equally adept at taking flight from the water and is far more apt to do so than is the Common Loon.

ORDER COLYMBIFORMES

Grebes: *Family Colymbidae*

Holboell's Red-necked Grebe
Colymbus grisegena holbollii (Reinhardt)

GENERAL DISTRIBUTION: Breeds from northeastern Siberia, northern Alaska, and Mackenzie south to northern Washington, North Dakota, southern Minnesota, and New Brunswick. Winters on the Atlantic Coast from Maine to Florida, on the Pacific Coast from the Aleutian Islands to southern California, and on the Great Lakes.

STATUS IN GEORGIA: Until recently, known as a rare winter visitant on the coast, and as an equally rare late fall and early spring transient in other parts of the state; now apparently fairly common on the coast during the winter months.

Definite records for Georgia have until recent years been few in number. Two specimens were taken by Eugene E. Murphey at Augusta, Richmond County, on February 13, 1904; and another was collected by Isaac F. Arnow at the mouth of the Cumberland River, in Camden County, on February 18, 1904. Griffin [1941] lists this large grebe as a rare winter visitant about Atlanta and gives the extreme dates of occurrence as November 4 (1932) and March 9 (1930). A later date for the spring migration, however, is of a single bird observed at Atlanta by J. M. Sanford on March 27, 1917. Murphey reports seeing two individuals on Lake Olmstead on March 3, 1927. Hebard [letter] states that this species now winters commonly in Cumberland Sound; seven birds were seen there by him December 2, 1950, his earliest date of occurrence in the fall; fifteen were seen on February 16, 1951, and forty-four on December 18, 1951.

HABITS AND RECOGNITION: Anyone familiar with the appearance of a grebe should have no difficulty in readily recognizing this species if fortunate enough to see one in Georgia. It is noticeably larger than the Horned Grebe, with which it might be confused, and during the winter months has a pale grayish chin and throat that contrasts sharply with the much darker gray of the neck. When alarmed, it usually seeks safety by diving, but if forced to fly, it reveals two white patches in each wing that will at once identify it. Holboell's Red-necked Grebe is an extremely wary bird, and can be looked for only on the larger bodies of water. It will dive at the slightest alarm, and, being adept at remaining almost entirely submerged for long intervals, it may not be seen again.

Horned Grebe
Colymbus auritus (Linnaeus)

GENERAL DISTRIBUTION: Breeds from central Alaska and northern Mackenzie east to Ontario and south to southern British Columbia, southern Wisconsin, northern Nebraska, and Maine. Winters on the Atlantic Coast from Maine to Florida, on the Pacific Coast from southern Alaska to southern California, and to some extent in the interior from the Great Lakes to the Gulf Coast.

STATUS IN GEORGIA: Occurs as a scarce transient and winter visitant in the interior of the state and as a common winter resident on the coast.

At Atlanta its status is that of an uncommon winter visitant, extreme dates of occurrence as cited by Griffin [MS] being November 20 (1932) and May 7 (1949). At Athens [Burleigh, 1938], it was noted at rather infrequent intervals in the fall, extreme dates being September 26 (1925) and December 4 (1927). On one occasion only was more than a single individual seen. This was on November 25, 1926, when six birds were found on the small lake on the grounds of Athens Country Club and two on Lake Kirota, on the campus of the University of Georgia. There are no records for the winter months and but one for the spring migration—a single bird, in full breeding plumage, being seen on April 10, 1927. Jones [1942] found this species a rare transient and winter visitant at Mt. Berry, in Floyd County, his dates of occurrence being November 23-24, 1936; November 23 and 26, and December 24, 1939; and March 24-27 and April 15, 1941. There is one record for Milledgeville, March 16, 1945 [Tait, 1946]. In Baker County, Hopkins [1951] noted it on four occasions in 1950, single birds being seen on February 13 and 24, and on March 6 and 21.

Murphey had a specimen in his collection taken in McIntosh County on January 2, 1900, and Hebard [1941] records two on the St. Marys River on December 9, 1940, one south of Camden and the other south of the Charlton County line. Fleetwood [1947] observed it on two occasions in the Okefenokee Swamp, a single bird on January 23, 1947 on the "prairie" at Stump Lake and two the following day at Lake Seagrove. It has been reported on the coast as a common winter resident at Darien, Savannah, and Blackbeard Island, and Hebard [letter] states that he has noted this grebe during the winter months in unusually large numbers on Cumberland Sound. On February 16, 1951, when he was accompanied by Herbert L. Stoddard, fifty-one were seen, and on December 8, 1951 fully five hundred were observed in this same general area.

BLACK VULTURE CHICKS
Coragyps atratus

Finding this nest was no accident. Knowing from experience that Black
Vultures nest in caves, hollow logs, and dense thickets, I watched the
birds' comings and goings, crawled about on hands and knees through a
greenbriar tangle I knew they liked, and finally found the chicks
under a great log. The very next day, in this oddest of studios, I painted
my picture, direct from the living babies. They made not a sound.
I was aware of the circling of the old birds above me because a
rapidly moving shadow often passed close.

Family Colymbidae: GREBES

HABITS AND RECOGNITION: It is only in its rather drab winter plumage that this small grebe will, almost without exception, be seen in Georgia. In full breeding plumage it is a handsome bird, and one not easily confused with any other species, but its fall moult is completed before its arrival in the state in late September, and its spring moult is usually incomplete at the time of its normal departure in March. Its size is that of a small duck, but its pointed bill and long, slender neck will readily identify it as a grebe, and its gray back and pure white underparts are equally diagnostic. Singly—and rarely in small flocks—it can be found at infrequent intervals on the ponds and larger bodies of water throughout the state, and as it is not especially shy, can be satisfactorily observed.

Northern Pied-billed Grebe
Podilymbus podiceps podiceps (Linnaeus)

GENERAL DISTRIBUTION: Breeds locally throughout most of North America from central British Columbia east to Nova Scotia, and south to Florida, Texas, and Mexico. Winters largely in the southern United States and Mexico, a few individuals being found at this season of the year as far north as Vancouver Island on the Pacific Coast, and on the Atlantic Coast as far north as New York.

STATUS IN GEORGIA: Breeds locally in the extreme eastern and southern part of the state, and occurs throughout the state as a common transient. Winters commonly south of the fall line, and in smaller numbers in the northern part of the state.

At Athens [Burleigh, 1938] migrants usually appear during March (March 8, 1927, March 16, 1928, and March 30, 1929), but single birds or small flocks have been seen there during every month of the year. A few remain throughout the winter when the lakes and scattered ponds, as happens at times, do not freeze over in late December or early January, single birds having been noted on February 4, 1927, and January 3, 1928. These birds were unusually plentiful on April 5, 1925, when forty-six individuals were counted on the three lakes in the vicinity of Athens, and on October 15, 1926, when twenty-two were seen in a flock on the city reservoir and several more on Lake Kirota. A single bird that was possibly injured, or may have represented a non-breeding individual, lingered on Lake Kirota from June 3 through July 4, 1925. Johnston [1945] gives extreme dates of occurrence for the Atlanta area as June 18 (1942) and May 22 (1932). Jones [1942] found it a "frequent but not common transient" at Mt. Berry (Floyd County), his extreme dates of occurrence in the spring, over an interval of nine years, being March 3 (1940) and May 21 (1939), and in the fall, September 23 (1939) and December 28 (1940). Dorsey [letter] considers this little grebe an uncommon winter resident at Rome, his extreme dates of occurrence being September 11 (1945) and April 6 (1945). Murphey had specimens taken in Richmond County on November 6, 1898, and January 6, 1911, and reported the bird as breeding there. At Macon Johnston [MS] gives as extreme dates of occurrence August 31 (1936) and May 23. Norris and Hopkins [1953] report it at Tifton on July 15, 1933, and at Fitzgerald as late in the spring as May 28, 1941. Wright and Harper [1913] report it as uncommon in winter in the Okefenokee Swamp, and Hebard [1941] likewise considers it scarce there. He noted it at intervals in January, 1926, and on November 1 and November 26, 1932, December 1, 1934, and November 25, 1937. He has one record for Folkston, December 2, 1940, and stated that John Burch saw twelve on the St. Marys River on September 12, 1941. On the coast it is resident and may possibly breed; it was seen at St. Marys by Helme on January 16 and 22, 1902, and in Liberty County by Hoxie on February 27, 1904.

The first definite breeding record for the state is that of a nest found near Newton in Baker County on April 30, 1926, with eight slightly incubated eggs [Burleigh, 1927]. It was in a rather open growth of reeds fringing the shore of what is known locally as Alligator Pond, and was floating in two feet of water. In construction it was characteristic, being a large wet mass of reeds twenty inches across and about as deep, with a shallow cavity in the top in which the eggs were lying, covered by a thin wet layer of coarse fragments of the reeds. Both birds were heard, but only once were they seen, appearing for a minute or two in the open water well out from the shore. This wariness is characteristic of this species during the breeding season, at which time the bird is more often heard than seen.

Two other nests, seemingly fully built, but empty, were found this same day in another pond near by. Twenty-one years later, on June 3, 1947, Stoddard [1947] again found this grebe nesting at the same spot—three nests with eggs; in two, four each; and in one, seven. A number of empty nests and several broods of young were found in Alligator Pond. On another pond near Albany, in Dougherty County, at least six broods of young were seen. This would indicate that under favorable conditions this species has increased noticeably as a breeding bird in southwestern Georgia since it was first found nesting there. Stoddard [MS] reports this little grebe nesting on Susina Plantation in Grady County in 1944, an adult with three striped young being noted there on June 23. In 1948 a pair reared a brood of young on a pond on Birdsong Plantation, the nest when examined on May 2 holding seven eggs.

HABITS AND RECOGNITION: The Pied-billed Grebe is the common grebe of Georgia, and the one most frequently seen on the ponds and larger bodies of water. Its plumage is rather drab, largely grayish brown, and it can be easily recognized also by its small size and thick, round-tipped bill. In breeding plumage it has a black throat patch and a black line across the bill, but these are lacking during the winter months. In summer it is also distinctly browner in appearance. In migration it can be found wherever there is sufficient water to afford it a food supply and protection from its enemies, and consequently its distribution is general over much of Georgia. Even in moments of extreme danger it is very reluctant to fly, and will almost invariably attempt to escape by diving under the water. It is remarkably adept at remaining submerged for long intervals, with only the bill above the surface of the water, and this is a source of amazement to many unfamiliar with this trait, for having once disappeared, it may not be seen again. If not unduly alarmed, it will, when too closely approached, sink slowly out of sight, but it can, when necessary, dive with surprising speed.

Stoddard, in his unpublished manuscript on the birds of Grady County, comments on a rather unusual trait displayed by the Pied-billed Grebe in that part of the state:

> The writer has noticed an interesting association of these little grebes with alligators on several occasions. When the gator swims, one or more of the grebes may be in close attendance, swimming usually just a few feet from the head of the reptile. Whether it is a matter of companionship, curiosity, or profit in some way from the habit is unknown. In any case, it has been observed on several occasions both during the breeding season and at other times.

ORDER PROCELLARIIFORMES

Shearwaters and Petrels: *Family Procellariidae*

Greater Shearwater
Puffinus gravis (O'Reilly)

GENERAL DISTRIBUTION: Breeds only on Inaccessible Island, in the South Atlantic, but throughout much of the year is found over the entire Atlantic Ocean, from northern Europe and Greenland to South Africa and southern South America.

STATUS IN GEORGIA: One of the rarest birds known to occur in the state, there being but two records of it.

The first is that of a dead bird picked up on the beach on Tybee Island on June 11, 1911, by Hoxie [1911]. Hebard [letter] states that on February 25, 1949, "4 or 5 were seen at the end of the St. Marys Jetties following the shrimp boats, after an eastern storm the day before."

HABITS AND RECOGNITION: Shearwaters are birds of the open ocean and, except during the breeding season, are found near land only when forced in by severe storms. Spending most of their lives on the vast expanse of the Atlantic Ocean, they are able to cope with all but the most tempestuous hurricanes, and as a result it is only rarely that they will be seen near shore. Anyone fortunate enough to observe a Greater Shearwater on the Georgia coast will recognize it with little difficulty. Unlike the gulls, its body is characteristically tapering and cylindrical in appearance, and its long wings are curved and pointed, and it can be distinguished from the other shearwaters by its black bill, white underparts, grayish-brown back and head, and white patch at the base of the tail.

Stormy Petrels: *Family Hydrobatidae*

Atlantic Wilson's Petrel
Oceanites oceanicus oceanicus   (Kuhl)

GENERAL DISTRIBUTION: Breeds on islands in the Antarctic and in the Indian Ocean, wandering north after the breeding season and being found during the late spring and summer months over most of the oceans. On the Atlantic Coast it is found then north to Labrador.

Family *Hydrobatidae:* STORMY PETRELS

STATUS IN GEORGIA: A rare summer visitant on the coast.

There are but three records for the occurrence of this species in the state. Gilbert R. Rossignol reports two specimens taken some fifteen or twenty miles off the mouth of the Savannah River in September, 1926. Don Eyles [1938e] picked up a bird on the beach at Tybee Island on August 8, 1937, that was apparently in too weakened a condition to fly, but he liberated it the following day when it appeared stronger and able to care for itself. Sciple [1939], while deep sea fishing on June 16, 1939, about twenty miles offshore from St. Simons Island, observed one of these petrels as it circled about his anchored boat.

HABITS AND RECOGNITION: Like the shearwaters, petrels are, for the larger part of the year, birds of the open ocean, and except during severe storms will not be seen in the proximity of land. Even then it takes exceptionally violent and protracted gales to drive them near shore, so the sight of one on the Georgia coast is rare. Since they breed in the Antarctic, their young are reared during our winter months, and the appearance of petrels on the Atlantic Coast of the United States in late June, rarely earlier, is merely their means of escaping the rigorous winter weather on their breeding grounds. Wilson's Petrel is an easy bird to identify in life. It is slightly smaller than a Purple Martin, but with its black plumage and graceful swallow-like flight, is somewhat suggestive of that species. It has, however, a distinctive white rump patch, and its feet, with yellow webs, extend far enough beyond the tail as to be easily noticeable.

ORDER PELECANIFORMES

Pelicans: *Family Pelecanidae*

White Pelican
Pelecanus erythrorhynchos   Gmelin

GENERAL DISTRIBUTION: Breeds from Great Slave Lake south to southern California, Nevada, Utah, and Manitoba, and on the coast of Texas. Winters from northern California south along the Pacific Coast to Panama, on the Gulf Coast, and in Florida.

STATUS IN GEORGIA: A rare fall transient, found both on the coast and in the interior.

Actual records for the state are few in number. Arnow [1904] writes of the capture of three individuals, said to have been in an exhausted condition, in the fall of 1903, one in the St. Marys River opposite Kings Ferry, Florida, another in the Satilla River, near Satilla Bluff, and the third on the Stafford Plantation on Cumberland Island. Rossignol [1913] records one shot at the wharves on the Savannah River on October 9, 1912. Sprunt [1930] saw one taken off St. Catherine's Island in October, 1929. Eyles [1938] observed one on Oysterbed Island on July 3, 1938. It was said to have first appeared there on June 2, and was still present on August 15. Howe [1947] reports two seen October 13, 1946, on the Savannah River, near Tybee Light, by members of the Georgia Ornithological Society attending the annual fall meeting on Cockspur Island. The most recent record for the coast is that of two birds seen by Hebard, November 28, 1950, on Kings Bay River opposite the Stafford Plantation on Cumberland Island.

In the interior of the state it has been recorded from three localities. Murphey [1937] listed a specimen in his collection taken on the Savannah River, in Richmond County, on September 14, 1916. Greene [1933] records one specimen taken and two others seen near Lithonia, DeKalb County, about October 1, 1926, and one seen September 16, 1930, on the East Lake Country Club lake at Atlanta. Spratt [1936] reports one "on the Atlanta reservoir" on July 27, 1935, where it was observed at close range as it rested on the water. A recent record is of one bird seen by Fletcher [1946] on October 10, 1945, at Cordele, in Crisp County.

HABITS AND RECOGNITION: The White Pelican is an impressive bird that cannot be mistaken for any other species. Its large size, white plumage, and

88

characteristic flight are unmistakable. When seen in the air, its alternate flapping and soaring and its habit of carrying its head well back on its shoulders and not extended as with the other large water birds are a ready means of identification. It is of only casual occurrence in the state, and its appearance at rather infrequent intervals in the late summer and fall months seem to indicate that Georgia sees only stragglers that have wandered east of the regular path of migration. Its size precludes its appearance on any but the larger bodies of water, and only on the coast does it linger for more than a day.

Eastern Brown Pelican
Pelecanus occidentalis carolinensis (Gmelin)

GENERAL DISTRIBUTION: Breeds locally on the south Atlantic and Gulf coasts of the United States from South Carolina to Texas, and on the Atlantic Coast of Central and South America south to Brazil, also in the Bahamas and the West Indies. Winters from Florida (rarely Georgia) and the Gulf Coast south throughout its breeding range.

STATUS IN GEORGIA: Does not breed but occurs commonly on the coast throughout the larger part of the year, being scarce or absent only during late December and January. There is only one record for the interior of the state.

Nesting as they do both north and south of Georgia's coast line, it is not surprising that Brown Pelicans can be found in the state throughout much of the year. In the spring and in the fall, migrating flocks are much in evidence, while non-breeding birds can be found in small numbers throughout the summer months. Possibly because it is such a common bird, ornithologists have failed to record it in due proportion. Worthington reports this species common in February and March, 1890, near the mouth of the Altamaha River. Helme observed 150 to 200 on Cumberland Island April 12 to 14, 1902. Mrs. Bassett has noted it at intervals in Chatham County from March 11 to May 18, 1928. I saw a flock of approximately 60 birds flying over Ossabaw Sound on May 1, 1921, and on April 30, 1922, found the birds plentiful along the ocean beach near the mouth of the Savannah River. Norris noted this species almost daily in June, 1939, on St. Simons and Sea Islands. A few are usually recorded on Christmas censuses taken in late December, but there is apparently but one record for January. Thomas [1945] saw a single bird at Sea Island on January 16, 1945. The single record for the interior of the state is of one bird that appeared on a lake at Albany on or about August 20, 1952, and remained there for three weeks [Giffen, 1953].

HABITS AND RECOGNITION: The Brown Pelican is a common and characteristic bird of the south Atlantic Coast region, and one that never fails to excite interest when seen for the first time. Its large size and somewhat grotesque appearance set it apart from the other species with which it associates, and as it shows little fear of man, usually no difficulty is experienced in becoming acquainted with it. The tops of old pilings in the harbors or stretches of unfrequented beach are spots where one or more can be found throughout much of the day, although they can just as often be seen resting on the water near shore. Their food is entirely fish, and these they secure by watching for them from the air and then plunging into the water with a violence that sends the spray in all directions. Their flight is so typical that even at a distance they can be recognized with little difficulty. They invariably fly in a straight line, with alternate flapping and soaring, and where there are two or more, one follows the other with a precision equalled by few other species.

There are breeding colonies both in South Carolina and in Florida, but, oddly enough, the Brown Pelican has never been found nesting in Georgia. This is difficult to understand, for there are islands lying off the coast well suited for this purpose. Once established, their breeding colonies, unless disturbed, occupy the same island year after year. With protection, their numbers have been increasing in recent years, and it is quite possible that this increase will ultimately result in the establishment of a breeding colony on the Georgia coast.

Boobies and Gannets: *Family Sulidae*

Gannet
Morus bassanus (Linnaeus)

GENERAL DISTRIBUTION: Breeds in the Gulf of St. Lawrence and in Newfoundland, also in Iceland and the British Isles. Winters from the coast of Virginia (rarely of Massachusetts), south to Cuba and the Gulf of Mexico, and on the coasts of North Africa, the Canaries, and the Azores.

STATUS IN GEORGIA: A winter resident along the coast, probably commoner than the few records would indicate.

What is apparently the first definite record for the state is that of a dead bird picked up on the beach on Cumberland Island by Arthur H. Helme in the winter of 1903. Helmuth [1920] records the species as common on February 25, 1918, off the entrance to the Savannah River, and Tomkins has observed it at this same spot on January 24 and February 26, 1931; January 3, 1932; and December 4, 1938. A single bird was seen by

Family Phalacrocoracidae: CORMORANTS

Griffin [1941] near the mouth of the Blackbanks River on St. Simons Island, Glynn County, on November 16, 1941. Thomas [1945] saw one at Sea Island on January 13, 1945, and considered this species fairly common twenty-five miles offshore from Brunswick on January 18, 1945. Johnston and Major [1950] reported seeing at least forty gannets a few miles offshore from the south end of Sapelo Island on March 18, 1950, fully half of which were in immature plumage. They succeeded in collecting four of these birds, two of them adults, and these are probably the only extant specimens from the state.

HABITS AND RECOGNITION: The Gannet is another species so thoroughly at home on the vast expanses of the Atlantic Ocean that only rarely does it approach the shore. Adults are unmistakable, for they are large white birds with black wing tips, easily twice the size of a Herring Gull, and with long pointed wings and slender, pointed tails. Young birds appear dark gray all over, but their characteristic appearance and actions as they circle over the water will readily identify them. Both in flight and in its method of obtaining food, the Gannet is suggestive of a pelican. When seen offshore, they will be flying close to the water, with alternate flapping and soaring. They are far less sociable than pelicans, however, and do not follow each other with the precision the pelicans display. Their food is almost entirely fish, and this they get by spectacular plunges that frequently reach a depth of fifty feet or more below the surface of the water.

Cormorants: *Family Phalacrocoracidae*

Atlantic Common Cormorant
Phalacrocorax carbo carbo (Linnaeus)

GENERAL DISTRIBUTION: Breeds from the coast of western Greenland south to Nova Scotia, and in Iceland, Scandinavia, northern Russia, and the British Isles. Winters from southern Greenland to New York, and casually to Georgia, and from the Mediterranean south to the Canary Islands.

STATUS IN GEORGIA: A rare winter visitant on the coast.

To Ivan R. Tomkins belongs the credit for adding this species to the state list, for to date he alone has recorded it in Georgia. A specimen was taken by him on October 19, 1930, on the north jetty at the Savannah River Entrance, and he has recorded [1941] single birds seen February 14, 1932, and April 20, 1941. The latter bird was on a piling at the north end of

Blackbeard Island, and compared with several other cormorants close by, was conspicuously whiter beneath.

HABITS AND RECOGNITION: Its larger size and the whiter underparts of the immature birds are the characters that distinguish this species from the other cormorants found in Georgia during the winter months, and a direct comparison is to a large degree essential for satisfactory identification. Consequently, sight records are rather unsatisfactory, and except under the most favorable circumstances must be accepted with a certain amount of reservation. During the breeding season these cormorants have a conspicuous white patch on the flanks, but it is doubtful that birds reaching Georgia in the fall or early winter linger long enough in the spring to acquire this adornment, so useful as a field mark. Because of persecution on its northern breeding grounds this species has until recent years been rather scarce on the Atlantic Coast. However, it is increasing in numbers again, and may in time occur regularly in Georgia during the winter months.

Northern Double-crested Cormorant
Phalacrocorax auritus auritus (Lesson)

GENERAL DISTRIBUTION: Breeds from central Alberta east through Saskatchewan and northern Ontario to Newfoundland, and south to central Illinois, northeastern Arkansas, and the coast of Maine. Winters on the Atlantic and Gulf coasts from New Jersey to Florida and Louisiana.

STATUS IN GEORGIA: Does not breed, but is resident on the coast, occurring as a common winter visitant, and in smaller numbers throughout the summer months. In the interior it is a fairly common winter resident in the southern part of the state and infrequently found north of the fall line during migration.

As is the case with other common birds, actual records are not very numerous. Worthington reported cormorants common in winter near the mouth of the Altamaha River. James Henry Rice, Jr., found them abundant on the Isle of Hope and Colonel's Island, December 14, 1916. I noted a number on the lower Savannah River, January 7, 1923, and on Blackbeard Island, January 21, 1932. Pearson [1922] observed ten birds on Cumberland Island, May 2 to 6, 1921. Mrs. Bassett recorded this species in Chatham County, May 19, 1928, November 4, 1931, and May 28, 1932. Apparently the only specimen taken on the coast is a female collected in Chatham County by G. R. Rossignol, Jr., on December 7, 1908. In the interior, Eyles [1937] reports a flock of twenty of these birds seen on the Chattahoochee River, about eight miles from Palmetto, in Coweta County, on

October 30 and 31, 1936. He personally examined the head and foot of one that was shot then, and verified the identification. Griffin [MS] cites an additional record for the Atlanta area, October 27, 1945 (Major, fide Johnston).

Jones [1942] found this species an uncommon transient at Mt. Berry (Floyd County), his extreme dates of occurrence in the spring being March 15 (1939) and April 16 (1939), and in the fall November 16 (1941) and December 26 (1940). He states that almost invariably single individuals were seen. Norris and Gaulding collected a specimen at Tifton on February 10, 1943, that was identified by Herbert Friedmann as the nominate race [Johnston, 1948]. In Grady County, Stoddard [MS] reports the Double-crested Cormorant "a winter resident, sometimes numerous." He has noted it from late December (December 23, 1945) until April (April 11, 1945). Neal [1949b] noted a single bird on a lake at Demorest on November 24, 1948.

HABITS AND RECOGNITION: In Georgia the cormorant is essentially a bird of the coastal areas, and as common throughout much of the year as is the Brown Pelican. It can be seen singly or in small flocks, and whether in flight or perching on a buoy or an old piling, can be easily recognized. When resting above the water, it appears as a large dark bird with an upright posture. In such a position its slender neck and long tail are equally diagnostic. At close range its hooked bill will distinguish it at once, but as the average bird is wary and difficult to approach, this field mark cannot be taken advantage of very often. When flocks fly by overhead or a short distance offshore, they suggest geese, individual birds following each other in V-formation, or in a long, straight line. Seen on the water, they might be confused with loons were it not for their long necks that are usually held upright. Their food is almost entirely fish, and these they secure by pursuing them under water. They are therefore far less spectacular in their appearance and habits than are the pelicans and, while a characteristic feature of the Georgia coast, excite little attention.

Florida Double-crested Cormorant
Phalacrocorax auritus floridanus (Audubon)

GENERAL DISTRIBUTION: Largely resident from North Carolina south to extreme southern Florida, and west on the Gulf Coast to Louisiana; known to breed, however, only in North Carolina, Florida, and Louisiana. Found also in the Bahama Islands and on the Isle of Pines.

STATUS IN GEORGIA: Possibly a not uncommon winter visitant on the coast, although at present there are only three definite records of its occurrence in the state.

A specimen was taken at Summerville, Chattooga County, on March 1, 1886, and identified as *floridanus* by C. Hart Merriam. Johnston [1948] found a juvenile female of this southern race in the Isaac F. Arnow collection in the University of Georgia Museum, collected by H. P. Hopkins at St. Marys on May 9, 1908. The identification was confirmed by Herbert Friedmann. Stoddard reports a female collected on Sherwood Plantation in Grady County on February 27, 1947. Norris [letter] saw a cormorant at Fitzgerald, Ben Hill County, on July 4, 1939, and it is quite possible that this was an individual of this southern race. This possibility applies also to two birds seen by Grimm [1946] at Hinesville, Liberty County, on April 25, 1945.

HABITS AND RECOGNITION: This subspecies differs from typical *auritus* in size only, being smaller but otherwise indistinguishable from the Double-crested Cormorant. For this reason specimens are necessary to determine its actual status in the state, but breeding as it does in North Carolina, it doubtless occurs on the Georgia coast during the winter months; this, however, has yet to be determined.

Darters: *Family Anhingidae*

Northern Anhinga
Anhinga anhinga leucogaster   (Vieillot)

GENERAL DISTRIBUTION: Breeds from southern North Carolina, Arkansas, and Texas south to Paraguay. Winters throughout most of its breeding range, occurring at this season of the year north to central Arkansas, central Alabama, and southern Georgia.

STATUS IN GEORGIA: Resident in the southern part of the state, and a casual transient north of the fall line.

There are breeding records from Chatham, Liberty, Charlton, Grady, Baker, Dougherty, Ben Hill, Jenkins, Emanuel, Burke, and Jefferson counties, and from St. Simons and Blackbeard Islands. Wright and Harper [1913] record the species as common in the Okefenokee Swamp, nests being found there on May 21 and June 18. Mrs. Bassett [1937] records a nesting colony at King's Pond, Liberty County, that was visited at frequent intervals during 1932. In all, about thirty nests were found; these held eggs on dates varying from May 17 to July 13. The colony was last inspected on August 7, and despite the late date, a number of the nests were found still to contain young. Stevenson [1940] found four pairs nesting on the "Big Pond" near Waynesboro, in Burke County, on May 20, 1939. Three of the nests seen that day contained young, and the other three, fresh eggs.

94

Family Anhingidae: DARTERS

Stoddard [MS] reports one pair nesting on Sherwood Plantation in Grady County in 1940, the nest when examined in June holding five eggs. He also found "about a dozen pairs" nesting on Big Cypress Pond in Dougherty County on June 3, 1947, all the nests examined that day holding young of varying age [Stoddard, 1947]. Norris [1951c] noted "adults and immatures" on Big Cypress Pond, Early County, in June, 1948, and surmised that this species possibly nested there. Odum [letter] reports finding three pairs nesting at McKinney's Pond, in Emanuel County, on May 15, 1953, the nests that day holding fully grown young.

Casual transients have been noted at Macon on October 24, 1931, March 20, 1955, and September 21, 1955 [Johnston, MS], and at Athens on March 25, 1935 [Denton and Byrd, 1935]. Murphey had specimens in his collection taken in Jenkins County on October 31, 1907, and May 10 and June 10, 1910, and at Augusta on September 18, 1942. Hebard [1941] states that this species winters in the Okefenokee Swamp in relatively small numbers, the majority of the birds leaving before the end of October and not returning until late February. From 1929 to 1936 he noted several birds each winter along the Big Water and near the west end of the Suwanee Canal.

HABITS AND RECOGNITION: The Anhinga, or Water-Turkey, is one of the characteristic birds of the larger swamp areas of the southeastern United States, and while it is rather local in its occurrence in Georgia, it can be found, at least in small numbers, wherever there is suitable habitat. It apparently has a definite aversion to salt water, and in this respect differs radically from the herons and other species with which it associates. It is a curious bird in both appearance and actions, and one that cannot be confused with any other. When not feeding, small groups can be found sitting quietly upright in the trees bordering open water, and here their long, sinuous, slender necks, small bodies, and long tails can be seen to advantage. If approached, they frequently drop to the water and swim away with only their heads and long necks above the surface, suggesting at once the name snakebird by which they are commonly known. They are strong, powerful swimmers, and have no difficulty in capturing the fish that form the bulk of their food. They are equally adept in the air, and it is not uncommon during the spring months to see one or more circling overhead until they have reached such a height that they are practically out of sight. In southern Georgia the Water-Turkey nests singly or in small groups, and it is usually the middle of April before breeding activities are well under way. The nests are generally near open water and are in the tops of bushes or on the lower branches of the larger trees, the height varying from five to twenty feet. They are substantial, but crude, platforms of coarse twigs and dead leaves. Three to five chalky-white eggs are laid.

95

Frigate-birds: *Family Fregatidae*

Caribbean Magnificent Frigate-bird
Fregata magnificens rothschildi   Mathews

GENERAL DISTRIBUTION: Breeds from the Bahamas and the West Indies south to the coast of Venezuela. In the late spring and early summer there is a definite northward movement, and this species is found regularly then in Florida and on the Gulf Coast.

STATUS IN GEORGIA: A rare summer visitant on the coast.

Georgia is a little north of the coastal areas where this species is customarily found during the summer months, so there are not many records of its occurrence. Palmer [1912] records a specimen taken at the Sapelo Lighthouse, McIntosh County, on June 8, 1912, by W. G. Cromley. Mrs. Bassett reports the capture of a specimen at Townsend in 1928. Tomkins [1934] records a specimen obtained by G. R. Rossignol on Wassaw Island, Chatham County, on May 16, 1933. The most recent records are those of John Oney: two birds seen at St. Simons Island on September 18, 1947, and single birds in St. Simons Sound on July 6 and August 28, 1949.

HABITS AND RECOGNITION: The Frigate-bird is one of the most spectacular of our sea birds, and it is unfortunate that it is found so rarely in the state. It gets much of its food from the surface of the water, and here its agility because of its small, weak feet, but in the air it is unsurpassed by any other species. With its relatively small body and wide expanse of wing it can move with a speed and precision that cannot fail to impress the onlooker. Even in the calmest weather it remains aloft with no visible movement of wings. It is the exceptional storm that can master its supremacy in the air. It gets much of its food from the surface of the water, and here its agility in picking up small fish or other edible morsels, without wetting a feather, is remarkable to behold. It shows no reluctance, however, in robbing gulls and other species with which it associates of any visible food they may be carrying. It never fails to effect its piracy once its victim has been sighted. The invariable result, after an ineffectual effort by its victim to escape, is the dropping or disgorging of the fish or other desirable morsel which is retrieved in the air by the winged pirate. Seen even at a distance, the Frigate-bird can hardly be confused with any other bird. Its wing expanse of seven and one-half feet, long forked tail, and dark appearance make it readily identifiable.

ORDER CICONIIFORMES

Herons, Egrets, and Bitterns: *Family Ardeidae*

Northern Great Blue Heron
Ardea herodias herodias   Linnaeus

GENERAL DISTRIBUTION: Breeds from southeastern British Columbia and
eastern Washington east through Saskatchewan, Manitoba, and Ontario,
to southern Quebec, south to Iowa, Illinois, Indiana, eastern Tennessee,
and South Carolina. Winters from New York south to Florida and the Gulf
Coast, and in the Bermuda Islands.

STATUS IN GEORGIA: Of casual occurrence north of the fall line throughout the year, and possibly a fairly common winter visitant in the southern
part of the state.

At Athens it was never seen in any numbers, but it occurred throughout the larger part of the year, being absent only for a short interval during
the winter months and again in late spring. Its presence was influenced to
a large extent by the weather, for it was far more plentiful in the summer
if rains were frequent, and, in mild winters, it lingered well into December. Average dates of arrival and departure in Clarke County are March
25 (1926) and November 7 (1924), other dates of occurrence being February 12 (1928), May 29 (1921), June 6 (1929), and December 15 (1926).
At Atlanta, Greene [1933] and Griffin [1941] list this species as a permanent resident, but not known to breed, and Jones [1942] gives it the
same status at Mt. Berry (Floyd County). At Milledgeville, Blanche Tait
[1946] records extreme dates of occurrence as March 27 (1936) and July 5
(1939). It has been reported at Macon from October through January. A
specimen taken by D. V. Hembree at Roswell, in Fulton County, on September 20, 1914, has been found referable to this northern race.

HABITS AND RECOGNITION: It is possible that the Great Blue Heron breeds
sparingly in the northern part of the state, but as yet there is no definite evidence to that effect. An occasional bird is apt to be seen at almost any time
wherever there is enough water to afford it an ample supply of food. Single
pairs have been known to breed in wooded areas where access to the nesting site was so difficult that the nests were seldom found or molested, and
this is possibly the case in Georgia. However, since it is equally possible
that the birds seen during the spring months were non-breeding indi-

Eastern Bobwhite

Colinus virginianus virginianus

Herbert Stoddard can, with a loud, inhalant, whistled imitation of the
Bobwhite's cry of challenge, bring a male bird unbelievably close. Such
birds were not, however, very good as models, for they did not stand
still and they usually whirred off when they failed to find a rival.
The male I painted had certain stubs and branches from which he
whistled his "Bob, Bob-white!" of loneliness. The grass about him is
broom sedge, the yellow-flowered plant a legume called rattlebox.

viduals that had lingered south of their normal breeding range, further study is necessary before any definite conclusions can be reached. Seen in flight or standing quietly at the edge of open water, this heron can be readily recognized by its large size and characteristic appearance. Its color is predominantly blue-gray, and with its height of four feet and its long legs, long slender neck, and long sharp bill, it should not be confused with any other species. In common with other herons, it usually nests in rookeries of varying size, but in migration it is far less sociable, and in Georgia is commonly observed singly, or in groups of two or three. It is at all times a wary bird, and one whose acquaintance can be made only at a distance.

Ward's Great Blue Heron
Ardea herodias wardi   Ridgway

GENERAL DISTRIBUTION: Breeds from Kansas east through Iowa, Illinois, and Indiana to southern South Carolina, and south to the Florida Keys and the Gulf Coast. Winters from southern Georgia, southern Alabama, and the Gulf Coast of Texas south to central Mexico.

STATUS IN GEORGIA: Resident in the southern part of the state.

Erichsen [1921] stated that about Savannah it bred in the more heavily forested areas of the larger coast islands and was at one time a common breeding bird on Little Tybee Island, but there are no recent records of its nesting on any of these islands. This statement is borne out by Rossignol's egg catalog which lists ten sets of eggs taken on Little Tybee Island on May 15, 1906, April 23, 1907, May 4, 1909, and April 7, 1910. Rossignol also took a set of five eggs on Wassaw Island April 19, 1906, and five sets of four eggs each on Goat Hammock, March 25, 1923. Erichsen was present the day the rookery on Goat Hammock was investigated and states [MS] that twenty-two nests were found there: eighteen contained four eggs each, three held three eggs, and one an incomplete set of two eggs. The nests were all in live oaks, averaging twenty-four feet above the ground, and were roughly constructed of coarse dead branches, lined to a varying degree with moss, green leaves, and dry grasses. It is said still to nest at the mouth of the Altamaha River, and Wright and Harper [1913] considered it a fairly common breeding bird in the Okefenokee Swamp.

Stoddard [1947] found a small breeding colony on Big Cypress Pond, in Dougherty County, on June 3, 1947. A dozen occupied nests were seen, in the larger cypress trees, and ranged from twenty to seventy feet above the water. All contained well-grown young on that date. Norris [letter] reports a specimen identified as *wardi* that was taken near Camilla, Mitchell County, on August 5, 1948, that is now at the Emory Field Station in Baker County. Another taken by Norris at Tifton on August 29, 1951, and now preserved as a skeleton at the Museum of Vertebrate Zoology, Berkeley, California, has also been identified as this race.

HABITS AND RECOGNITION: This southeastern race of the Great Blue Heron can be distinguished by its larger size, by its whiter underparts, and by its olive, instead of black, legs. Its habits are similar to those of its more northern relatives, although it is apparently less wary and more easily approached. Although rather local in its distribution during the breeding season, it was at one time a fairly common bird in the southern part of the state. The inroads of civilization, however, have deprived it of many of its former nesting sites, and at present it is known to nest at only a few spots.

American Common Egret
Casmerodius albus egretta (Gmelin)

GENERAL DISTRIBUTION: Breeds from Arkansas, Tennessee, and New Jersey south to Florida and the Gulf Coast, and through Mexico south to Patagonia; also in Oregon and California. Winters throughout the larger part of its breeding range, north to South Carolina and the Gulf Coast, and on the Pacific Coast to Oregon.

STATUS IN GEORGIA: Resident in the southern part of the state, and a summer resident on the eastern edge as far north as Richmond County; of casual occurrence elsewhere during the late spring and summer months.

Breeding rookeries have been reported on Cumberland Island, by Helme, in 1902, and by Pearson [1922] in 1921; by Wright and Harper [1913] in the Okefenokee Swamp in June, 1912; on Ferry Island in Chatham County in June, 1929; and by Greene on Little St. Simons Island in April, 1934. Three birds seen by me at Newton, in Baker County, on May 10, 1931, were feeding at the edge of a large shallow pond, and, because of the date, suggested the possibility that this species might be breeding in one of the near-by swamps. Murphey [1937] recorded the species as extremely scarce in Richmond County thirty years ago, but fairly common now and breeding. Odum [letter] reports 239 occupied nests in a rookery at McKinney's Pond, in Emanuel County, all holding well-grown young when examined on May 15, 1953.

My only experience with a breeding colony of Egrets in Georgia was on Ossabaw Island, in Chatham County, on April 30, 1921. Erichsen [1921] had reported ten or twelve pairs of these birds nesting at this spot in May, 1915, so it was gratifying to me to note a perceptible increase in their number. On the day of my visit approximately forty pairs were found nesting in a small swamp in the middle of the island, with possibly thirty pairs of Snowy Egrets, one hundred pairs of Little Blue Herons, two hundred pairs of Tricolored Herons, and ten pairs of Green Herons. The nests were in small willows that were scattered in small clumps through the swamp and were easily recognized on account of their large size. They were situated ten to twelve feet up from the water and were substantially built of coarse twigs and sticks. Usually there was but one nest in one tree, although as many as four were found together, frequently with nests of the other species in the same tree. Of those examined, ten held small young, and twenty-four, eggs, varying in incubation from fresh to well incubated, and in number from one to four, three, however, being the commonest. Two nests held four eggs each, while in fourteen there were three eggs; in five, two; and in the remainder, one. The birds themselves were not very timid, for, while a sudden noise would startle them, it was not difficult to approach within fifty feet of them.

Although occurring during the winter months in the southern part of the state, it is only in the Okefenokee Swamp that the Egret is found in any numbers in winter. Hebard [1941] records 85 seen by Francis Harper on Floyd's Island Prairie in January, 1917, and estimates that he himself saw about 500 on Chase Prairie in January, 1930. Three years later, on November 25, 1932, he reports fully 2,000 at this same spot. Hopkins [1951] reports 4 seen in Dougherty County on January 11, 1950, and 70 in Baker County on February 24, 1950.

In common with other herons, the Egret wanders north after the nesting season and can be found then in small numbers throughout the northern part of the state until early fall. A very early record is that of a single bird seen by Jones [1942] at Mt. Berry (Floyd County) on April 16, 1941; and Greene [1933] records one near Atlanta on May 20, 1928. Otherwise it is late June or early July before the first individuals are noted north of the fall line. Hembree took a specimen at Roswell, in Fulton County, on June 24, 1927, and Jones reports this species a rare summer visitant at Mt. Berry, one to four individuals being seen throughout July and August. An exceptionally late date of occurrence is that of four birds which were reported seen at the River Farm on November 29, 1935. Griffin [1941] lists the extreme dates of occurrence for the Atlanta area (excluding the single May record) as July 9 (1940) and September 29 (1929). At Athens I recorded this species on rather infrequent occasions, extreme dates of occurrence being July 6 (1947) and July 31 (1926). Johnston [MS] considers the Egret a summer visitant at Macon, giving as extreme dates of occurrence April 4 (1955) and October 11 (1952). There is one winter record, February 28, 1953 (Whitney).

HABITS AND RECOGNITION: Once a common bird in the southern part of the state, the Egret was almost exterminated by the depredations of plume hunters, and had not this practice of killing the birds for their plumes during the nesting season been stopped by rigid laws, it is doubtful that any would be left today. Fortunately, protection was accorded this handsome bird before the last remnants were gone, and today it has increased in numbers to the point where it is as common as it was many years ago. There is no more picturesque sight than that of an Egret standing quietly at the edge of a pool or wending its way low over the top of a somber cypress swamp. Under such conditions its pure white plumage stands out to best advantage and cannot fail to impress even the most casual observer. There are several so-called white herons, but even at a distance the Egret is easily identified. Not only is it considerably larger than either the Snowy Egret or the immature Little Blue Heron with which it might be confused, but it has a distinctive yellow bill and black legs and feet.

Common Snowy Egret
Leucophoyx thula thula (Molina)

GENERAL DISTRIBUTION: Breeds locally in the United States from North Carolina south to Florida and the Gulf Coast of Louisiana and Texas, and south of the United States to Chile and Argentina. Winters throughout its breeding range north to South Carolina, southern Georgia, and the coasts of Louisiana and Texas.

STATUS IN GEORGIA: Breeds commonly along the coast, and regularly occurs there during the winter months. A rare summer visitant elsewhere in the state.

In recent years breeding colonies have been reported from St. Marys, Blackbeard Island, Cumberland Island, Ossabaw Island, St. Simons Island, the mouth of the Altamaha River, Tybee Island, and Everett's Pond, Chatham County. Erichsen [1921] considered that, in May, 1915, not more than twelve pairs of these birds were nesting on Ossabaw Island, but on my visit to this rookery on April 30, 1921, I found that in six years the number had increased to at least thirty pairs. Like those of the other herons, their nests were built in the small willows that were scattered through the swamp and were on the average five or six feet above the surface of the water. All held eggs, usually four, but not infrequently three, and, more rarely, one or two. The rookery on Tybee Island was in quite a different situation, for here the birds were nesting in a small grove of live oaks that stood within one hundred yards of the open beach on one side and the same distance from the Savannah highway on the opposite side. I first visited this rookery on April 26, 1926, and on that date I estimated that there were approximately fifty pairs of Snowy Egrets nesting there, in addition to fully three hundred pairs of Tricolored Herons. Seven years later, on May 10, 1933, I again visited this spot and found the Egrets had increased materially in number, my estimate that day totaling two hundred pairs of these attractive herons. Yet the Tricolored Herons had decreased in number, for not over one hundred pairs were using the rookery that year. In 1926 the nests all held eggs, but in 1933 nesting must have begun much earlier for practically all the nests held three or four small young. Nests were placed literally everywhere in the live oaks, frequently six or more in one tree, and were, without exception, crude platforms of sticks and coarse twigs. Don Eyles [1938] made an exhaustive study of the rookery in June and July, 1937, and found an even more noticeable increase in the number of Snowy Egrets nesting there, his estimate being about 1,000 pairs.

Until recent years this species has been seen on the coast only at infrequent intervals during the winter months, the majority apparently going farther south at the approach of cold weather. Erichsen [MS] reports seeing single birds on Tybee Island January 7, 1923, January 1, 1929, December 27, 1931, and December 24, 1940; and Hebard [1941] noted one bird in the Okefenokee Swamp on December 1, 1932. Tomkins [letter] states that at the present time the species "may be seen in fair numbers all winter long on the coast."

A noticeable characteristic of the Snowy Egret is its partiality for salt water. For this reason, although as in the case of the other herons there is a definite northward movement during the summer months, there are not many records then for the interior of the state. I have never recorded it at Athens, and Griffin [1941] cites but one record for the Atlanta area, a single bird seen July 23, 1939. Bell [1939] reports this species seen in Morgan County from the first of July through the middle of August, 1939. Johnston [MS] cites two records for Macon, May 30 and October 12, 1955. Norris [letter] observed a single bird at Tifton from September 24 to October 8, 1941, and considers this a rather late date for this species there. Stoddard states that in Grady County the Snowy Egret can be seen in small numbers from March (earliest record March 13, 1944) until October, but it is not known to breed in the county. Norris [1951] has noted it throughout the summer months in southwestern Georgia, but states that it apparently does not breed there.

HABITS AND RECOGNITION: As was the case with the larger egret, this beautiful little heron was for years mercilessly slaughtered by plume hunters during the nesting season, until for a time it appeared on the verge of extinction. Protection over a period of years, however, has restored it almost to its former numbers, and today flourishing colonies exist on the coast of Georgia. Its snow-white plumage and graceful movements give it the distinction of being the most attractive of all our marsh birds, especially during the spring months when its nuptial plumes add materially to its beauty.

Normally, heron rookeries are located in the most inaccessible swamps, where observation is possible only at the expense of much effort and personal discomfort, but the Snowy Egrets have obligingly established a thriving colony on Tybee Island, where they can be seen to advantage almost from the main highway. Here it is possible to watch them without alarming them by your presence, for they have become accustomed to the close proximity of human beings, and apparently realize the protection they are afforded at this spot. At this season of the year they are easily distinguished from immature Little Blue Herons, also white and practically the same size, by their nuptial plumes. However, the best field mark at any time of the year is their deep black legs and bright yellow feet, the contrast being readily noticeable even at a distance. In the field, size is often rather deceptive, but during the nesting season this species can be distinguished from the larger egret by its black, rather than yellow, bill.

Stoddard [MS] makes an interesting comment on the feeding habits of this egret in his part of the state:

> It may be quite numerous in late summer when a dozen or more may be seen associating with cattle or other grazing animals in closely cropped pastures either near or distant from water. The birds dart about for insects, at times almost under the feet of the grazing herd. Sometimes one will pick at a fly or other insect on the tender belly of a cow, the reaction to the dagger-like beak being instantaneous and violent. We have in one instance observed a Snowy Egret on the back of a cow; in another case standing sedately on the back of a hog.

Reddish Egret
Dicromanassa rufescens rufescens (Gmelin)

GENERAL DISTRIBUTION: Breeds from southern Texas, Louisiana, and Florida south to Guatemala, and in the Bahamas and the West Indies. Occasional individuals wander north of this breeding range, there being records for Colorado, Illinois, and Georgia.

STATUS IN GEORGIA: Of accidental occurrence on the coast.

There is but one record for the occurrence of this species in Georgia. A bird in immature plumage was collected by William Brewster at St. Marys on April 20, 1877, and is now in the Museum of Comparative Zoology at Cambridge, Massachusetts [Hebard, 1949].

Family Ardeidae: HERONS, EGRETS, & BITTERNS

HABITS AND RECOGNITION: The Reddish Egret was at one time a common bird throughout much of Florida, but persecution by plume hunters so reduced it in numbers that by 1890 it had practically disappeared. In recent years it has appeared again in small numbers, and with continued protection it may regain, to some extent at least, its former status as one of the characteristic birds of the state. It is a slender, medium-sized heron that can be recognized in any plumage by its flesh-colored, black-tipped bill. It can usually be found associating with other herons, and appears at home in fresh-water marshes and about the sloughs and open channels in the salt marsh. When observed feeding in shallow water, it gives the impression of grace and agility, pursuing the small fish with more energy than is displayed by the other herons.

Louisiana Tricolored Heron
Hydranassa tricolor ruficollis   (Gosse)

GENERAL DISTRIBUTION: Breeds from North Carolina and the Gulf states south to the West Indies and Central America and on the Pacific Coast of Mexico. Winters north to South Carolina and Lower California.

STATUS IN GEORGIA: Breeds commonly along the coast, and is casual there during the winter months. Found infrequently elsewhere in the state during the summer months.

It has been recorded as breeding at St. Marys, Cumberland Island [Pearson, 1922], Ossabaw Island [Erichsen, 1921], Altamaha River Swamp, Liberty County [Erichsen, 1919], Blackbeard Island, and Tybee Island. When he visited the rookery on Ossabaw Island in May, 1915, Erichsen estimated that approximately two hundred pairs of Tricolored Herons were nesting there. Six years later, on April 30, 1921, I spent part of the day at this same rookery and found no noticeable increase in their number. The other herons had apparently profited by the protection afforded them, but as far as I could determine, there were again on this date about two hundred pairs of Tricolored Herons nesting on the island. Every available willow had its nests, in the larger ones as many as eight, and few with less than four or five. Even so, a few pairs had been forced to build their nests in thick clumps of cat-tails within a foot or so of the water. All the nests held well-incubated eggs, usually four, but in an occasional instance, three. The nests themselves were substantially built platforms of coarse willow twigs, with a slight depression in which the eggs were lying.

At the rookery on Tybee Island, which I visited on April 26, 1926, I found possibly three hundred pairs of these herons nesting in the live oaks. Here the nests varied from six to twenty feet above the ground and were either at the outer ends of the larger branches or in the very tops of the trees. Despite the date, breeding activities were apparently barely well started, for half the nests held but one or two eggs each, and where there were four, the eggs were invariably fresh. When I returned to this rookery seven years later, on May 10, 1933, I was surprised to find a radical decrease in the number of these herons nesting here, my figures that day including but one hundred pairs of Tricolored Herons. However, this decrease was apparently of short duration, for when Eyles [1938] made a careful study of this breeding colony in June and July, 1937, he stated that, in his opinion, fully eight hundred pairs were represented by nests holding broods of young.

Although found on the Georgia coast during the winter months, this heron is only of casual occurrence then, and there are few definite records. Worthington noted two birds at the mouth of the Altamaha River on December 19, 1889, and again on January 5, 1890. Mrs. Bassett saw a single individual on Ossabaw Island on February 22, 1924, and I personally recorded one on Blackbeard Island on January 21, 1932. The only winter records for the interior are from the Okefenokee Swamp, where Hebard [1941] saw single birds January 1, 1930, and November 25, 1932.

Postnuptial wandering in this species is apparently restricted to relatively few individuals, and only at infrequent intervals is a Tricolored Heron seen north of its breeding range. At Athens I recorded it but once, a single bird appearing on Lake Kirota, on the college campus, on July 21, 1927, where for nine days it was seen daily. Greene [1933] cites two records for the Atlanta area: single birds seen August 19, 1928, and August 11, 1932. Murphey [1937] considers it casual in Richmond County, and Johnston [MS] a rare summer visitor at Macon, occurring between the dates of July 27 (1952) and October 9 (1949). Stoddard reports it in Grady County, August 14, 1944, and from July 13 through August 25, 1945, while in Baker County it was noted twice in 1949, a specimen being taken on July 13 and two seen July 29 [Norris, 1951], and again on two occasions in 1950, a single bird being seen on August 1 and two on August 9 [Hopkins, 1951].

HABITS AND RECOGNITION: Since its nuptial plumes lacked the appeal of those of the two egrets and had no commercial value, the Tricolored Heron was never persecuted by plume hunters, and as a result has always been a common bird throughout its breeding range. In Georgia it has shown a definite partiality for the proximity of salt water, and, while scattered rookeries exist near the coast, it has never been known to breed in the many fresh-water marshes in the interior of the state. It is a medium-sized slender heron with blue, gray, and brown its predominating colors, its appearance being so unlike that of the other herons that no difficulty should be experienced in readily identifying it. Possibly its best field character is its white belly that stands out in such contrast to the rest of its underparts. Along the coast it is a common bird throughout the larger part of the year, and can be seen wherever there is shallow water that affords a suitable food supply. Pools in the open salt marsh are favorite spots, but it can also be found along drainage ditches and at the edges of streams and larger bodies of water. It is energetic and agile in its feeding habits, rarely showing any of the deliberateness of its larger relatives as it pursues small minnows and other aquatic life that form the bulk of its food.

Northern Little Blue Heron
Florida caerulea caerulea (Linnaeus)

GENERAL DISTRIBUTION: Breeds from Delaware south to Florida and the Gulf Coast, and from central Texas south through Mexico and Central America. Winters north to South Carolina and the Gulf Coast of Louisiana. Wanders north regularly during the summer months and occurs casually then as far north as Nova Scotia and Newfoundland.

STATUS IN GEORGIA: Breeds commonly in the southeastern corner of the state, and is of casual occurrence there during the winter months. A regular and fairly common summer visitant throughout the remainder of the state.

Breeding colonies have been reported at St. Marys, Cumberland Island, Ossabaw Island, Mimsville, Tybee Island, the Okefenokee Swamp, Fitzgerald, Emanuel County, and Richmond County. Wright and Harper [1913] examined a colony of several hundred birds in the Swamp in May, 1912. Erichsen [1921] estimated that possibly one hundred pairs were nesting on Ossabaw Island in May, 1915. I visited this same rookery on April 30, 1921, and found approximately the same number of birds. The nests were in the lower branches of the small willows, usually within five feet of the water, and were well built of small sticks and coarse twigs. All held well-incubated eggs, usually four, but occasionally three.

On June 13, 1927, I had the opportunity of visiting the heron rookery on Tybee Island, and estimated that on that date at least one hundred pairs of Little Blue Herons were nesting there in the live oaks. Fully grown young were numerous, while half the nests held other young, in various stages of development, or well-incubated eggs. The nests that had been built earlier in the season and were now empty were quite substantial, while those then in use were in many cases rather frail and constructed of twigs and coarse grass stems. Apparently nesting material had become difficult to obtain. Don Eyles [1938] reports approximately fifty pairs using this rookery in June, 1937, but suggests this estimate may be conservative, so it is possible that no actual decrease has occurred in recent years.

Hopkins [1942] found this species nesting ten miles north of Fitz-gerald on June 3, 1942, there being possibly fifty pairs using the rookeries that he succeeded in locating. On that date the young were well grown, but still unable to fly. Odum [letter] reports finding ninety pairs nesting in the rookery at McKinney's Pond, in Emanuel County, on May 15, 1953, most of the nests still containing eggs.

Although the species is known to winter in the southern part of the state, there are rather infrequent records. Erichsen [MS] reports seeing the Little Blue Heron in Chatham County, December 8, 1918, January 7, 1923, January 1, 1929, December 27, 1931, December 30, 1934, and December 24, 1940. I saw a single bird on Tybee Island, December 15, 1933. Hebard [1941] has observed it casually in the Okefenokee Swamp, one or more being seen on January 4, 1930, November 25, and December 1, 2, and 3, 1932, December 3, 1934, and February 28, 1936. Norris and Hopkins [1953] report seeing four of these herons at Tifton on December 21 and 26, 1941.

The northward movement in the spring occurs in early March, and by the middle of the month many of the birds are back on their breeding grounds. Stoddard [MS] states that the Little Blue Heron appears in Grady County in late February (earliest record February 25, 1950), and is common by early April. Norris and Hopkins [1953] cite as their earliest record for the spring migration at Tifton, March 22 (1932). The birds are of casual occurrence then in the northern part of the state, having been re-corded at Athens on March 25, 1926, at Atlanta by Greene [1933] on March 26, 1932, and at Macon [Johnston, MS] on April 2, 1955.

With no other species is postnuptial wandering during the summer months more pronounced than with the Little Blue Heron. At Athens it invariably appeared by the middle of June, although the numbers seen then were influenced to some extent by the weather. During periods of drought relatively few were observed, while heavy rains in July and Au-gust, resulting in flooded bottom lands, attracted Little Blues. Throughout July, 1926, the open Sandy Creek bottoms were flooded under several feet of water, and by the twenty-seventh of that month twenty of these herons had congregated there, although normally only one or two would be seen. Usually these birds appeared by the middle of June and remained until the first week in September, my extreme dates of arrival and departure being June 13 (1929) and September 30 (1926). At Atlanta, Eyles [1937a] has recorded this species as early in the summer as May 28 (1932). John-ston [1945] gives extreme dates for the Atlanta region as June 24 (1944) and October 2 (1943). Jones [1942] found this species an irregular sum-mer visitant at Mt. Berry (Floyd County). Five birds were seen at Victory Lake on July 22, 1937, and were observed there in varying numbers June 9 to July 15, 1941. The maximum concentration was noted on July 6, twenty-one Little Blue Herons being present that day.

HABITS AND RECOGNITION: As with the Tricolored Heron, this species was rarely molested by the plume hunters, its nuptial plumes having little commercial value. As a result, its numbers were never depleted to any extent, and it has always been fairly common throughout its breeding range in the state. In appearance it is a medium-sized, slender heron, individuals in adult plumage being easily recognized by their dark slate-blue body and dull brownish-red head and neck. Young birds can be easily confused with the Snowy Egret, for they are essentially the same size, and likewise appear pure white in color. The Little Blue Heron's primaries are tipped with bluish gray, but as this is extremely difficult to detect in the field, the best character to rely upon is the color of the legs and feet. This is a uniform dull green, in contrast to the black legs and bright yellow feet of the Snowy Egret. The Little Blue Heron shows a distinct preference for fresh-water marshes, and, being comparatively unwary, is a species likely to be seen by the casual observer. Sociable at all times, it can be found feeding in little groups wherever sufficient shallow water provides the aquatic life that forms the larger part of its food supply. Usually deliberate in its movements, it at times displays considerable agility in pursuing its prey, and it is the exceptional small fish or frog that escapes it then.

Eastern Green Heron
Butorides virescens virescens (Linnaeus)

GENERAL DISTRIBUTION: Breeds from Nova Scotia, Quebec, Ontario, Wisconsin, Minnesota, and North Dakota south to Guatemala and Honduras, and west to Colorado and New Mexico. Winters throughout its breeding range north to South Carolina, Georgia, and the Gulf Coast of Louisiana and Texas.

STATUS IN GEORGIA: A fairly common breeding bird throughout the state, and of casual occurrence during the winter months both on the coast and in the interior.

It has been found breeding in various localities throughout Georgia, but it is unquestionably more numerous on the coast. Here it nests in small colonies, in contrast to the single pairs normally observed elsewhere. Erichsen [1921] comments on the large number nesting in a dense thicket of stunted water-oaks on Wilmington Island, where, on April 18, 1915, the nests were all found to hold full sets of eggs. He records another colony of similar size on Sylvan's Island, on the Herb River, three miles from the town of Thunderbolt, where the nests were placed in the extreme tops of tall pine saplings. Quite a different site was the one I found on Ossabaw Island on April 30, 1921, where possibly ten pairs of these birds were found nesting in the populous rookery in the center of the island. Here the willows had all been pre-empted by the larger herons, and, doubtless because of necessity, the Green Herons had built their nests in thick clumps of cattails within a foot or so of the water. On this date the nests all held slightly incubated eggs, usually four, but occasionally three. That this species is less aggressive than its near relatives is borne out by the history of the rookery on Tybee Island. Erichsen [1921] recorded only the Green Heron there in 1915, and stated that "they were so numerous that every available nesting site was occupied." On my first visit to this spot, however, on April 26, 1926, not a single pair remained, the available sites being all occupied by Tricolored Herons and Snowy Egrets.

Characteristic of the nesting of this species away from the coast is a nest that I found at Athens on May 24, 1925. It held three half-grown young, and was twenty feet from the ground in the top of a small wild cherry tree in underbrush at the foot of a wooded hillside bordering an open swamp. In construction it was typical of nests of these small herons, being a compact and slightly hollowed platform of coarse twigs. Griffin [1940] cites as nesting-season extremes for the Atlanta area, three eggs, incubation undetermined, on April 21, 1922, and four eggs, partly incubated, on May 14, 1905. Apparently the only example of colonization during the breeding season in the interior of the state is that cited by Griffin and Major [1947]. On May 18, 1946, Major and Terry A. McGowan "discovered five occupied nests of this species in a small swampy area near the south fork of Peachtree Creek off Clairmont Road in DeKalb County. On that date two nests contained 4 eggs each, one nest contained 5 eggs, one nest contained 3 eggs and one newly hatched young, and one contained 4 downy young. Two young birds just out of the nest and barely able to fly were climbing about the branches near an unoccupied nest, indicating that six pairs nested in the area during the season. All the nests were located from 2 to 7 feet above standing water in black willow (*Salix nigra*) or buttonbush (*Cephalanthus occidentalis*), and all were within an area less than 75 feet in diameter."

Although an occasional bird winters both on the coast and in the interior, the majority leave the state in October and do not return until the following March. First arrivals in the spring were noted at St. Marys, February 8, 1902; Savannah, March 13, 1904; Cumberland Island, March 21, 1902; Grady County, March 19, 1944; Fitzgerald, March 17 (1942); Atlanta, March 23, 1906; Athens, March 27, 1925; Mt. Berry, March 14, 1939. Dates of birds last seen include Rome, October 7, 1950; Athens, October 30, 1942; Atlanta, October 24, 1942; Macon, October 10 (1952); and St. Marys, October 24, 1905.

Family Ardeidae: HERONS, EGRETS, & BITTERNS

Erichsen [1921] has noted this species at Savannah during the winter months, and Hebard [1941] has seen single birds in the Okefenokee Swamp on January 6, 1930, and January 31, 1931. Norris reports a single bird seen at Tifton by Stephens on December 22, 1932. I saw one of these small herons on South Peachtree Creek, at the edge of Atlanta, on December 26, 1946. It had been seen at this same spot several days previously by Griffin and others.

HABITS AND RECOGNITION: There are probably few birds more familiar to those whose time, to some extent, is spent outdoors, than is the Green Heron. It is less sociable by nature than are the other herons and widely distributed, so that there are few streams and ponds in the state where, at one time or another, this species will not be seen. Being rarely molested, it is not very timid, and will usually permit a reasonably close approach before taking flight. Thus seen, it is easily identified, for it is a small dark heron, with short legs for this group of birds and a short tail. Normally quiet, when flushed it utters an explosive "skeow," that leaves no question about its identity. Its feeding habits are more deliberate than those of the other herons, for it commonly remains for long intervals standing quietly at the edge of a shallow pool waiting for an unwary minnow or other aquatic prey. On occasion, however, it can move with surprising rapidity.

American Black-crowned Night Heron
Nycticorax nycticorax hoactli   (Gmelin)

GENERAL DISTRIBUTION: Breeds from northern Oregon, southern Wyoming, southern Manitoba and southern Quebec south to Paraguay. Occurs regularly in winter north to central California and North Carolina, and casually to Massachusetts, New York, Illinois, Colorado, Utah, and Nevada.

STATUS IN GEORGIA: A fairly common breeding bird on the coast, occurring there in smaller numbers during the winter months. An uncommon migrant and summer visitant throughout the rest of the state.

Breeding colonies have been reported at St. Marys, Cumberland Island, Ossabaw Island, Blackbeard Island, Tybee Island, and at the mouth of the Altamaha River. Erichsen [1921] found a few pairs nesting in the rookery on Ossabaw Island in May, 1915, but I failed to note this species there when I visited the spot in 1921. I estimated not over five or six pairs of these birds nesting in the rookery on Tybee Island on May 10, 1933, and Eyles [1938] found the same meager population there during the studies he made in June, 1937. The nests were noticeably larger than those of the other herons and were built of coarser sticks and twigs, and thus were easily recognized. Erichsen [MS] states that his earliest breeding record for the Tybee Island rookery is a nest that held four fresh eggs on April 22 (1938), his latest one with three incubated eggs, examined on June 9 (1940). Hebard [letter] reports a single pair breeding on Mill Creek, western Camden County, in 1948, the nest when examined on June 8 holding three well-grown young.

During the winter there is a noticeable decrease in the number of Night Herons on the coast, and it is early March before the northward movement is well under way. Helme observed a few birds at St. Marys, January 15 and 28 and February 22, 1902. On Cumberland Island he found this species abundant from March 8 to April 15, 1902, when large numbers came into the marshes each night. Murphey [1937] states that in Richmond County the bird is far less numerous during the winter months. Hebard [1941] saw single birds in the Okefenokee Swamp on October 31, November 2, and November 25, 1932. In Grady County, Stoddard [MS] noted this species on August 4, 1942, September 11, 1944, and April 10, 1949. Norris and Hopkins [1953] state that it is a winter visitant in both Tift and Ben Hill counties, the earliest fall record at Fitzgerald being November 2 (1940) and the latest spring record at Tifton April 2 (1933). At Macon it has been noted on April 13, 1932, in the fall from August 16 (1949) to October 21 (1955), and on December 31, 1949 [Johnston, MS]. At Athens it was scarce during the spring months, my few records being April 30, 1925, and April 16 and 21, 1926. During the summer, however, it was noted at frequent intervals, extreme dates for arrival and departure being July 12 (1927) and September 17 (1927). Griffin [1941] considers it a scarce spring transient in the Atlanta region, his extreme dates being March 19 (1932) and May 16 (1932). There is one recent record for the summer months, August 5, 1950 (Parks, fide Griffin). A single bird was seen at Lake Rutledge, Morgan County, on October 13, 1940 [Griffin, 1940].

HABITS AND RECOGNITION: Because of its relative scarcity and nocturnal habits, this heron is only infrequently seen in Georgia by the casual observer. As its name implies, it is inactive throughout much of the day, remaining quietly in the shelter of the reeds or roosting in trees bordering open water, where it is an inconspicuous feature of the landscape. If frightened by too close an approach, it utters a hoarse "wock" as it departs hurriedly, its flight then being strong, direct, and far swifter than that of the other herons. This characteristic and its stout appearance readily identify it, although in adult plumage, black above and white beneath, it should not be confused with any other species. Young birds are brown, streaked with white, so are radically different in appearance, but their chunky build and short legs are equally diagnostic.

Family Ardeidae: HERONS, EGRETS, & BITTERNS

Eastern Yellow-crowned Night Heron
Nyctanassa violacea violacea (Linnaeus)

GENERAL DISTRIBUTION: Breeds from New Jersey, Illinois, Indiana, Missouri, Kansas, and Oklahoma south to the Bahamas, the West Indies, Brazil, and Peru. Not known to occur during the winter months north of Florida and southern Texas.

STATUS IN GEORGIA: A fairly common summer resident on the coast, and locally common during the breeding season in the Okefenokee Swamp and in Jenkins and Richmond counties. Uncommon and of local occurrence elsewhere in the state.

It has been reported as breeding at St. Marys, Cumberland Island, Little St. Simons Island, the mouth of the Altamaha River, Savannah, the Okefenokee Swamp, and in Jenkins and Richmond counties. In each case the number of birds seen was rather small in comparison to the numbers of the other species with which they were associating. Rossignol [letter] reports a small breeding colony found in Camden County April 26, 1909, six nests examined that day holding either four or five slightly incubated eggs. Stoddard found three pairs nesting on Sherwood Plantation in Grady County in 1938, two nests examined on May 27 holding two and three eggs each. Sprunt [1945] reports four nests found May 18 to 24, 1945, on Altama Plantation in Glynn County.

The northward movement in spring apparently takes place in March and early April. At Darien, first arrivals were noted on April 3 (1890), and at Savannah on March 13 (1904) and March 12 (1905). At Athens I found this species a rather scarce transient. In the spring I recorded it but twice, on April 19, 1924, and on April 6, 1926, while my only fall record is that of two birds seen September 11, 1925. Griffin [MS] lists it as an uncommon summer resident in the Atlanta area, giving as extreme dates of occurrence May 6 (1945) and September 12 (1946). On July 27, 1937, Giles [1937] saw an immature bird that had been shot the previous day in the southwestern part of Atlanta. Another immature bird was observed by Giles and others from July 20, 1937, through August 6, 1937, at a small pond on Lakeview Avenue in northeastern Atlanta. A bird in immature plumage was found "feeding leisurely along the banks of Armuchee Creek seven miles north of the center of Rome" on August 21, 1949 [Griffin, 1950]. Hebard [1941] reports a bird seen by Francis Harper in the Okefenokee Swamp on November 6, 1935, a late date for its appearance in the state. Norris [1951] states that this heron was not uncommon locally in southwestern Georgia during the summer of 1948.

HABITS AND RECOGNITION: Despite its name, the Yellow-crowned Night Heron is active throughout most of the day, and can be found feeding

EASTERN TURKEY

Meleagris gallopavo silvestris

This, the most controversial of my paintings, was based on several life-sketches made from a blind, on a detailed sketch of a turkey's head made some years ago by Owen J. Gromme, and on a magnificent gobbler mounted by Herbert Stoddard. Waiting in the blind was exhausting. When, at last, a gobbler did show up, he walked straight toward me, head high, suspicious, very proud looking. I was so excited my hand shook. Details I painted from the mounted specimens placed full in the afternoon sun. In some lights a turkey looks dark, almost black; but put it in the sun and its plumage lights up and shines with the brilliance of burnished metal.

about pools and at the edges of streams where crawfish and crabs, its favorite food, are most easily obtained. In Georgia it is far less common than
the other herons, and except in the vicinity of nesting sites it is not often
seen. It is more slender in appearance than the Black-crowned Night
Heron, but nevertheless gives the impression of chunkiness that is a good
field character. The adult bird, seen at a distance, appears gray, with the
top of the head black, and should not be confused with any other species.
The young bird, however, is so similar in appearance to the young of the
Black-crowned Night Heron that field identification is often rather difficult.
It is darker, and its relatively long legs extend well beyond the tail in flight.
This latter characteristic, if seen clearly, will distinguish it at once from its
near relative, the Black-crowned Night Heron, which has shorter legs.

American Bittern
Botaurus lentiginosus (Montagu)

GENERAL DISTRIBUTION: Breeds from British Columbia east to Newfoundland and south to southern California, Colorado, the Ohio Valley,
and Florida. Winters over much of its breeding range and south to Cuba,
Puerto Rico, and Panama.

STATUS IN GEORGIA: A fairly common spring and fall transient throughout the state, and a rare winter resident wherever conditions are suitable.
Possibly breeds in the Okefenokee Swamp.

The Bittern occurs as a transient in Georgia throughout much of the
spring and fall months. In the spring it has been observed from early
March until the middle of May, and it is possible that late February records
indicate the beginning of the northward movement. In the fall it has been
recorded as early as the middle of July, and regularly in September and all
of October.

Helme reports one on Cumberland Island on March 8, 1902, and Mrs.
Bassett has noted it at Savannah on March 9 and 11, 1929. Erichsen [MS]
considers this species a fairly common winter resident on the coast, extreme
dates of occurrence being October 14 (1917) and May 1 (1921). Stoddard
[MS] reports single birds seen in Thomas County, May 5, 1945, and in
Grady County, April 23, 1948, and March 27, 1949. Norris and Hopkins
[1953] cite as their extreme dates of occurrence for Tifton, December 7
(1941) and April 16 (1933), while Johnston [MS] gives as extreme dates
of occurrence for Macon March 7 (1945) and May 4 (1935), and September 7 (1934). At Athens I found it a scarce but regular transient from the
middle of March through the first week in May, extreme dates of occurrence being March 14 (1946) and May 15 (1922). Griffin [1941] found its
status in the Atlanta region much the same, his extreme dates being March

20 (1932) and May 15 (1932). Johnston [1945] records one Bittern at Atlanta as early as February 21 (1943), but this note may possibly refer to an individual that wintered. At Mt. Berry Jones [1942] observed one on April 10, 1935.

An early record for the fall migration is for the Atlanta region, Johnston [1945] listing a bittern seen there on August 22 (1942). The latest fall date for the Atlanta region is November 3 (1905), as cited by Eyles [1937a] in his list of migration extremes for the area. At Athens I found it a regular and not uncommon transient in fall, extreme dates of occurrence being September 2 (1928) and October 30 (1921). At St. Marys it was noted on September 12, 1905, and in Grady County, by Stoddard, on August 30, 1942, and July 13 and August 7, 1948, by E. V. Komarek.

Definite winter records are not abundant. It is said to occur during the winter months at St. Marys, and Hebard [1941] records individuals seen in the Okefenokee Swamp on January 7, 1930, December 31, 1935, and January 13, 1941. Another bird he saw there February 27, 1936, was possibly an early migrant. I have but one winter record for Athens, a single bird being seen in the open Sandy Creek bottoms on December 1, 1937, while at Atlanta, Johnston [1945] records one seen on January 21, 1944. That it possibly breeds at least sparingly in the Okefenokee Swamp is suggested by the fact that Wright and Harper [1913] flushed a bird at the edge of the Suwanee River on June 17, 1912. This species has been found nesting in Florida, so it is not improbable that eventually it will be added to the list of birds known to breed in Georgia.

HABITS AND RECOGNITION: No bird is more solitary or seclusive in its habits than the Bittern. Except during the breeding season it lives alone, spending its days hidden in the densest vegetation bordering the marshes or sloughs where it can procure the crawfish and frogs that are its favorite food. Deliberate in its movements, it will stand quietly for long intervals, moving only when, with a sudden swift thrust of its bill, it spears its prey. Its brown plumage blends so well with its surroundings that it is rarely seen until it flies, and the average individual is almost stepped on before it takes flight. It is a large, stocky brown heron, with black wing tips which at once distinguish it from immature night herons. Otherwise inconspicuous, the Bittern is well known because of the loud, booming notes that it utters during the spring months. These sounds have been variously described as "pumping" or "stake driving," and when heard in the depths of a swamp cannot fail to attract attention.

Eastern Least Bittern
Ixobrychus exilis exilis (Gmelin)

GENERAL DISTRIBUTION: Breeds from southern Quebec, Ontario, southern Maine, southern Vermont, Wisconsin, Minnesota, and North Dakota south to the West Indies and southern Mexico. Winters from Florida and southern Texas south to eastern Guatemala.

STATUS IN GEORGIA: A fairly common summer resident on the coast and of local occurrence elsewhere in the state during the summer months.

Because of the obstacles encountered in studying the home life of the Least Bittern, but few nests have been found in the state. Erichsen [1921] records two nests found on Ossabaw Island in May, 1915, one on the eleventh with three heavily incubated eggs, and one on the fourteenth with one fresh egg. They were well concealed in clumps of cat-tails, and were shallow platforms composed "of the dead stalks and blades of the different species of vegetation growing in the pond." At this same spot, on April 30, 1921, I found another nest that held four newly hatched young. Like the others, it was in a clump of cat-tails, a foot or so above the water, and was a substantial, slightly cupped bed of dry pieces of cat-tails. This bittern has been reported as breeding at St. Marys, and Murphey [1937] states that in Richmond County it is common in the marshes, but because of its retiring habits, is rarely seen. Denton [letter] reports it a fairly common breeding bird at Macon and at McKinney's Pond, in Emanuel County. Major and Johnston [1944] found the first nest for the Atlanta area on June 26, 1944. This empty nest and three downy young in the reeds close by were located on Candler Lake. The following year Major [1945] noted a pair at this same spot, and succeeded in finding a nest that, on May 26, 1945, held four eggs. He describes the nest as being a platform of dead rushes a few inches above the water.

Migration records for the state are very few in number. Bent [1926] gives March 6 as an arrival date for Savannah. At Athens I recorded this species but once in the spring, a single bird being flushed on March 25, 1928, from the edge of a stretch of open marsh in the Sandy Creek bottoms. A fall date is given by Greene [1933] for Atlanta, a single bird being picked up injured in the city limits on August 29, 1932. Norris [in litt.] has recorded this species at Tifton on September 24, 1941, and in Cook County on August 14, 1951, and Hebard [1941] reports one bird seen in the Okefenokee Swamp on November 1, 1932.

HABITS AND RECOGNITION: This diminutive heron is so secretive in its habits that it is probably commoner in the state than is indicated by the preceding scanty records. Its days are spent in the thicker stretches of cattails and reeds that characterize the fresh-water marshes, and so reluctant is it to expose itself that only rarely is it flushed. If too closely approached and unable to escape otherwise, it will fly for a short distance just above the top of the reeds and disappear, not to be seen again. Its flight at such a time gives the appearance of weakness and of reluctance to leave even momentarily the protection of the vegetation in which it conceals itself so successfully. Under these conditions, its small size and distinctive plumage readily identify it. The large buffy wing patches and glossy black back and top of head will distinguish it at once from the larger rails with which it might be confused. Few birds are better adapted to marsh life than is this small bittern. Its body is long and narrow, enabling it to move with ease through the densest vegetation, and its plumage blends so well with its surroundings that when quiet it becomes almost invisible.

Erichsen [MS] says that "During the breeding season the birds have a low mournful note that bears some resemblance to one of the common calls of the Yellow-billed Cuckoo. This mellow 'coo-coo-coo,' coming apparently from a distance, is a very peculiar sound, difficult to describe." It is a difficult bird to become acquainted with, and the usual reward for hours spent in its haunts is an occasional glimpse of one slipping quietly away in the reeds.

Wood Ibises: *Family Ciconiidae*

Wood Ibis
Mycteria americana   (Linnaeus)

GENERAL DISTRIBUTION: Breeds from South Carolina, Florida, and Texas south to Argentina and Peru. Wanders north during the summer months to California and Arizona and, rarely, to Montana, Wisconsin, Ontario, and the New England states.

STATUS IN GEORGIA: A fairly common summer visitant on the coast and in the Okefenokee Swamp and of casual occurrence during the summer months north to the fall line; accidental in the Piedmont, where it has been recorded but once. Seldom seen during the winter months.

There are very few spring records for the state, although the bird possibly occurs regularly on the coast at that time. Mrs. Bassett recorded it at Savannah on April 26, 1928, and again on March 29 and May 14, 1931. Summer and fall records are more numerous. At Savannah, in 1912, Hoxie observed five or six birds on June 25, but saw no more until August 9, when they became common; the last were seen on October 10. Erichsen [MS] gives as his extreme dates for Chatham County, June 7 (1919) and December 8 (1918). At Mimsville this species was reported on July 2 and September 4, 1902. On Blackbeard Island the federal warden, M. F. Boisclair, reported the birds abundant in the summer of 1917.

Wright and Harper [1913] record the Wood Ibis as fairly common in the Okefenokee Swamp. They say: "While a few were seen in May and June, they began in July to assemble in flocks. In descending the Suwanee on July 13, our party flushed flock after flock until 200 or more birds were sailing overhead." In October, 1931, I spent four days in the swamp, from the fifteenth through the eighteenth, and found this species plentiful. Hebard [1941] states that numbers remained in the swamp throughout the winter of 1931–32. The only birds he saw, however, were two that had been shot on November 1 by a local hunter. Stoddard [MS] reports seeing this species frequently in Grady County from late spring until fall, and on one occasion during the winter, a single bird on Sherwood Plantation, December 21 and 22, 1946.

I saw a single bird at Newton, Baker County, on July 14, 1929, and Norris [1951] reports this species locally common to abundant in southwestern Georgia "during the latter half of the summer." In 1947 and 1948, he saw several flocks that "numbered more than 40 birds." Norris and Hopkins [1953] state that the Wood Ibis has been noted at Fitzgerald at irregular intervals between the dates of March 15 (1941) and October 7 (1952). Murphey [1937] reports that this species "frequently appears in August and September [in Richmond County] in large flocks, twenty to thirty or more which are composed in the main of the young of the year." At Macon it has been noted on June 8, 1955 (Rohwer), and in the fall between the dates of August 26 (1935) and October 5 (1955) [Johnston, MS]. Bell [1939] records two birds seen in Morgan County, June 25 and July 1, 1939, the only occasion on which this species has been noted in the Piedmont.

HABITS AND RECOGNITION: The Wood Ibis is misnamed, for it is not an ibis but a stork, and is the only representative of this widely distributed family indigenous to North America. It is a large, impressive-looking bird, and while it might be confused with a heron at a distance, its stout downcurved bill will at once identify it. It is at all times extremely wary and almost impossible to approach closely. When it is seen in the top of a tall tree or feeding in an open marsh, its white plumage, with black-tipped wings and tail, is readily diagnostic. On the ground it at times appears awkward and somewhat ungainly, but when soaring in small groups overhead, as it commonly does, a totally different picture is presented. Unlike the herons and the true ibises, the head of the Wood Ibis is naked, and the dark, coarse, exposed skin has given it the rather appropriate name of "flinthead." Because of its wariness and the fact that its flesh is tough and rarely eaten, this species is seldom molested, and as a result it has always been a common bird within its range.

Ibises and Spoonbills: *Family Threskiornithidae*

Eastern Glossy Ibis
Plegadis falcinellus falcinellus (Linnaeus)

GENERAL DISTRIBUTION: Breeds locally in southern Louisiana and central Florida and in the West Indies. Occurs casually as far north as Nova Scotia, Quebec, Ontario, Michigan, and Wisconsin.

STATUS IN GEORGIA: A rare transient on the coast; accidental in the interior.

Actual records of occurrence in the state are few in number. Tomkins has seen single birds on four occasions at the mouth of the Savannah River, on June 14 and again on August 12, 1928, and on October 23 and 25, 1932. Sprunt [1933] records a single bird seen on Cumberland Island on April 7, 1933. Thomas [1945] reports one bird seen at the clay pits near Augusta on May 17, 1945. The most recent records are of single birds seen at Savannah [Tomkins letter] August 14, 15, and 16, 1953. On the sixteenth a male in immature plumage was collected, the first specimen to be recorded from the state.

HABITS AND RECOGNITION: The various species of ibises are easily told from herons by their long down-curved bills, and the Glossy Ibis in adult plumage can be recognized at once by its rich reddish-chestnut plumage. Young birds are less highly plumaged, being a glossy metallic green above and dull grayish-brown beneath, but their uniformly dark appearance, even at a distance, will readily distinguish them from immature White Ibises. Nowhere in the United States is this species a common bird, and anyone fortunate enough to see one in Georgia will probably find it associating with herons about the pools or open channels in salt marsh.

White Ibis
Eudocimus albus (Linnaeus)

GENERAL DISTRIBUTION: Breeds from South Carolina, the Gulf Coast of Louisiana and Texas, and Lower California south to the West Indies, Venezuela, and Peru. Wanders casually north after the breeding season to South Dakota, Illinois, and the New England states.

STATUS IN GEORGIA: Breeds fairly commonly on the coast and in the Okefenokee Swamp, and occurs casually in this general region during the winter months. A summer visitant elsewhere in the state.

Although there is no question that this species nests in fresh-water swamps in the southern part of the state, there is little actual data available on its breeding habits. S. W. Wilson, who collected eggs on the Georgia coast between 1853 and 1865, recorded the White Ibis as breeding in the Altamaha River swamp [Bailey, 1883]. B. H. King reported the arrival of thirty adult birds at Mimsville on April 17, 1902, which stayed in the vicinity until July 25; on August 2 a small flock of immature birds was seen, these remaining for several days. From these records it seems probable that the birds bred in that vicinity. Pearson [1922] recorded nineteen birds seen on Cumberland Island May 2 to 6, 1921, and stated that they were nesting there. Mrs. Bassett reported the presence of a large rookery on Terrell's Pond, approximately two miles from Hinesville, in Liberty County. She visited the pond on April 10, 1931, and estimated that the colony numbered about 1,500 birds. She saw no nests, but she was told that the birds nested each year in a relatively inaccessible part of the swamp.

Grimm [1946] considered this species a common summer resident in the vicinity of Camp Stewart, this reservation comprising some 280,000 acres lying in Liberty, Bryan, Long, and Evans counties. A flock of sixty birds was seen on May 30, 1945, at a cypress pond a few miles northwest of Hinesville, about half of which were fully grown young of the year. Wright and Harper [1913] list it as breeding in the Okefenokee Swamp. Stoddard and Greene [1937] found a large breeding rookery in Camden County, in Big Thour Swamp, lying on the north side of the Satilla River between Woodbine and White Oak, which, they estimated, contained at least 15,000 birds. On the day that they visited this rookery, July 25, 1937, the hundreds of nests that they saw were empty, the young birds being already well grown, and were concentrated in the tops of the larger willows. They described the nests as being "on the hummocks on the swamp floor and up to the tops of the willows some fifteen feet higher, frequently being placed so close together as to almost touch."

Relatively few White Ibises remain in the state during the winter months, the majority leaving in October and returning the following March or early April. Bent [1926] gives March 17 (1904) as an arrival date at St. Marys, and Arnow records a flock of 500 seen there on March 31, 1905. Grimm [1946] recorded it for the first time in the spring of April 1, 1944 (a flock of 75 near Fleming) and on April 4, 1945 (a flock of 150 at Camp Stewart). Stoddard's extreme dates for Grady County are April 1 (1945) and September 12 (1945).

Although the White Ibis is said to winter in small numbers on the coast, the only definite record for this season of the year is of a single bird seen in the Okefenokee Swamp on November 25 and again on December 28, 1932 [Hebard, 1941].

After the breeding season this species appears regularly in the vicinity of Augusta [Murphey, 1937], and Griffin [1941] records it as a rare sum-

121

mer visitant at Atlanta, his extreme dates being July 17 (1921) and September 14 (1934). Greene [1933] saw two birds on the Chattahoochee River near Atlanta on July 17 and 23, and a single bird on July 24, 1921. There is a single record for Macon, September 2, 1950 [Farrar]. Norris and Hopkins [1953] noted this species at Fitzgerald as early as May 25 (1940) and as late as August 6 (1952). Norris [1951] also reports this species as locally common during the summer months in the northwestern corner of the state, as many as eighty being observed in flocks present there during 1947 and 1948.

HABITS AND RECOGNITION: The White Ibis is an extremely social bird, much more so than any of the herons, occurring in flocks of varying size throughout the year. Its breeding colonies are located in the depths of the most inaccessible swamps, but as its food is procured some distance from the rookeries, it can be commonly observed feeding about many of the ponds and sloughs along the coast. Flocks seen under these conditions can be easily recognized. Size and general appearance suggest both the Snowy Egret and the immature Little Blue Heron, but the black-tipped wings and long down-curved bill will readily distinguish the birds as White Ibises. Almost equally diagnostic is the fact that the flocks feed in rather compact groups, a habit never observed in any of the herons. Young birds resemble immature Glossy Ibises, but the underparts, lower back, and rump are white. When they are frightened from a shallow pool or from the edge of a stream, the flight of these ibises is direct and fairly swift, short intervals of soaring relieving the otherwise steady beat of the wings. If not unduly alarmed, they will frequently alight in the top of a large tree and remain there for some time, giving the observer the opportunity to admire their immaculate plumage and graceful shape.

Roseate Spoonbill
Ajaia ajaja (Linnaeus)

GENERAL DISTRIBUTION: Breeds on the Gulf Coast of Texas and Louisiana and in southern Florida, south through the Bahamas, Cuba, and central Mexico to Argentina and Chile. Occurs accidentally north to California, Utah, Colorado, Kansas, and Wisconsin.

STATUS IN GEORGIA: An extremely rare visitant in the southeastern corner of the state.

There is apparently but one definite record for this species in the state. Sprunt [1936] reports a single bird seen by Mrs. H. W. Butler and Mrs. Victor Bassett during the summer of 1934 at King's Pond, Liberty County. Mrs. Butler succeeded in getting a clear photograph of this bird on one of her visits to the Pond in July; thus there can be no question as to the reliability of this record. Other records include two birds reported by A. H. Helme as seen by Captain Swan, keeper of the light on Little Cumberland Island, on April 13, 1902; one seen by Hoxie at Savannah in the fall of 1911; and the mention by Wright and Harper [1913] of the finding of feathers of this species by a local hunter in the Okefenokee Swamp.

HABITS AND RECOGNITION: This unique and strikingly colored bird was at one time common throughout much of Florida and possibly then regularly appeared on the coast of Georgia. Unfortunately, it was subject for years to slaughter by plume hunters, and its number was so reduced that at the present time only a few small breeding colonies remain in the more in accessible swamps. With the protection now accorded it, it is hoped that it will increase in number, and again be seen in areas where for many years now it has been but a memory. Anyone fortunate enough to observe one in the southern part of the state will have no difficulty in recognizing it. In appearance it suggests a medium-sized heron, but its broad, spoon-shaped bill and conspicuous pink color will identify it beyond any question.

ORDER ANSERIFORMES

Ducks, Geese, and Swans: *Family Anatidae*

Whistling Swan
Olor columbianus (Ord)

GENERAL DISTRIBUTION: Breeds mainly north of the Arctic Circle from northern Alaska to Baffin Island, south to the barren grounds of Canada and the Alaska peninsula. Winters on the Atlantic Coast from Maryland to North Carolina and, rarely, south to Florida and the Gulf Coast of Louisiana and Texas; also on the Pacific Coast from southern Alaska to northern Lower California.

STATUS IN GEORGIA: A rare transient and winter resident.

There are only a few records of this magnificent bird in the state. Hoxie reports one bird seen at Savannah, April 9, 1910, apparently the first record for Georgia. Werner [1945] states that two were seen on Pine Lake, ten miles southeast of Atlanta, on February 25, 1945. Smith [1945] records one killed on Lake Blackshear, near Cordele, on or about January 22, 1945, and Norris [1940] reports the possession of a specimen killed in Ben Hill County on November 15, 1940. Greene was shown the remains of one killed in the Okefenokee Swamp in December, 1934. Belger [1950] collected a bird in immature plumage on the Savannah River, five miles below Augusta, November 21, 1949. Sprunt [1936] saw two birds off Cumberland Island on April 17, 1932. The most recent record is that of eight birds seen on the Berry College Campus, in Floyd County, from November 23, 1951, through March 8, 1952 [Bell, 1952].

HABITS AND RECOGNITION: Since Georgia is south of the main wintering grounds of the Whistling Swan on the Atlantic Coast, it is probable that only an occasional straggler reaches the state. Consequently, this is one species, which, even if searched for, will rarely be seen. Feeding is invariably carried on in shallow water, but as the swan is a wary bird, it will usually be observed on the larger bodies of water and at a safe distance from shore. Under these conditions, and despite the distance, it can be readily recognized, its long neck, large size, and pure white plumage leaving little doubt of its identity.

Family Anatidae: DUCKS, GEESE, & SWANS

Hudson Bay Canada Goose
Branta canadensis interior   Todd

GENERAL DISTRIBUTION: Breeds in western Labrador, northern Quebec, Ontario, and Manitoba (Hudson and James Bays), south to about longitude 52° N. Winters from Ontario, Michigan, Wisconsin, Minnesota, and Illinois south to the Gulf Coast and on the Atlantic Coast from Maryland to Florida.

STATUS IN GEORGIA: A fairly common spring and fall transient and a locally common winter resident.

In fall the first flocks usually appear in Georgia the latter part of October, and, especially on the coast, are fairly common for a month or more. The earliest date of arrival is that given by Stoddard [MS] for Grady County, a flock being seen by E. V. Komarek on September 5, 1945. Tomkins [1931] noted first arrivals at the mouth of the Savannah River on October 21, 1927, and October 25, 1930, and Hoxie reports a flock of fourteen at Savannah on October 31, 1908. Stoddard saw a flock of about eighty near Thomasville on October 29, 1925, and Johnston [MS] gives November 15 (1938) as the earliest date of arrival at Macon. At Athens, my earliest record for the fall migration is that of a flock of approximately one hundred of these geese on November 6, 1921. Griffin [1941] gives October 21, 1940, as the earliest date of arrival in the Atlanta region, and Jones [1942], October 29, 1935, for Mt. Berry (Floyd County).

The height of the spring migration apparently is in March, although stragglers have been observed much later in the spring. Hoxie reported flocks at Savannah on March 27, 1910, March 28, 1912, and April 14, 1914; Tomkins noted a flock there on February 13 and 14, 1932. Handley saw five birds near Beachton, Grady County, on March 17, 1925. I flushed a single bird in the open Sandy Creek bottoms, then under several feet of water, near Athens, on March 20, 1929. At Macon the latest date for the spring is March 12 (1932) [Johnston, MS], and Jones gives March 14 (1936) as the date of the latest flock observed in the spring at Mt. Berry. The latest date for the spring migration is that given by Greene [1933] for the Atlanta region, two birds being seen May 22, 1932, in the South River bottoms.

During the winter months these geese have been found in but a few widely separated localities. Greene [1933] states that they winter along the Chattahoochee River north of Atlanta, and Murphey [1937] found large flocks during the winter months on the Savannah River both above and below Augusta. Stoddard reports a flock seen near Rocky Hill, in Grady County, which during the winter of 1937 fed for weeks in a large grain field. Late records, that possibly indicate wintering birds, are (Tomkins) December 2, 1932, at Savannah, and (Hebard) December 6, 1934, in the Okefenokee Swamp, and December 5, 1940, at Folkston.

Studies made of the distribution and migration of this interior race of the Canada Goose [Hanson and Smith, 1950] show beyond question that *interior* is the principal form occurring in Georgia, both as a transient and as a possible winter resident. Other recognized races may be present in small numbers from time to time, but in view of the lack of specimens it seems advisable to attribute all sight records to this dark-colored race from the interior of the country.

HABITS AND RECOGNITION: The Canada Goose is undoubtedly the best known of any of our waterfowl, for it is familiar not only to those possessing a special interest in birds, but to the layman as well. One of the first birds to migrate north in the spring, it is greeted as a harbinger of spring, and the sight of a flock flying high overhead never fails to excite interest. Flying by night as well as by day, a flock of these geese rarely fails to attract attention. One or more of the birds are continually uttering their loud, resonant, honking notes, and the clamor announces the presence of a flock when, as frequently happens, darkness or distance renders it invisible. In clear weather these birds fly very high, but even then the characteristic V-shaped formation of the flock is diagnostic. The slow, steady wing-beats do not suggest speed, but actually the flight is strong and swift. A bird as familiar as this to even the casual observer needs no detailed description. Its large size, black head and neck, and conspicuous white cheek patches readily identify it wherever it is seen.

Athabaska Canada Goose
Branta canadensis parvipes   Cassin

GENERAL DISTRIBUTION: Breeds in northern Saskatchewan, northern Alberta, and southwestern Mackenzie. Winters from Texas to Louisiana and northern Mexico.

STATUS IN GEORGIA: Recorded only in the southern part of the state, where its occurrence is possibly casual.

In Georgia it has been taken but once. Stoddard collected a female goose at Rocky Hill, in southeastern Grady County, on March 8, 1937, that has been identified by John W. Aldrich as representing this race.

HABITS AND RECOGNITION: In appearance this goose is merely a small Canada Goose, and cannot be satisfactorily identified in the field. There are no color differences, and accurate measurements are necessary to determine its identity.

Family Anatidae: DUCKS, GEESE, & SWANS

American Brant
Branta bernicla hrota   (Müller)

GENERAL DISTRIBUTION: Breeds in the Arctic regions of eastern North America, on both coasts of Greenland, and apparently in the Spitzbergen archipelago. Winters largely on the Atlantic Coast of the United States from Massachusetts to North Carolina, casually to Florida.

STATUS IN GEORGIA: A rare transient on the coast.

At present there are but two records of this species in the state. Worthington took two specimens at Egg Island, at the mouth of the Altamaha River, on March 10, 1897, and Sciple collected a female at Sea Island, in Glynn County, from a flock of six, on December 29, 1948 [Sciple, 1950b].

HABITS AND RECOGNITION: The Brant is a small goose, about half the size of a large Canada Goose, with a black head, neck, and breast that readily distinguish it from its larger relatives. It is strictly a maritime species, the chief food of which during the winter months was formerly eelgrass (*Zostera marina*). When eelgrass was almost wiped out along the Atlantic Coast by disease a few years ago, the Brant was hard pressed for food on its wintering grounds. Although the Brant population was severely threatened by this catastrophe, the birds fortunately were able to adapt themselves to a diet of sea lettuce, which continued to be an abundant if not equally acceptable food supply. Unlike the Canada geese, Brant do not fly in V-shaped flocks, and when in the air their irregular formation suggests the pattern followed by the ducks. In Georgia, however, as only an occasional straggler probably will be seen, this characteristic is not likely to be observed.

Pacific White-fronted Goose
Anser albifrons frontalis   (Baird)

GENERAL DISTRIBUTION: Breeds in Alaska and probably Mackenzie. Winters in the western United States and south to central Mexico.

STATUS IN GEORGIA: A rare transient that has been recorded only twice, in the early spring.

There are apparently but two authentic records for this species in the state. Murphey [1937] records a specimen that was shot on the Savannah River, seven miles above Augusta, in February, 1891. Norris states that J. L. Stephens collected a White-fronted Goose at Tifton on March 17, 1932, which he had mounted, and has in his possession at the present time.

This specimen was critically examined by Allen J. Duvall and identified as *frontalis*.

HABITS AND RECOGNITION: As the winter range of the White-fronted Goose lies, to a very large extent, west of the Mississippi River, it is probable that only at infrequent intervals will an occasional bird be seen in Georgia. Such a straggler may be alone or in company with other geese, but it is distinctive enough in appearance to be readily recognized. It is noticeably smaller than the Canada Goose, and at a distance appears uniformly grayish-brown. A closer view, if the bird is in adult plumage, will reveal the black markings of the underparts and the white forehead. The young are very similar in appearance to those of the Blue Goose, and can only be distinguished with certainty if the feet and legs are closely observed. In the White-fronted Goose these are yellowish, while in the Blue Goose they are dull pink.

Greater Snow Goose
Chen hyperborea atlantica   Kennard

GENERAL DISTRIBUTION: Breeds at McCormick Bay, Greenland, and on north Baffin and Ellesmere islands. Winters on the Atlantic Coast of Maryland, Virginia, and North Carolina.

STATUS IN GEORGIA: A rare fall transient on the coast.

At present there is but one authentic record for this bird in Georgia. Tomkins [1932] saw a single bird near Savannah on November 24, 1931, resting with gulls on a sand bar in the Savannah River. He was fortunately able to collect it, and it proved to be an adult male with measurements clearly referable to this larger race. Other records of snow geese in Georgia probably refer to the Lesser Snow Goose (*Chen hyperborea hyperborea*), but, in the absence of specimens, this can only be assumed at this time. Stoddard [1942] has pointed out that the smaller race migrates and winters with the Blue Goose on the Gulf Coast, and in Grady County the snow geese he has observed were almost invariably with larger numbers of blue geese. Some of the following records, therefore, very probably refer to *hyperborea*, but since this identification is merely tentative, it seems desirable to list here all available records of snow geese, without subspecific assignment. Tomkins [1938] noted small flocks at Savannah in the fall of 1937 and 1938, and Jones [1942] saw a flock in Floyd County on October 26, 1941. Stoddard [1942] observed a large flock in Thomas County in October, 1924, and four flocks totaling over one hundred snow and blue geese in Grady County on October 25, 1941. Land [1949] reports one bird seen at Marietta on February 28, 1949. Cottam [1951] noted a single bird, in immature plumage, on the Ogeechee River near Richmond Hill Plantation, Richmond Hill, October 26, 1949. Hopkins [1951] observed one flying by overhead in Colquitt County on March 29, 1950.

HABITS AND RECOGNITION: Snow geese are handsome birds with their pure white plumage offset by black wing tips, and it is unfortunate that they are so rarely seen in the state. As with the Brant, the Greater Snow Goose winters on a relatively short and narrow stretch of the Atlantic Coast, and it is doubtful that many individuals venture south of Core Sound, North Carolina. In the air these geese usually fly in long diagonal lines, and are far less noisy than other geese, flocks observed going to, or from, their winter quarters passing by overhead with hardly a sound.

Blue Goose
Chen caerulescens   (Linnaeus)

GENERAL DISTRIBUTION: Breeds in the interior of Baffin Island and on the southwestern coast of Southampton Island. Winter range is largely restricted to the coast of Louisiana, although there are casual records from Texas, Mississippi, Florida, the Bahamas, and Cuba.

STATUS IN GEORGIA: A rare fall transient and winter resident.

The first definite record for the state is that of a male taken at Axon, in Atkinson County, November 20, 1920, and now in Murphey's collection [Tomkins, 1935]. Tomkins [1930] saw three birds at the Savannah River entrance November 9 and 10, 1929, and took an immature bird there November 1, 1934. Stoddard [1942] reports three flocks flying southwestward over Grady County on October 25, 1941. A female was collected by him on Sherwood Plantation, in Grady County, October 28, 1944. Apparently the only records for the spring migration are those of a single bird seen by E. P. Creaser at the south end of Blackbeard Island on March 31, 1941 [Tomkins, 1942], and a flock of eighty-one seen flying north over St. Simons Island on April 22, 1952 [Hebard, 1952b]. Hebard [1942] found three Blue Geese on Mill Creek, in western Camden County, on January 1, 1942, and for a week thereafter. Neal [1949] saw a single bird on Lake Demorest, in Habersham County, November 17–24, 1948, and Ambrosen [1950] reports a dead bird found on Five Points Lake in the Piedmont National Wildlife Refuge on November 13, 1949. Griffin [letter] reports a single bird near Decatur from November 9, 1952, to March 15, 1953, and Rotchford [1953], one bird on McKinley Lake, at Milledgeville, October 24–26, 1952.

HABITS AND RECOGNITION: Within its rather restricted range, the Blue Goose is, during the winter months, an exceedingly abundant bird. Rela-

PURPLE GALLINULE

Porphyrula martinica

To show me these gorgeous birds on their nesting ground, Herbert Stoddard
drove me to a large pond on Suzina Plantation, several miles east of
Sherwood. One end of the pond was choked with large white water lilies,
and here the gallinules were—walking about on the grassy leaves, lifting
their wings as if in courtship display, occasionally folding a leaf back and
holding it down with one foot while finding food on the under surface.

tively few individuals, however, wander far from the direct route taken to and from their breeding grounds in the far north, so it is only in the Mississippi Valley that this species appears regularly in migration. In Georgia it occurs only casually, and while flocks have been observed in the fall flying high overhead inland, on the coast the few records pertain to one or two birds seen at extremely infrequent intervals. Adults are easily identified, for they are smaller than Canada geese, and have all-white heads, which distinguish them at once from any other geese that might be seen in this region. Young birds resemble the young of the White-fronted Goose, but can be recognized by their pink, rather than yellow, feet and legs.

Common Mallard
Anas platyrhynchos platyrhynchos   Linnaeus

GENERAL DISTRIBUTION: Of wide distribution in the Northern Hemisphere. Breeds in North America from Alaska and Mackenzie south to Lower California, New Mexico, southern Texas, Kansas, Illinois, Ohio, and Virginia. Also in Iceland, throughout Europe south of the Arctic Circle, in the Azores and northern Africa, and from Siberia to China and Japan. Winters in North America largely in the Southern and Middle states as far north as open water is found, although found at that season north to central Alaska and south to southern Mexico, the Lesser Antilles, and Panama.

STATUS IN GEORGIA: A fairly common winter resident over much of the state, being less numerous on the coast, where it is largely limited to freshwater marshes.

Although fall migrants usually do not appear in Georgia before the latter part of October or early November, occasional birds can be seen much earlier than this. At Athens the first week in November was the average date when the first flocks were seen, but Mallards have been recorded there on October 1, 1925, and, on what is probably the earliest record for the state, September 19, 1929. The largest flock noted during the winter months was one containing thirty birds that was flushed in the open Sandy Creek bottoms on January 6, 1924. A smaller flock of eighteen birds was found at this same spot on January 11, 1925. In the spring this species was rarely seen later than the middle of April, average late dates being April 11 (1926) and April 12 (1927). The latest date reports a single bird, a female, found on Lake Kirota on May 3, 1925.

At Atlanta, Griffin [1941] records the Mallard as a winter resident, with extreme dates of November 9 (1940) and April 5 (1939). Jones [1942] gives it the same status at Mt. Berry (Floyd County), his extreme dates being October 17 (1940) and April 18 (1938). Murphey [1937] considers it fairly abundant at Augusta, while at Macon [Johnston, MS], extreme dates are October 27 (1934) and May 21 (1955). Hebard [1941] states that it winters in large numbers in the Okefenokee Swamp. He found that from 1910 until 1936 it decreased noticeably in number, apparently because of logging operations then being carried on, but it is now relatively numerous again. Stoddard [MS] gives as extreme dates for Grady County November 4 (1945) and March 18 (1945), and Norris [in litt.] cites as the earliest fall record for Tifton, October 27 (1933). Tomkins reports it uncommon in the coastal area, where he has noted small flocks at the mouth of the Savannah River on October 25, 1926, and November 30, 1933. Erichsen [MS] cites as extreme dates of occurrence for Chatham County, October 11 (1930) and April 10 (1927).

HABITS AND RECOGNITION: The Mallard is unquestionably the most widely distributed, most abundant, and best known of our wild ducks. In recent years it has become somewhat reduced in numbers, but even so, many flocks can be observed in Georgia from late October until early March, and it is the species that is most often shot by the hunters of the state. It is essentially a bird of the fresh-water streams and marshes, obtaining its food by tipping up in shallow water near the shore, this method of feeding being commonly known as "puddling." It is averse to diving, and while it can and does do so to escape capture if wounded, it will otherwise submerge only part of its body in reaching the bottom of a pool or stream. In a few favored spots in the state, as the Okefenokee Swamp, large numbers concentrate during the winter, but ordinarily flocks of ten or twelve birds, rarely more, will be seen. It is at all times a wary bird, and it is a fortunate hunter who is able to get his bag limit in the course of a day's hunting.

It is unquestionably a favorite among waterfowl hunters because of its large size and excellent flesh. Being easily domesticated, it can be found about many farmyards, thus is a familiar bird even to those who do not know it in the wild. The males are unmistakable, with their glossy green heads, white ring around the neck, and ruddy breasts. Females are less easily identified, but their large size and conspicuous white patches on the tail will distinguish them from other mottled brown ducks in flight.

Black Duck
Anas rubripes Brewster

GENERAL DISTRIBUTION: Breeds from northern Quebec (Ungava), northern Manitoba, and northern Ontario south to northern Indiana, Wisconsin, and Delaware, and casually in North Carolina and possibly in Georgia.

Winters from the Great Lakes and New England south to Texas, Louisiana, and Florida.

STATUS IN GEORGIA: A common transient and winter visitant, and a possible local summer resident in the eastern part of the state.

In the fall the first small flocks usually appear in Georgia shortly after the middle of October, and are present thereafter wherever conditions are suitable until the following April. At Athens, I recorded this species only as a regular, but not common, spring and fall transient, but it is possible that it occurs, at least sparingly, during the winter months. My extreme dates in the fall are October 16 (1926) and December 3 (1927), and for the spring migration, March 9 (1927) and March 31 (1926). Griffin [1941] considers it a regular winter resident about Atlanta, his extreme dates being September 11 (1932) and April 18 (1932).

Jones [1942] lists it as common and a regular visitant during the winter months at Mt. Berry (Floyd County), his earliest date of arrival in the fall being October 22 (1939), and his latest date of departure in the spring, April 18 (1938). At Macon [Johnston, MS], extreme dates are September 26 (1954) and April 29 (1933). Hebard [1941] gives October 19 (1940) as the earliest date of arrival at Coleraine, and states that it winters in large numbers in the Okefenokee Swamp. He estimates that in December, 1934, fully 1,500 Black Ducks could be found in Chase Prairie. At Newton, in Baker County, on December 27, 1924, I observed a number of small flocks dropping down into a shallow, cypress-bordered pond just at dark, apparently to feed there throughout the night. Stoddard [MS] gives as extreme dates for Grady County, November 8 (1945) and March 18 (1945); and Erichsen, for Chatham County, October 24 (1926) and April 8 (1921). A specimen was taken at Waynesboro on November 30, 1922, and two birds were noted at Macon, April 22, 1931.

Individuals banded at Lake Scugog, Ontario, were shot in the state at the following localities: Cave Spring, February 7, 1924; Hawkinsville, September 6 and December 15, 1923; Rome, October 1, 1923, and January 1, 1925; Savannah, March 10, 1925.

The Black Duck is not known definitely to breed south of Currituck Sound, in eastern North Carolina, but available records, while somewhat inconclusive, indicate that it possibly nests locally in Georgia. Attempting to verify a rumor that an occasional brood of young was seen on the Alcovy River south of Covington, I spent the larger part of the day, July 17, 1937, on this stretch of the river, accompanied by Charles N. Elliott, then director of the Georgia Game and Fish Commission. We found no nests or broods of young, but did see two adult birds that flushed from a bend of the river as we approached in a boat.

Davis and Johnston [1946] report flushing four birds from a slough at the edge of the Chattahoochee River north of Atlanta on August 3, 1946, a date that further confirms the likelihood of this species nesting in the state. Davis likewise saw two birds on August 2, 1947, on the Twin Lakes, ten miles south of Valdosta, Lowndes County, but, as he pointed out, since this is in the extreme southern part of the state, there is a possibility that these were Mottled Ducks, *Anas fulvigula.* A nest with six eggs, found on Blackbeard Island on July 2, 1917, by M. F. Boisclair, was considered at the time to be that of a Black Duck. However, this identification was never fully confirmed. Neill [1949] reports two birds seen at Augusta on July 5, 1948, scattered pairs and single birds at McKinney's Pond, in northern Emanuel County, July 11–17, 1948, and a single bird at Miller's Pond, in northern Burke County, on August 28, 1948.

HABITS AND RECOGNITION: The Black Duck is one of the few ducks limited in its distribution to eastern North America, but within its range it is an abundant and well-known bird. On the northern Atlantic Coast it outnumbers even the Mallard, and in the fall it is probably the bird most sought by the many waterfowl hunters afield there during the open season. It is usually found in small flocks, rarely more than eight or ten birds being seen together, and these flocks are so wary and so constantly on the alert that it is the exceptional sportsman who even approaches the bag limit.

Unlike other ducks, it is equally at home in fresh-water swamps and in salt-water marshes, feeding in the shallower water near the shore, where it secures its food by tipping up, and partially submerging, its body. It apparently is averse to diving and, while capable of doing so, has never been known to feed in deep water. It is normally more active at night than during the daytime, especially during the fall months, the days being spent then resting and sleeping in stretches of open water, where there is little danger of being taken unawares. Although known as the Black Duck, it actually is dark brown rather than black, and at a distance resembles, both in size and general appearance, a dark female Mallard. In flight, however, it can be recognized at once by the silvery-white lining of its wings and the lack of white in the tail. There is no difference in the plumage of the two sexes of the Black Duck.

Florida Mottled Duck
Anas fulvigula fulvigula Ridgway

GENERAL DISTRIBUTION: Resident on the Florida peninsula north to Alachua County.

STATUS IN GEORGIA: Of accidental occurrence.

There is apparently but one record of this species in the state, a specimen taken by A. H. Helme on Cumberland Island, on December 23, 1902, being found referable to *fulvigula*. It is possible, however, that it occurs regularly in the southern part of the state but has been overlooked because of its similarity to the relatively abundant Black Duck.

HABITS AND RECOGNITION: The Florida Mottled Duck resembles the Black Duck, but is slightly smaller and paler. It is essentially a bird of the fresh-water marshes, but otherwise its habits are similar in every respect to its more northern relative, though it is said to be less wary.

Gadwall
Anas strepera   Linnaeus

GENERAL DISTRIBUTION: Has a wide range in the Northern Hemisphere. In North America it breeds from northern Saskatchewan and Hudson Bay south to California, New Mexico, Kansas, Iowa, central Minnesota, and southern Wisconsin. Also in the British Isles and temperate Europe and Asia. Winters in North America from Maryland, Illinois, Arkansas, Colorado, and southern British Columbia south into Mexico, and in Jamaica, and also is found in winter in the British Isles, the Mediterranean countries, northern India, China, and Japan.

STATUS IN GEORGIA: Apparently an irregular and rather local winter resident in the southern part of the state, and a scarce transient north of the fall line.

Definite records are rather few in number, but it is probable that the bird occurs more frequently than is generally supposed. Few hunters seem to know it by name, and it can undoubtedly be confused with other species unless seen under favorable conditions. At Athens, I recorded it only during the fall migration of 1929, a female being taken on October 28 and a male on November 7. Griffin [1941] considers it a rare winter resident about Atlanta, and gives as extreme dates November 18 (1938), and March 13 (1938). However, a single bird was reported seen by Sanford at Atlanta on March 24, 1917. At Mt. Berry (Floyd County), Jones [1942] gives it this same status, his few records being of two birds seen December 6, 1940, and single birds December 15, 1940, and February 3–4 and March 16, 1941. Murphey [1937] found it an irregular winter visitant in Richmond County, and had specimens in his collection taken there on November 25, 1922, and December 6, 1931. At Macon there is a single record, March 8, 1945 (Meanley).

Stoddard [MS] has noted it but twice in Grady County, single males being seen there January 25, 1945, and November 30, 1947. Norris and Hopkins [1953] have records for the Tifton-Fitzgerald region from December 7 (1941) to December 22 (1940). Hebard [1941] records one shot on Floyd's Island Prairie on November 30, 1928, and states that "at least 14 frequented the Rice Pond at Coleraine in November and December, 1940." He reports a pair seen at Silco, Camden County, on November 25, 1940, and a single bird that same day on the St. Marys River in Charlton County. Tomkins says the Gadwall appears irregularly on the coast at the mouth of the Savannah River, being noted there in February, 1923, in January, 1924, on November 12, 1929, and on November 6 and 23, 1930. Erichsen [MS] has a single record for Chatham County, December 30, 1934.

HABITS AND RECOGNITION: The Gadwall is one of the surface-feeding ducks, and is commonly found associated with other species with similar habits. Its preference is for fresh-water ponds and swamps, and here it feeds in the shallower water near the shore. It has no liking for salt water, and in the extensive coast marshes it is only rarely seen. In the eastern United States it is, to a large extent, a bird of the interior, and it is doubtful if at any time flocks of any size occur in Georgia. Normally one or two are observed with such species as the Pintail or the American Widgeon, although it is not uncommon to find them alone. Superficially this species suggests a Black Duck, but its smaller size, slender appearance, and white wing patch should readily identify it. Seen at reasonably close range, its gray plumage is equally diagnostic.

Pintail
Anas acuta   Linnaeus

GENERAL DISTRIBUTION: Breeds from northwestern Alaska and northern Mackenzie east to Labrador and south to central Iowa, central Nebraska, northern Colorado, northern Utah, and southern California. Winters from southern British Columbia, Colorado, Missouri, southern Illinois, and Maryland south to the Gulf Coast, the Bahamas, the West Indies, and Panama.

STATUS IN GEORGIA: A regular, but uncommon, winter resident and transient throughout the state where suitable conditions occur.

Murphey [1937] noted this species as a regular winter resident at Augusta, flocks being frequently observed feeding among the willows on the banks of the Savannah River. A specimen in his collection was taken in Richmond County on December 1, 1903. At Athens, I found it a scarce migrant both in the spring and in the fall, my extreme dates for it being

February 16 (1929) and April 5 (1925), and October 29 (1925) and December 14 (1926). Despite the present lack of records, however, it doubtless occurs during mild winters where food and cover are available. Griffin [MS] records the Pintail as an uncommon winter resident about Atlanta, his extreme dates being October 31 (1942), and April 8 (1934). Jones [1942] considers it a fairly regular, but uncommon, winter visitant at Mt. Berry (Floyd County), his earliest date of arrival in the fall being November 6 (1941), and latest in the spring, June 23 (1940). At Milledgeville [Tait, 1946], it was noted on March 17, 1941; at Macon, Mrs. Mounts observed a flock of nine birds on December 8, 1928; and Straw [1947] observed a pair on the Chattahoochee River, near Columbus, on April 10, 1946. Norris [1939] reports a female killed fourteen miles from Fitzgerald on September 29, 1939, the earliest fall record for the state. Stoddard [MS] considers it a winter resident in Grady County, his extreme dates being November 3 (1943) and April 11 (1945).

One was taken in the Okefenokee Swamp, December 29, 1916, and Harper saw several there on January 4, 1917. Hebard [1941] considers it uncommon in the swamp, although he states that 100 were found on Chase Prairie on February 10, 1935. He observed it first at Coleraine on October 28, 1940. Another early record for the state in the fall is that of a small flock seen at the mouth of the Savannah River on October 8, 1932. This species was also recorded there in spring on March 15 and April 12, 1931.

HABITS AND RECOGNITION: Because of its wide distribution and unique appearance, the Pintail is probably nearly as well known throughout the country as the Mallard or the Black Duck. Always wary and alert, it is a favorite with the hunter who is more interested in sporty shooting than he is in getting the bag limit. Being another of the surface-feeding ducks, it can be found associating with Widgeons and Shovelers, procuring its food in shallow pools where the bottom can be reached by tilting up rather than diving. It is commonly seen in fresh-water marshes and streams, but is not averse to salt water, and is found equally often in the sloughs and open channels in the coast marshes.

It is one of the earliest ducks to migrate in the spring, following closely the retreating ice and snow as it pushes northward toward its breeding grounds in the far north. In the fall, however, it apparently moves south long before the freeze-up in the north, and by late August or early September the first flocks have started south. No duck is more easily recognized. Even at a distance its long, slender neck, and long, pointed tail identify it readily, these characters being the same in both sexes. On the water, females suggest female Mallards, but their slender build and graceful buoyancy should be apparent within reasonable range. Males are unmistakable, with their white underparts, gray back, and slender brown head and upper neck.

Green-winged Teal
Anas carolinensis Gmelin

GENERAL DISTRIBUTION: Breeds from northern Alaska and Mackenzie south to central California, northern New Mexico, Nebraska, southern Minnesota, northern Michigan, western New York, southern Ontario, and southern Quebec. Winters from southern British Columbia, Montana, Nebraska, southern Illinois, and Maryland south to the West Indies, British Honduras, and southern Mexico.

STATUS IN GEORGIA: An uncommon transient and winter resident except on the coast where it winters commonly.

At Athens, I noted it but once, two birds being seen February 14, 1927, in the Sandy Creek bottoms. Griffin [1941] considers it a rare winter resident about Atlanta, and gives as dates of occurrence November 22–28, 1936, and December 20, 1938. He cites an additional fall record [Griffin, 1942] of a single bird seen by Paxton on December 26, 1941. Johnston [1944] reports a female seen on the Piedmont Park Lake, within the Atlanta city limits, on March 30, 1944. At Lake Rutledge, Morgan County, a single bird was seen on October 12, 1940 [Griffin, 1940].

Jones [1942] found it a rare winter visitant at Mt. Berry (Floyd County), his few records being April 8, 1939, and October 25 and December 26, 1940. Dorsey [letter] reports four birds seen at Rome on April 21, 1952. At Augusta, Murphey [1937] states that, while it was formerly abundant, it is now rare, although a few are observed each winter. For Macon there is a single record, January 24, 1953 (Whitney). In the bird distribution files of the Fish and Wildlife Service there is a record of one noted at Ways Station, Bryan County, on November 9, 1886. Norris and Hopkins [1953] report it at Tifton, April 16 to 20, 1932, and Stoddard [MS] considers it a fairly common winter resident in Grady County, his extreme dates being November 27 (1944) and March 28 (1945).

Hebard [1941] reports it present in the Okefenokee Swamp in small but increasing numbers between 1928 and 1936. Members of the Georgia Society of Naturalists saw twenty-four on Chase Prairie between December 1 and 7, 1934, and ninety were observed at this same spot between January 24 and 27, 1935. On the coast, it has been noted in Chatham County by Erichsen at rather infrequent intervals, his extreme dates being September 27 (1924) and March 15 (1938). However, Tomkins [letter] states that he has found this little duck wintering commonly on the coast.

Family Anatidae: DUCKS, GEESE, & SWANS

HABITS AND RECOGNITION: The Green-winged Teal is another of the so-called "puddle ducks" that feeds by preference in shallow water, and frequents pools and sloughs in marshes. It apparently experiences no difficulty in diving, and can do so when occasion demands, but only rarely will it be seen feeding in deep water. It is unusually agile on land, walking or running with ease, and this agility makes it possible for it to supplement its usual diet with seeds and grain that it picks up in the farmer's fields. Few birds can fly faster than this little duck, and its evolutions in the air are so disconcerting to the average hunter that only the more skillful and experienced can hit this elusive target. Unfortunately for its own preservation, it is rather unsuspicious and easily approached when on the water, and this has, all too often, proved its undoing. It is one of the hardier ducks, being among the first to start the long flight north in the spring and one of the last to appear in the fall. In Georgia it is rarely seen after the first week in March, and it is November before the first small flocks reappear. Few ducks are easier to identify. Its small size will distinguish it at once from all but the Blue-winged Teal, and it can be told from this species by the lack of large, light-blue patches on the wings in either sex and in the male by the presence of a vertical white stripe in front of the wing.

Blue-winged Teal
Anas discors Linnaeus

GENERAL DISTRIBUTION: Breeds from central British Columbia and southern Mackenzie south to northern Nevada, central Utah, northern New Mexico, Missouri, Indiana, Ohio, and western New York, and in small numbers in Texas, Louisiana, and Florida. Winters to a large extent in Central and South America south to Brazil, and casually in the southern United States north to southern Illinois and Maryland.

STATUS IN GEORGIA: A fairly common spring and fall transient, and a local and rather scarce winter resident in the extreme eastern edge of the state.

At Athens I found this species a fairly common transient, small flocks being seen at frequent intervals throughout most of April, and again in September. As a usual thing the flocks observed contained four or five birds, exceptions being a group of thirteen found feeding in a shallow pool in the open Sandy Creek bottoms on April 16, 1926, and a flock of ten at the same spot on September 7, 1926. Extreme dates of occurrence recorded by me in the spring are March 26 (1928) and April 27 (1928), and in the fall, September 7 (1926) and October 15 (1926). Griffin [MS] records it as a common transient in the Atlanta area, extreme dates being March 18 (1939) and May 16 (1944), and August 27 (1938) and October

139

15 (1930). Johnston [1945] reports a single bird wintering at Atlanta, being seen from October 16, 1943, through May 6, 1944. At Mt. Berry (Floyd County) Jones [1942] found the Blue-winged Teal "an irregular transient occurring usually in pairs or alone." His extreme dates for the spring migration are March 20 (1938) and May 1 (1940), and for the fall migration, September 29 (1941) and October 8 (1940). Murphey [1937] considers this species "still a frequent winter resident, but in greatly diminished numbers." His earliest recorded date of arrival in Richmond County in the fall is September 9, and the latest date of departure in the spring, April 26. At Macon, Johnston [MS] gives as extreme dates of occurrence March 8 (1945) and May 12 (1928), and August 31 (1936) and September 26 (1954).

At Milledgeville, Tait [1946] cites one record, April 19, 1942. Dreyfoos [1946] has recorded it on the Fort Benning Reservation at Columbus on several occasions in 1945, two birds being seen on one pond, April 9 through 15, and six on another pond, April 13. Hopkins [in litt.] gives as extreme dates for Fitzgerald, September 9 (1939) and April 27 (1952), and in Grady County, Stoddard [MS] reports small flocks present in the fall from August 27 (1941) until late November, and in the spring from March 18 (1945) to April 28 (1945). Grimm [1946] found it present in small numbers on a pond at Flemington, in Liberty County, in 1944, four birds being noted on March 31, and six April 1 through April 6. Hebard [1941] has recorded it but once in the Okefenokee Swamp, a pair being seen on Chase Prairie on November 25, 1932. He states that "numbers frequented the Rice Pond at Coleraine in September and October, 1940, and were last noted November 2." He has noted it at Coleraine as late in the spring as May 14 (1953) [Hebard, letter].

On the coast Tomkins has observed this species in the spring at the mouth of the Savannah River as early as February 16 (1929) and as late as April 24 (1932). A few individuals apparently linger here in the fall well into December, and may possibly remain throughout the winter. Eight were killed on December 5, 1883, when they struck the lighthouse on Tybee Island, and on December 28, 1904, Helme took a specimen on Cumberland Island. Erichsen [MS] cites as his extreme dates of occurrence for Chatham County September 15 (1923) and April 18 (1926).

HABITS AND RECOGNITION: The Blue-winged Teal is unique in its reluctance to experience even a touch of winter, for it leaves the northern part of its breeding range so early in the fall that it escapes to a large extent even the first heavy frosts. In Georgia the first small flocks arrive as early as the latter part of August, and by the middle of September are present over much of the state. The weather then is usually hot and dry and more suggestive of midsummer rather than early fall, but these teal never fail to put in their appearance in certain favored pools and quiet streams. The spring migration is rarely well under way before the middle of March, and although the bulk of the birds are gone by the latter part of April, it is not uncommon to see a few small flocks as late as the first week in May.

Shallow pools and slow, sluggish streams are spots sought by these small ducks during their sojourn in the state, and here they feed on aquatic vegetation that can be had from the surface of the water, or by merely submerging their heads. Normally unsuspicious and easily approached, when alarmed they are one of the swiftest of the ducks in flight, and once in the air, are said to be able to attain a speed of 90 to 100 miles an hour. In migration they fly in small, compact flocks of their own, but when resting or feeding, they commonly associate with such species as the Widgeon and the Shoveller. The small size and conspicuous, light-blue wing patch will readily identify this species regardless of sex. Males are unmistakable, if seen within reasonable range, because of the broad white crescent in front of the eye.

European Widgeon
Mareca penelope (Linnaeus)

GENERAL DISTRIBUTION: Breeds in Greenland, Iceland, the British Isles, northern Europe, and Asia east to Kamchatka. Of casual occurrence in North America both in migration and during the winter months, having been recorded on the Atlantic Coast south to Florida, in the Mississippi Valley south to Louisiana, and on the Pacific Coast from Alaska to California.

STATUS IN GEORGIA: A rare transient and winter resident in the southeastern corner of the state.

The first definite record for the European Widgeon for Georgia is that of a male taken by A. H. Helme on Cumberland Island on December 28, 1904. At the University of Georgia, at Athens, there is a specimen taken in Chatham County by Walter Hoxie on November 18, 1908, and in the state museum at Atlanta is another specimen taken near Savannah. Hebard [1941] records a single bird shot on Floyd's Island Prairie, in the Okefenokee Swamp, on January 31, 1931, and what appears to be the most recent record there is that of a male seen by G. Edgar Folk on Wassaw Island, Chatham County, on March 12, 1938 [Folk, 1939].

HABITS AND RECOGNITION: Although able to secure its food by diving where the water is not too deep, the European Widgeon prefers to feed near the shore of a pond or quiet stream where it is not necessary to submerge its entire body. For this reason, the occasional bird seen in this country is found with small flocks of American Widgeons or other surface-feeding ducks. Within its breeding range, it shows a definite partiality for salt water, but this is apparently not the case in so far as North American stragglers are concerned, fresh-water pools and marshes being preferred. In appearance this species suggests the American Widgeon. The males, however, can be easily distinguished by their reddish-brown, rather than gray, heads, and by the fact that the forehead and crown are buffy instead of white. Females and young are less distinct, but, like the males, are characterized by a distinctly brown head that lacks any suggestion of gray. In both sexes the axillars in the wing are gray, while in the American Widgeon they are white.

American Widgeon
Mareca americana (Gmelin)

GENERAL DISTRIBUTION: Breeds from Alaska and Mackenzie south to southern California, Utah, Colorado, central Nebraska, and central Iowa. Winters from southern British Columbia, Nevada, Utah, Colorado, the Ohio Valley, and Maryland, south to Central America and the Lesser Antilles.

STATUS IN GEORGIA: An uncommon winter resident in the southern part of the state, and a fairly common transient north of the fall line (although apparently less numerous in autumn than in spring).

In Georgia the American Widgeon is one of the last ducks to migrate north in the spring, the small flocks observed being most numerous the last two weeks in March. Farther north the fall migration is well under way by the latter part of September, but this far south it is usually October, or even later if the weather is mild, before the first flocks appear.

At Athens I recorded one flock of five birds as early as February 15 (1927), but otherwise my extreme dates for the spring migration are March 7 (1926), and April 1 (1926). I have but one record for the fall migration, a single bird being seen on Lake Kirota on November 10, 1927, and for two days thereafter. Griffin [1941] gives as the extreme dates for the spring migration in the Atlanta area, February 25 (1932) and April 8 (1938). He, too, cites but one record for the fall migration, November 2, 1935. Johnston [1945] reports the first occurrence of this species wintering about Atlanta, a single bird appearing October 14, 1943, and being seen at intervals then through May 18, 1944. Jones [1942] found it "a fairly common, but irregular, winter visitant," the earliest date of arrival in the fall recorded by him being October 22 (1939), and latest in the spring, June

18 (1941). Murphey [1937] considers the American Widgeon a regular, but uncommon, winter visitor about Augusta. Specimens in his collection were taken in Richmond County on September 13 and 15. At Macon [Johnston, MS] it was noted on February 28, 1953, and May 27 and September 13, 1955. Norris [in litt.] gives his earliest fall record at Tifton, November 2 (1941), and Stoddard [MS] states that this species is a common winter resident in Grady County, being seen from November 3 (1943) through March 31 (1946).

Hebard [1941] reports it uncommon in the Okefenokee Swamp during the winter months, and states that fifteen American Widgeons were seen on Chase Prairie December 1 to 7, 1934. He first observed it at Coleraine on October 24, 1940. Mrs. Bassett has recorded this species in Liberty County on December 17, 1931, and February 11 and March 21, 1932. Tomkins found it an irregular visitant at the mouth of the Savannah River, noting it there on November 12 and December 14, 1929, October 8, 1932, and November 11, 1933. Erichsen [MS] cites extreme dates of occurrence for Chatham County as October 29 (1927) and April 7 (1916). Specimens were taken in Chatham County on November 8, 1908, and on Blackbeard Island.

HABITS AND RECOGNITION: The American Widgeon is another of the surface-feeding ducks that obtains the bulk of its food in the shallower pools and streams. Not only is it reluctant to dive at any time, but it also apparently experiences considerable difficulty in going very far beneath the surface of the water or remaining there for any length of time. For this reason it has developed a habit unique among our ducks which aids it in getting the food it prefers. It associates with such species as the Scaups, the Redhead, and, even more frequently, the Coot. All are skillful divers, and the Widgeon, taking advantage of this, waits for individual birds to come up to the surface whereupon it robs the diver of part of its booty of aquatic plants. So common is this habit that, in many parts of its range, the Widgeon is often referred to as the Poacher.

This is one of the commoner ducks found in the state in migration, and, especially during the spring months, small flocks can be found on many of the larger pools and streams. During the hunting season they learn to be constantly on the alert, but for the greater part of the year they are relatively unsuspicious and easily approached. Males are readily recognized, for their color pattern is quite distinctive. The best field character is the conspicuous white forehead and crown, although in flight the broad white patch on the forewing will distinguish this species even at a distance. Females have the same wing mark, and, while they can be confused with the European Widgeon, if they are seen under favorable conditions, the gray (instead of brownish) head and neck should identify them.

Shoveler
Spatula clypeata   (Linnaeus)

GENERAL DISTRIBUTION: Has a wide range in the Northern Hemisphere. In North America it breeds from Alaska and northern Mackenzie south to southern California, central Arizona, northern New Mexico, Kansas, Iowa, northern Illinois, and northern Indiana. Also from the Arctic Circle to southern Europe and central Asia, and from Great Britain to Kamchatka and the Commander Islands. Winters in North America from southern British Columbia, central California, Arizona, New Mexico, Texas, Missouri, southern Illinois, and the coast of Virginia, south to the Pacific Coast of Mexico, Central America, and the West Indies.

STATUS IN GEORGIA: A regular but uncommon transient north of the fall line and a locally uncommon winter resident in the southern part of the state.

At Athens I found this species to be a rather scarce transient, and noted it only in the spring, although it doubtless occurs in small numbers in the fall. My few records for its occurrence are: a flock of seven birds April 5, 1925 (Lake Kirota); five, April 2, 1926 (Sandy Creek bottoms); four, March 16, 1928 (City Reservoir); and twenty, March 22, 1929 (Sandy Creek bottoms). Griffin [1941] lists it as a transient in the Atlanta area, and gives as extreme dates of occurrence February 28 (1932) and April 26 (1932), October 29 (1932) and November 9 (1932). At Mt. Berry, in Floyd County, Jones [1942] found it a rare transient, extreme dates being October 8 (1940) and December 2 (1934), March 24 (1941) and April 9 (1941).

Murphey [1937] considers it not uncommon about Augusta, and states that it remains quite late in the spring, his latest dates of departure being April 16 and April 19. Specimens in his collection were taken in Richmond County on December 6, 1903, and April 2, 1906. At Macon it has been reported by Denton in the fall on the unusually early date of August 31, 1937, and also [Johnston, MS] on October 11, 1952, and April 10, 1954.

Hebard [1941] found it wintering in small numbers in the Okefenokee Swamp, its center of abundance apparently being on Grand Prairie and Honey Island Prairie. He records a female seen by Herbert L. Stoddard on Chase Prairie on December 3, 1934, and a male shot by John M. Hopkins at this same spot on December 22, 1934. He also has records for this species on Mill Creek, in western Camden County, single birds, December 23, 1939 and December 5, 1940, and for Silco (December 11, 1940) and Rice Pond (December 14, 1940). Records for the coast are largely limited to observations made by Ivan Tomkins at the mouth of the Savannah River. He reports "a few in the salt marshes each year from 1923 to 1931," and gives as dates of arrival there in the fall, September 22, 1930, and October 24, 1933, and departure in the spring, April 3, 1931, and April 23, 1932. Erichsen [MS] cites extreme dates of occurrence for Chatham County as October 14 (1917) and April 7 (1940).

HABITS AND RECOGNITION: The Shoveler is a duck that can hardly be confused with any other species. Not only is the color pattern of the male so striking as to be instantly recognizable, but the long, broad spatulate bill in both sexes will identify at once any bird seen within reasonable distance. This highly specialized bill makes it possible for the Shoveler to secure its food from the surface of the water, and as a result it is usually found feeding in the shallower pools, or at the shore line of slow-flowing streams. Its associates then are generally the Blue-winged Teal and the Widgeon, and compared with these species, its relatively small size, not much larger than a teal, is readily apparent. It is one of the least suspicious of the ducks and is easily approached, but, when alarmed, can rise from the water and depart with considerable speed. Like the Blue-winged Teal, it is apparently not a hardy bird, for it leaves its breeding grounds in September at the first hint of winter and does not reappear in the spring until April or later. In Georgia the small flocks in which it normally travels are most numerous in late March and the first half of April, and again in late September and October.

Wood Duck
Aix sponsa   (Linnaeus)

GENERAL DISTRIBUTION: Breeds locally throughout the United States, and north in Canada to southern British Columbia, southern Manitoba, southeastern Ontario, and central Labrador. Winters largely in the southern United States, north casually to British Columbia, southern Illinois, and Virginia, and south to central Mexico and Jamaica.

STATUS IN GEORGIA: A locally common resident throughout the state, and an abundant winter resident south of the fall line.

At Athens this species has increased perceptibly since 1920, and can now be seen throughout the year on the Oconee River. Young recently out of the nest were reported to me early in May, 1927, and that the Wood Duck remained to breed that year was further verified by my seeing two birds in the Sandy Creek bottoms July 22. My first definite winter record was that of three birds seen at the edge of the river January 27, 1928.

Griffin [1941] lists the Wood Duck as a permanent resident in the Atlanta area and records a nest found there by Barkalow on May 3, 1932, with twelve eggs [Griffin, 1940]. Greene [1933] saw two adult birds on

EASTERN AMERICAN OYSTER-CATCHER

Haematopus palliatus palliatus

This big, robust shore bird we saw in the vicinity of Savannah. It is a wary
and not at all common species which rests on islands at high tide and flies
out to the salt-water flats to feed at low tide. The roughness of its soles helps
it to run about the wet rocks without slipping.

the Flint River near Jonesboro, on May 22, 1929, and reports that four days later Norman Giles, Jr., saw three young at this same spot. At Rome, Jones [1947] records a nest with eggs found in a hollow stump on April 5, 1929, and a brood of eleven young seen May 9, 1943. Murphey [1937] considers this handsome duck abundant about Augusta, where it breeds in early March. He states that previous to 1930, "it was greatly diminished in numbers, but under protection its numbers are steadily increasing." Denton reports a female with three half-grown young on Spirit Creek, in Richmond County, May 1, 1952. Hopkins [in litt.] reports broods of small young at Fitzgerald April 11 and June 20, 1940, and May 3, 1941. Stoddard [MS] reports broods of small young in Grady County, May 8, 1940, July 19, 1944, and April 15, 1945, these dates indicating a long breeding season for this species in the southern part of the state.

In December, 1917, Francis Harper estimated the number of resident Wood Ducks in the Okefenokee Swamp at 500 or more, and Hebard [1941] cites winter concentrations in various parts of the swamp that show a noticeable increase in recent years. He states that 400 were seen on Spanish Creek in 1934, and 287 on Chase Prairie from January 24 to 27, 1935. The partiality of this species for acorns was clearly indicated by the fact that, when the oaks on the mainland bore heavily, relatively few Wood Ducks would be found in the swamp. In November and December, 1940, apparently because of a severe drought that left much of the swamp dry, there was an unusual concentration of these ducks at Coleraine, fully 5,000 being found then on Mill Creek above the dam. Grimm [1946] considered these ducks a fairly common permanent resident in Liberty County in 1944, finding them especially numerous along the Canoochee River on June 18. The Savannah Wildlife Refuge on the coast probably has a larger population of Wood Ducks than any other area in the state. E. B. Whitehead, federal game protector, reports seeing more than 2,000 there in January, 1930, and in early April of that year, many small young.

HABITS AND RECOGNITION: Too many of our birds have common names that are either inappropriate or wholly misleading, but the Wood Duck is not one of these. Regardless of season or circumstance, this species can be found in wooded swamps rather than open marshes, and unlike the other surface-feeding ducks, it shows a decided preference for the swifter-running streams bordered by heavy timber. A certain proportion of its food is obtained in shallow water, but it is quite agile on land, and because of its fondness for the smaller acorns and other seeds and berries, can be found often feeding in wooded areas some distance from the nearest water. Surprised under these conditions, it demonstrates both speed on the wing and an adeptness in threading its way through the forest growth that is a marvel to see.

Except during the breeding season, it is found in small flocks, and while in no sense of the word unsociable, because of the nature of its haunts, it is rarely seen associating with other ducks. With the possible exception of the Hooded Merganser, this species is the only duck that is now known to nest in the state. A natural cavity in a large tree is the site usually selected, although hollow stumps or old woodpecker holes are utilized if they are large enough. The height from the ground is seemingly immaterial. The downy young seem to be able to reach the ground without harm by simply fluttering down within a few hours after they are hatched. After they have all assembled on the ground they follow the mother on foot to the nearest water.

Redhead
Aythya americana   (Eyton)

GENERAL DISTRIBUTION: Breeds from central British Columbia and Manitoba south to southern California, central Nevada, northern New Mexico, central Nebraska, and southern Wisconsin. Winters from southern British Columbia to Mexico, and from Colorado, Arkansas, southern Illinois, and Maryland south to the West Indies.

STATUS IN GEORGIA: A locally uncommon transient and winter resident throughout the state.

At Athens I found it a scarce transient, and one that was seen only at infrequent intervals. Extreme dates of occurrence I recorded there for the spring migration are March 15 (1925) and March 31 (1926); and for the fall migration, November 4 (1924) and November 28 (1929). At Atlanta migration extremes are November 13 (1927) [Greene, 1933] and April 29 (1943) [Johnston, 1945]. Jones [1942] found this species a rare spring transient at Mt. Berry, near Rome, small flocks being seen March 10, 1938, and March 16, 23, and 24, 1941. Murphey [1937] considers it an irregular winter visitant about Augusta, and states that but a single individual was noted from 1933 through 1937. A specimen in his possession was taken in Richmond County in January, 1907. For Macon there is a single record, December 19, 1920 (Beryl T. Mounts). In Grady County, Stoddard [MS] has noted this species on but three occasions, on December 9, 23, and 25, 1945. Hebard [1941] reports it an uncommon duck in the Okefenokee Swamp from 1925 to 1936, the largest number shot in a day being four, on Chase Prairie, on December 3, 1932. Additional records he cites are a single bird shot on Mill Creek, in western Camden County, on December 3, 1939; one seen at the Rice Pond, in eastern Charlton County, on October 14, 1940; and a pair at Silco on December 10, 1940. On the coast, Tomkins has recorded it but once, a specimen having been taken at the mouth of the Savannah River on February 13, 1928.

HABITS AND RECOGNITION: The Redhead is one of the hardier ducks, wintering in numbers as far north as it can find open water; however, the major wintering ground is along the Gulf Coast of Texas. It is not a common bird in Georgia, and only rather small flocks or single birds are seen. It is equally at home in fresh water or salt water, and commonly associates throughout much of the year with such species as the Lesser Scaup and the Ring-necked Duck. As its food is largely aquatic vegetation, it is an excellent table bird, and always a favorite with waterfowl hunters. It is a swift flier, but decoys readily, and, as a consequence, is shot in numbers throughout the legal hunting season.

Ring-necked Duck
Aythya collaris (Donovan)

GENERAL DISTRIBUTION: Breeds from central British Columbia east through Alberta, Saskatchewan, Manitoba, Ontario, and the Maritime Provinces, and south to central Arizona, northern Utah, northern Nebraska, northern Iowa, southern Wisconsin, and Maine. Winters in the southern United States, north casually to Chesapeake Bay, southern Illinois, northern Arkansas, northern Texas, and southern British Columbia, in the Bahamas, and through Mexico to Guatemala.

STATUS IN GEORGIA: A fairly common transient and locally common winter resident throughout the state.

At Athens I found this duck a regular but uncommon transient, small flocks being noted at infrequent intervals both in the spring and in the fall. I have no records for the winter months, extreme dates of occurrence being March 5 (1929) and April 16 (1925), and October 30 (1929) and December 6 (1927). Griffin [MS] considers it a winter resident about Atlanta, extreme dates being October 15 (1944) and May 21 (1932). Murphey [1937] states that in Richmond County it is "very common, and frequents particularly the deep wooded creeks and the ponds and lagoons which lie close to the banks of the Savannah River." Specimens in his collection were taken in December, 1896, and on February 10 and March 12, 1935. His latest date for the spring migration is March 29.

Jones [1942] regards it as a common winter resident and the most abundant duck at Mt. Berry, in Floyd County, flocks of over 100 being frequently seen during March. He gives as extreme dates of occurrence in this northwestern corner of Georgia October 26 (1939) and April 29 (1941). Johnston [MS] reports it from Macon in 1953 between the dates of March 7 and April 26. In Grady County, Stoddard [MS] considers it a common winter resident, occurring from October 3 (1943) until early April. He has noted it, however, as late as May 20, 1952, a flock of six, in Thomas County. Norris and Hopkins [1953] cite as their earliest fall record, for Fitzgerald, October 29 (1952), and as their latest spring record, for Irwin County, March 25 (1952).

Harper reports this species a common winter resident in the Okefenokee Swamp, and this is verified by Hebard [1941], who found it the most abundant duck there during the winter months. His comments are interesting, and worth quoting in detail:

> From the number estimated at about 1,000 using Chase and Floyd's Island Prairies in 1925–26 the 'Bulls' increased to 10,000 as estimated by Gad Roddenberry in 1930–31. I believe this estimate to have been much too low as two flocks at least a mile long and several hundred yards deep flew west over Floyd's Island in January, 1931, each evening on their way to their roost on Floyd's Island Prairie. Not over 5,000 were present the next two years, although I saw over 2,000 coursing back and forth over Chase Prairie on December 16, 1933.

The earliest date of arrival reported to him was October 23, 1938, and small numbers were still present in the swamp as late as March 11 (1931). He reports this species at Coleraine until April 4 (1939), and at St. Marys until April 12 (1939). Helme considers it not uncommon on the coast; he saw three birds at Brunswick on January 13, 1902, and six on Cumberland Island on March 7, 1902. Tomkins recorded two flocks on the lower Savannah River, one of fourteen birds on February 8, 1933, and the other of similar size on March 25, 1935. In the collection of the University of Georgia are two specimens taken in Chatham County November 7 and 13, 1908.

HABITS AND RECOGNITION: Because of its similarity in both appearance and actions to the Scaup Duck, the Ring-necked Duck is not well known to the average hunter. Consequently, it was at one time thought to be rather scarce in the state, and only in recent years has its relative abundance been recognized. It is essentially a bird of the interior, frequenting fresh-water ponds and marshes and only rarely found in salt water. Its food is largely aquatic vegetation, and this it obtains by diving to the bottom of pools and slower-flowing streams where the water is four to six feet in depth. It is a swift flyer, but rather erratic in flight, and while it decoys readily, the open formation of the flocks renders this species less vulnerable than other ducks. Those familiar with its habits comment on the fact that it favors certain ponds or lakes to the exclusion of others apparently equally favorable, and regardless of how much it is hunted, will consistently return to these spots. The male Ring-necked Duck is most likely to be confused with the Scaups, and from these it can be readily distinguished by its black, rather than gray, back, and by the broad white band on the bill. The females have this same band on the bill, which distinguishes them from female Redheads; they lack the white patch at the base of the bill and the white stripe in the wing that characterizes the female Scaups.

Canvasback
Aythya valisineria   (Wilson)

GENERAL DISTRIBUTION: Breeds from central Alaska and northern Mackenzie south to western Nevada, northern Utah, northern New Mexico, western Nebraska, southern Wisconsin, and southern Minnesota. Winters from southern British Columbia south along the Pacific Coast to Mexico, and from Montana, Colorado, Arkansas, southern Illinois, and Maryland south to the Gulf Coast.

STATUS IN GEORGIA: An uncommon and irregular transient and winter resident in the interior of the state, and a fairly common winter resident on the coast.

Records of the Canvasback in the interior of the state are not numerous. Jones [1942] considers it an uncommon winter resident at Mt. Berry in Floyd County, small flocks being seen from November 9 (1935) through March 25 (1940). Greene [1933] lists it as a rare winter resident about Atlanta, with extreme dates of occurrence November 20 (1932) and April 13 (1933). In Richmond County, Murphey [1937] found it an "irregular winter visitant, usually appearing during, or after, the cold spells of January or February." He collected several specimens on the Savannah River, near Augusta, on January 16, 1905. There are two records for Macon, November 27, 1931, and March 19, 1932 (Denton). Stoddard [MS] has but a single record for Grady County, January 27, 1946, and Hopkins [1951] noted a single bird, a male, on a pond in Baker County on the unusually late date of May 16, 1950.

In the Okefenokee Swamp, it is apparently rare during the winter months, for Hebard [1941] cites but two records: January 15, 1930, and December 2, 1932. He likewise has but one record for Camden County, a single bird being seen on the St. Marys River, above Mill Creek, on November 28, 1932. On the coast, it is apparently a fairly common winter resident. Tomkins reports this species unusually plentiful during the winter of 1933–34 and states that there were four feeding grounds on the lower Savannah River where these birds could always be found. He gives as dates of arrival November 23, 1928 and 1930. On February 10, 1935, three flocks, totaling forty-eight birds, were seen.

HABITS AND RECOGNITION: The Canvasback is the duck so highly praised by epicures, and when it has been feeding to a large extent on wild celery, of which it is exceptionally fond, it is unquestionably an excellent table bird. Under other circumstances, however, its flesh is no better than that of many of the other ducks with which it associates, and in some instances, where it has been feeding on small fishes, mollusks, crustaceans, and other salt-water life, it is inferior to those which have been feeding on plants. Having large powerful feet, it is a very good diver and a strong swimmer, and accordingly can secure its food in water where it is necessary to reach a depth of twenty to twenty-five feet.

It is a hardy species, being one of the last to leave its northern breeding grounds in the fall, and one of the first to start the long flight north in the spring. Canvasbacks concentrate in large numbers during the winter months in the Chesapeake Bay region. South of this point on the Atlantic Coast they are far less numerous, and in Georgia only small scattered flocks are seen. Both in migration and throughout the winter this species occurs impartially in either fresh or salt water and can be found wherever an adequate food supply exists. With its reddish-brown head and neck, the male Canvasback bears a superficial resemblance to the Redhead, but can readily be distinguished by its noticeably white, rather than gray, back. In either sex the flattened forehead and long wedge-shaped bill showing a straight sloping line from tip to tip of head identify this species at a reasonable distance.

American Greater Scaup
Aythya marila nearctica   Stejneger

GENERAL DISTRIBUTION: Breeds from the Aleutian Islands and the Arctic Coast of Alaska and Canada, south to central Alaska and central Mackenzie. Winters on the Pacific Coast south to southern California, on the Gulf Coast, on the Atlantic Coast from Maine to Florida, and in small numbers on the Great Lakes and in the Southwestern states.

STATUS IN GEORGIA: Apparently a rare and rather local winter resident in the eastern edge of the state.

Authentic records of its occurrence are very few in number, but, as it is easily overlooked among the common Lesser Scaups, it may be commoner than is generally supposed. At Augusta, Murphey [1937] states that it is "never very abundant"; he had several specimens taken there. Hebard [1941] cites two records for the Okefenokee Swamp: a male killed there on Chase Prairie on December 30, 1929, and five males shot at this same spot on January 15, 1930.

HABITS AND RECOGNITION: The Greater Scaup is so similar in appearance to the Lesser Scaup that it is difficult to identify in the field except under very favorable circumstances. It is slightly larger, and the head of the male is glossed with green in contrast to dull purple in the smaller bird; otherwise, the two species look very much alike when seen sitting on the water. In flight both sexes of the Greater Scaup show longer white strips in the wings than the Lesser Scaup. The Greater Scaup is noticeably maritime in its habits, and on the Atlantic Coast is rarely seen on inland waters, seeming to prefer salt-water bays and sounds where it gathers in dense rafts. It is a powerful swimmer, and a skillful diver, and normally secures its food, principally mollusks living on the bottom, well offshore in water that is eight to ten feet deep.

Lesser Scaup
Aythya affinis   (Eyton)

GENERAL DISTRIBUTION: Breeds from southern Alaska east through northern Canada to the west coast of Hudson Bay, and south to Colorado, Iowa, southern Wisconsin, and northern Ohio. Winters from southern British Columbia, Colorado, Arkansas, southern Illinois, and Maryland south to the Bahamas, the Lesser Antilles, and Panama.

STATUS IN GEORGIA: A common transient and winter resident throughout the state.

At Athens I found this species a common transient both in the spring and in the fall, flocks of varying size being frequently seen. The lakes and ponds in this part of the state are usually frozen over in December, and only once was the Lesser Scaup observed in January. The winter of 1926–27 was characterized by relatively mild weather that lasted until the middle of January, and this was taken advantage of by seventeen of these ducks that remained on the lake on the grounds of the Athens Country Club from the middle of December through January 15. Infrequent records during the summer months are probably of crippled birds that had not recovered sufficiently after being injured in the fall to make the long flight north in the spring. Such records include a female seen on Lake Kirota on June 21, 1926, and a male found on the Oconee River July 5, 1927. My extreme dates of occurrence in the spring are March 8 (1927) and May 23 (1927 and 1928), and in the fall, October 24 (1926) and December 20 (1925).

Griffin [1941] lists this species as a winter resident about Atlanta, and gives as extreme dates October 19 (1930) and June 5 (1932). Jones [1942] found it a common winter resident at Mt. Berry, in Floyd County, and states that its maximum numbers were reached in March, when flocks of fifty were observed. The earliest date of arrival in the fall which he recorded is October 8 (1934), the latest date of departure in the spring, June 15 (1941). Greene reports a flock of fourteen birds, six males and eight females, on Rabun Lake June 11, 1930, and a single bird there June 28. At Macon extreme dates of occurrence are November 12 (1928) and May 7 (1932) [Johnston, MS]. Norris and Hopkins [1953] give as their earliest fall record for Fitzgerald, October 25 (1942) and as their latest spring record for Tifton, April 28 (1933). In Grady County, Stoddard [MS] considers this species an irregular winter resident, abundant in some years, but in others somewhat scarce. His extreme dates are November 4 (1945) and April 2 (1945). At Augusta, Murphey [1937] considers it common during the winter months, but with a noticeable decrease in numbers in recent years.

In the Okefenokee Swamp, Hebard [1941] found it "not an uncommon duck," although varying in numbers from year to year. He states that five hundred were noted at Silco on December 31, 1940. On the coast, Tomkins noticed a definite decrease in numbers after 1930, the large flocks that formerly wintered on the lower Savannah River being reduced to an average of fifty individuals. However, in recent years this species has regained its former numbers and now is an abundant winter resident. He gives as arrival dates there October 25, 1927, and October 20, 1930. What is apparently the earliest date of arrival in the state in the fall is a single bird seen by Arnow in Chatham County on October 5, 1906. Howell reports seeing several flying near the mouth of the Savannah River June 14, 1927, and a flock of twelve at this same spot May 10, 1933.

HABITS AND RECOGNITION: The Lesser Scaup is probably the commonest duck found in Georgia both in migration and during the winter months. It is probably also one of the best-known to both the sportsman and the amateur ornithologist. At all times it shows a preference for fresh water, and the many small flocks, which reach the state from the interior of the continent, can be found at one time or another on practically all the smaller lakes and ponds that afford sufficient protection and food supply. Being excellent swimmers and divers, these ducks remain well offshore, and feed by diving to the bottom, where the water reaches a depth of six or eight feet, and searching for edible aquatic vegetation. To some extent such animal food as small fish, tadpoles, small mollusks, and water insects are eaten, although on the whole, vegetable matter forms the bulk of their diet. They are capable of remaining under water for some time and appear to be as adept at this as other species of ducks that feed in deeper water.

While not unsociable by nature, the Lesser Scaups are usually found pretty much by themselves, in flocks of varying size, resting or feeding with apparent unconcern for any other ducks that may be present. They are swift and somewhat erratic fliers, but decoy readily, and consequently frequently find their way into sportsmen's bags. Where undisturbed, they are relatively unsuspicious, and can be identified with relatively little difficulty if the diagnostic characters are seen. The males are characterized by dark head and front end of the body, white middle section (grayish on back), and black tail; in addition, the blue bill and conspicuous white stripe on the wing (in flight) distinguish them from any other ducks. Females are far less distinctive, being mostly dull brown, but if seen alone, can be recognized by the white area on the face at the base of the bill and by the narrow white stripe on the wing in flight. This species can be distinguished from the much rarer Greater Scaup in the hand by the smaller size and narrower bill, but in the field the shorter white stripe running lengthwise of the wing, and seen in flight, is usually the only visible sign of difference. This slight difference makes it very difficult to identify these two species individually in the field.

American Common Golden-eye
Bucephala clangula americana   (Bonaparte)

GENERAL DISTRIBUTION: Breeds from central Alaska east to northern Labrador, and south to central British Columbia, northern Montana, northern Minnesota, northern Michigan, northern New York, and northern Vermont. Winters on the Pacific Coast from the Aleutian Islands south to Lower California, on the Gulf Coast, and on the Atlantic Coast from Maine to Florida; also casually on the Great Lakes and in the interior.

STATUS IN GEORGIA: An uncommon winter resident throughout the state.

At Athens I found the Golden-eye a rather uncommon winter resident, single birds being seen at infrequent intervals on the city reservoir and on the Oconee River. My earliest date of arrival in the fall is November 25 (1926), the latest date in the spring March 11 (1926). Griffin [1941] lists it as a winter resident about Atlanta, with extreme dates of occurrence November 26 (1931) and March 26 (1939). Johnston [1945] recorded it slightly earlier in the fall at Atlanta, noting it there on November 23, 1943. At Mt. Berry, in Floyd County, Jones [1942] found this species an uncommon transient. He has no records for the winter months, extreme dates of occurrence being November 11 (1939) and November 28 (1936), and February 26 (1940) and April 5 (1938). At Augusta, Murphey [1937] considers the Golden-eye "an irregular or casual winter visitant, confined largely to the [Savannah] river." Norris [in litt.] has but one record for

Tift County, December 11, 1941, while in Grady County, Stoddard [MS] has noted this species but twice, single birds being seen November 26, 1933, and December 9, 1945. Hebard [1941] has but one record for the Okefenokee Swamp, two specimens being taken on Floyd's Island Prairie on November 30, 1928. Apparently the only definite record for the coast is that of a specimen taken in Chatham County on February 1, 1909, and now at the University of Georgia at Athens.

HABITS AND RECOGNITION: Since it is one of the hardiest of our ducks, and winters as far north as it can find open water, the Golden-eye is not a common bird in any of the Southern states. Always wary and constantly on the alert, it prefers the larger bodies of water, and being a skillful swimmer and diver, can obtain its food well offshore. On the Atlantic Coast it is a characteristic bird of the open ocean, but it is equally at home in fresh water, and in the interior, winters in numbers on the larger lakes. Its flight is swift, and usually at a considerable height above the water. Even at a distance it is easily recognized, being stout in appearance, with a short neck and large head and with a large amount of white in the plumage. In the air its wings produce a winnowing whistle that is audible while the bird is still some distance away, and gives this species the vernacular name of "whistler." Aquatic vegetation, especially eelgrass, forms a part of its food, but during the winter months it feeds largely on small mussels and crustaceans which it secures by diving to the bottom of water frequently eight or ten feet in depth.

Bufflehead
Bucephala albeola (Linnaeus)

GENERAL DISTRIBUTION: Breeds from west central Alaska and northern Mackenzie east to northern Ontario and south to southern British Columbia and northern Montana. Winters on the Pacific Coast from the Aleutian Islands south to Lower California; in the interior, from northern Montana to the Gulf Coast; and on the Atlantic Coast from Maine to Florida.

STATUS IN GEORGIA: An uncommon transient and winter resident throughout the state.

At Athens I found this species a rather scarce transient, rarely observing it more than once or twice either in the spring or in the fall. My extreme dates of occurrence in the fall are November 6 (1927) and November 27 (1928), and in the spring, February 4 (1923) and March 20 (1926). Griffin [1941] considers it a winter resident about Atlanta, his extreme dates of occurrence being December 12 (1931) and March 22 (1940). Johnston [1945] has, however, recorded it at Atlanta on April 6 (1942).

At Mt. Berry, in Floyd County, Jones [1942] lists it as a rare winter visitant, his earliest date of arrival in the fall being November 28 (1936), and his latest date of departure in the spring March 24 (1940). Murphey [1937] states that about Augusta it is a regular winter visitant. Specimens in his collection were taken in McIntosh County on December 18, 1899, and in Richmond County on February 2, 1908. Hopkins [letter] gives as extreme dates at Fitzgerald, November 27 (1942) and April 26 (1941). In the Okefenokee Swamp it does not appear to be a very common bird. Hebard [1941] cites but three records for its occurrence there; December 13, 1932, December 3, 1934, and November 23, 1935, all for Chase Prairie. He reports a single bird, a female, seen on Mill Creek, in Camden County, on November 28, 1932. On the coast, specimens were taken on Sapelo Island by Worthington on December 9 and 17, 1887, and by Hoxie in Chatham County on November 18 and December 17, 1908.

HABITS AND RECOGNITION: This handsome little duck is apparently immune to low temperatures and severe winter storms, for it winters as far north as it can find open water. As a result, relatively few Buffleheads reach the Southern states, single birds, rarely small flocks, being seen at infrequent intervals on the larger ponds and lakes. They are exceptionally skillful divers and so adept at swimming under water that they experience no difficulty in catching the small fish that form the bulk of their food. Such a diet renders their flesh rather unpalatable, and this fact, together with their small size, smaller even than a Blue-winged Teal, saves them from being shot by any but the most undiscriminating sportsman. In the fall they are invariably very fat, this characteristic giving them the common name of "butterball." Few ducks are swifter in their motions. If alarmed while feeding under water, they are capable of emerging into the air, flying, at a surprising speed, and are soon out of sight. Little difficulty should be experienced in identifying this little duck wherever it is seen. The conspicuous white patch on the back of the puffy head and the black and white pattern of the body and wings of males are unmistakable, while the females can be recognized by their small size and the small white patch behind the eye.

Oldsquaw
Clangula hyemalis (Linnaeus)

GENERAL DISTRIBUTION: Breeds on the Arctic Coast of both hemispheres, south on the North American continent to the Aleutian Islands, Hudson Bay, and northern Labrador. Winters on the Pacific Coast south to southern California, on the Great Lakes, on the Gulf Coast, and on the Atlantic Coast from the Gulf of the St. Lawrence to Florida.

STATUS IN GEORGIA: A rather uncommon winter resident throughout the state.

At Athens I recorded the Oldsquaw on but three occasions. A female appeared on the lake on the grounds of the Athens Country Club on December 19, 1926, and remained there for almost a month, being last seen January 16, when the lake, except for one small area, was frozen over. Another female was found on the city reservoir on April 10, 1927, and a third female was seen there on December 20, 1929. Jones [1942] states that at Mt. Berry, in Floyd County, it is a rare spring migrant. It was observed there by Lynds Jones on March 10, 1938, and by Harold C. Jones on March 23, 1941. There is apparently but one definite record for the Atlanta area, March 4–16, 1934 (Werner). At Augusta, Murphey [1937] considers it "an irregular winter visitant, appearing on the Savannah River during the periods of coldest weather." Specimens in his collection were taken in Richmond County on February 18, 1899, and February 10, 1904. Thomas [1945] records a single bird seen at Augusta on January 7 and 8, 1945. Stoddard [MS] reports an immature male seen at Mason's Pond, in Grady County, on March 9, 1928. Specimens have been taken on the Savannah River, in Chatham County, in January, 1899, and on December 5, 1908, and Tomkins observed one bird at the mouth of the river in January and part of February, 1929, and two the following winter in this same locality.

HABITS AND RECOGNITION: Because of its extreme hardiness and its partiality for the large bodies of water, the Oldsquaw is not a common bird in the southeastern United States. It winters as far north as it can find open water and is thoroughly at home in the roughest waters, where its skill in swimming and diving are ably demonstrated. It is considered one of the most skillful of the diving ducks, and while its food is largely obtained in water of moderate depth, it is said to be capable of reaching a depth of one hundred feet or more. Its flight is swift and rather erratic, and quite unlike that of other ducks. Flocks seen at a distance can usually be recognized by the sudden and unexpected twists and turns that are made, suggestive of the flight of some of the smaller shore birds. Although a certain amount of aquatic vegetation is eaten, the food of the Oldsquaw consists to a large extent of mussels and other mollusks. Possibly because of this diet, its flesh is rank and tough, and only the less experienced hunter will attempt to eat one. Farther north this species is seen in flocks of varying size, but in Georgia only single birds are usually found, and these are almost invariably females. They are rather drab in appearance, but can be recognized by the white head and neck offset by a black crown and a conspicuous black patch behind the eye.

King Eider
Somateria spectabilis   (Linnaeus)

GENERAL DISTRIBUTION: Breeds in Greenland and from the Arctic Coast of Canada and Alaska south to northern Labrador, Hudson Strait, northern Hudson Bay, and the St. Matthew Islands, Bering Sea; also in Siberia, Novaya Zemlya, and Spitzbergen. Winters on the Atlantic Coast from southern Greenland south to Massachusetts and locally to Georgia; on the Great Lakes; and on the Pacific Coast from the Bering Sea south regularly to the Aleutian Islands, and casually to California.

STATUS IN GEORGIA: Of casual occurrence on the coast.

Worthington [1890] first recorded this species for the state when he took two specimens at the mouth of the Altamaha River on April 25 and May 5, 1890. On the latter date he saw a flock of seven of these eiders, four males and three females. Wayne [1910] reports it at Ossabaw Island on December 1, 1904, and at St. Catherine's Island on December 3, 1904. In the American Museum of Natural History there is a specimen from Ossabaw Island taken December 2, 1904.

HABITS AND RECOGNITION: In common with the other eider ducks, the King Eider is essentially a bird of the open ocean, where its extreme hardiness enables it to exist under the most adverse conditions. An excellent swimmer and a skillful diver, it is little concerned about the roughest seas. Its food during the winter months consists largely of mollusks and crustaceans, and these it obtains without difficulty in relatively deep water. It winters as far north as there is open water, and while common off the New England coast, it is found irregularly and rarely observed farther south. It probably reaches Georgia only during exceptionally severe winters, and even then in very small numbers. In appearance it is a large, heavy duck, with a swift, direct flight that is usually sustained a few feet above the water and consists, when it is not alarmed, of alternate flapping and sailing. This characteristic flight is a ready means of identification, for no other duck flies in this manner.

Surf Scoter
Melanitta perspicillata   (Linnaeus)

GENERAL DISTRIBUTION: Breeds from northwestern Alaska and northern Canada casually to Greenland, south to Alberta, northern Saskatchewan, James Bay, and the Gulf of St. Lawrence. Winters on the Pacific Coast from the Aleutian Islands to Lower California; on the Great Lakes (rarely south to Louisiana); and on the Atlantic Coast from the Bay of Fundy to Florida.

STATUS IN GEORGIA: An uncommon winter resident on the coast.

This species was first recorded for the state by Isaac F. Arnow, who collected three specimens on the Cumberland Jetties, Camden County, [Johnston, 1949a]. These were a male and a female taken November 17, 1903, and a male taken March 19, 1904. Pearson [1922] reports five birds seen near Dungeness Wharf on Cumberland Island May 6, 1921, and Tomkins has observed single birds at Oysterbed Island, Chatham County, on October 10, 1937, and in St. Catherine's Sound on February 18, 1943.

HABITS AND RECOGNITION: The Surf Scoter is well named, for it is a bird of the open ocean, feeding along the shore just beyond the surf, where its skill in swimming and diving enables it to feed in the roughest waters. It is doubtful that it occurs at any time on the ponds and lakes in the interior. Farther north on the New England coast it is abundant during the winter months, but being a hardy species, it is uncommon and rather local in its occurrence this far south. In appearance it is a large, dark, stout-looking duck with a suggestion of heaviness that is emphasized by its lack of agility in leaving the water when forced to fly. Once in the air, however, its flight is swift and strong. It resembles the other scoters closely, but can be recognized in either sex by the white patches on the head.

American Black Scoter
Oidemia nigra americana   Swainson

GENERAL DISTRIBUTION: Breeds in northeastern Siberia and from northern Alaska and northern Mackenzie south to James Bay and Newfoundland. Winters on the Pacific Coast from the Aleutian Islands to southern California, on the Great Lakes, and on the Atlantic Coast from the Gulf of St. Lawrence to New Jersey, and rarely to Georgia and Florida.

STATUS IN GEORGIA: Apparently of accidental occurrence on the coast.

There seems to be but a single authentic record of this species in the state, although it appears in the list of Georgia birds prepared by John LeConte [White, 1949]. A female was collected by Arnow on November 17, 1903, on the "jetties north of Cumberland Sound, Georgia," and this specimen is in Eugene E. Murphey's collection now in the Charleston Museum.

HABITS AND RECOGNITION: The American Scoter is another typical sea duck, which, by preference, spends the winter months on the open ocean.

The roughest waters hold no terrors for a species as skillful in swimming and diving as is this scoter, and it is doubtful that even the severest winter storms do more than force it into the more sheltered bays or inlets. Its food is largely mussels, which it secures by diving to ledges of rock frequently twenty feet or more below the surface of the water. It is the least common of the three scoters found on the Atlantic Coast, and since it is an extremely hardy bird, it is probable that very few individuals come as far south as the Georgia coast even during the severest winters. The male is our only duck with entirely black plumage, while the female is uniformly dusky brown.

Ruddy Duck
Oxyura jamaicensis rubida   (Wilson)

GENERAL DISTRIBUTION: Breeds from central British Columbia, Alberta, and northern Manitoba south to northern Lower California, central Arizona, central Texas, northern Illinois, Minnesota, and Iowa; also locally and casually east to Maine and Massachusetts. Winters on the Pacific Coast from southern British Columbia to Costa Rica, in the interior from southern Illinois and Pennsylvania to central Arizona, and on the Atlantic Coast from Massachusetts to Florida, the Bahamas, and the West Indies.

STATUS IN GEORGIA: A fairly common transient and uncommon winter resident throughout the state, but local in its occurrence.

At Athens I recorded this species as a fairly common transient, observing it at frequent intervals both in the spring and in the fall. I have no records for the winter months, extreme dates of occurrence being March 9 (1928) and May 27 (1926), and October 29 (1925) and December 15 (1926). Greene [1933] listed it as an uncommon winter resident about Atlanta, his earliest date of arrival in the fall being October 27 (1932) and his latest date of departure in the spring, May 20 (1923). His only definite winter record is that of a single bird seen on the lake in Piedmont Park on January 18, 1929. Jones [1942] considers it a rare transient at Mt. Berry, in Floyd County, observing it in the spring between the dates of March 10 (1938) and April 22 (1940), and in the fall between the dates of November 7 (1940) and December 14 (1941).

At Augusta, Murphey [1937] states that the Ruddy Duck was formerly abundant, but is now much less numerous. He had a specimen in his collection taken in Richmond County on December 14, 1934. There is a single record for Macon, March 19, 1932 [Denton]. Stoddard [MS] has a single record for Grady County: two birds seen on the Susina Plantation November 26, 1943. The bird is also apparently rather uncommon in the Okefenokee Swamp, for Hebard [1941] cites but one record, a female shot

WILSON'S THICK-BILLED PLOVERS
Charadrius wilsonia wilsonia

These pretty shore birds, which we saw on the ocean shore near
Savannah, were readily identifiable, even at considerable distance, from
the big bill and the simple dark chest-band. Their usual cry was a not
very loud "quip-ip." Since they were not wary, I had a good opportunity
to study them at close range.

on Floyd's Island Prairie on November 28, 1928. At Coleraine, single birds were seen December 3 and 13, 1940, on the Rice Pond, and a male on the St. Marys River, in Camden County, on December 9, 1940. On the coast, Worthington took four specimens on Sapelo Island January 3, 1888, and Tomkins reports this species common at the mouth of the Savannah River both in the fall and in the spring. Erichsen [MS] cites as extreme dates of occurrence for Chatham County November 6 (1927) and April 28 (1917).

HABITS AND RECOGNITION: The Ruddy Duck is unique in many respects, its appearance and actions distinguishing it at once from the other species with which it associates. It is one of the smallest of the ducks, with a short, chunky body, a short, thick neck, and stiff, pointed tail feathers that are often held erect much in the manner of a wren. It is more at home in the water than in the air and, like the grebes, prefers to dive when alarmed rather than seek safety in flight. Its normal manner of swimming is low on the water, the body partly submerged, and in disappearing below the surface, it can sink rapidly out of sight without actually diving. Although it breeds in the interior, it apparently has no dislike for salt water, and in Georgia is equally common on the coast and on the inland ponds and lakes. Its food is largely aquatic vegetation, and this it obtains from the bottom in relatively shallow water. In the spring the males with their deep red plumage are unmistakable, and can hardly be confused with any other ducks. Females, and males during the fall and winter months, are uniformly gray, with light cheeks, this latter character, in connection with their small size and chunky appearance, readily identifying them.

Hooded Merganser
Lophodytes cucullatus (Linnaeus)

GENERAL DISTRIBUTION: Breeds locally from central British Columbia east to New Brunswick and south to Oregon, northern New Mexico, Arkansas, and the Gulf states. Winters largely in the southern United States north to Massachusetts, Pennsylvania, Lake Michigan, Nebraska, Colorado, Utah, and British Columbia, and south to Cuba and central eastern Mexico.

STATUS IN GEORGIA: Fairly common locally as a transient and winter resident throughout the state and a possible summer resident on the coast.

At Athens I found this species a regular but rather uncommon transient both in the spring and in the fall, extreme dates of occurrence being February 9 (1928) and March 22 (1928), and November 10 (1926) and December 6 (1925). It is possible that a few individuals winter, although I have no actual evidence to that effect. Griffin [1941] considers it resident

about Atlanta, but there are no breeding records, and the exact status of
the few birds seen during the summer months has yet to be determined.
Greene [1933] has recorded single birds in the vicinity of Atlanta on the
following dates: November 26, 1931, and March 20, March 26, May 1,
August 11, and October 20, 1932. All were females or immature males.
Jones [1942] reports it a fairly common winter visitant at Mt. Berry, in
Floyd County, extreme dates of occurrence being October 29 (1939) and
April 4 (1941). At Augusta, Murphey [1937] lists it as a regular winter
visitant, being "abundant both in river lagoons and deep ponds." Stoddard
[MS] reports a flock of nine in Grady County January 1, 1945, and a single
female there March 25, 1945, and states that it is "not infrequently noted
on quiet woodland ponds and small lakes."

Wright and Harper [1913] reported it common in the Okefenokee
Swamp throughout the winter, and Hebard [1941] gives it the same status.
He states that Thomas and James Roddenberry saw 363 on Chase Prairie
from January 24 to 27, 1935, and that he himself found it common on
Chase Prairie on February 27, 1936, and November 25, 1937. Norris [in
litt.] reports this species near Tifton, in Tift County, on November 19,
1933 (J. L. Stephens) and December 11, 1941 (Norris). On the coast it
has been reported common during the winter at St. Marys by Helme, and
at the mouth of the Altamaha River by Worthington. Erichsen [MS] states
that although definite evidence is lacking, there is a possibility that this
species breeds sparingly in Chatham County. He noted a pair on the Ogeechee River, June 4, 1918, another pair in a "wooded swamp near the mouth
of Black Creek," May 30, 1925, and an occasional bird frequently in August, from 1926 to 1935, "in the swampy woodlands that line the low flat
shores of the Ogeechee River below Morgan's Bridge." Specimens have
been taken at Sapelo Island on November 21, 1887, and January 24, 1888,
and in Chatham County on November 28, 1908.

HABITS AND RECOGNITION: The Hooded Merganser is so similar in its
habits to the Wood Duck that in many parts of the country it is known by
that name. Its nest is placed in a cavity of a tree or old snag. Ponds and
streams bordered by woodland are its preferred haunts throughout much
of the year, and only in migration will it be found in the open marshes, or
on the larger bodies of water in association with other ducks. It apparently
has no liking for salt water, and only rarely will be found in the bays and
inlets along the coast. It is a swift flier, but is so thoroughly at home in the
water that when alarmed it is more apt to escape by diving, then reappearing on the surface well out of reach of any harm. Much of its food consists
of small fish, which it has little difficulty in securing, for it is an energetic
and skillful swimmer under the water.

Like the Wood Duck, it is quite adept at finding its way through heavy timber, flying through the upper branches of the larger trees at an astonishing rate of speed. Being a very hardy species, it winters as far north as it can find open water, and its relative abundance in the Southeastern states during the winter months varies with the severity of the weather farther north. Mergansers are usually called "fish ducks," and can be distinguished from the other ducks by their slender bills with toothed edges that serve them so well in seizing and holding live fish. The Hooded Merganser is much smaller than the other two species found in the state, and the male is unmistakable because of the conspicuous bi-colored, fan-shaped crest on its head. Females are not so easily recognized, but seen at reasonable range, they can be identified by the uniform dark coloration, except for white patches in the wing, and by the slender bill and small size.

American Common Merganser
Mergus merganser americanus   Cassin

GENERAL DISTRIBUTION: Breeds from the Alaska Peninsula east across the continent to Newfoundland and south to central California, central Arizona, northern New Mexico, Minnesota, Michigan, New York, and the New England states. Winters mainly within the United States from southern British Columbia, the Great Lakes, and the St. Lawrence Valley south to the Gulf Coast and northern Mexico.

STATUS IN GEORGIA: An uncommon winter visitant.

Definite records for the occurrence of this species in the state are few in number. Murphey [1937] says that it is a rare winter visitant about Augusta, but cites no actual records. Griffin [1941] gives it this same status for the Atlanta region; extreme dates of occurrence, however, November 23 (1938) and January 1 (1939), would suggest that this merganser is actually a late fall transient. At Mt. Berry, in Floyd County, Jones [1942] considers it a very rare winter visitant, seen between the dates of November 16, 1935, and February 16, 1936. I did not see it at Athens, nor has it been observed at any time in the Okefenokee Swamp. A specimen was taken in Richmond County on January 5, 1900, and in Chatham County on April 5, 1908. The most recent record is that of a flock seen by Tomkins in St. Catherine's Sound on February 18, 1943.

HABITS AND RECOGNITION: This merganser is one of the hardiest of the ducks, wintering as far north as it can find any open water. Consequently relatively few reach the Southern states, and in Georgia it is only seen at rather infrequent intervals. Although a rather heavily built bird and awkward on land, it is extremely skillful in the water. In diving, it can submerge its body slowly, much like a grebe, or disappear under the surface with surprising speed. Its food is largely fish, which it secures by pursuing them under water. It is capable of swimming under the water with great rapidity. Probably no bird is more unpopular among sportsmen than is this so-called fish duck, for it has a voracious appetite and unquestionably eats large numbers of fish. If game species are present, it gets some of these, too. However, a study of its food habits has shown that it destroys large numbers of such predatory fish as the pickerel, and so balances the harm it does. Mergansers are not difficult ducks to identify, for they are long-bodied birds that sit low in the water and, at a distance, suggest the appearance of a loon. Males of this species are unmistakable, for their plumage is conspicuously white, the black markings on the back and glossy green head standing out in sharp contrast. Females are largely gray, the head with its prominent pointed crest being cinnamon brown, offset by a distinct white chin and white neck and breast.

Lesser Red-breasted Merganser
Mergus serrator serrator Linnaeus

GENERAL DISTRIBUTION: Breeds from the Arctic Coast of Alaska east across the continent to central Greenland, and south to northern British Columbia, southern Manitoba, Minnesota, Michigan, northern New York, and the coast of Maine. Winters on the Pacific Coast from British Columbia to southern Lower California, in the interior from the Great Lakes southward, and on the Atlantic Coast from Maine to Florida and Texas.

STATUS IN GEORGIA: An irregular and rather uncommon transient and winter resident in the interior, and a fairly common winter resident on the coast.

At Augusta, Murphey [1937] considers this species an "occasional winter visitant; never abundant," while at Athens I found it a rather scarce and irregular transient. Only once was it observed in Clarke County in any numbers. On April 9, 1927, during a period of rain and fog, small flocks were found on all bodies of water of any size, and the following day sixteen of these birds, in a compact group, were seen on the city reservoir. My only other record for the spring migration is that of two birds seen March 18, 1925, while in the fall this bird was noted on November 4 and December 3, 1927, and on November 7 and November 16, 1929. Griffin [1941] lists it as a transient in the Atlanta area, extreme dates of occurrence in the fall being November 16 (1935) and November 26 (1931), and in the spring, February 17 (1940) and May 7 (1931). At Mt. Berry, in Floyd County, Jones [1942] found it a scarce winter visitor, occurring in small flocks between the dates of November 11 (1939) and April 29 (1941).

Hebard [1941] cites but one record for the Okefenokee Swamp, a single bird seen on Chase Prairie on December 1, 1934. Norris and Hopkins [1953] give as extreme dates for Tifton, November 27 (1933) and March 30 (1933). On the coast, Worthington records it as common in winter at the mouth of the Altamaha River; he took two specimens on Egg Island, April 10, 1890. Helme saw approximately fifty birds off Cumberland Island on March 10, 1902, and noted the last there on April 14. At St. Marys he found them abundant on February 1, 1902. Howell observed several birds in Wassaw Sound on May 10, 1933. Erichsen [MS] cites as extreme dates of occurrence for Chatham County, November 7 (1926) and March 31 (1940).

HABITS AND RECOGNITION: This species is probably the commonest of the mergansers along the coast and the one most often seen on salt water. While it is a hardy bird and abundant on the New England coast during the winter months, large numbers reach the Southern states at this season of the year. Flocks seen then, however, consist largely of females and immature males, the adult males apparently preferring to remain farther north. It is a typical fish duck, and thoroughly at home in even the roughest waters. The position of its legs well back toward the end of its body is an asset in swimming rapidly under water, but on land makes it rather awkward. Being heavy-bodied, it is slow in leaving the water, often flapping along the surface for some distance when first alarmed, but once it is in the air, its flight is swift and direct. It is essentially a bird of the coves and estuaries along the coast. It is very skillful at diving and at swimming under water and, being at all times a wary bird, is well able to elude the average sportsman. In any plumage this merganser can be recognized by its long neck, head, and bill, its noticeably flat body, and the conspicuous white in the wing. Adult males are unmistakable with their reddish breasts and long, pointed crests. Females and young can be confused with the American Merganser, but can be distinguished at a reasonable range by the less clearly defined white throat and gradual blending of the dark head with the light underparts.

ORDER FALCONIFORMES

Vultures: *Family Cathartidae*

Eastern Turkey Vulture
Cathartes aura septentrionalis Wied

GENERAL DISTRIBUTION: Breeds from southern New England and central New York west to eastern Iowa and south to the Gulf states. Winters throughout all but the northernmost parts of its range; casual in Ontario, Quebec, the Canadian Maritime Provinces, and northern New England.

STATUS IN GEORGIA: A common permanent resident throughout the state.

Nesting usually begins in early April, the eggs, almost invariably two in number, being laid on the ground, in hollow logs, under overhanging rocks, or in the middle of dense, tangled thickets. Suitable nesting sites for a bird as large as this are never very numerous, and one that has been selected and found satisfactory is generally used year after year. Such at least was my experience at Athens. On May 22, 1925, I frightened a Turkey Vulture from two well-incubated eggs that were lying on fragments of rotten wood near the center of an old hollow pine log, in a well-wooded ravine. The log was fairly well concealed by the surrounding underbrush and a thick growth of honeysuckle vines covering the ground and was eighteen feet in length, with the eggs six feet from the larger entrance. Passing the same spot on April 24, 1927, I found a bird incubating two almost fresh eggs, and the same experience was repeated on April 17, 1933, when two fresh eggs were again found in this now extremely dilapidated log. The turkey vulture is said to nest not oftener than every two years, possibly even less frequently, so it is not unlikely that the same bird had continued to use this old pine log, in which to rear its young.

At Atlanta, Greene [1933] reports a nest shown to him on June 11, 1932, that held one egg (there had been two when the nest was first found two weeks earlier) and was under an overhanging rock on a hillside facing the Chattahoochee River. Griffin [1940] cites as the earliest breeding record for the Atlanta area a nest with two eggs found by him on April 16, 1938. At Mt. Berry, in Floyd County, Jones [1947] found a nest the second week in April, 1930, and two others, with eggs and young, on June 16 and 18, 1939, one in a cave and the other in a hollow log. In the southern part of the state nesting is occasionally earlier than north of the fall line, for Hopkins [letter] reports a nest with two eggs at Fitzgerald on March 23,

1940, and Grimm [1946] found two downy young "beneath a tangle of green briar on April 4, 1942" on the Camp Stewart Reservation, near Hinesville. An early breeding record for Grady County is reported by Stoddard [MS], who found a nest on Sherwood Plantation, March 12, 1950, that held one incubated egg. However, the average pair probably is not incubating the normal clutch of two eggs until early April. Two nests found by Erichsen in Chatham County [MS] held respectively two slightly incubated eggs on April 19, 1930, and two well-incubated eggs on April 20, 1934, while a third nest found in Bryan County had two incubated eggs on April 10, 1927.

HABITS AND RECOGNITION: It is doubtful that any bird is more typical of the southeastern United States than is the Turkey Vulture. Almost universally known as the Turkey Buzzard, it is present everywhere throughout the year, and except during intervals of rainy weather, one or more will be in sight overhead from daylight until dark. In Georgia it is less numerous in the mountain counties, but elsewhere in the state it is a common bird and varies little in numbers, regardless of the season. Few birds have mastered the art of flying so successfully as has the Turkey Vulture. Taking advantage of air currents and of the prevailing winds, it is able to remain in the air for hours with barely a movement of its wings, soaring high overhead or coursing back and forth over open fields at lower altitudes. On the ground, however, it is clumsy and awkward, and its small naked head, dull red in color, and dingy brown plumage present a singularly unattractive picture.

Its proficiency as a scavenger is well known, and this characteristic gives it economic value throughout the South. Apparently lacking the ability to kill its prey, it depends for a food supply on animals that have died from one cause or another, and the quick disposal of such carrion undoubtedly has a beneficial effect in any community. It has at times been accused of spreading such diseases as hog cholera, but careful investigation each time has proved such rumors entirely false. It is true that this vulture has no reluctance in eating animals that have died of disease, but the virus is destroyed in the bird's intestinal tract and so rendered harmless. It probably locates the dead animals on which it feeds primarily by its keen vision. To what extent the sense of smell plays a part is a debated question which has not as yet been satisfactorily determined. There is no doubt that a dead animal, even if partially concealed, is found within a remarkably short time.

In the northern part of its breeding range it is present during the summer months only, but in Georgia the normally mild winters inconvenience it so little that it is doubtful that many individuals leave the state.

Black Vulture
Coragyps atratus (Meyer)

GENERAL DISTRIBUTION: Resident from Kansas, southern Illinois, southern Indiana, eastern Maryland, and southeastern Virginia south through the Southern states to Mexico, Central America, and South America.

STATUS IN GEORGIA: A common permanent resident throughout the state except in the mountain counties, where it is rarely seen.

Despite its relative abundance, not many nests of the black vulture have been found in the state. Rossignol [in litt.] succeeded in finding six in the vicinity of Savannah, the earliest holding two fresh eggs on February 7 (1907), the latest two well-incubated eggs on April 14 (1917). In Grady County [MS], Stoddard reports a young bird almost full grown on Sherwood Plantation, August 13, 1924, and a single young bird approximately two weeks old on Springwood Plantation April 1, 1944. At Athens I found my first nest on April 21, 1923, the two fresh eggs lying in the hollow butt of a recently uprooted tree. Several years later, on March 24, 1929, a bird was flushed from two slightly incubated eggs that were lying on fragments of dead leaves at the foot of a large, partly decayed yellow poplar in woods bordering Sandy Creek. Griffin [1940] gives but one breeding record for the Atlanta area, a single young bird being found on June 4, 1939. At Rome, Jones [1947] records a nest with two eggs found March 3, 1938. Denton [1945] reports a nest found at Cochran, Bleckley County, on March 31, 1933 that held two fresh eggs and was "on the ground beside a large rotting log in a small gum swamp." He also has a breeding record for Madison County, two eggs on April 13, 1935, and one for Richmond County, two apparently fresh eggs on March 9, 1951.

HABITS AND RECOGNITION: This species is a usually more abundant bird than the Turkey Vulture and is more sociable in its disposition. It can be seen soaring alone overhead, but more often than not, several others will be in sight at the same time, and in roosting or feeding on carrion, it will be found commonly in groups. Ten to twenty are usually observed together, but on several occasions as many as fifty have been seen feeding on a dead cow, and Greene [1933] reports over one hundred together in the South River section near Atlanta. It is a heavy-bodied bird, with shorter wings and tail than the Turkey Vulture, and consequently is noticeably less graceful in flight. It is capable of remaining in the air for long periods, however, although it is forced to flap its wings at frequent intervals, alternating this flapping with periods of soaring. Because of its numbers and its willingness to accept any food that is digestible, regardless of state of decomposition, its value as a scavenger has long been recognized, and it is seldom molested.

Milton Hopkins [1953c] has found that in southern Georgia the Black Vulture appears to be changing its food habits and becoming to some extent an actual predator. He states:

> It is generally believed, and the belief is largely true, that vultures in the South live almost exclusively on dead animals and their remains. However, the Black Vulture (*Coragyps atratus*) has from time to time become a predatory bird to be reckoned with, especially in restricted localities. Whether or not this predatory tendency is sporadic will have to be determined by further observations. With the movement towards disease eradication and improvement of breeds among our livestock in Georgia, stock owners tend more and more to remove dead animals from pastures; this is especially true because rendering companies are offering free removal of dead carcasses from stock-keepers' premises. Possibly this partial removal of the buzzards' food supply has left them no other choice than that of killing living animals inasmuch as the few small animals killed on the highways cannot possibly supply the needs of the buzzard population existing in some localities.
>
> Losses have, in large part, been restricted to swine. . . . During different periods of March, April, and May, 1952, I had knowledge of or observed the killing and partial consumption of 18 Duroc pigs on a farm in Irwin County. On several occasions the flock of vultures molesting these pigs were frightened "out of sight" of the area by gunfire only to be found back at work again on the days following. Local residents agreed that Black Vultures were the predators in several cases that they were aware of, although one man told of a "red-headed buzzard" that had plucked the eyes from a new-born Hereford calf before the owner was able to locate it. . . . The actual method of predation on swine, as observed by myself, was very similar to that described by Lovell (1952) in which he states the buzzards taking part attacked the tail and rectum and pulled out the intestines of new-born pigs. On several occasions during the spring and early summer here in Irwin County I have observed four or five Black Vultures with outspread wings to surround a small pig and to peck near its eyes and anal region. These vultures were quite bold, for observations were made from a vehicle only 25–30 yards away in an open pasture. These vultures would fly off only when disturbed by my approaching them on foot, but would be back at work shortly.

Not only its plumage, but its naked head as well, is black, and this has given it the common name of Carrion Crow. In the air its short, square tail, and the grayish white patch on the under surface of the wing will readily identify it.

Kites, Hawks, and Eagles: *Family Accipitriidae*

Northern Swallow-tailed Kite
Elanoides forficatus forficatus   (Linnaeus)

GENERAL DISTRIBUTION: Formerly bred locally from northern Minnesota, southern Wisconsin, southern Indiana, and North Carolina south through eastern Mexico; now largely extirpated from the United States; winters almost entirely south of our borders.

STATUS IN GEORGIA: Formerly a fairly common summer resident in the southern part of the state, but at the present time scarce. At one time of casual occurrence along the Savannah River as far north as Augusta, where it at one time nested, but is now rarely seen.

Definite records in Georgia are rather few. Wright and Harper [1913] recorded it as fairly common in the Okefenokee Swamp, and this is the one spot in the state where it is of more than casual occurrence today. Hebard [1941] states that it does not winter there, the earliest date of arrival in the spring being March 20, 1936. At Augusta, Murphey [1937] found this species "for many years an abundant resident," arriving in the spring as early as April 12 and not seen after September 15. These kites nested in the deep swamps bordering the Savannah River, and here a single nest was found that contained young birds. It was ninety feet from the ground in the top of a tall, slender tree and was so inaccessible that its contents could be determined only from a distance. Logging operations and the common practice of shooting all hawks in sight rapidly reduced the numbers of these birds, and in August, 1919, Murphey recorded the last pair to be seen in Richmond County for many years. It was almost two decades before he observed this kite again in the vicinity of Augusta, two birds being seen on July 19, 1938, circling over the Savannah River twelve miles below the city, Murphey [1938c]. In his collection were two specimens taken in Richmond County, on July 7, 1901, and August 16, 1909. Wharton [1941] reports an immature male shot near Conley on September 3, 1941.

Apparently the most recent records north of the fall line are those of a single bird seen at Milledgeville, on April 19, 1942, by Frank Fitch, Thomas Hall, and Thomas Bivens [1942], and one bird seen in Richmond County by Thomas [1943] on May 26–27, 1943. Other records for the state are a single bird seen by Helme on Cumberland Island on April 4,

1902, and [Brewster, 1882] one seen by a Mr. Fordham at St. Marys on April 17, 1877. Denton reports a bird seen at Macon by L. H. Mounts on December 6 and 26, 1924.

HABITS AND RECOGNITION: It is unfortunate that the indiscriminate shooting of all hawks in Georgia has so reduced the numbers of the Swallow-tailed Kite that it is now a scarce bird everywhere in the state. Attractive in appearance and entirely beneficial in its food habits, it deserved protection at all times, and its present scarcity is a sad commentary on the general attitude towards our birds of prey. At a distance it suggests a large swallow, and this appearance is emphasized by its flight, which is surpassed by few other birds in skill and gracefulness. It spends much of the day on the wing, catching and devouring its food as it flies, and, while normally seen low overhead, it ascends at times to great heights, where it performs aerial evolutions that demonstrate its mastery of the air.

Its favorite food consists of such large insects as grasshoppers and dragonflies; lizards and snakes are also taken as opportunity offers and form a substantial part of its diet. It drinks from the surface of a lake or stream much in the manner of a swallow, and has frequently been observed bathing by dipping momentarily into the water again and again until its desires are satisfied. No bird is easier to identify, even at a distance. Its long, forked tail, white head and underparts, and black back, wings, and tail will distinguish it at once as a Swallow-tailed Kite, wherever and whenever seen.

Mississippi Kite
Ictinia misisippiensis   (Wilson)

GENERAL DISTRIBUTION: Breeds from northeastern Kansas, southern Illinois, southern Indiana, and South Carolina south to Texas and Florida Winters in central Florida and southern Texas south to Guatemala.

STATUS IN GEORGIA: Formerly a fairly common summer resident in the coastal plain and along the Savannah River as far north as Augusta, but now rather scarce anywhere in the state.

From the few records available it would appear that in the spring this kite is first seen in Georgia in late April or early May, and is last seen in the fall in early September. Murphey [1937] states that it arrives in Richmond County the first week in May, rarely late April, and departs in early September. At Macon extreme dates of occurrence are May 6 (1945) and August 29 (1950) [Johnston, MS]. A pair that nested at Mimsville in 1905 arrived on May 1 and departed on September 4.

Nesting is normally under way by the middle of May, the nests being built in the tops of the largest trees available and usually over water. What is probably the first definite breeding record for the state is that of a set of eggs taken in the Altamaha River Swamp on June 8, between the years 1853 and 1865 [Bailey, 1883]. Murphey [1937] records a nest found in Richmond County in 1936 that was in a large white oak, and states that four breeding pairs were located that year. Henderson [1936] found another nest that same year, on June 28, that was in a large cypress swamp ten miles below the city of Augusta. The birds had used an old, abandoned hawk's nest in the top of a tall cypress, and had merely added an additional layer of twigs and leaves. The nest, when examined, was seen to hold large young. Denton [1944] reports a pair of these kites apparently nesting in swampy woods at the edge of the Ocmulgee River a short distance south of Macon. Both were seen in the hay fields adjoining the levee on June 18, 1944, and one was observed carrying a stick about ten inches long. There is a specimen in the U.S. National Museum taken at Macon in June, 1849, and six specimens are in existence that were taken in Richmond County between the years 1891 and 1910.

A. H. Howell and I saw a single bird at Montezuma on May 23, 1933, and another later the same day in the Flint River bottoms near Marshallville. Stoddard [MS] reports a single record for Grady County, a specimen taken near Beachton, July 8, 1926. Norris [1951] noted this kite in Chattahoochee County, July 10 to August 8, 1947, and reports one bird seen by Hopkins, at Newton, Baker County, on August 9, 1950. Johnston [1954] reports seeing a bird at Athens on June 9, 1949.

HABITS AND RECOGNITION: While not so spectacular a bird as the Swallow-tailed Kite, this species is nevertheless swift and graceful in the air, displaying an agility that cannot fail to impress the observer. Even at a distance its swallow-like flight will readily distinguish it as a kite, and its subdued colors, pale gray beneath, darker above, will at once identify it as a Mississippi Kite.

Its food consists chiefly of insects. Cicadas, grasshoppers, and the larger beetles apparently are preferred where available, and these are invariably picked up and eaten while the bird is in flight. It is wholly beneficial in its habits, but as it is normally unsuspicious and easily approached and its appearance unfortunately that of a hawk, its numbers have been materially reduced in recent years. Eugene E. Murphey [1937] has given us an excellent description of its haunts and feeding habits in the vicinity of Augusta which is worth quoting in detail. He says:

Beginning at the fall line at Augusta, the valley of the Savannah is from two to four miles in width, bounded on both sides by dense swamps, much of which is cypress and tupelo, but with elevated

174

ridges covered with deciduous trees and some pines. This valley is subject to overflow at each rise of the river, its soil a rich alluvial silt, and numerous lagoons and "dead rivers" exist which mark former river courses and which are refilled whenever the water reaches a certain height. This valley has for many years been given over almost entirely to the raising of hay, and enormous numbers of grasshoppers are found therein. It is upon these grasshoppers that the kites exist. They are late to appear over their feeding grounds, but may be observed sitting, sometimes four or five in a group, at the top of some dead cypress or other favorable observation point from sunrise until about eight o'clock, at which time they begin to feed over the hay-fields. During the time of mowing they follow the horse-drawn reapers, hovering or circling a little in advance of the teams, and as the grasshoppers rise in front of the machine, they swoop down in parabolic flight, take their prey on the wing, and immediately ascend to their normal cruising height of about two hundred feet. When the mowing machines were not in the fields, the birds beat backward and forward over the fields and pick out and stoop to their individual prey as it rests on some high grass stalk. The food is then eaten while on the wing.

Northern Sharp-shinned Hawk
Accipiter striatus velox   (Wilson)

GENERAL DISTRIBUTION: Breeds from northwestern Alaska, northwestern Mackenzie, central Quebec, and Newfoundland south to central California, Arizona, Texas, Louisiana, Alabama, and northern Florida. Winters from southern British Columbia, Montana, Minnesota, southern Ontario, Ohio, and New England south to Panama.

STATUS IN GEORGIA: A fairly common winter resident throughout the state. Reasonably conclusive evidence indicates that an occasional pair nests in the northern counties.

At Athens, I found this species a fairly plentiful winter resident, being most numerous in October and but infrequently seen after the middle of February. Extreme dates of occurrence are October 9 (1927) and February 27 (1921). At Atlanta, Greene [1933] and Griffin [1941] consider it a permanent resident, but as available records apparently include only the months from August to April, I would be inclined to modify that statement. My personal opinion is that this little hawk follows the smaller birds south in the fall and north in the spring, and under these circumstances the appearance of an occasional sharp-shin as early as August, or as late as April, could be more or less expected.

Jones [1947] says that it occurs at Rome during the summer months, but a nest has yet to be found there, and it is possible that these are non-breeding birds that have lingered south of their normal range. There is, however, evidence that the Sharp-shinned Hawk has actually been found nesting in Georgia in past years. Writing under date of June 2, 1952, William W. Griffin states that D. V. Hembree claims to have taken sets of eggs of this hawk at Roswell "in several successive seasons." These eggs were sold to an oölogist in Pennsylvania whose name he could not recall, and attempts to locate their present whereabouts have met with no success. It so happens, however, that an adult at one of the nests was collected at the time the eggs were taken, on June 5, 1916, and this skin is now in the collection of Albert F. Ganier, of Nashville, Tennessee. As it is a Sharp-shinned Hawk, and as Hembree is a reliable reporter, there seems no reason to doubt that this species does at times nest in the state.

Murphey [1937] records it as a regular and common winter resident about Augusta. At Macon the earliest date of arrival in the fall is September 4 (1934) [Johnston, MS]. In Grady County, Stoddard [MS] reports it wintering in small numbers, appearing in late September (September 28, 1940) and being rarely seen after the first of April. Norris and Hopkins [1953] cite October 13 (1940) as their earliest fall record for Fitzgerald, and March 11 (1942) as their latest spring record for Tifton. In the Okefenokee Swamp it has been noted by Hebard [1941] as relatively uncommon during the winter months, extreme dates of occurrence being November 19 (1940) and February 15 (1941). In Chatham County, Erichsen [MS] likewise considers it an uncommon winter resident, extreme dates of occurrence being October 2 (1927) and April 14 (1929). Worthington found it common about Darien in the winter, his latest record there being April 10 (1890). There are May records for Macon and for Wilmington Island, but without actual specimens these must be considered rather doubtful. Female Sharp-shinned Hawks and male Cooper's Hawks are in many cases nearly identical in size and appearance, and easily confused except under the most favorable circumstances.

HABITS AND RECOGNITION: The Sharp-shinned Hawk is one of the few birds about which little good can be said. Its food consists almost entirely of small birds, and these it pursues relentlessly. It shows no hesitation in taking small chickens from farmyards and even from enclosures where access is not too difficult, and so has earned the enmity of farmers. It is probably no exaggeration to say that, to a large extent, the ill repute in which all of our hawks are held is due to the depredations of this and the Cooper's Hawk. It is audacious in hunting its prey, and the luckless bird that appeals to its voracious appetite rarely escapes. Its method of hunting is to fly low at the edge of thick woods, or in the shelter of underbrush or hedgerows, and by combining stealth with speed, strike its victim by an unexpected pounce. Various hawks delight in soaring high overhead for long periods, but the sharp-shin has little liking for open country, and its days are spent skulking in or near woodland. Its normal flight is quite characteristic, for, unless alarmed, it will glide for a short distance, flap its wings rapidly to regain momentum, and then glide again. In size it suggests both the Sparrow Hawk and the Pigeon Hawk, but its short rounded wings and long tail will readily distinguish it from these two species. In adults the upperparts are uniform bluish-gray, and this coloration, along with their pouncing upon prey, has given them the common name of "Blue Darter."

Cooper's Hawk
Accipiter cooperii (Bonaparte)

GENERAL DISTRIBUTION: Breeds from southern British Columbia east through central Alberta and southern Quebec to Prince Edward Island, and south to the southern border of the United States and northern Mexico. Winters from Oregon, Colorado, Nebraska, southern Michigan, and Massachusetts south to Costa Rica.

STATUS IN GEORGIA: A fairly common permanent resident throughout the state.

In the breeding season it has been recorded at Athens, Atlanta, Covington, Rome, Young Harris, Hall County, Macon, Beachton, the Okefenokee Swamp, Hinesville, Cumberland Island, and Savannah. Actual breeding records, however, are not numerous. Helme reported this species as breeding on Cumberland Island in 1902, two nests being found on April 11 that were fully built but still empty. Rossignol [in litt.] reports two nests found at Savannah, the first with four incubated eggs on May 19, 1914, the second with three fresh eggs on May 16, 1915. A much earlier breeding record is cited by Erichsen [MS] for Chatham County, a nest found by him April 16, 1929, holding three slightly incubated eggs.

At Athens a pair of these birds nested for two years in open pine woods on a hillside facing the open Sandy Creek bottoms, using the same nest each year. It was sixty feet from the ground in a crotch of a large loblolly pine (*Pinus taeda*), and was substantially built of sticks and twigs, the slight hollow being thickly lined with large flakes of pine bark. When first found, on May 10, 1923, it held four half-incubated eggs, while the following year the female was flushed from four fresh eggs on April 19. At Atlanta, Griffin [1940] cites as nesting dates five partially incubated eggs on April 23, 1920 (Wallace Rogers) and three young on June 2, 1939 (Griffin). An even later record for this area, however, is a nest found near

Northern Black Skimmers

Rynchops nigra nigra

The Black Skimmer is one of the world's strangest birds. I never see a skimmer, living or dead, without marveling at the oddly shaped, almost knife-thin bill and at the inexorable evolutionary forces which have produced it. The specimen on which I based my painting was shot near Savannah. Now that I have seen, heard, skinned, and painted a Black Skimmer, I am forced to believe that there really is such bird!

Marietta, in Cobb County, that held three young on June 27, 1935 [Barkalow, 1940]. Fleetwood [1945] reports a nest on the Piedmont National Wildlife Refuge, in Jones County, which was twenty-five feet from the ground in a sweetgum (*Liquidambar styraciflua*), and held three nestlings June 2, 1939. Dorsey [letter] found a nest at Rome on May 4, 1953 with five eggs.

HABITS AND RECOGNITION: In practically all respects this species is a large facsimile of the Sharp-shinned Hawk, not only in appearance but in habits as well. It is exceedingly destructive to bird life, and because of its large size, few birds are immune to its attacks. Chickens are apparently considered especially desirable, and where unprotected from this bold marauder, barnyard flocks are frequently much reduced in numbers. If any hawk deserves the name of "chicken hawk" it is the Cooper's Hawk, and it is safe to say that the losses suffered by farmers through the actions of this species will always make it difficult to arouse much interest or sympathy in the protection of other raptores that are largely beneficial in their habits.

It is essentially a bird of the more heavily timbered areas, and the one factor that governs its presence in any locality during the greater part of the year is a stretch of woodland large enough to afford a suitable nesting site. Logging operations in various parts of the state have in recent years left open slashings unsuitable for the needs of this species, and it is consequently less numerous than it was. It is especially well adapted to secure its prey in thick woods, its short rounded wings and long tail enabling it to thread through thickets and underbrush with singular skill. Like the Sharp-shinned Hawk, it is commonly referred to in Georgia as the "Blue Darter," an appropriate name when one considers its swift flight, and the uniform bluish-gray coloration of the upperparts of the adults.

Eastern Red-tailed Hawk
Buteo jamaicensis borealis   (Gmelin)

GENERAL DISTRIBUTION: Breeds from the Yukon, Mackenzie, Manitoba, and Quebec south to Texas, Oklahoma, Arkansas, and northern Florida. Winters from southern Kansas, Illinois, New York, and New England south to the Gulf Coast.

STATUS IN GEORGIA: An uncommon resident throughout the state, more numerous during the winter months.

Although there are very few definite breeding records for Georgia, the red-tail has been reported as nesting in the Okefenokee Swamp, on Wilmington Island (near Savannah), at the mouth of the Savannah River, on Cumberland Island, and at Fitzgerald. A pair of these birds nested for several years in a stretch of thick woods near Whitehall, in Clarke County, but with the cutting of this timber in 1926 they disappeared, and it is doubtful that this species now breeds about Athens. The nest, when first found on April 19, 1921, held three newly hatched young, and was seventy feet from the ground in a crotch of a large shortleaf pine. It was substantially built of sticks and coarse twigs, with a slight lining of fresh oak leaves. Two years later, on April 4, 1923, this same nest had been repaired and was again being used, holding on that date two fresh eggs. At Marietta, in Cobb County, a nest was found by T. Lawrence on April 10, 1933, with two fresh eggs, in a large hickory tree near Kennesaw Mountain [Barkalow, 1940]. Stoddard [MS] reports a nest in Thomas County that held two fresh eggs on February 15, a rather early date even for the southern part of the state. On Sherwood Plantation, in Grady County, young recently out of the nest have been seen as early as the latter part of April, and on one occasion near the middle of July. Hebard [1946] found a nest in southeastern Camden County that was being built in late January, 1946, in the top of a tall cypress, and that held, on April 26, two well-grown young.

The red-tail is noticeably more numerous in the state in the winter, birds that have nested farther north appearing in the late fall and lingering until almost the first of April.

HABITS AND RECOGNITION: Although always wary and never permitting a close approach, the Red-tailed Hawk has, nevertheless, been so consistently persecuted by farmers and sportsmen that in recent years it has become a rather scarce bird in the state. This is unfortunate, for not only is it largely beneficial in its habits, but it is an attractive part of the landscape well worthy of perpetuating for future generations. It is a large, powerful hawk that delights in soaring in wide circles high overhead, attaining great heights with an ease that well displays its powers of flight. Under these circumstances it is, of course, far from inconspicuous, and if about this time a chicken disappears from a farmyard, the soaring hawk may be condemned for an act of which it is entirely innocent. Careful study has shown that not over 10 per cent of its food consists of birds, the remainder being largely injurious rodents, and this fact alone is an argument for its protection.

It is a big, heavy-bodied bird, and this appearance is emphasized by its normal flight, which seems slow and deliberate. However, it is capable of real speed when the occasion demands, as is ably demonstrated when, from the top of a tall tree, it suddenly drops to the ground and flies off with a mouse in its talons. In common with the other *buteos* it has broad, rounded wings, and adult birds can be recognized at a reasonable distance

Family Accipitriidae: KITES, HAWKS, & EAGLES

by the uniform red coloration of the broad, short tail. Young birds are more confusing, for the tail lacks any suggestion of red and is faintly barred. However, their size and the absence of any markings on the throat and upper belly are diagnostic.

Krider's Red-tailed Hawk
Buteo jamaicensis kriderii (Hoopes)

GENERAL DISTRIBUTION: Breeds from southern Alberta, southern Saskatchewan, southern Manitoba, Wyoming, North Dakota, and Minnesota south to Nebraska and Missouri. Winters from the southern part of its breeding range to the Gulf Coast.

STATUS IN GEORGIA: Of casual occurrence during the winter months, but possibly commoner than the few records indicate.

There are at present but three definite records of this subspecies in Georgia. W. W. Worthington took a specimen on Sapelo Island on February 16, 1888 [Brewster, 1889]; a male was collected on February 3, 1904, near St. Marys, Camden County, by Isaac Arnow [Arnow, 1904]; and Eugene E. Murphey took a female on the Savannah River, in Screven County, on January 2, 1909 [Murphey, 1937].

HABITS AND RECOGNITION: Krider's Red-tailed Hawk is a well-marked race that is distinguished from others of this species by its pale coloration. Within reasonable distance it is possible to identify it with some degree of certainty, but as intergradation occurs with other races, records, to be reliable, must be based on actual specimens. In general appearance and actions it is similar in every respect to *borealis*, and as its food is largely rodents, it can be considered beneficial during its visits to the state.

Western Red-tailed Hawk
Buteo jamaicensis calurus Cassin

GENERAL DISTRIBUTION: Breeds from Alaska and central western Mackenzie south to Lower California and east to the edge of the Great Plains. Winters from the southern part of its breeding range south to the Gulf Coast.

STATUS IN GEORGIA: Known from but one specimen taken in the southern part of the state, but possibly occurs casually in Georgia during the winter months.

Hebard [1941] reports a bird shot by Hamp Colson in eastern Charlton County on February 20, 1941, that was identified by Josselyn Van Tyne as typical of this western race.

HABITS AND RECOGNITION: This western race of the Red-tailed Hawk, unlike other forms of this species has two distinct color phases. One, the light phase, is similar to *borealis,* while the other is characterized by being uniformly dark, sooty-brown, with the exception of the red tail. Its habits differ in no way from those of the eastern bird, and as it is difficult to distinguish in the field, it is quite possible that an occasional Red-tailed Hawk seen during the winter months soaring overhead or perched in the top of a tall tree is this visitor from the Western states.

Fuertes' Red-tailed Hawk
Buteo jamaicensis fuertesi   Sutton and Van Tyne

GENERAL DISTRIBUTION: Southwestern Texas; probably also southern New Mexico and at least northern Chihuahua and Coahuila.

STATUS IN GEORGIA: Of accidental occurrence in the southern part of the state.

The only record for the occurrence of this southwestern race of the Red-tailed Hawk in Georgia is that of a male collected by Arnow at Griffin's Neck, in Camden County, on March 8, 1906, and identified as *fuertesi* by Allen J. Duvall of the Fish and Wildlife Service.

HABITS AND RECOGNITION: Fuertes' Red-tailed Hawk is distinguished by its pale, relatively unmarked underparts, a character frequently apparent in the field if the bird, as happens on occasion, is within two hundred yards of the observer. However, where subspecies are concerned, specimens are necessary for satisfactory identification, and to the average person a Red-tailed Hawk soaring overhead can be recognized only to the species. In actions, this race differs in no way from the Eastern Red-tailed Hawk and, in view of its restricted range, should not be looked for in Georgia other than as an accidental visitant.

Northern Red-shouldered Hawk
Buteo lineatus lineatus   (Gmelin)

GENERAL DISTRIBUTION: Breeds from southern Ontario, Quebec, and Prince Edward Island south to Kansas, Missouri, and North Carolina. Winters from southern Ontario and the New England states south to the Gulf Coast and Georgia.

STATUS IN GEORGIA: A fairly common winter resident throughout the state.

The Red-shouldered Hawk is noticeably more numerous during the winter months than during the rest of the year, and this is unquestionably due to the immigration of individuals that have nested farther north. The northward movement in the spring apparently occurs in early February, for it is then that this species is most abundant about Athens. For a few days Red-shouldered Hawks will be seen in all the stretches of woods bordering the Oconee River, whereas only an occasional pair can be observed throughout the spring and summer months. Identification of this northern race in the field is largely guesswork, and as not many specimens have been taken in Georgia, its relative abundance in the winter has yet to be determined. At present there are but five definite records. It was first recorded for the state by Arnow, who collected a specimen at St. Marys on December 4, 1903. A specimen in the collection of Eugene E. Murphey was taken in Richmond County on November 2, 1908, another at Emory University was taken at Oxford on February 12, 1909, and one was collected by N. H. Giles in Pickens County on September 4, 1933. The most recent record is of a specimen collected by William W. Griffin at Atlanta on January 15, 1949.

HABITS AND RECOGNITION: This hawk is essentially a bird of the wooded bottomlands, but as it has a wide distribution, it is possibly the commonest raptor in the eastern United States. Like the red-tail, it has been given the name of "chicken hawk," and this is unfortunate, for actually it is one of our least harmful birds of prey. A careful study of its food habits has shown that birds, including poultry, constitute but 2 per cent of its diet, 65 per cent being injurious rodents, and the remainder such miscellaneous items as frogs, snakes, and the larger insects. Like the other *buteos*, it has broad, rounded wings and a broad tail, but its flight is swift and graceful, lacking the apparent heaviness of other members of this genus.

Its partiality for the vicinity of water persists throughout the year, so in Georgia it can be looked for during the winter months in wooded river bottoms and the edges of cypress swamps. During the breeding season this species is noisy and much in evidence, but in late summer it becomes silent, and birds seen in the winter are quiet and relatively inconspicuous. It delights then, however, in soaring high overhead on clear, sunny days, and under these circumstances can be readily identified by its uniformly light reddish-brown underparts and conspicuous barred tail.

Florida Red-shouldered Hawk
Buteo lineatus alleni Ridgway

GENERAL DISTRIBUTION: Resident from Oklahoma and eastern Texas east to South Carolina and south to southern Florida.

STATUS IN GEORGIA: A fairly common permanent resident throughout the state.

Although more numerous about the big swamps south of the fall line, this hawk has a wide distribution over the state, and there are probably few wooded river bottoms where at least one pair cannot be found during the breeding season. There are not many definite breeding records, but it has been recorded common during the summer months in the Okefenokee Swamp [Wright and Harper, 1913], in Grady County [Stoddard, MS], at Augusta [Murphey, 1937], at Americus [Denton, 1942], and at Columbus [Straw, 1947]. At Athens, it nested in the Sandy Creek bottoms, and here I succeeded in finding a nest on May 1, 1923, that held three well-incubated eggs. It was fifty-five feet from the ground in a crotch of a large loblolly pine and was well built of sticks and coarse twigs, the hollow in the top being thickly lined with cornhusks and dry pine needles and containing a single spray of green oak leaves. The following year, on March 22, a bird was flushed from this same nest, and investigation showed that, despite the early date, it held two fresh eggs.

At Atlanta, Greene [1933] reports three occupied nests in the South River section on March 23, 1930, April 11, 1931, and March 22, 1933. Concerning this last nest, he says, "According to Don Eyles, it contained five eggs on March 18." Griffin [1940] cites as a late record for Atlanta a nest that on May 13, 1939, held three young. Apparently the first definite breeding record for the southern part of the state is a nest I found at Newton, in Baker County, on March 20, 1927, with three fresh eggs. Grimm [1946] reports a nest on the Camp Stewart Reservation, near Hinesville, that held well-grown young on May 1, 1943, and was forty feet from the ground in a slash pine. In Grady County, Stoddard [MS] noted an incubating bird on March 31, 1946, and frequently observed young out of the nest in late May and early June.

Specimens have been examined from St. Marys (December 4, 1903, Arnow), Riceboro, the Okefenokee Swamp, Preston, Burke County, and Atlanta.

HABITS AND RECOGNITION: Possibly no bird is more characteristic of the wooded swamps of the Southeastern states than is the Red-shouldered Hawk. It is usually the first bird one sees and hears on entering such an area, and as it is normally unsuspicious and easily approached, its identity will not long remain in doubt. It is unquestionably the commonest hawk occurring in the state, and as it is largely beneficial in its habits, it is hoped that future years will see no decrease in its numbers. As for food habits, rodents are taken to some extent, but in contrast to individuals breeding farther north, it seems to prefer snakes, lizards, and frogs, which form a large proportion of its diet. During the early spring months it is one of the noisiest of the hawks, but after the eggs are laid and the female begins to incubate, both birds become quiet, and only when the vicinity of a nest is approached will the loud scream be heard. Its habit, however, of soaring overhead at intervals during the day makes it a bird not easily overlooked, and it will usually be seen immediately wherever it is present.

Adults of *alleni* are characterized by being smaller and paler than the northern race, while the young are noticeably darker both above and below. As with most subspecies, this is not apparent in the field, so only breeding birds can be safely identified as this form.

Northern Broad-winged Hawk
Buteo platypterus platypterus (Vieillot)

GENERAL DISTRIBUTION: Breeds from central Alberta through central Saskatchewan, southern Manitoba, Ontario, central Quebec, and New Brunswick to Cape Breton Island, and south to central Texas and the Gulf Coast. Winters from southern Florida and southern Mexico through Central America to Colombia, Venezuela, and Peru; casually farther north to Indiana and Illinois.

STATUS IN GEORGIA: A fairly common summer resident over the northern half of the state and a rather scarce summer resident south of the fall line; of casual occurrence during the winter months as far north as Fulton County.

It is possible that the Broad-winged Hawk is commoner in the state than the available data indicate. At present, however, there are very few definite breeding records. It has been observed during the summer months in Cherokee County, where a specimen was taken on July 11, 1905, at Rome [Jones, 1947], and at Athens, where I found it in small numbers but did not succeed in locating a nest. Griffin [1940] cites as extreme breeding records for the Atlanta area a nest with young on April 29, 1939 (Ramsey, Hill) and one with four eggs on May 25, 1932 (Barkalow). Apparently the only breeding record for the southern part of the state is a nest found by Stoddard in Grady County, on May 12, 1924, that held two eggs.

In the spring, this species normally appears in late March or early April, and is only infrequently seen after the latter part of September. My extreme dates of occurrence for Athens are March 27 (1921) and September 15 (1926); while at Atlanta, Griffin [1941] gives as extreme dates March 19 (1941) and October 2 (1935). At Macon it was first noted on March 31, 1928, and April 1, 1934, and last seen in the fall on November 21, 1925, and October 25, 1930. Tait [1946] first observed it at Milledgeville on April 1, 1941, and April 19, 1942. It was not found during the summer months at Columbus, but was seen there by Dreyfoos [1946] on

April 5 and 13, 1945, and by Straw [1947] from April 14 to April 30, 1946. In Grady County, Stoddard considers it a rather scarce summer resident, appearing in late March (March 25, 1924) and being rather infrequently seen after the end of July. On the coast, a specimen was taken at Savannah by Hoxie on March 11, 1908.

At Augusta, Murphey [1937] considers the Broad-winged Hawk a fairly common transient, with an occasional individual remaining throughout the winter months. He had specimens taken in Richmond County on February 20, 1901, and September 19, 1904, and states that "one was observed at close range January 1, 1935." Johnston [1949] reports an immature female taken by Isaac F. Arnow at St. Marys, Camden County, on December 29, 1902. The only other winter records are from Atlanta, single birds being seen December 24, 1938, and December 30, 1940 [Griffin, 1941], from Macon, December 26, 1953 (Rohwer), and from Irwin County, one bird seen December 29, 1951 [Norris and Hopkins, 1953].

HABITS AND RECOGNITION: The Broad-winged Hawk is one of the least suspicious of the hawks and normally permits a fairly close approach before becoming alarmed. It has accordingly suffered more from indiscriminate shooting at the hands of hunters and farmers than other more wary species and has become much reduced in numbers in recent years. This is unfortunate, for actually it is one of the most beneficial of the birds of prey, its food consisting almost entirely of harmful rodents, reptiles, and such large insects as grasshoppers, the larvae of the larger moths, and beetles. It deserves protection at all times. There is an evident trend for more and more states to pass laws against indiscriminate shooting of all hawks, and it is hoped that this enlightened attitude will become widespread soon enough to prevent dangerous depletion in the numbers of such valuable and attractive species as the Broad-winged Hawk.

This is one of the less conspicuous of the larger hawks, for it is normally found in the thicker stretches of woods, where it leads a quiet and rather sedentary existence. It will sit for long intervals on a favored perch, watching for any slight movement beneath it and then dropping down swiftly on an unwary mouse or lizard. During the mating season, however, in early May, it can be seen soaring in wide circles overhead, and its actions then belie the suggestion of sluggishness noticeable in the late summer and fall months. Its shrill scream, so unlike that of the other hawks, can be frequently heard then, and is a ready means of identification. Adults can be recognized at any time of the year by their relatively small size, as compared with other soaring hawks, and their conspicuous black and white banded tail, but immature birds so closely resemble Red-shouldered Hawks that their identity is often open to question.

Family Accipitriidae: KITES, HAWKS, & EAGLES

American Rough-legged Hawk
Buteo lagopus s. johannis (Gmelin)

GENERAL DISTRIBUTION: Breeds from the Aleutian Islands, northwestern Alaska, Victoria Island, southwestern Baffin Island, northern Quebec (Ungava), and northeastern Labrador south to northern Alberta, the north shore of the Gulf of St. Lawrence, and Newfoundland. Winters from southern British Columbia east through Colorado and Minnesota to southern Ontario, and south to southern California, southern New Mexico, Texas, Louisiana, and Georgia.

STATUS IN GEORGIA: Possibly of general, although casual occurrence, during the winter months, but at present recorded only from the southern part of the state.

It was first recorded in February, 1925, when a specimen was taken by Homer Williams three miles south of Thomasville [Stoddard, 1928]. Hebard [1941] observed three of these large hawks in the Okefenokee Swamp on March 13, 1931, and in eastern Charlton County January 3, 1943, and February 15, 1945 [Hebard, 1945].

HABITS AND RECOGNITION: As the food of the Rough-legged Hawk is almost entirely rodents, it will usually be seen during the winter months soaring low over the open fields and pastures or perching quietly on the top of a fence post watching for its prey. Its actions then suggest those of a Marsh Hawk, but its larger size, dark color, broad wings, and noticeably shorter tail are good field characters for identification. Its flight appears slow and leisurely, but it is a strong, skillful flier, and capable of remaining in the air for long periods of time. Nesting as it does in the far north, it is a hardy bird and probably does not come any farther south in the winter months than is necessary to obtain an ample food supply. It is possible that a few reach Georgia each year in the late fall, but the sight of one of these large hawks in the state will always be a noteworthy event.

American Golden Eagle
Aquila chrysaëtos canadensis (Linnaeus)

GENERAL DISTRIBUTION: Breeds from northern Alaska, northwestern Mackenzie, and northern Ungava south to northern Lower California and central Mexico; formerly in New England, and in the Southern Appalachians to North Carolina. Casual in the winter to the Gulf Coast, from eastern Texas to northwestern Florida.

STATUS IN GEORGIA: Of casual occurrence in the state throughout the year.

Gerhardt [1855], who lived at Varnell's Station, in Whitfield County, stated that this species was found in Georgia during the winter months, but it was not until April 23, 1913, when a male Golden Eagle was collected in Butts County [Griffin, 1941], that it was definitely added to the state list. Since that date it has been seen or taken at infrequent intervals and, with but one exception, during the winter months. Summarized briefly, the following records show the known occurrence of this eagle in the state in recent years:

1919: A male caught in a steel trap on the summit of Brasstown Bald by Bonnell H. Stone on December 18 [Griffin, 1941].

1930: A bird taken alive by Dr. W. A. Clarke on the Oconee River, twenty miles south of Athens, in Oglethorpe County, on November 1 [Greene, 1931].

1931: One caught in a steel trap at Bellville, Evans County, on November 5 [Greene, 1932].

1932: One shot on Brier Creek, in Burke County, on December 14 [Stevenson, 1936].

1935: One shot at Midville, near the Ogeechee River, on January 14 [Stevenson, 1936].

1938: A female killed in northeastern Charlton County on January 20 [Hebard, 1938].

1939: One seen in the extreme northern part of Lumpkin County on July 3 [Sciple and Griffin, 1939].
An immature male shot by a deer hunter on the Ocklochnee River, in Grady County south of Cairo, on December 16 [Stoddard, 1940]; one shot in Thomas County on December 27 [Stoddard, 1940].

1941: One caught in a steel trap by Wildlife Ranger Webster W. Dockery in the Chattahoochee National Forest, near Vogel State Park, on January 10; one shot by Carl Fitts on his farm, four miles east of Jasper, on February 14. Both of the above specimens were given to Charles Wharton, who mounted them for the state museum [Griffin, 1941].

1943: One seen on Coleraine Plantation, eastern Charlton County, on December 3 [Hebard, 1945].

1944: An adult male shot by Aubrey Jones on the Oconee River, five miles east of Milledgeville, on January 7 [Rogers, 1944]. One bird seen by Glenn W. Bell on June 8 "circling the peak of a mountain above Lake Rabun, near Lakemont, Georgia." Despite the date, there was no question about its being a Golden Eagle, for as it wheeled overhead, the white band in the tail was clearly seen [Bell, 1944].

1948: One seen on Sherwood Plantation, Grady County, November 7 [Stoddard, MS].

1951: A bird found dead on the edge of a cypress pond in Dougherty County on April 15 [Hopkins, 1951]; one seen in Grady County, on Sherwood Plantation, on December 16 [Stoddard, MS].

1952: One shot at Athens, November 15 (Eugene P. Odum).

Murphey [1937] states that specimens have been taken in Richmond, Burke, and Lincoln counties. A taxidermist at Brunswick is reported by Stoddard to have in his possession two mounted specimens, taken locally.

HABITS AND RECOGNITION: This majestic bird is at the present time characteristic of the rugged mountains of the Western states and is only infrequently seen in the East. Since scattered pairs are said to have nested for many years in the southern Appalachians, it is possible that at one time it occurred as a breeding bird in the mountains of northern Georgia. I was told of a nest found on the slopes of Brasstown Bald some years ago that was said to have been an eagle's nest, but, unfortunately, there was no possibility of verifying that statement.

The Golden Eagle is a large, powerful bird, with the ability to kill and carry off young lambs and pigs and even small fawns; therefore, it is not surprising that it was gradually extirpated from the Eastern states. In the Western states, such mammals as prairie dogs, jackrabbits, and the larger ground squirrels form a large portion of its diet, and there it is probably more beneficial than harmful. In Georgia, however, and elsewhere in the southern mountains, such native game birds as the wild turkey and ruffed grouse, as well as livestock, unquestionably suffered from the depredations of this eagle, and this added to the unpopularity in which all birds of prey are generally held. In the air the Golden Eagle is an impressive bird, and the sight of one soaring overhead never fails to arouse the interest of the most casual observer. At a distance it appears very dark, almost black, and this, with its large size, leaves little doubt of its identity. It is easy to confuse this species with young Bald Eagles, which likewise at a distance appear very dark. In any plumage, however, the Golden Eagle has a tail white at the base with a broad black terminal band and white patches near the ends of the wings. In contrast to the bare legs of the Bald Eagle, only the toes of the Golden Eagle are bare.

Southern Bald Eagle
Haliaeetus leucocephalus leucocephalus (Linnaeus)

GENERAL DISTRIBUTION: The United States, south to southern Lower California, breeding where conditions are suitable.

STATUS IN GEORGIA: A fairly common resident on the coast and in the Okefenokee Swamp, and of casual occurrence elsewhere in the state.

The Bald Eagle apparently wanders about extensively after the breeding season, for it has been seen from time to time in the interior of the state where it is not known to nest. Smith reports a Bald Eagle killed in DeKalb County on February 20, 1886, and Greene [1933] records specimens taken at Jonesboro on May 19, 1929, and at Austell on May 15, 1930. Murphey [1937] states that one in immature plumage was seen flying over Augusta on July 4, 1907. The following day what was apparently this same bird was killed at Waynesboro, in Burke County. Denton [letter] reports one bird, in adult plumage, at Augusta on May 5, 1953. There are three records for Macon, November 11 and December 30, 1925, and November 24, 1944 [Johnston, MS]. Norris and Hopkins [1953] report one record for

Irwin County, September 21, 1940. In Grady County, Stoddard [MS] has noted it but twice, on April 15, 1945, and September 5, 1948.

Broley [1947] has made an intensive study of the Bald Eagles that breed in Florida and has found that there is a noticeable, and apparently regular, northward movement of these birds after the breeding season. Six of those that he succeeded in banding while nestlings were recovered in Georgia, as follows: Swainsboro, May 22, 1940; Hilltonia, May 7, 1941; Rentz, November 26, 1942; Statesboro, April 20, 1944; Alma, June 1, 1944; Moniac, April 26, 1945.

Hebard [1941] cites a number of records for the Okefenokee Swamp for the winter months; a nest found there on the canal on February 28, 1936, held "two fairly well-grown young." On the coast, it has been reported breeding at St. Marys, Cumberland Island, Blackbeard Island, Darien, and Savannah. Rossignol's egg catalog lists twenty-six sets taken near Savannah from 1906 through 1922. In two instances but a single egg was laid; otherwise, each nest found held two eggs. December is the month that the Bald Eagle normally nests in Georgia, for only three nests were recorded in January and these held well-incubated eggs. Rossignol's extreme nesting dates are December 3 (1908), two slightly incubated eggs, and January 18 (1922), two well-incubated eggs.

On January 7, 1923, I spent the day with Walter J. Erichsen looking for occupied nests on the islands lying off the coast from Savannah, and we succeeded in finding one on Little Tybee Island that held two half-incubated eggs. The nest was fifty-five feet from the ground in the top of a large slash pine (*Pinus caribaea*) standing alone at the north end of the island at the edge of a wide stretch of salt marsh. Judging from its appearance, it had been used for several years, for it was a massive structure of broken limbs and somewhat smaller sticks, three feet high and fully six feet wide, the slight hollow in the top being thickly lined with grasses, gray moss, and dry pine needles. The incubating bird left the nest when I was over one hundred yards away and circled near by as I climbed the tree, uttering its characteristic cries that seem weak for the size of the bird.

HABITS AND RECOGNITION: The Bald Eagle, our national emblem, is one bird that needs no description. Whether it is seen in the top of a tall tree or soaring overhead, its impressive size and pure white head and tail leave no doubt of its identity. Like so many large birds, its flight seems heavy and labored, but actually it is a powerful flier, and when occasion demands, it is exceedingly swift in the air.

Throughout much of its range, fish constitute a major portion of its food, so it is in the vicinity of water that this eagle is normally seen. It is fully capable of taking from the water fish weighing several pounds or more, but is not averse to picking up any found dead at the water's edge.

Family Accipitriidae: KITES, HAWKS, & EAGLES

Its habit of robbing ospreys of fish they have caught is well known to everybody familiar with its habits. I have myself observed this rather spectacular performance on the Georgia coast. On seeing the osprey flying by with a large fish in its talons, the eagle left its perch in the top of a tall pine and, mounting into the air, approached the osprey with a swift dive that apparently so startled and frightened it that it at once dropped the fish and fled. The eagle had no difficulty in catching the fish before it reached the water and, carrying it back to the tree it had left, proceeded to eat it at its leisure. It is said that sometimes the osprey will protest and attempt to escape with the fish it is carrying, but the eagle is so much stronger and swifter that the outcome is never long in doubt.

Much has been written of the fierceness and destructiveness of the Bald Eagle, but this was largely imagination, or, if you will, wishful thinking. In Georgia certainly it well deserves the protection now afforded it by federal statutes, and it is to be hoped that it will long continue to maintain its numbers in the state.

American Marsh Hawk
Circus cyaneus hudsonius (Linnaeus)

GENERAL DISTRIBUTION: Breeds from northwestern Alaska, northwestern Mackenzie, central Quebec, and Newfoundland south to northern Lower California, southern Arizona, southern Texas, southern Illinois, southern Indiana, Ohio, Maryland, and southeastern Virginia, and casually to northern Florida. Winters from southern British Columbia, Montana, South Dakota, southern Wisconsin, southern New York, and New England south to the Bahamas, Cuba, and Colombia.

STATUS IN GEORGIA: A common winter resident throughout the state.

In fall, the Marsh Hawk usually arrives in the northern part of the state in early September, but occasionally appears in August and on one occasion has been seen in July. South of the fall line it has rarely been noted before the first week in October, but it is probable that an occasional individual appears in September. First arrivals were noted at Rome, August 16 (1953); Blairsville, August 19 (1940); Athens, August 10 (1925) (average date of arrival September 11); Atlanta, July 22 (1943) and August 24 (1930); Macon, August 29 (1936); Tifton, September 25 (1941); Grady County, September 16 (1944); Hinesville (Camp Stewart), October 10 (1943); Coleraine, October 10 (1940); Chatham County, August 19 (1935); and St. Marys, October 15 (1905).

In spring, this species is only infrequently seen after the middle of April, although a few birds linger into May. The latest records for the spring migration are: Athens, May 22 (1928); Atlanta, May 15 (1932);

Milledgeville, April 14 (1943); Macon, May 10 (1953); Americus, April 12 (1942); Fitzgerald, April 24 (1942); Grady County, May 1 (1940); Chatham County, May 15 (1931); Cumberland Island, May 3 (1921); and Cumberland Sound, May 18 (1952).

It has been reported common during the winter months on Cumberland Island, at St. Marys, and in the Okefenokee Swamp. At Athens I found it fairly plentiful at that season; eight were seen at dusk, on January 17, 1929, in the open Sandy Creek bottoms, where they apparently had assembled to spend the night. At Tarversville, in Twiggs County, I noted four birds on January 15, 1921.

HABITS AND RECOGNITION: The Marsh Hawk is essentially a bird of the open country, and only rarely will it be seen flying over wooded areas. It seldom alights in a tree, and the sight of one on a fence post or a low stump is decidedly uncommon. Its prey is eaten on the ground. At night it will roost in the middle of the largest open field or pasture that it can find. Its food is largely meadow mice when they are available, and these it gets by flying over the open fields and dropping suddenly on its prey. Considerable difference of opinion exists as to whether this species is harmful or beneficial. It does take an occasional bird and it has been known to carry off small chickens, but the bulk of its food is harmful rodents, and it should, I think, be considered one of our beneficial hawks. Odum [1947] shows clearly the benefit farmers derive from the presence of Marsh Hawks during the winter months. He states:

> During the fall and winter months of 1946–47 cotton rats (*Sigmodon hispidus*) were more abundant at Athens than in any of five years that we have been carrying out systematic trapping operations. In a large broom-grass field near the campus, cotton rats were estimated to be 60 to 100 per acre. . . . In this field a large number of Marsh Hawks congregated during the late winter, far more than we have ever noted in this location previously. The hawks roosted in depressions in the grass usually near the tops of hills. Nine of these roosting places were counted on February 9, and as many as three birds could be seen flying over the field at one time. Most of the roosting places contained many pellets, which on examination proved to contain in all cases the remains of cotton rats. In fact, nothing but cotton rat bones and skulls was found in a series of 50 pellets brought to the laboratory for examination.

The flight of the Marsh Hawk is light and graceful, and it is apparently a tireless flier, for it spends much of the day on the wing. Seen beating low over an open meadow or river bottom, it can readily be identified by its slender build, long, slim tail, noticeably long wings, and white patch at the base of the tail. Adult males are unmistakable, their light gray plumage giving an impression of whiteness possessed by no other hawk. Females and young are brown, but in any plumage the conspicuous white rump is a good field mark.

Ospreys: *Family Pandionidae*

American Osprey
Pandion haliaetus carolinensis (Gmelin)

GENERAL DISTRIBUTION: Breeds from northwestern Alaska east through northwestern Mackenzie, northern Manitoba, and central Quebec to Newfoundland, south to Lower California, western Mexico, and extreme southern Florida. Winters from Georgia and the Gulf states to the West Indies and Central America.

STATUS IN GEORGIA: A fairly common summer resident on the coast and in the Okefenokee Swamp and an uncommon transient elsewhere in the state. Largely of accidental occurrence during the winter months below the fall line.

The Osprey has been reported as breeding at Savannah, St. Marys, St. Catherine's Island, Little St. Simons Island, Cumberland Island, and in the Okefenokee Swamp. Verified records, however, are with one exception apparently limited to the Savannah region. Here Rossignol [letter] succeeded in finding forty occupied nests on the islands lying off the coast. With few exceptions they held three eggs each, either fresh or slightly incubated, in late April or early May. His extreme breeding records are a nest with three fresh eggs found April 9 (1910) and one that on May 18 (1915) held three well-incubated eggs. On May 5, 1929, in the Okefenokee Swamp, I saw a bird incubating on a nest that was fifty feet from the ground in the top of a large dead cypress standing near the middle of one of the numerous open "prairies."

Although a few rarely winter, most of the birds have usually left the state by the latter part of November, and it is the last of February or early March before they reappear.

The earliest migrants in the spring were recorded at Athens, April 9 (1927); Atlanta, March 30 (1932); Milledgeville, April 19 (1942); Baker County, February 13 (1950); Tifton, March 15 (1933); Grady County, February 27 (1940); Okefenokee Swamp, February 10 (1935); Savannah, February 24 (1912); Darien, March 10 (1890); Sea Island, March 3; and St. Marys, February 24 (1902). They were last seen in the interior of the

EASTERN GROUND DOVES
Columbigallina passerina passerina

I watched these tiny doves from a hiding place in the brush. When I first saw
them, they were on the ground, feeding. The seeds they found must have
been very small, for though their heads moved rapidly up and down,
their beaks never seemed to open, and they swallowed so fast that I saw
no movement of their throat muscles. Disturbed, they flew with a noisy *flut,*
flut of wings, to a low perch, whence, having assured themselves
that all was well, they flew back to the ground. The male of the pair is above.

state, where they do not nest, on the following dates: Athens, May 21 (1926); Atlanta, May 19 (1946); Canton, May 21 (1916); and Toccoa Reservoir, May 27 (1916).

The fall migration begins in August, for individuals have been observed as early as August 10 (1940) at Lake Rutledge, and August 16 (1928) at Athens. At Atlanta the earliest fall date is September 18 (1946). Latest dates of departure in the fall are: Athens, September 27 (1926); Atlanta, November 18 (1938); Tifton, October 18 (1941); and the Okefenokee Swamp, November 25 (1932 and 1937).

There are only a few records for the occurrence of this species in the state during the winter. Hebard [1941] reports six birds on Chase Prairie, January 24–27, 1934, and a single bird on Floyd's Island, Okefenokee Swamp, December 2, 1934. Tomkins [1942] saw one bird on the Savannah River, three miles east of Savannah, on January 18, 1938. Norris and Hopkins [1953] saw single birds at Fitzgerald, January 6, 1940, and at Tifton, December 21, 1942.

HABITS AND RECOGNITION: The Osprey is probably better known to most observers as the fish hawk, and it must be admitted that this is an appropriate name. Its food consists entirely of fish, which it almost invariably catches for itself. Dead fish lying on the shore are rarely touched and are completely ignored if not entirely fresh. Its methods of fishing are familiar to all who have watched one for any length of time. Flying within fifty feet of the water, it searches for any fish swimming near the surface, hovering at times on rapidly beating wings if it detects any movement beneath it. Suddenly it plunges downward with half closed wings, and its body may be completely submerged before it rises again with a fish clutched in its talons. It is common practice for a Bald Eagle to rob an Osprey of a fish that it is carrying, but being an expert fisherman, the hawk finds this piracy more an annoyance than anything else.

There should never be any uncertainty in recognizing the Osprey. A large hawk that is dark above and white beneath, seen in the vicinity of water, will readily be recognized as the fish hawk.

Falcons: *Family Falconidae*

American Peregrine Falcon
Falco peregrinus anatum   Bonaparte

GENERAL DISTRIBUTION: Breeds locally from northwestern Alaska, northern Mackenzie, and central Greenland south to central Lower California, central Mexico, central Texas, northeastern Louisiana, Missouri, Indiana, Pennsylvania, Connecticut, and northern Alabama, and in the mountains of North Carolina, South Carolina, and Georgia. Winters from southern British Columbia, Colorado, Nebraska, southern Illinois, Indiana, Pennsylvania, New York, and Massachusetts south to the West Indies and South America.

STATUS IN GEORGIA: A rare winter resident throughout the state. There is one breeding record for Dade County, and there is a possibility of its nesting in Rabun County.

The Peregrine Falcon reaches Georgia in the fall in November, rarely earlier, and lingers in the spring until early May. South of the mountains it has been seen at Atlanta on February 28 and March 1 to 5, 1930 (Greene); February 10 and November 2, 1935, and December 23, 1936 (Dorsey); August 8, 1940 (Griffin); and March 27, 1943 (Johnston); at Milledgeville, February 27, 1942 (Tait); at Macon, Decmber 13, 1952 (Whitney); in Grady County, October 28, 1924, November 19, 1942, and December 9, 23, and 25, 1945 (Stoddard); in the Okefenokee Swamp, December 1, 1932 (Chesser Prairie), and December 2 (Floyd's Island Prairie) and December 3 (Chase Prairie), 1934 (Hebard); Savannah, December 30, 1934 (Erichsen), and November, 1944, to March, 1945 (Tomkins); Cumberland Island, March 20 and April 10, 1902 (Helme), and May 4, 1921 (Pearson); and Pelican Island, Glynn County, March 11, 1948 (Woodward).

There is a specimen in the United States National Museum taken in Liberty County in December, 1848, and two in Dr. Murphey's collection taken in Richmond County, January 14, 1909, and at Augusta on December 17, 1912. A juvenile female, banded at Montreal, Quebec, by C. E. Hall, June 16, 1943, was shot by S. G. Braswell three miles from Swainsboro on October 7, 1943 (Duvall, letter).

The only definite breeding record for the state is that of a nest found on a ledge of a cliff on Lookout Mountain, in Dade County, April 23, 1942, that held three young [Herbert, Peterson, and Spofford, 1943]. Eyles [1936] had seen a bird at this same spot on Lookout Mountain on May 24, 1936, whose actions suggested that there was a nest in the vicinity, but he was unsuccessful in finding it.

HABITS AND RECOGNITION: The Peregrine Falcon of the North American continent is a subspecies, or geographic race, of the famous peregrine of the Old World, a bird long renowned because of its use through the centuries in the noble sport of falconry. It is a bold, audacious hawk, so swift on the wing that anything it attacks seldom escapes. Birds form the bulk of its food, and whether it be a crow, a swallow, or a duck, once the chase is joined, the issue is rarely in doubt. Its victim is usually attacked from above, and sometimes considerable time is spent in gaining sufficient altitudinal superiority for a successful pounce. Dropping with incredible speed, in what is known as the "stoop," the peregrine either strikes its prey from above or pulls up into a horizontal rush which quickly reaches the fleeing prey from behind. The thrust of the talons into the prey usually results in its almost instant death. There are definite records of Peregrine Falcons attaining a speed of 150 to 200 miles an hour. Faster speeds than this are undoubtedly reached in the "stoop." Thus even the swiftly flying ducks and pigeons are seldom able to escape a hunting Peregrine. One cannot but admire the daring and agility of this falcon, and as it is nowhere a common bird, its depredations will never be serious enough to cause much concern.

During migration, shore birds seem to be a favorite food, and consequently, in Georgia, it is on the coast that it is most frequently seen. Pigeons in the larger cities have attracted it in recent years, and where these birds exist in sufficient numbers, an occasional Peregrine Falcon will be found frequenting the ledges of the taller buildings during the winter months. Wherever seen it will be at once recognized as a falcon, for no other hawks have the long, pointed wings, long tail, and rapid wing-beats of this genus. It can be distinguished from the other falcons by its large size and the black markings on its face.

Eastern Pigeon Hawk
Falco columbarius columbarius Linnaeus

GENERAL DISTRIBUTION: Breeds from southeastern Mackenzie east through Ungava to Newfoundland and south to southern Manitoba, northern Michigan, central Ontario, and northern Maine. Winters from the Gulf states and the West Indies south to Ecuador and Venezuela.

STATUS IN GEORGIA: An uncommon transient and winter resident throughout the state.

Records for this species in Georgia are relatively few in number, but as it resembles somewhat the Sparrow Hawk, it is possible that occasional individuals have been overlooked and that it is commoner than is generally supposed. At Athens I noted it but once, a single bird on February 2, 1928. There are three records for the Atlanta area, November 10, 1932 (Hembree), April 16, 1949 (Griffin), and April 12, 1952 (Griffin). Murphey [1937] considers it uncommon about Augusta; a specimen in his collection was taken January 1, 1935, and he reports seeing single birds March 17 and April 16, 1935. At Columbus it was observed by Straw [1947] on April 28, 1946, and at Macon (Meanley) on December 12, 1943, and April 23, 1945. Stoddard [MS] has three records for Grady County, single birds seen September 24, 1938, December 3, 1947, and September

2, 1948, and Hebard reports one bird at Coleraine on February 19, 1950. Erichsen [MS] reports four spring records for Chatham County, March 9, 1935, April 7, 1940, March 25, 1945, and April 1, 1947. Worthington took specimens on Sapelo Island on December 21, 1887, and on Egg Island, at the mouth of the Altamaha River, on April 15 and 18, 1890. Helme noted single birds on Cumberland Island on March 8 and April 5 and 15, 1902, and collected two specimens there on January 5 and April 23, 1905.

HABITS AND RECOGNITION: In many respects the Pigeon Hawk is a miniature of the Peregrine Falcon. Its long, pointed wings, long tail, and rapid wing-beats identify it readily as a falcon, and on the wing it is swift and agile in its pursuit of the smaller birds which constitute the bulk of its food. It is essentially a bird of the open country and, when seen in Georgia, will generally be found perching on a fence post or the top of a telephone pole. Nesting as it does in the far north, where man is seldom seen, it has never learned the desirability of keeping well out of gunshot range. Consequently it is usually unsuspicious and easily approached. Birds larger than a jay or a pigeon are rarely molested by the pigeon hawk, but such species as sparrows and thrushes undoubtedly pay a heavy toll. In direct flight in the open the intended victim has little chance to escape, but many instances are known where a small bird's ability to dodge and reach the shelter of underbrush has deprived this falcon of its prospective meal. Apparently it is unable to change suddenly the direction in which it is flying or to penetrate thickets, regardless of how open they may be.

The Sparrow Hawk is the only species with which the Pigeon Hawk could be confused, but the dark-banded tail of the latter, lacking any trace of red, should readily identify it.

Western Pigeon Hawk
Falco columbarius bendirei   Swann

GENERAL DISTRIBUTION: Breeds from northwestern Alaska, Yukon, and northwestern Mackenzie south to British Columbia, Alberta, and northern Saskatchewan, and in the mountains to northern California. Winters south through California and New Mexico to Lower California and northeastern Mexico. Of casual occurrence during the winter months in the Southeastern states.

STATUS IN GEORGIA: Recorded once in the southern part of the state.

A female collected at St. Marys on December 7, 1903, by Isaac F. Arnow has been identified by Allen J. Duvall as *bendirei*. This specimen is now in the Museum of Zoology, University of Georgia, Athens [Hebard and Johnston, 1951].

198

HABITS AND RECOGNITION: This western race of the Pigeon Hawk differs from its eastern relative in being paler and, in immature plumage, browner. There is apparently no size difference. Its actions are similar, and as its food is almost entirely small birds, it is probably just as well for small birds that it is not more common in the state.

Northern Sparrow Hawk
Falco sparverius sparverius Linnaeus

GENERAL DISTRIBUTION: Breeds from the Upper Yukon east through northwestern Mackenzie, Alberta, Saskatchewan, Manitoba, and northern Ontario to southern Quebec, south to northwestern California, Colorado, Texas, and the northern part of the Gulf states. Winters from southern British Columbia, Kansas, Indiana, central Illinois, Ohio, and Massachusetts south through eastern Mexico to Panama.

STATUS IN GEORGIA: Resident and fairly common as a breeding bird in the northern part of the state; elsewhere a fairly common transient and winter resident.

During the winter there is a noticeable increase in the number of Sparrow Hawks in the southern part of the state on account of the arrival of migrant birds from the northern part of the range of the species. Specimens from southwestern Georgia taken February 20, 1903, and from Beachton, March 8, 1926, and November 4, 1951, were found to be typical of *sparverius*. A bird banded at Norristown, Pennsylvania, on June 11, 1932, was shot at Augusta on November 17, 1932. Tomkins [1942] reports taking several specimens at Savannah that are referable to this race and states that transients from the north arrive in September and depart the following April.

At Athens, I found the Sparrow Hawk fairly common during the summer and succeeded in locating several nests. One found April 18, 1922, from which I flushed the incubating bird, was eighty feet from the ground in the trunk of a large shortleaf pine on a wooded hillside. Another that held five eggs on April 16, 1926, was forty-five feet from the ground in an old flicker's hole in the top of a decayed red oak stub at the edge of a wood. A male, one of a pair nesting on the University of Georgia campus, was collected May 21, 1929, and proved to be typical of this northern race. Griffin [1940] cites, as extreme dates for the Atlanta area, nests found by himself on March 13 (1938), four eggs, and June 5 (1939), young.

HABITS AND RECOGNITION: This handsome little hawk is a familiar sight along the highways throughout the state, for it is characteristically a bird of the open country and finds the tops of telephone poles much to its liking as perches. Passing traffic causes it little concern, and only when approached on foot will it fly to the top of another pole, there to await patiently the movement of a mouse or grasshopper in the grass beneath it. Its food is to a large extent rodents and insects, and these it picks up from the ground in the open fields or pastures that it prefers to frequent. At times it will hover with rapidly beating wings over a spot that has aroused its interest, suddenly dropping down with a quick pounce and then flying off with its prey in its talons. Birds are rarely molested, although during the winter months, especially if snow covers the ground, it has been known to kill and eat sparrows and, rarely, larger species such as the Robin. In Georgia the nest is invariably in the cavity of a tree, the tree or stub chosen usually standing well out in an open field or slashing. Here the four or five eggs are laid on fragments of rotting wood, there being no attempt to build a nest of any kind.

Its small size and reddish upperparts and tail should readily distinguish this little falcon wherever it is seen. Its call notes are equally distinctive, being loud and shrill and suggesting the syllables "killy, killy, killy."

Little Sparrow Hawk
Falco sparverius paulus   (Howe and King)

GENERAL DISTRIBUTION: Resident on the Gulf Coast and from southern Alabama, southern Georgia, and the coast of South Carolina south to the Florida Keys.

STATUS IN GEORGIA: Resident in the southern half of the state, but rather local in its distribution and nowhere common.

Sparrow Hawks have been reported breeding on Cumberland and Blackbeard Islands, at St. Marys, and in the Okefenokee Swamp. Erichsen [MS] reports a nest found in Chatham County on May 14, 1934, that held small young; Grimes [letter], one at Folkston in May, 1932, that also held young; and Hopkins [letter], one at Fitzgerald on May 5, 1941, that held five eggs. Specimens representing this small race have been examined from Thomasville, Thomas County, December 4, 1910; Sylvania, Screven County, January 19, 1929; Baxley, Appling County, November 24, 1929; and Newton, Baker County, July 15, 1929. Tomkins [1942] states, on the basis of specimens, that *paulus* occurs in Burke and Washington counties, but that as yet there is no definite evidence of its breeding there.

HABITS AND RECOGNITION: This southern race of the Sparrow Hawk is characterized by being smaller than *sparverius,* darker reddish brown above, and having a larger, heavier bill. None of these characters are apparent in the field; therefore, only when specimens are available can it be satisfactorily identified. Its actions differ in no way from those of its larger relative. It frequents open country and shows a similar liking for perching on the top of a telephone pole at the side of a road. Tomkins [1948] studied briefly the food habits of several of these birds that he and Don Eyles watched near Ludowici on April 20, 1941, and was interested to note that the male would bring the female a lizard rather than a mouse or a grasshopper. Since this same preference had been noticed in Florida, he suggests the possibility of the presence or absence of an abundance of lizards as being the determining factor in the local distribution of this species in southern Georgia.

The nest found by Erichsen near Savannah was only nine feet from the ground in a natural cavity in a live oak stub, while that found by Grimes at Folkston was thirty feet from the ground in an old flicker's hole.

ORDER GALLIFORMES

Curassows and Guans: *Family Cracidae*

Northern Chachalaca
Ortalis vetula Mccalli   Baird

GENERAL DISTRIBUTION: Resident from the lower Río Grande Valley in Texas south through Mexico to northern Vera Cruz and San Luis Potosí.

STATUS IN GEORGIA: Occurs only on Sapelo Island, where it was introduced in 1923 [Phillips, 1928] and has apparently become well established, and in smaller numbers on near-by Blackbeard Island.

Jenkins [1949] reports that on June 4, 1948, at least six of these birds were found at the south end of Sapelo Island, and later in the day three at the north end. On subsequent visits, July 15 and August 11, they were again observed. Residents on the island state that they have seen young birds on many occasions.

HABITS AND RECOGNITION: Being a rather wary bird, the Chachalaca would go largely unnoticed were it not for its loud, discordant notes. These suggest the name by which it is known and readily identify this unique species wherever heard. In size it suggests a small turkey, but otherwise is distinct enough, for it has a rather small head and a large, rounded tail. It is rarely seen on the ground, its food of berries, buds, and an occasional insect being obtained as it hops about on the branches of the larger shrubs and trees. The nest is also built in a tree, being usually from five to fifteen feet from the ground, and is composed of short, stout twigs and leaves. Three eggs are normally laid and but one brood reared each year. Little is known of the habits of the Chachalaca in Georgia, but they probably are similar to those of the birds occurring naturally along the Río Grande in Texas.

Grouse and Ptarmigans: *Family Tetraonidae*

Appalachian Ruffed Grouse
Bonasa umbellus monticola   Todd

GENERAL DISTRIBUTION: Resident from southeastern Michigan, northeastern Ohio, and northeastern Pennsylvania south to northeastern Alabama and northern Georgia.

Family Tetraonidae: GROUSE & PTARMIGANS

STATUS IN GEORGIA: A fairly common to scarce resident in mountainous areas in the northern part of the state.

Howell [1909] reported this species at Ellijay and on Mt. Oglethorpe and in small numbers on Brasstown Bald in 1908. In 1922 I flushed two birds from the lower slopes of Brasstown Bald on June 25, and on July 16 heard a bird drumming near this same spot. Near Margret, in Fannin County, I saw a single bird on June 28, 1921, in thick woods in a ravine. Hoxie, in 1923, recorded this species as rare at Cloudland, on Lookout Mountain, and Pindar [1926] lists it for Chickamauga Park. Odum [1945] noted a single bird on Burnt Mountain, in Pickens County, on July 28, 1945.

Apparently there are only three definite breeding records for the state. One is that of a nest with eggs found in May, 1937, four miles from Toccoa, in Stephens County [Smith, 1945]. Another is that of a female with downy young on Burnt Mountain noted by Odum and Griffin on May 26, 1946 [Griffin, letter]. The third definite breeding locality for Georgia is Tray Mountain, where Denton and Neal [1951] report "small chicks" early in June, 1948, and on June 18, 1949, and broods of half-grown young on August 6 and 15, 1949.

HABITS AND RECOGNITION: In the Northern states the Ruffed Grouse is highly esteemed as a game bird, but in Georgia it does not occur in large enough numbers, or over a wide enough area, to be of much importance in this respect. It is doubtless hunted to a limited extent, but it is the exceptional sportsman who trudges the steep mountain slopes in expectation of a shot at one of these wary birds. If approached as it feeds on the ground, it will remain motionless, and undetected, until it feels that it is threatened with real danger. Then it will suddenly burst from the ground with a roar of wings that is both startling and disconcerting, and disappear through the trees with impressive speed. Even the experienced hunter is frequently taken unaware, and misses the shot that he has waited for with such anticipation.

The drumming of the male is a familiar sound in grouse country during the spring months, and one that never fails to arouse a thrill. For many years considerable difference of opinion existed as to how this sound was made, but it is generally accepted now that it is caused by the rapid beating of the wings against the air, the log on which the bird stands being merely the spot chosen for this unique mating performance. When heard at a distance, it has a muffled tone, but it is sufficiently clear to disclose the slow, deliberate beats that gradually increase to a rapid tempo and then abruptly stop. The nest is a slight hollow in the ground lined with dead leaves and is usually at the base of a tree or near a large rock. Normally nine to twelve eggs are laid, and but a single brood is reared each year.

The Ruffed Grouse is now known to be susceptible to maladies which cause considerable mortality among these birds. This is considered the probable reason for the years of extreme scarcity that occur periodically. In Georgia there have been years when this species has been rarely seen and others when it was fairly common. Since excessive hunting has never been the cause of serious depletion in the number of these birds in this state, the fluctuation in number must be accepted as normal in the life history of this grouse.

Partridges and Quails: *Family Perdicidae*

Eastern Bobwhite
Colinus virginianus virginianus   (Linnaeus)

GENERAL DISTRIBUTION: Resident from southeastern Virginia south to southeastern Alabama, Georgia, and northern Florida.

STATUS IN GEORGIA: A common permanent resident throughout the state.

There is no county in the state in which this species cannot be found, its relative abundance depending on the amount of open country with food and shelter sufficient for its needs. It is probably more numerous south of the fall line, although even in the mountains it is a common bird.

Only one brood is reared each year, although nests with eggs have been found as early as the latter part of April and as late as October. During the summer of 1922, I found two nests at Young Harris, in Towns County. One held seventeen slightly incubated eggs on July 7. In the middle of an open clearing on a mountainside, it was sunk flush with the ground at the base of an old stump and partially concealed by a dead limb covering it. It was a substantial bed of dead leaves, grasses, and dry pine needles. The other nest held twelve fresh eggs on July 27 and was well concealed under the edge of a brush pile in an open field. At Athens, I flushed a covey of young birds on October 12, 1922, that were but half-grown at that late date. Griffin [1940] gives as extreme nesting dates for the Atlanta area a nest with ten eggs on May 18 (1932, Barkalow), and one with twelve eggs on August 18 (1939, Griffin). Jones [1947] reports a nest at Rome that held three eggs on April 23, 1929, and a brood of young on May 18, 1939. A nest found near Fitzgerald on May 26, 1940 held eight eggs [Hopkins, in litt.]. Stoddard [MS] considers May, June, July, and August the important nesting months in Grady County, extreme dates being April 28 (1927) and October 8 (1925). Erichsen [MS] cites as nesting extremes for Chatham County (nineteen nests) a nest with fourteen fresh eggs on May 14 (1916) and one that held ten incubated eggs on June 20 (1926).

HABITS AND RECOGNITION: Probably no bird is better known throughout the eastern United States than is the Bobwhite. No lover of thick woods or mountaintops, it seeks the haunts of man and is commonly found in the pastures and at the edges of the cultivated fields near farms. Here its clear, ringing "bob-white, bob-white" can be heard throughout the spring and early summer months, and is one of the sounds that soon comes to be associated with such open country. During the fall and winter it is found in small coveys, and it is then that it affords pleasure to countless sportsmen who justifiably consider it our outstanding upland game bird. On the approach of a hunter a covey will crouch motionless at the spot where it has been feeding, depending on protective coloration for concealment and only flying when almost underfoot. The sudden noisy flushing of the birds and the speed with which they depart is sufficiently startling to confuse all but the experienced hunter, and the novice rarely brings in many birds at the end of a day's hunt. At this season of the year the bob-white is wary and wild, but on the approach of spring the coveys break up, and birds seen then are noticeably less timid.

Aside from its value as a game bird, this species has considerable economic value and is a decided asset to the farmer. Each bird consumes, in the course of a year, a large quantity of noxious weed seeds, as well as injurious insects. Its natural enemies are unfortunately numerous and persistent, but since it is prolific and well able to take care of itself, only the actions of man threaten its existence. Its popularity, however, should always insure its presence in normal numbers throughout the state, especially since Georgia is particularly fortunate in now having available the results of a thorough and detailed investigation of the many factors affecting the welfare of this outstanding game species. Begun in March, 1924, by Herbert L. Stoddard, Sr., with field headquarters near Beachton, this study continued until July, 1929, and resulted in a monumental treatise [Stoddard, 1931] that has proved invaluable in formulating techniques for increasing and perpetuating the numbers of this game bird in the Southeastern states.

Turkeys: *Family Meleagrididae*

Eastern Turkey
Meleagris gallopavo silvestris   Vieillot

GENERAL DISTRIBUTION: Now resident from western Oklahoma, southeastern Missouri, eastern Kentucky, and central Pennsylvania south to eastern Texas, the Gulf Coast, and southern Georgia. Formerly occurred north to Nebraska, Kansas, South Dakota, southwestern Ontario, and southern Maine.

STATUS IN GEORGIA: Although originally found throughout the state, it is now limited to the coastal plain, where it is locally fairly common, and to the mountain counties.

Perry [1911] stated that this species was found at St. Marys. Wright and Harper [1913] recorded it as scarce in the Okefenokee Swamp in 1912, but present in larger numbers in the wooded areas west of the Swamp. Hebard [1941] questions whether any now occur there, but reports wild turkeys common in 1933 and again in 1935 at Coleraine, in western Camden County, and in eastern Charlton County. Stoddard [MS] considers this species common on game preserves at the present time in Grady and Thomas counties. Two males taken in Grady County have been identified by Alexander Wetmore as intermediate in characters, but, while approaching the Florida Turkey (*Meleagris gallopavo osceola*) in their wing pattern, they are otherwise definitely referable to *silvestris*. Wild turkeys were reported by Hoxie as fairly common in McIntosh County, and Sprunt [1945] saw two broods of young on May 22 and 24, 1945, on the Altama Plantation eight miles south of Darien. Pearson [1922] found it common on Cumberland Island in 1921, and apparently increasing in numbers there. Whitehead reports seeing a good many turkeys near Montieth, in Chatham County, in September, 1932. Meanley [1945] observed several in the Ocmulgee River bottoms in Bibb County and in Ben Hill County in 1945, and Norris [1951] states that a nest with fourteen eggs was found by Robert F. Thorne in Early County on May 22, 1947. Murphey [1937] considers it still fairly common about Augusta, while in the mountains it has been reported from Brasstown Bald and Rich Mountain [Howell, 1909], on Cowpen Mountain, and on Tray Mountain [Denton and Neal, 1951].

HABITS AND RECOGNITION: This is one species that needs no description, for to the casual eye it is identical in appearance to the domestic turkey; the bird seen in the farmyard has the tail feathers tipped with white, the wild turkey in the woods has the tail tipped with chestnut. This distinction obviously is not too noticeable, and there have been actual instances when hunters have been outwitted by wild birds that appeared too tame when first approached. It was at one time a common bird over much of the state, but human occupation of its range, along with its excellence as a table bird, has been instrumental in eliminating it from all but the most remote areas and protected game refuges. Where consistently hunted, it becomes extremely wary, and considerable skill is required to bag one. It normally attempts to elude the hunter by running, but if closely pursued will take flight and travel for a long distance before coming to the ground again. During the fall and winter months, males and females are found in separate flocks, but on the approach of spring these flocks break up, and it is then that the familiar gobble of the male can be heard on the mountain ridges, or in river bottoms.

There is no record of a nest's being found in the northern part of the state, but in southern Georgia the eggs are usually laid in early April, and by the middle of May broods of young are commonly seen. The nest is merely a slight hollow in the ground, lined with dead leaves, and is usually placed in a dense thicket where it is well concealed. The few nests I have seen would, I am sure, have been passed unobserved had not the females flushed when the nests were approached. Normally from eight to fifteen eggs are laid, but as the young turkeys have many enemies to contend with, broods of well-grown young are rarely this large. Although essentially a bird that prefers the ground throughout the daylight hours, it spends the nights in the upper branches of the taller trees. Favored trees are used night after night and are occupied from dusk until well after daylight, the birds always making sure they are unobserved before flying to the ground to feed.

In his unpublished manuscript on the birds of Grady County, Herbert L. Stoddard, Sr., has discussed in considerable detail the habits of this famous game species in southern Georgia, and his comments are here quoted:

Grady and nearby counties (Thomas in Georgia and Leon and Jefferson in Florida), famous for their beautiful forested game preserves, are fortunate in having one of the heaviest stockings of pure Wild Turkey to be found in the United States. The writer has estimated a fall population up to ten thousand of the great birds for the four-county area. Probably at least two thousand of these occur in Grady County.

They are given a measure of protection from their worst natural enemies, wildcats and foxes, while the kill by man is adjusted by the landowners and plantation personnel as closely as possible to the annual increase. Few or no turkeys can long persist except where such special protection is extended.

There are numerous good turkey "roosts" in the form of permanent ponds and sloughs grown up to stands of gum or cypress in areas where most of the turkeys occur. They also roost readily in old forest growth along creeks or "branches," the Ocklochnee River, or even hammocks and pinelands. It is an interesting sight to see and hear a large turkey group going to roost at nightfall. A flock of around fifty were seen to particularly good advantage taking up their roosting places in a huge Water Oak and neighboring hardwood trees in a creek "hammock" on Sherwood [Plantation] between 5:15 and 6:00 P.M. on December 7, 1947. The birds started to fly in from several hundred yards distant, one by one, and at first at intervals of a half-minute or more. They would alight near by and lower, then make their way higher and from tree to tree by short flights and a tremendous beating of wings, meanwhile keeping up an animated undertone of clucks and soft conversation. The hub-bub and wing beating continued for over forty minutes, exciting the numerous squirrels who chattered and scolded, and the Hermit Thrushes which clucked and nervously flitted their wings. By six, when dusk was closing in, the birds were largely settled for the night, over thirty-five feet high in the big oak and others near by, and just an occasional wing-beat was heard.

Gobbling begins to ring through the pinelands in late February or March and reaches its height in April, when the hens are laying their eggs in carefully concealed nests, built as a rule on the edge of openings in partially wooded sections. The nests are usually located in patches of comparatively heavy ground cover that has escaped the general burning for two or three years. The eggs are usually well concealed from all angles by hardwood sprouts or low shrubs. Unless more than one hen is laying in a nest, the clutch is usually eleven or twelve eggs; twenty or more may be found in dual nests. Following are a few representative nestings of many that have been noted by the writer in Grady County: Springwood Plantation May 9, 1925, twelve eggs, Sherwood April 13, 1940, fourteen eggs, Springwood April 6, 1944, two nests about seventy-five yards apart, one with nine eggs and the other with twenty-one.

While most of the nesting is in April and May, late nests are not rare. On July 15, 1946, the writer found a brood of ten to twelve young only two or three days old in a roadside ditch on Sherwood.

Hens with their broods combine forces as the young poults develop, three or more adults and thirty or more young being frequently seen. As the poults develop, they seek their food of insects and grass seeds by preference in open improved pastures or closely mowed hay or small grain fields. It is an interesting and lively sight to see them catching grasshoppers. On Birdsong Plantation, within a half-mile of where this account is being written, a paradise for growing turkeys occurs in the form of large highly improved pastures surrounding an ancestral roosting swamp of some seventy acres. Flocks of varying size totaling one hundred or more young birds may be seen at times within an hour. The groups average in size from a dozen to forty poults, with one to four adult hens in each. The hens begin to bring their young to these pastures from all the surrounding country by the second week in May. By early June they are at their maximum number, as comparatively few are hatched after June 10. They frequent these pastures during the entire period of fast growth, still being numerous there to the beginning of the "open" season in November.

EASTERN YELLOW-BILLED CUCKOO

Coccyzus americanus americanus

These "rain crows" were fairly common in deciduous woodland, but I rarely
found them in the pines. Their odd, throaty songs I heard daily,
but getting a really good look at a bird required careful scrutiny
of the leafage overhead. The bird in my picture is perched on a branch
of the tulip poplar in full flower.

ORDER GRUIFORMES

Cranes: *Family Gruidae*

Whooping Crane
Grus americana (Linnaeus)

GENERAL DISTRIBUTION: Formerly bred from northern Mackenzie and Hudson Bay south to Illinois and Iowa; now apparently restricted during the summer months to southern Mackenzie. Occurs in winter on the coast of Texas.

STATUS IN GEORGIA: Of casual occurrence in the state in early years.

Definite evidence that this species once occurred in Georgia is fortunately not lacking. In the Academy of Natural Sciences in Philadelphia there is a sternum and trachea from St. Simons Island, and in the United States National Museum a humerus, the label bearing no specific locality other than Georgia. Griffin [letter] states that a mounted specimen has been found at Macon that "was shot near Macon on November 12, 1885, by a Richard Hodgins." It had been stored in a basement for some time, but was still in good condition and is now on exhibit at the state museum at Atlanta. Catesby [1771] mentions the presence of this species in 1722-23 at the mouth of the Altamaha River, and also at the mouth of the Savannah River. The latter locality, however, could refer to either Georgia or South Carolina.

HABITS AND RECOGNITION: This magnificent bird, at one time abundant, has been so reduced in numbers that at the present time it is almost on the verge of extinction. The few that winter on the Texas coast have fluctuated in abundance but have shown practically no over-all increase in number in recent years. Fortunately these only surviving birds, numbering twenty-five in 1952, chose to winter on a federal migratory bird refuge, but even so their chance of continued survival is precarious in the extreme. A discouraging feature is the relatively small number of young they bring south from their far northern breeding grounds each fall. The Whooping Crane is a tall and stately bird, and once seen will never be forgotten. Always wary and on the alert, it will not permit a close approach, but its size and white plumage leave no doubt of its identity.

Florida Sandhill Crane
Grus canadensis pratensis   Meyer

GENERAL DISTRIBUTION: Resident on the Florida peninsula and north to the Okefenokee Swamp in Georgia and on the Gulf Coast of Alabama, Mississippi, and Louisiana.

STATUS IN GEORGIA: Resident and fairly common in the Okefenokee Swamp.

Many observers have reported this species in the Swamp, and until recent years in relatively small numbers. Consistently hunted for food, these cranes barely managed to hold their own, but with protection they have increased and are now common in this rather limited area. Harper [1912] observed ten birds in May, 1912, and I saw the same number on March 16, 1921. Stoddard reports a flock of from ten to twenty on December 29, 1932. Hebard [1941] states that it was in 1932 that the first increase in number was noted. Prior to that year flocks seen during the winter totaled from eight to fourteen birds. On November 3, 1932, twenty-five were seen on Chase and Floyd's Island Prairies, and from January 24 to 27, 1935, ninety-four were counted on Chase Prairie. Hebard gives as definite localities where this crane has been recorded "the Canal near Camp Cornelia; along the Canal over Chesser Prairie; over the small prairies between the Canal and Buck Lake; crossing the Canal near Bugaboo Landing; and in Chase and Floyd's Island Prairies." Apparently the only record for this southern race outside the Swamp is for April, 1932, when a bad fire drove them east into western Camden County.

Walkinshaw [1947] spent the first week of April, 1945, studying the nesting habits of this crane in the vicinity of Chesser Island. During this period 53 birds were observed and 48 others heard, a total of 101. He succeeded in finding six nests, three of them on April 1; five held eggs, and the sixth, newly hatched young.

Farther north in the state this species has been recorded as a rare transient, and while specimens must be examined before any definite conclusions can be reached, there is little doubt that these records pertain to one or both of the races nesting farther north. Murphey [1937] observed two birds near Augusta in May, 1894; Wharton [1940] reports a flock of forty at Jackson Lake, in Jasper County, on March 24, 1940; Fleetwood [1942] saw fifteen flying south over the Piedmont National Wildlife Refuge, in Jones County, on November 1, 1942; Ambrosen [1950] saw a flock of similar size there on October 31, 1949, and a flock of sixty on March 6, 1952; Peters [1952] reports three in northern Fulton County on November 1, 1951; Johnston [letter] states that two flocks, one of six birds, the other of thirteen, were seen at Macon on March 20, 1955.

Family Aramidae: LIMPKINS

HABITS AND RECOGNITION: Anyone visiting the Okefenokee Swamp for the first time has a memorable experience awaiting him, not the least feature of which is the sight of the Sandhill Crane, feeding in an open "prairie," or flying overhead uttering its loud, sonorous, trumpeting notes. Seen at a distance, its gray plumage blends well with its surroundings, but it is nevertheless an impressive bird, for it stands almost as tall as a man, and either afoot or on the wing gives no impression of awkwardness. Its food is gathered as it walks sedately in the open marsh, and being ever on the alert and able, because of its height, to see for long distances, it is rarely taken unawares. In the air it is excelled by few birds. Rising in wide spirals, it will, when the mood strikes it, ascend to such a height as to be barely visible to the naked eye and circle for long intervals with no apparent effort. In flight it can be readily distinguished from the larger herons because of its habit of carrying its long neck extended rather than drawn back to its shoulders.

Walkinshaw [1947] has published notes on six nests found near Chesser Island between April 1 and 5, 1945, and these are of sufficient interest to quote in some detail. He states:

> Five of the six nests were built in patches of maiden cane (*Panicum hemitomon*) through which grew considerable moss. One nest was found in a clump of sawgrass (*Cladium jamaicense*). All of the nests were built in the open some distance from neighboring hammocks of cypress, bays, maples, and slash pine with their tangles of bamboo and shrubbery beneath and Spanish moss draped above. All were constructed of material at hand, mostly the maiden cane, with wads of moss and sawgrass when that grew near the nest. All were little crane-made islands in water, except one that was built on a little five-foot island less than a foot from the water. The six nests measured in diameter across the base 90x92 cm.,[1] 135x138 cm., 90x90 cm., 100 cm., 92x92 cm., and 36 cm. (the latter was the one on the small island). The water depth varied between 21 cm. and 46 cm., averaging 34 cm. The nests stood from 8 to 15 cm. above the water, averaging 12 cm. in height, and all were slightly hollowed in the center of the mass for the eggs.

Limpkins: *Family Aramidae*

Northern Limpkin
Aramus guarauna pictus (Meyer)

GENERAL DISTRIBUTION: Resident in Cuba and in Florida and extreme southeastern Georgia. Of casual occurrence in South Carolina.

[1] 10 cm. = about 4 inches.

STATUS IN GEORGIA: Of casual occurrence in the southeastern corner of the state, where it possibly breeds sparingly.

The Limpkin was first recorded for the state by Bartram [1791] at the mouth of the Altamaha River; Bailey [1883] mentions eggs taken by Dr. S. W. Wilson, between the years 1853 and 1865, in the coast region, the nests being "in brackish or salt ponds near the sea." Wright and Harper [1913] noted several birds in the Okefenokee Swamp on May 13, 1912, but considered them merely stragglers. Hebard [1941] has observed single birds in eastern Charlton County on November 30, 1932, and January 19, 1938, and on Mill Creek, in western Camden County, on February 24, 1936. The latter bird was again seen by Francis Harper five days later. Hebard likewise states that one bird was noted at intervals on Mill Creek "from the summer of 1938 until the late winter of 1939–40," and [Hebard, 1945a] that a single bird was also seen there on July 18, 1943.

Sprunt [1946] reports two birds seen by himself and E. B. Chamberlain on May 22, 1945, on the Altama Plantation in Glynn County, approximately eight miles south of Darien and sixteen miles north of Brunswick. He states: "The birds were flushed from sawgrass in the midst of a large cypress-gum swamp on the edge of a canal. One of them alighted on a small cypress just across the narrow canal where it stood, jerking its tail and bobbing the head in characteristic fashion. We approached to within seventy-five feet. Search was made for the nest as we were confident the birds must have been breeding but we were unsuccessful." Apparently the only specimen taken in the state is one collected at St. Marys on December 1, 1887, and now in the Museum of Vertebrate Zoology at Berkeley, California [Johnston, letter].

HABITS AND RECOGNITION: The Limpkin is in many respects a curious bird. As it feeds beside a pool or at the edge of an open channel in a marsh, it suggests an overgrown rail. On being frightened, however, it flies off with slow steady wing-beats and long, extended neck, in the manner of a crane. When it is seen on the ground, the reason for its name is at once apparent, for it walks with a jerky, limping movement that is characteristic of this species alone. Much of its time is spent on the ground, but it is equally at home in a tree, moving about among the branches with ease. It is a noisy bird, and when alarmed, as well as on other occasions, it utters a loud, piercing wail that is usually repeated by others that are within hearing. Its food apparently consists almost exclusively of large freshwater snails of the genus *Pomacea*, and because of this fact it will never be of more than casual occurrence in Georgia. In all other respects such areas as the Okefenokee Swamp are ideally suited for its needs, but the scarcity of these snails effectively limits the possibility of the Limpkin's occurring there in any numbers.

Rails, Gallinules, and Coots: *Family Rallidae*

Northern King Rail
Rallus elegans elegans Audubon

GENERAL DISTRIBUTION: Breeds from Nebraska, southern Minnesota, Ontario, New York, and Massachusetts south to Texas, Louisiana, and Florida. Winters from the southern part of its breeding range north locally to New Jersey.

STATUS IN GEORGIA: A fairly common breeding bird in its restricted habitat throughout the state, except in the mountains, and of local occurrence below the fall line during the winter months.

At Athens, I found this rail a fairly plentiful summer resident in the Sandy Creek bottoms; elsewhere it occurred in limited numbers where conditions were suitable. The earliest date of arrival in the spring was April 10 (1925), while in the fall the latest date on which one was observed was September 14 (1927). Greene [1933] noted it at Atlanta, on the South River, as early as March 16 (1930), while Griffin [MS] gives as extreme dates of occurrence for the Atlanta region March 13 (1938) and October 30 (1951). At Mt. Berry, near Rome, it was recorded only as a rare spring transient, a single bird being seen April 22, 1944 [Jones, 1944]. Murphey [1937] considers it common about Augusta, where it is apparently, to some extent at least, resident. Specimens in his collection were taken in Richmond County on October 8, 1903, May 7, 1910, and November 7, 1923. Extreme dates of occurrence at Macon are April 24 (1932) and October 8 (1954) [Johnston, MS]. Grimm [1946] reports a single bird at Clyde, in Bryan County, on April 1, 1944, and Hopkins [MS] gives as his earliest spring record for Fitzgerald, April 22 (1941). Definite winter records are not numerous. A specimen was taken on Sapelo Island on December 15, 1887, and an occasional bird has been noted during the winter months at Savannah and at Brunswick. Hebard [1941] considers it common at that season in the Okefenokee Swamp, but states that it is more often heard than seen. He likewise considers it common in suitable localities in western Camden County and eastern Charlton County.

Although it breeds throughout the state, not many nests have been found. At Athens, I had but one definite breeding record, a brood of downy young recently hatched being seen in the Sandy Creek bottoms on May 22, 1921. Johnston [1954] reports a nest found there on April 17, 1949, that held nine eggs. Griffin [1940] gives as extreme nesting dates for the Atlanta region a nest with eight eggs found May 18 (Griffin, 1939), and one that held ten eggs on May 21 (Bell, 1939), but he later [1947] reported a nest with thirteen eggs found May 5, 1946, in a stretch of open marsh on the Flint River in Clayton County. "It was constructed of grasses and sedges and was located in a clump of cattails (*Typha latifolia*) and unidentified sedge about four inches above the water." Norris [in litt.] reports a nest found at Albany, in Dougherty County, by Jimmy Major, that held seven eggs on June 17, 1948. Bailey [1883] states that on the coast eggs were found at Savannah on April 17 and June 18; at Allenhurst, April 25; and on Butler's Island, July 18. Erichsen [1921] reports a set of ten eggs in the collection of T. D. Perry that were taken near Savannah on April 20, 1911, "in a small reedy pond along the right of way of the Atlantic Coast Line Railroad near its junction with the Ogeechee Road."

HABITS AND RECOGNITION: Despite its size, that of a one-third-grown chicken, the King Rail is so secretive in its habits that it is rarely seen. Its days are spent skulking in the reeds and marsh grass of the fresh-water swamps that it inhabits, and were it not for its harsh, cackling notes, its presence would go largely undetected. When alarmed, it prefers to escape by running silently, causing no perceptible movement of the surrounding vegetation. Approached unexpectedly, however, it will spring into the air, fly for a short distance with legs dangling, and disappear again. Its flight is direct and rather slow, the wings being short in proportion to the size of the body and apparently incapable of providing much speed. The nest is usually built over water and is a well-concealed and substantially formed bed of dry fragments of such vegetation as can be most easily procured in the vicinity. The young, coal black in color when first hatched, leave the nest within a few minutes of the time they have emerged from the shell, and at once follow their parents into the marsh.

Its large size will readily distinguish this species from all of its tribe but the Clapper Rail, from which it can be recognized by its reddish rather than gray plumage. Unlike the Clapper Rail, it has no liking for salt water, and only rarely will it be seen in any but fresh-water marshes.

Northern Clapper Rail
Rallus longirostris crepitans Gmelin

GENERAL DISTRIBUTION: Breeds in the salt marshes of the Atlantic Coast from Connecticut south to North Carolina. Winters from New Jersey south to Florida.

STATUS IN GEORGIA: A winter resident on the coast.

The first ornithologist in the state to take one was W. W. Worthington, who collected a specimen on Sapelo Island, December 16, 1887. Two specimens in the Arnow collection, now at the University of Georgia, a male taken October 22, 1902, and a female January 29, 1903, were found typical of this northern race, as was also another specimen taken by John Oney in Glynn County, October 29, 1948.

Stewart [1951] states that in the bird-banding files of the Fish and Wildlife Service there are records of a Clapper Rail that was banded at Ocean City, New Jersey, May 31, 1949, and recovered on Wassaw Island, Chatham County, October 23, 1949; and of another that was banded at Chincoteague, Virginia, August 6, 1950, and recovered in Glynn County, November 28, 1950. He points out that five other birds banded in Virginia were all recovered in a narrow coastal area extending from Charleston, South Carolina, to Jacksonville, Florida, a fact suggesting that this area is the major wintering ground for the Northern Clapper Rail.

HABITS AND RECOGNITION: The Northern Clapper Rail can be distinguished from the southern race by the lighter coloring of the gray barring of its flanks, less ashy upperparts, and more heavily marked under tail-coverts. Unlike the King Rail, it has no liking for fresh water, and is rarely seen away from the salt marsh bordering the coast. In common with all the rails it is extremely secretive in its habits, hiding during the day in the thick marsh vegetation and being seldom seen. It would probably remain entirely undetected were it not for its loud, cackling notes, which, especially during the spring months, can be heard both in the daytime and throughout much of the night.

Wayne's Clapper Rail
Rallus longirostris waynei Brewster

GENERAL DISTRIBUTION: Resident in the coastal salt marshes from southeastern North Carolina to central Florida.

STATUS IN GEORGIA: An abundant resident in the salt marshes on the coast.

Specimens representing this race have been taken by John Oney in Glynn County on October 29, 1948, and January 5 and 6, and August 27, 1949, and in Camden County November 29, 1948.

Nests with eggs have been reported from Egg Island, McIntosh County, March 29 and April 16, 1890, and Cumberland Island, April 23, 1903. Rossignol's egg catalog lists fifteen sets of eggs taken near Savannah from 1907 through 1921. His earliest breeding record is of a nest found April 18 (1915) with seven fresh eggs; his latest, a nest that held nine slightly incubated eggs on June 18 (1911). Erichsen [MS] states that the nesting activities of this species in Chatham County extend from the middle of April to the middle of July, his extreme breeding records among forty-two nests being one with six fresh eggs, April 14 (1918) and one with seven eggs, July 11 (1920). On St. Catherine's Island, Liberty County, he found two nests in 1913, one with eleven eggs on May 9, the other with seven eggs on July 19.

HABITS AND RECOGNITION: Within its habitat this rail is a common bird, being found throughout the year in salt marshes fringing the coast. Always secretive and shy, it is rarely seen, but its presence is revealed by its loud, cackling notes heard at intervals during the day. While the tide is out, it remains in the depths of the thickest marsh vegetation, but periods of high tide frequently submerge the larger part of its feeding grounds, and it can be found then on higher ground where it is more easily observed. Only when thoroughly frightened will it fly, and then, with legs dangling and short wings beating the air, it will go but a short distance before dropping out of sight again. It is able to swim with ease, and frequently escapes pursuit by crossing a stretch of deep water and disappearing in the reeds on the opposite side. The nest is usually over water and is a substantial though well-concealed bed of fragments of reeds and marsh grass, slightly cupped to hold the clutches of nine to twelve eggs. In common with the other rails, the young when hatched are covered with a soft, thick, glossy black down and bear no resemblance to their parents. They desert the nest very soon after they have left the egg, and follow their parents into the more inaccessible parts of the marsh where they are relatively safe.

In the field, this race of the Clapper Rail is indistinguishable from birds breeding farther north on the Atlantic Coast, and only during the summer months can it be recognized with certainty. The principal characters that separate it are its gray upperparts and dark flanks.

Northern Virginia Rail
Rallus limicola limicola   Vieillot

GENERAL DISTRIBUTION: Breeds from British Columbia east through Saskatchewan, Manitoba, Ontario, and southern Quebec to New Brunswick, and south to northern Lower California, Utah, Colorado, Nebraska, Kentucky, and North Carolina; also in Toluca Valley, Mexico. Winters from southern British Columbia, Utah, Colorado, Arkansas, and North Carolina (casually Massachusetts) south to Guatemala, and on the Gulf Coast from Texas to Florida.

STATUS IN GEORGIA: A fairly common transient and winter resident on the Savannah River as far north as Augusta, and on the coast; elsewhere in the state a scarce transient.

At Athens, I found this rail a rather scarce spring transient, noting it in the Sandy Creek bottoms on May 20, 1922, May 16, 1926, and May 15, 1929. Smith [1903] lists specimens taken at Kirkwood, in DeKalb County, on October 14, 1898, and in February, 1899; Johnston [1947] reports a single bird seen on the South River, near Atlanta, on November 2, 1946, and Parks [1951] a dead bird found on a street in Atlanta on September 19, 1950. Murphey [1937] considers it fairly common about Augusta. The only record for the Okefenokee Swamp is that of a single bird killed by Morgan Hebard on Floyd's Island Prairie on December 17, 1933 [Hebard, 1941]. Stoddard [MS] has but two records for Grady County, a specimen taken on November 1, 1939, and one bird seen August 28, 1946.

On the coast, specimens were taken by Worthington at Broro Neck, McIntosh County, on March 16, 1889, and on Egg Island on January 24, 1890, and by Helme at St. Marys on February 11, 1903. Hoxie noted it at Savannah on March 8, 1908; Mrs. Bassett observed several near the Savannah River Bridge on March 8, 1929; and Erichsen reports single birds seen in Chatham County, November 16, 1918, December 3, 1931, and March 18, 1939. Single birds struck Tybee Light on September 23 and 29, and October 21, 1928. What is apparently the earliest record in the fall is that of a bird seen by Tomkins at the mouth of the Savannah River on August 7, 1932.

HABITS AND RECOGNITION: The apparent scarcity of the Virginia Rail as a transient in the interior of the state may be due to its extreme secretiveness. Few birds are more difficult to observe in their normal habitats. Its life is passed in the densest marsh vegetation, where it is a noteworthy event actually to see one. Only when hard pressed will it fly, and then it will go but a short distance before dropping to the ground again and completely disappearing. The exact spot where it was last seen may be carefully marked, but despite exhaustive search the bird will not be flushed again. Its thin body and long muscular legs enable it to pass through the thickest reeds with ease and speed, and there is no perceptible movement of the vegetation as it slips away. To one familiar with its notes, its presence in the spring is soon revealed, but in migration it is silent, and in its winter quarters it is rarely heard to utter a sound. Unlike most of the other rails it has no preference for fresh or salt water, and while found during the summer months in fresh-water swamps, it occurs commonly in the salt marsh throughout the winter.

Although rarely seen and then for but a brief moment, the Virginia Rail is not a difficult bird to recognize. Its relatively small size, approximately half that of the King Rail, reddish coloration, and long slender bill will distinguish it at once if observed within reasonable range.

Sora
Porzana carolina (Linnaeus)

GENERAL DISTRIBUTION: Breeds from central British Columbia east through southern Mackenzie, Saskatchewan, and Manitoba to New Brunswick and Nova Scotia, and south to northern Lower California, Utah, Colorado, Kansas, Missouri, Illinois, Ohio, Pennsylvania, and Maryland. Winters from California, Arizona, Texas, the Gulf Coast, and Georgia south through the West Indies and Central America to Venezuela and Peru.

STATUS IN GEORGIA: An uncommon transient throughout the state and of local occurrence during the winter months at Augusta, in the Okefenokee Swamp, and on the coast.

At Athens, I noted this species but twice, single birds being seen on September 19 and November 5, 1927. Griffin [MS] considers it a rare transient about Atlanta, giving as extreme dates of occurrence March 31 (1896) and May 12 (1897) and September 22 (1908) and November 14 (1899). Additional records for this part of the state are of single birds seen at Kirkwood, in DeKalb County, on May 12, 1897, and at East Point on September 30, 1902 [Smith, 1903], and one observed on the South River on May 2, 1948 [Werner, 1949]. Murphey [1937] states that it winters about Augusta, being noted there from September until April. There are two records for Macon, May 24, 1953, and October 8, 1954 [Johnston, MS]. Stoddard [MS] collected a male in Thomas County on May 9, 1940, and reports three records for adjoining Grady County, May 6, 1940, and October 4 and November 5, 1943. He likewise reports a single bird seen in Thomas County by E. V. Komarek on September 19, 1949. Norris and Hopkins [1953] have recorded it at Fitzgerald from April 13 (1941) to May 25 (1940). Hebard [1941] has noted it but once in the Okefenokee Swamp, a single bird on Chesser Prairie, near Sego Lake, on November 26, 1932.

On the coast, it is fairly common in fresh-water marshes both in the spring and in the fall, and is apparently of regular occurrence during the winter months. It has been noted by Erichsen [MS] in Chatham County as early in the fall as August 29 (1926), and as late in the spring as May 6 (1923).

There is apparently a definite movement southward in late September, for at the Tybee Light one was killed on September 24, 1924, two on September 23, 1928, and one on September 29, 1930. Winter records include a bird reported from Sapelo Island, January 20, 1888; several observed by Hoxie at Savannah on February 21, 1912; a specimen collected by Tomkins near Savannah on January 29, 1933; and a casual bird observed by me on Tybee Island on December 15, 1933.

HABITS AND RECOGNITION: Because of its wide distribution and abundance the Sora is probably the most generally known of the rails. It is essentially a bird of the fresh-water marshes, and while characteristically secretive and shy, it can often be found feeding in open spots where the cautious observer is able to watch its movements. Searching for food at the edge of a stagnant pool, it moves with long steps, its short tail jerking spasmodically and its head bobbing up and down in a manner quite suggestive of a dove. Seen under these conditions, its short yellow bill, black throat and face, and grayish-brown plumage will readily identify it.

It is apparently less reluctant to fly than are the other rails, but its flight appears equally feeble and labored, and it never goes far before dropping out of sight in a thick stretch of marsh vegetation. It is adept at swimming and diving, and has been known to escape pursuit by swimming across a stretch of deep water rather than by flying. Like the other rails, its thin body and long strong legs enable it to move through the thickest reeds or marsh grass with speed and ease, this being accomplished with no movement of the vegetation to betray its progress. On its breeding grounds it is noisy, and its presence is soon revealed to anyone familiar with its notes; in migration, however, it is usually silent. During most of the year the food of the Sora consists largely of small mollusks and aquatic insects, but in the fall the seeds of various aquatic plants are given preference. It is excellent eating then, and because of its abundance and the ease with which it can be shot, it is in many localities a popular game bird.

Northern Yellow Rail
Coturnicops noveboracensis noveboracensis (Gmelin)

GENERAL DISTRIBUTION: Breeds from southern Mackenzie, Hudson Bay, and Ungava south to Minnesota, Wisconsin, and Maine. Winters in the Gulf states (casually north to North Carolina) and in California.

STATUS IN GEORGIA: A rare transient and winter resident, although possibly commoner than the available records would indicate.

This species was first listed for the state by LeConte [in White, 1849, Suppl., p. 10], but without comment. Murphey [1937] considers it "an irregular or accidental winter visitant" about Augusta and says that specimens have been taken in Richmond County. Griffin [MS] reports one taken by R. W. Smith near Atlanta on November 17, 1900. Hamilton [1945] reports one captured alive near Tunnel Hill in Whitfield County, on October 6, 1944. It was later sent to H. C. Oberholser for examination and the identification confirmed. Hebard [1941] states that it is not uncommon during the winter months in eastern Charlton County, where one was collected on December 3, 1937, and in eastern Camden County, where one was taken in March, 1940, and single birds seen December 7, 1940, and January 16, 1941. On the coast, Worthington took a specimen on Egg Island, at the mouth of the Altamaha River, on March 29, 1890, and Mrs. Bassett reports one seen at Savannah late in March, 1927, and one killed at the Tybee Light on September 28, 1930.

HABITS AND RECOGNITION: The Yellow Rail is so secretive that it is rarely seen, and there is still much to be learned about its mode of living. It is entirely possible that it is not uncommon in Georgia during the winter months, but it is so elusive that the element of luck is a big factor in seeing one. Under ordinary circumstances it is extremely difficult to cause one to fly, and if flushed, it goes but a short distance over the top of the grass before dropping out of sight. Unlike the other rails, its existence is not dependent on extensive stretches of marsh, for during the summer it is found in wet meadows, and in the winter it sometimes occurs in dry, broom-sedge fields. Anyone fortunate enough to see one will have little difficulty in recognizing it from its small size, yellowish-brown plumage and white wing patch.

Eastern Black Rail
Laterallus jamaicensis jamaicensis   (Gmelin)

GENERAL DISTRIBUTION: Breeds from Minnesota, southern Ontario, and Massachusetts south to Florida. Winters in Guatemala and Jamaica and casually north to southern Louisiana, southern Georgia, and Florida.

STATUS IN GEORGIA: A rare transient and winter resident, possibly breeding locally where conditions are suitable.

At Athens, it may breed sparingly. Although I had suspected for some time that this species nested in the Sandy Creek bottoms, it was not until July 31, 1929, that this suspicion was at least partially verified. To quote from my notebook:

> Two birds seen, flushed when almost walked on, from a stretch of rather open marsh grass at the upper end of the Open Sandy Creek bottoms. They flew but a short distance into a thicket of alders and blackberry bushes, and although they could be heard for a moment or two uttering their characteristic notes, it proved impossible to flush them again. I had suspected for some time that calls heard from time to time in certain stretches of marsh grass could be attributed to this species, but not until today were my suspicions verified. Undoubtedly the fact that the bottoms are now under several feet of water, due

to an unusually heavy rain last night, was responsible for my finding these two birds in such a relatively exposed position, although it was almost dusk at the time and rather cloudy. [Burleigh, 1938.]

It has been recorded [Mounts, 1930] at Macon on May 13, 1928, and April 20 and May 6, 1929; and Hebard [1941] considers this species a regular and not uncommon winter resident in western Camden County and eastern Charlton County. Efforts to collect a specimen were unsuccessful, but he reports it there on November 2, 22, and 26, and December 14, 1940, and January 13, 16, 27, and 29, 1941. A specimen was taken at Savannah on October 29, 1917, and several have been reported as having struck Tybee Light.

HABITS AND RECOGNITION: Because of its small size and secretiveness (characteristic of all the rails), this diminutive species is almost as difficult to observe as a field mouse. In fact, the sight of one running swiftly out of sight in dense marsh grass is so suggestive of a mouse that it can be easily mistaken for a small mammal. One can only guess its relative abundance in migration, for with its extreme reluctance to fly, its presence can long remain undetected. When it is seen in the air, its flight seems feeble and uncertain, and it usually goes but a few yards before, with legs dangling, it drops to the ground again. There are instances of its being caught by dogs or by men when cornered in scant vegetation, as then it makes no effort to fly. It is only during the breeding season that its characteristic notes are generally heard, but as I found from personal experience in the Sandy Creek bottoms, it is extremely hard even then to find the bird. The "song" I heard there on successive evenings in late July has been aptly described by Arthur T. Wayne as "kik, kik, kik, kik," or "kuk, kuk, kuk, kuk," and was apparently that of the male, the notes of the female being said to be noticeably different. The nest is well concealed in thick marsh grass and is built of fine grasses, slightly cupped to hold the clutches of six to ten eggs.

Purple Gallinule
Porphyrula martinica (Linnaeus)

GENERAL DISTRIBUTION: Breeds from southern Mississippi, southern Alabama, and South Carolina (casually to southern Virginia), south through Mexico and the West Indies to Argentina. Winters from the Gulf Coast and Florida south throughout its breeding range.

STATUS IN GEORGIA: A fairly common but local summer resident in the southern part of the state and on the Savannah River as far north as Augusta; of casual occurrence elsewhere.

Helme took a specimen on Cumberland Island on April 11, 1903, and this is apparently a normal date of arrival for this species on the coast. Pearson [1922] noted several Purple Gallinules there May 2 to 6, 1921. In Murphey's collection there was a specimen taken on Wilmington Island, October 1, 1928. Nests with eggs have been found at Savannah on May 16 and at Butler's Island on July 18 [Bailey, 1883]. Erichsen [MS] found a nest on Ossabaw Island on May 4, 1929 that held six eggs. Tomkins reports a nest at the mouth of the Savannah River that when found, June 1, 1931, held one fresh egg. On June 12 the bird was incubating nine eggs, and on June 28 the eggs were just hatching.

Murphey [1937] considers this species a rare but regular summer resident about Augusta, its favorite habitat being "some shallow pond densely grown up in bushes and tall grass." In Grady County, Stoddard [MS] gives as extreme dates of occurrence April 29 (1940) and September 20 (1944). He reports at least eight pairs nesting on Mitchell Pond (Susina Plantation) in 1947, broods of young of varying size being seen there on July 17. It has been noted in the Okefenokee Swamp [Wright and Harper, 1913]; at Fitzgerald on May 11, 1942, and May 24, 1943; and in Cook County, August 14, 1951 [Norris and Hopkins, 1953]; at Marshallville; and at Macon on May 5 and 12, 1928, and June 9, 1953. Griffin [1948] reports the first record for this gallinule in the Atlanta area, a female being captured alive May 5, 1948, on the Oxford Road near Emory University, in DeKalb County. Stoddard [1947] found at least a dozen pairs breeding in Alligator Pond in Baker County where, on June 3, 1947, the nests were all in the process of construction. That same day, in Dougherty County, he noted even larger numbers in Big Cypress Pond, where one nest with five eggs was found, and many partially built. At still a third pond, Hurricane, a nest held three eggs.

HABITS AND RECOGNITION: The Purple Gallinule is unquestionably the handsomest of our marsh birds. With its glossy purple head and underparts and bright green back, it presents a very attractive picture when seen at the edge of a marsh pool. In some respects it suggests a rail, for it dislikes to fly and, if forced to do so, will go but a short distance over the top of the reeds and marsh grass before, long legs dangling, it suddenly drops out of sight. Like that of the rails, its flight then appears weak, and it also has the habit of raising its wings over its back just before disappearing from view. It is by no means as secretive as the rails, however, and with due caution it is possible to watch one as it walks with ease over lily pads and other vegetation reaching the surface of the water. Its long toes support its weight admirably, but if it becomes partially submerged, as at times happens, it has no difficulty in swimming to a place where footing is more secure. Throughout much of the year it is a rather noisy bird, and its presence in a marsh is soon revealed by its loud cackling notes, especially noticeable during the breeding season. The nest is usually built over deep water, and is a compact bed of reeds and marsh grass, well cupped to hold the six to eight eggs that are normally laid. They are partially concealed in the thicker stretches of reeds, but are not difficult to find.

Florida Common Gallinule
Gallinula chloropus cachinnans Bangs

GENERAL DISTRIBUTION: Breeds from Minnesota, Wisconsin, Michigan, Ontario, and southern Quebec south throughout the eastern United States, in Central America, and in South America to Chile and Argentina; also locally in central California and in Arizona. Winters from southern California, Arizona, the Gulf Coast, and South Carolina south throughout its breeding range.

STATUS IN GEORGIA: Resident and locally fairly common in the southern part of the state and about Augusta. Of casual occurrence north of the fall line in migration.

Erichsen [1921] found a number of these gallinules breeding in a fresh-water pond on Ossabaw Island in 1915 and succeeded in locating four nests. The first was found on May 11 with seven fresh eggs, and three on May 14 with eight slightly incubated eggs, five fresh eggs, and one egg, respectively. He describes these as "built a foot above water, in tall reeds and cat-tail flags, composed of dead and water-soaked stalks and leaves of these plants." I visited this same spot on April 30, 1921, and found the birds even more numerous, eight nests being found within a short time. Three were empty, while five held eggs, in numbers of seven, five, three, two, and one. All were substantially built of dry pieces of cattails and were a foot or so from the water in isolated clumps of cattails in or at the edge of open water. Pearson [1922] noted this species on Cumberland Island, May 2 to 6, 1921. About Augusta it is apparently resident, having been recorded in Richmond County in every month except January and February, when it was possibly overlooked [Murphy, 1937]. Pearson suggests that two broods are probably raised each year, a nest with fresh eggs having been found in August, 1897.

At Tifton it has been noted on March 18, 1933, March 28, 1934, and September 30, 1932 [Norris and Hopkins, 1953], and on March 26, 1945 [Gaulding, 1945]. Norris [letter] states that he found this gallinule a fairly common breeding bird in the southwestern corner of the state in 1948. Adults and immatures were seen between Newton and Camilla, in Mitchell County, on June 11 and 16, and four adults and a brood of downy young on a pond in Dougherty County on June 17. Hebard [1941] considers it common in the Okefenokee Swamp during the winter months, and reports four birds seen on January 30, 1931. Stoddard [MS] reports single birds seen in Grady County April 2 and 13, 1945, and another that remained on a small pond on Birdsong Plantation from October 9, 1948, through May 1, 1949. Records north of the fall line are not numerous. Griffin [1941] considers it a rare spring transient about Atlanta, giving as extreme dates of occurrence, April 27 (1905) and May 10 (1929). Sanford, however, reports a bird caught within the Atlanta city limits on April 16, 1916, and it has been noted at College Park by Eyles [1937] on April 30, 1937, and at Atlanta by Johnston [1945] on April 26, 1943.

There are two records for Athens: specimens collected May 11, 1936 [Denton, 1936] and May 10, 1949 [Johnston, 1954]; and one for Americus, a specimen taken May 7, 1941 [Denton, 1942].

HABITS AND RECOGNITION: This gallinule is decidedly misnamed, for it has a wide distribution on the North American continent and is probably locally as common in other parts of the country as it is in Florida. It is by no means as attractive in appearance as the purple gallinule, its plumage being largely dark gray and brown. This is relieved by its deep red bill and frontal plate and long, yellowish-green legs. It is an inhabitant of open fresh-water marshes, where its days are spent in the shelter of the reeds and cattails. It is by no means as secretive as the rails, however, and being and adept swimmer can often be seen feeding in deep water or crossing an open channel. Under such circumstances the forward and backward movement of its head, so suggestive of a dove, is quite noticeable, as is also the conspicuous white of its under tail-coverts. Its long toes enable it to walk with ease on any vegetation that covers the water, and, rail-like, it escapes pursuit by slipping rapidly, and imperceptibly, through the reeds or cattails. It is always reluctant to fly and, if it feels the necessity of so doing, flutters awkwardly above the surface of the marsh for but a short distance before suddenly dropping out of sight. Except in migration it is a rather noisy bird, its loud cackling notes being one of the characteristic sounds of the marshes.

Northern American Coot
Fulica americana americana Gmelin

GENERAL DISTRIBUTION: Breeds from central British Columbia, Great Slave Lake, and southern Quebec south to Lower California, Arizona, Texas, northern Arkansas, western Tennessee, Ohio, and New Jersey; locally in southern Mississippi, southern Georgia, and Florida, through Mexico to Guatemala, and in Puerto Rico and Jamaica. Winters from Arizona, Texas, southern Illinois, and southern Virginia (casually Massachusetts)

Photograph by John M. Hopkins, Fish and Wildlife Service

Grand Prairie, in the Okefenokee Swamp.

Young Red-shouldered Hawks.

Swainson's Warbler on nest in canebreak over stagnant pond.

Photographs by Brooke Meanley

south throughout its breeding range, and on the Pacific Coast from southern British Columbia southward.

STATUS IN GEORGIA: A common winter resident on the coast and in the Okefenokee Swamp, and a common transient and uncommon winter resident in the interior of the state. Has been found nesting at Savannah and near Albany, in Dougherty County, and may breed locally elsewhere.

At Athens, the coot was a somewhat scarce transient, although noted in small numbers during each spring and fall migration. My extreme dates of occurrence in the spring were March 25 (1925) and May 12 (1926), and in the fall, September 24 (1925) and November 17 (1927). Johnston [1954], however, has noted it there as late as June 9, 1949, a single bird on Lake Kirota. Greene [1933] lists it a winter resident about Atlanta, his earliest date in the fall being October 13 (1932), his latest in the spring June 4 (1931). Johnston [1945] recorded it there as early as September 18 (1943) and reports that one individual remained throughout the summer of 1944. At Mt. Berry, in Floyd County, Jones [1944] found it a common transient, flocks being observed in late March, 1942, that totaled from 150 to 190 individuals. Extreme dates of occurrence for the spring migration are March 11 (1940) and May 3 (1942), and for the fall migration, August 10 (1943) and December 26 (1934). Dorsey [in litt.] reports this species at Rome as early in the spring as February 20 (1945) and as late as May 14 (1952). It has been noted at Milledgeville on April 11, 1936, and March 17, 1941 [Tait, 1946], and at Macon between the dates of October 17 (1931) and May 11 (1924) [Johnston, MS].

Murphey [1937] reports it a common winter resident about Augusta, "frequenting particularly open ponds with rush-grown banks but at times appearing in considerable numbers on the river." At Tifton, where it occurs as a winter resident, extreme dates are October 8 (1932) and May 15 (1932) (Norris). In Grady County, Stoddard [MS] considers it a common winter resident, extreme dates of occurrence being October 9 (1945) and May 5 (1945). Wright and Harper [1913] report it numerous during the fall and winter months in the Okefenokee Swamp, and Hebard [1941] recorded it there between the dates of November 1 (1932) and March 12 (1931).

On the coast, Helme found the coot plentiful on Cumberland Island from March 8 to April 12, 1902; and Mrs. Bassett reported it abundant on Colonel's Island during December, 1931, and January and February, 1932. Her earliest date in the fall is September 30, while Erichsen has noted it at Savannah as early as September 22 (1921). Troup D. Perry found this species to be a rare summer resident about Savannah, eggs being taken there on May 20. In Dougherty County, on July 16, 1929, I found coots breeding on a large pond near Albany, and succeeded in locating five nests. Three were empty, and judging by their appearance, the young had hatched successfully. The remaining two held eggs, in one, three, possibly half-incubated, and in the other, two. The nests were all in the thicker clumps of reeds and, being arched over, were fairly well concealed. They were fifty feet out from the shore, in water that was knee deep, and were compactly and substantially built of fragments of reeds.

HABITS AND RECOGNITION: Because of its wide distribution and relative abundance the coot is one of the better known water birds of the United States. While its habits suggest those of both ducks and gallinules, it is distinct from both, although closely related to the gallinules. Few birds are more gregarious; an occasional individual may be seen in migration, but normally it is found in flocks, and in the marshes where it breeds it is usually the most abundant species. Its food is largely obtained from the surface of the water or from the bottom when the water is shallow enough to permit it to feed by partially submerging its body. Sometimes, however, it gathers in dense rafts on open water and feeds by diving to the bottom as do various species of ducks.

It will fly only when hard pressed, and then will spatter along the top of the water until it has gained sufficient momentum, meanwhile splashing vigorously with its feet and wings and creating quite a commotion. Once in the air, however, its flight is strong and direct. It seldom flies far and, unless pursued, soon reverts to its normal activities. In swimming, it has a dovelike nod of the head that coincides with the thrust of its large webbed feet under the water, and this trait will readily identify it at some distance. Close at hand, its uniformly dark-gray plumage and conspicuous white bill will distinguish it at once. Marsh birds are characteristically noisy, and the coot is no exception. Its harsh cackle suggests that of a rail, but it also has a varied repertoire of guttural squawks and croaks that can be heard both day and night.

ORDER CHARADRIIFORMES

Oyster-catchers: *Family Haematopodidae*

Eastern American Oyster-catcher
Haematopus palliatus palliatus Temminck

GENERAL DISTRIBUTION: Breeds on the Atlantic and Gulf coasts from southern Virginia (formerly New Jersey) to Texas, on both coasts of Mexico, the West Indies (except the Bahama Islands), and south to Argentina and central Chile. Winters south of Virginia.

STATUS IN GEORGIA: A fairly common resident on the coast.

At one time the Oyster-catcher was a common bird on the Georgia coast, and while it has decreased in numbers in recent years, it is estimated that about thirty-five pairs still nest on the outer beaches. Helme reported it common on Cumberland Island in 1902, seeing nine there on March 24, but Pearson [1922] noted but a single bird on this island on May 4, 1921. Howell saw four on Oysterbed Island on June 14, 1927, and I observed two small flocks there on February 26, 1933, that totaled ten individuals. Tomkins [1936] states that flocks of as many as sixty-five have been seen during the winter in the Savannah region.

The first nests with eggs were reported on Egg Island, at the mouth of the Altamaha River, on April 19, 1888, and on Tybee Island, June 12, 1892. Rossignol's egg catalog records forty-eight occupied nests found on the islands from 1907 through 1934, sixteen with two eggs each, and thirty-two holding three. His earliest breeding record is three fresh eggs, March 27 (1927), his latest, two fresh eggs June 26 (1934). Bent [1929] gives as extreme breeding dates for South Carolina and Georgia (twenty-five records) March 27 to June 19. Erichsen [1921] found a nest with a single fresh egg on Raccoon Key on May 10, 1915, and another on Cabbage Island May 12, 1918 that held three slightly incubated eggs. In 1926 I had the opportunity of studying the breeding habits of this unique shore bird on the Georgia coast, and succeeded in finding three occupied nests. One was on Cabbage Island and held three fresh eggs on April 25, while the other two were on Oysterbed Island and held, on April 26, one fresh egg apiece. Several years later, on May 10, 1933, I was again on Cabbage Island and was shown a nest by Gilbert R. Rossignol that contained two fresh eggs. Norris [letter] found two nests in 1939 on the Pelican Banks (Sea Island) that held three eggs each, one on April 16 and the other on

June 14. Hebard reports two pairs in the marsh across the Sound from Jekyll Island, in Glynn County, in 1948, where on April 25, a nest with two eggs was found.

HABITS AND RECOGNITION: This large and strikingly colored shore bird has long had the reputation of being extremely wary and difficult to approach. Feeding as it does, however, on the open beaches, it is conspicuous at all times and is a bird that can hardly be overlooked. There should be no trouble in recognizing it, for no other bird of its size is so predominantly black and white, nor has such a long, deep-red bill. When the tide is low, it can be found on the exposed oyster beds, but at other times it feeds on the wider stretches of beach, probing in the sand for the mollusks that comprise the bulk of its diet. It is appropriately named, for oysters, when available, are eaten to the exclusion of any other marine life, the long powerful bill being well adapted to forcing open the shell and removing the succulent meat.

Except during the breeding season, it occurs in flocks of varying size, and those seen in Georgia during the winter are probably composed to a large extent of birds that have nested farther north. The few nests that I have seen in Georgia have been mere hollows in the sand, unlined, and far enough from the surf to be safe from the highest tides. In several instances they have been surrounded by fragments of oyster shells; Erichsen [1921] describes the two nests that he found as being on the top of a bank of oyster shell washed up by the surf. Normally two or three eggs are laid, rarely four, and the young leave the nest almost as soon as hatched, their protective coloring, resembling the beach sand, affording them protection.

Plovers, Turnstones, and Surf-birds: *Family Charadriidae*

Semipalmated Plover
Charadrius semipalmatus   Bonaparte

GENERAL DISTRIBUTION: Breeds on the Arctic Coast from Bering Sea to southern Baffin Island and Greenland south to southern Yukon, southern Mackenzie, James Bay, and Nova Scotia. Winters from central California, the Gulf Coast, and South Carolina to Chile, Patagonia, and the Galápagos Islands.

STATUS IN GEORGIA: A common transient and winter resident on the coast and an uncommon transient in the interior of the state. Non-breeding individuals occur sparingly on the coast during the summer.

At Athens, this small plover was found to be a rather scarce transient and the latest of the shore birds to appear in spring, my extreme dates for the occurrence of infrequent small flocks being May 3 (1925) and May 22 (1926). It was noted only once in the fall, a single bird being seen in the Sandy Creek bottoms September 12, 1926 [Burleigh, 1938]. At Atlanta, Greene [1933] recorded it in 1932 on May 12, 14, and 22, and again on August 27 and 31, and September 5. Griffin [1941] lists it as a "transient visitant" for the Atlanta region and gives as extreme dates of occurrence March 31 (1938) and May 27 (1932) and July 22 (1932) and September 5 (1932). At Lake Arrowhead, twelve miles north of Rome, a single bird was seen by Griffin [1950] on August 29, 1949. About Augusta, Murphey [1937] considers it "a regular migrant in spring and fall, and never abundant." He had a specimen taken in Richmond County on September 18, 1893. There are two records for Macon, April 30, 1932, and May 13, 1935; one for Tifton, September 2, 1946 (Norris); and one for Fitzgerald, April 27, 1952 (Hopkins). Stoddard [MS] has two records for Grady County: May 5, 1945, and September 7, 1947.

On the coast, Worthington reports twenty birds seen near the mouth of the Altamaha River, January 13, 1890, and forty on March 20, 1890; while Helme found this species common at Point Peter, at the mouth of the St. Marys River, January 22 and February 8, 1902, and equally common on Cumberland Island April 14, 1902. Pearson [1922] noted "perhaps twenty individuals" on Cumberland Island, May 3 and 4, 1921. I observed scattered small flocks on the open beach on Blackbeard Island on January 25, 1931, and considered this plover fairly common there that day. Tomkins [1936] records it as a permanent resident at Savannah, being most abundant in migration. Bent [1929] gives May 13 (1911) as a late departure date for Savannah. There are specimens at the University of Georgia taken in Chatham County, August 12 and September 30, 1908. Woodward [1949] noted this species on St. Simons Island from January through April, 1946–48, the largest number being observed in March and April.

HABITS AND RECOGNITION: Except for its darker plumage, the Semipalmated Plover is very similar in appearance and actions to the Piping Plover. The color of its upperparts has been compared to that of wet sand, and when the birds are seen feeding near the water's edge on an open beach, the appropriateness of this description is at once apparent. It is less partial than is the Piping Plover to sandy beaches, being frequently found on mud flats exposed by the low tide and occurring regularly in migration inland from the coast. When looking for food, which consists of small mollusks and crustaceans and other aquatic life, the small flocks spread out over a wide area, never remaining in a compact group as do the sandpipers. Each bird will run rapidly for a short distance, pause with bobbing head to scan the ground for a morsel of food, and then run on again. In flight, the flocks are usually compact and suggestive then of those of the smaller sandpipers, turning and twisting as they pass by and displaying an agility unsuspected in a bird which otherwise is so deliberate in its actions. Away from its breeding grounds, the Semipalmated Plover is a quiet bird and very seldom will its two-syllabled whistle be heard.

Eastern Piping Plover
Charadrius melodus melodus   Ord

GENERAL DISTRIBUTION: Breeds on the Atlantic Coast from Newfoundland south to North Carolina. Winters from Georgia south to northern Mexico and casually on the Gulf Coast from Florida to Texas.

STATUS IN GEORGIA: A fairly common transient and winter resident on the coast.

In 1890, Worthington saw fifteen birds at the mouth of the Altamaha River, January 27, and found them common there, March 12 to 20. An occasional bird was noted by Eugene E. Murphey on Wassaw Island, September 20 to 30, 1897; and Helme saw a few on Cumberland Island, March 10 to April 14, 1902. Sprunt [1931] reported them common at the mouth of the Savannah River during January, 1931, and Tomkins [1936] states that over an interval of eleven years he found the piping plover a regular spring and fall transient and a fairly common winter resident on the open beaches of Chatham County. Woodward [1949] found it fairly common on St. Simons Island from January through April, 1946–48. The earliest date that it has been recorded in the fall is August 14 (1897), on Wassaw Island, the latest in the spring May 11 (1910), at Savannah.

HABITS AND RECOGNITION: No bird is better adapted to its environment than is the Piping Plover. Its life is spent on the sandy beaches between the dunes and the surf, and so closely does its plumage match its surroundings that when quiet it is practically invisible. Unlike the sandpipers with which it associates, it is rather deliberate in its movements; when feeding, it will run along the sand for a short distance, pause to look about, and then, if unrewarded with a bit of food, will run on again. During these pauses it bobs its head in a manner characteristic of plovers, which trait distinguishes it from all sandpipers. In migration it occurs in small flocks, but, in feeding, the flocks never remain intact long, each bird moving in the direction that appeals to it at the moment, so that it is soon separated from its companions. During the winter months these birds are normally quiet and inconspicuous, the note most often heard then being soft and musical and so elusive in quality that it is no easy matter to locate its source.

Family Charadriidae: PLOVERS, TURNSTONES, & SURF-BIRDS

Of the three small plovers found on the Georgia coast, the Piping Plover is by far the palest and is further distinguished in the late fall and winter months by the absence of a black band across the breast. Seen in the spring when it has acquired its breeding plumage, this band is relatively narrow and usually broken in the middle; in this respect it is unlike either the Semipalmated Plover or the Thick-billed Plover which have neck bands unbroken in front.

Belted Piping Plover
Charadrius melodus circumcinctus (Ridgway)

GENERAL DISTRIBUTION: Breeds from southern Alberta, southern Saskatchewan, southern Manitoba, and the Gulf of St. Lawrence south to central Nebraska, northeastern Illinois, northwestern Indiana, northern Ohio, and northwestern Pennsylvania. Winters on the Gulf Coast from Mississippi to Texas and northern Mexico.

STATUS IN GEORGIA: Apparently a regular spring and fall transient and a possible winter resident on the coast.

At present the Belted Piping Plover is known as a Georgia bird from two specimens taken on Tybee Island, Chatham County, by Ivan R. Tomkins, on August 2 and 23, 1953. It would appear, however, that in previous years it has probably been overlooked, for Tomkins reports [letter] that "I have seen a number of these birds with complete throat rings: last spring in March and April (21 March, 4 April, 11 April, 18 April) and again on 31 July, 2 August, 8 August."

HABITS AND RECOGNITION: While in Georgia this interior race differs in no way in appearance and actions from typical *melodus*. It is a bird of the open beaches, where, singly or in small scattered flocks, it leads a quiet, unobtrusive existence and will rarely attract the attention of the casual observer. In breeding plumage it can be distinguished by the broad unbroken black band across the breast, but as with most subspecies, specimens are necessary for satisfactory identification.

Wilson's Thick-billed Plover
Charadrius wilsonia wilsonia Ord

GENERAL DISTRIBUTION: Breeds on the Atlantic Coast from southern Virginia (formerly New Jersey) south to Florida, on the Gulf Coast to Texas, and in the Bahamas. Winters from northern Florida and the coast of Louisiana and Texas south to Honduras and in the West Indies.

STATUS IN GEORGIA: A common summer resident on the coast.

Bent [1929] cites as the earliest dates of arrival in the spring, at Darien, March 19 (1890) and on Cumberland Island, March 18 (1902). Tomkins [1936] gives March 3 (1931) as his earliest spring date for Savannah; he states further that on March 15, 1931, he saw at least one hundred birds on Oysterbed Island, where the day before there were none; his latest date in the fall is October 17 (1931). Woodward [1949] noted this species on St. Simons Island on February 26, 1947, the earliest date it has been recorded in the spring.

This plover has been found breeding on practically all of the coastal islands, the nesting dates ranging from April 16 (Pelican Banks) to July 19 (St. Catherine's Island). Erichsen [MS] gives as his earliest breeding record a nest with three fresh eggs on Cockspur Island, April 24 (1938), his latest a nest with one fresh egg, also on Cockspur Island, July 4 (1940). Rossignol's egg catalog records 229 nests found on the islands from May 11, 1905 through April 25, 1935. Of this number, 24 held two eggs each; 204, three eggs; and a single nest (found on Oysterbed Island on May 18, 1924), four eggs. Fully 90 per cent of these nests were found in May, the extreme dates being April 24 (1932), three slightly incubated eggs, and June 21 (1907), two fresh eggs.

My experience with this species as a breeding bird on the coast of Georgia has been limited largely to Oysterbed Island, near the mouth of the Savannah River. Here in 1923, and again in 1925, I estimated the breeding population to be approximately thirty pairs. On my first visit, May 19, 1923, nesting activities were apparently just getting well started, for I succeeded in locating but seven nests, one with the full complement of three eggs, four with two, and two with but a single egg each. In 1925, I spent the morning of May 16 on the island, and within two hours had found twenty nests, twelve holding three eggs each, five with two, and three with but one. What is apparently the earliest breeding record for the state is that of a nest with two eggs reported by Norris [letter] as found on the Pelican Banks (Sea Island) on April 16, 1939.

HABITS AND RECOGNITION: This plover is one of the most characteristic breeding birds of the South Atlantic and Gulf Coast beaches. There are few beaches from southern Virginia to Texas where at least one pair cannot be found during the summer months, and on isolated islands where optimum conditions prevail, their numbers are sufficiently large to suggest a tendency to colonize. However, at other times the Thick-billed Plover is less gregarious than either the Piping or Semipalmated Plovers, and even in the early fall when the southward movement is at its height, flocks are rarely observed.

On its breeding grounds it is rather unsuspicious and easy to approach, and will be found to be less active and more deliberate in its actions than the other shore birds. Its food is obtained in typical plover fashion, but in running on a stretch of open beach, it appears less nimble, or less in a hurry, than are the others, and its pauses are longer. Its large, stout bill, dull black in color, will readily distinguish it from the other, smaller plovers with which it might be confused. The nests that I have found have been slight hollows in the sand, frequently lined with fragments of oyster shell, and were either in the open, with no concealment whatsoever, or at the base of a clump of myrtle sprouts. When leaving the nest, the incubating bird will run for a short distance before flying, so that there is invariably a line of well-defined footprints leading to the eggs. I have never found more than three eggs in a nest, and not infrequently but two are laid here in Georgia.

Northern Killdeer
Charadrius vociferus vociferus   Linnaeus

GENERAL DISTRIBUTION: Breeds from central British Columbia, southern Mackenzie, and northern Ontario south to southern Lower California, central Mexico, Florida, and the Bahamas. Winters from southern British Columbia, Colorado, Missouri, southern Illinois, western New York, and New Jersey south to Bermuda, the Greater Antilles, northern Venezuela, and northwestern Peru.

STATUS IN GEORGIA: A common permanent resident throughout the larger part of the state, being least numerous on the coast and during the summer months.

On the coast, where it rarely breeds, the first transients in the fall were noted at St. Marys on October 23 (1905) and at Savannah on October 17 (1925). Helme found the killdeer common on Cumberland Island, March 7, 1902, and Tomkins [1936] considers it a common winter resident about Savannah. Erichsen [MS] gives as his latest spring date for Chatham County, March 28 (1947).

At Athens [Burleigh, 1938], I found this species especially abundant in late February and March, when many flocks were noted in the open fields and pastures. A flock containing fully one hundred birds was seen in the open Sandy Creek bottoms on February 23, 1926. Hebard [1941] reports the killdeer common in the Okefenokee Swamp during the winter months.

It has been recorded as breeding at Augusta, Atlanta, Athens, Rome, Macon, Cochran, Marshallville, Baker County, Grady County, Savannah, and St. Simons Island. A nest found at Athens [Burleigh, 1938] on March 30, 1927, held four slightly incubated eggs and was on a slight slope on an open golf course. Another found in a similar situation on June 5, 1929, possibly a second brood, held four well-incubated eggs. There are two definite breeding records for the Atlanta area: a nest found by T. Lawrence at Marietta on May 17, 1931, with three eggs [Barkalow, 1940], and one found near Atlanta by Griffin on April 15, 1938 that held two eggs [Griffin, 1940]. Denton [1945] found newly hatched young at Cochran, Bleckley County, on April 7, 1933. He also reports a nest with four eggs at Macon on March 24, 1944. Although common during the winter months, the Killdeer is reported by Stoddard [MS] as being "a very rare breeder" in Grady County. His only breeding record is a nest that held four well-incubated eggs on June 9, 1939, when found by his son, Herbert L. Stoddard, Jr. Hopkins [in litt.] succeeded in finding four occupied nests in Baker County in June, 1950; one held four eggs on June 2, another three eggs on June 29.

HABITS AND RECOGNITION: The Killdeer is widely distributed in the United States and so numerous almost everywhere that it is known to almost everyone. In migration and during the winter months it is commonly seen in the vicinity of water, but in the nesting season scattered pairs can be found in open fields and pastures where ponds or streams are apparently of minor consideration. It is a noisy bird, constantly on the alert and protesting vociferously if its privacy is invaded; its note then is a loud, strident "killdee, killdee," which will at once identify it. In appearance and actions it is essentially a plover, running rapidly for a short distance and stopping with bobbing head as it scrutinizes the ground at its feet. Since it is now rarely molested, it shows little fear of man and, if approached as it feeds in an open field, will put what it considers a safe distance between itself and the intruder by running rather than flying. Its food throughout the year consists largely of insects, and as many of these are such destructive kinds as grasshoppers, May beetles, caterpillars, and weevils, it can be considered extremely beneficial and worthy of protection at all times.

The nest is a slight hollow in the ground, unlined, or lined with such material as is most easily obtained in the vicinity. One that I found at Athens had a fairly substantial lining of bits of rotten wood, fragments of weed stems, cotton seeds, small pieces of bark, and ash seeds. Another was much less elaborate, the eggs resting on a slight bed of crushed weed stems. The site is always in the open, where the incubating bird has an unobstructed view of its surroundings and can slip away if the nest is approached.

Atlantic American Golden Plover
Pluvialis dominica dominica (Müller)

GENERAL DISTRIBUTION: Breeds on the Barren Grounds from Point Barrow east to Hudson Bay and south to Ard Lake and Churchill, Manitoba. Winters on the *pampas* of Brazil, Argentina, Paraguay, Bolivia, and Uruguay.

STATUS IN GEORGIA: An extremely rare transient.

There are few records of this species in the state. Murphey [1937] says that it is a scarce fall transient in Richmond County, the most recent record there being of a single bird observed by Irvine Phinizy on October 6, 1925. Tomkins [1931] collected a male on Oysterbed Island on April 10, 1931, and reports three at Savannah on September 9, 1950. His most recent record (Tomkins, 1954) is that of a specimen taken three miles east of Savannah on November 8, 1953.

HABITS AND RECOGNITION: The Golden Plover will never be other than a casual transient in Georgia, as in spring its main route in migration is through the Mississippi Valley, while in fall most individuals fly from the coast of Nova Scotia over the ocean to the Lesser Antilles and then to the northern coast of South America. Thus only stragglers reach Georgia, and the sight of one will always be a noteworthy event. In appearance this species resembles closely the Black-bellied Plover, but is slightly smaller and lacks any white in the wings or on the upper tail coverts. When it is seen in flight at close range, it is possible to note the absence of black axillary feathers under the wings, but it must be admitted that this is a character difficult to see in the field. The Golden Plover can be found with other shore birds on the beaches, but it shows a decided preference for marshy meadows, and it feeds also in open fields and pastures.

Black-bellied Plover
Squatarola squatarola (Linnaeus)

GENERAL DISTRIBUTION: Nearly cosmopolitan. Breeds in North America on the Arctic Coast and islands from Point Barrow east to Southampton and western Baffin Island. Winters from southern British Columbia, the Gulf Coast, and North Carolina south to Brazil, Peru, and Chile.

STATUS IN GEORGIA: A common transient and winter resident on the coast and of casual occurrence there during the summer; apparently largely of accidental occurrence in the interior.

Helme observed three birds at St. Marys on January 15, 1902, and states that by February 8 these plover had become plentiful there. He

237

likewise found them common on Cumberland Island, March 18, 1902. Small flocks were reported at Savannah May 13, 1908 and May 11, 1910. I observed an occasional small flock on Oysterbed Island, May 16, 1925; an adult and a flock of eight in immature plumage at this same spot on June 14, 1927; and a single bird on Tybee Island on December 15, 1933. Woodward [1949] reports that this species was present in small numbers on Sea Island and St. Simons Island from January through April, 1946–48. What were apparently first arrivals in the fall were noted at Savannah, August 8 and 15, 1908, and in Bryan County, August 20 and 24, 1930. Tomkins [1936] considers the Black-bellied Plover a permanent resident on the coast, being most numerous in May and September.

The only records for the interior of the state are from Atlanta, single birds being seen there on August 26 and 27, 1932, and December 12, 1932 [Greene, 1933], January 3, 1942 [Griffin, 1942], and August 31, 1950 [Griffin, 1951].

HABITS AND RECOGNITION: In full breeding plumage the Black-bellied Plover well deserves the title of aristocrat of the shore birds. Its erect posture, dignified demeanor, and handsome plumage all serve to set it apart from the sandpipers with which it associates. In the fall, it loses its solid black underparts and is largely mottled gray and white, but even then it is one of the more impressive of the shore birds. Always wary and alert, it can rarely be closely approached as it feeds on the open beach, but even at a distance its large size and the conspicuous white in the wings and upper tail coverts will immediately identify it. Its stout body, large head, and short, heavy bill are equally unmistakable, as are its actions so typical of all the plovers. Its food, small mollusks and other marine life, is usually procured on mud flats and stretches of wet sand exposed by the falling tide; when the tide is high, it may be found feeding close to the water's edge, running swiftly just beyond the edge of the surf, with pauses to seize any morsels of food discovered.

In its long journeys to and from its breeding grounds in the far north, it can be found in flocks of varying size, but during the winter months it is less sociable and is as apt as not to be observed feeding alone. The notes of all the plovers, the Killdeer being the possible exception, are mellow and musical; that of the Black-bellied Plover is loud and clear, and suggestive of the syllables "pe-oo-ee."

American Ruddy Turnstone
Arenaria interpres morinella (Linnaeus)

GENERAL DISTRIBUTION: Breeds from western and northern Alaska east to Southampton and western Baffin Island. Winters from central California, the Gulf Coast, North Carolina, and Bermuda south to southern Brazil and central Chile.

STATUS IN GEORGIA: A common transient and winter resident on the coast, and of casual occurrence there during the summer.

Despite, or possibly because of, its relative abundance, there are few definite records for the occurrence of this species in the state. Hoxie reported what were apparently early fall transients at the mouth of the Savannah River on August 18, 1908, and late spring transients on Tybee Island on May 28, 1910. I observed five birds on Oysterbed Island on June 14, 1927, and at the time thought that because of the late date these might be non-breeders, which might possibly linger throughout the summer. However, I was again on Oysterbed Island on June 1, 1929, and noted small flocks throughout the morning, so it may be that the spring migration of the Ruddy Turnstone is sometimes prolonged into mid-June. A single bird seen on Cockspur Island on November 18, 1928, was so late that it may have wintered, as did scattered small flocks found on Blackbeard Island on January 25, 1931. Tomkins [1936] states that this species is a "permanent resident" on the coast. Woodward [1949] considered it fairly common on Sea Island and St. Simons Island from January through April, 1946–48.

HABITS AND RECOGNITION: Both in appearance and actions the turnstone is distinctive; it is a chunky, short-necked bird, with short orange legs and, in the spring and summer months, a variegated plumage of reddish-brown, black, and white that has given it the common name of "calico-bird." In the winter, it is less conspicuous, its predominating colors being brownish-gray and white, but its stout build and the white streaks on its back, wings, and tail that are revealed in flight, easily separate it from the sandpipers with which it is found. Its feeding habits are its own, for, as its name implies, it frequently secures the marine life that forms the larger part of its food by turning over small stones, as well as seaweed or any small objects littering the beach, with its short, stout bill. So preferred is this method of feeding that on sandy beaches it will often dig holes several inches deep rather than pick up what it can find on the surface in the manner of other shore birds. Both in migration and on the beaches that it frequents in the winter, it occurs in small flocks that show little fear of an intruder and are usually easy to approach. It is normally a quiet bird, but when flying it utters a short rapidly repeated note sounding like the syllables "kuk, kuk, kuk."

Snipe and Sandpipers: *Family Scolopacidae*

American Woodcock
Philohela minor (Gmelin)

GENERAL DISTRIBUTION: Breeds from Manitoba, southern Ontario, southern Quebec, and Nova Scotia south to eastern Colorado, southeastern Texas, southern Louisiana, and central Florida. Winters from southern Missouri, northern Indiana, and New Jersey south to the Gulf Coast and central Florida.

STATUS IN GEORGIA: Locally a fairly common resident throughout the state.

At Athens [Burleigh, 1938], I found this species rather scarce during the first year or so of my stay (1920–30), but after that it increased perceptibly in numbers, and at length became fairly plentiful throughout the year. On January 22, 1927, a male was for the first time heard giving its flight song, singing from dusk until well after dark over a marshy field at the upper end of the Sandy Creek bottoms. Two months later, on March 27, a brood of newly hatched young was found near this spot. The following year there was a noticeable increase in the number of these birds nesting on Sandy Creek, three pairs at least rearing their young there that spring. One pair nested rather early, for the four downy nestlings, already out of the egg a day or two, were found on March 18. A nest found four days later, on March 22, which held four well-incubated eggs, was hidden in the middle of a tangled briar thicket in a field partially overgrown with broom-sedge.

Griffin [1940] cites as breeding extremes for the Atlanta area a nest with four eggs found January 12 (1935) (Barkalow), and one that held four partially incubated eggs on March 15 (1904) (Mills). He reports another nest [Griffin, 1948], that held two eggs on March 2, 1947. Near Lawrenceville, in Gwinnett County, a nest with four eggs was found on April 4, 1952 (Odum). Murphey [1937] states that the Woodcock was formerly abundant about Augusta, but since 1907 has been much reduced in numbers.

At Rome, Jones [1947] reports well-grown young on May 2, 1942, and four young "quarter-grown," on April 9, 1944. It apparently breeds in Towns County, for at Young Harris single birds were seen by Howell on July 12, 1908, and by me on June 29, 1923, and I flushed another bird near the summit of Brasstown Bald on July 2, 1923. In Grady County there are no actual breeding records, but Stoddard [MS] believes it nests in small numbers, well-grown young having been seen on Sherwood Plantation in May.

240

Hebard [1941] considers it fairly common in the Okefenokee Swamp, the nuptial song having been heard over Floyd's Island in December and early January from 1930 through 1936. He reports young in western Camden County on March 9, 1939, and a nest with two newly hatched young and two pipped eggs at Coleraine, in Charlton County, on February 26, 1942.

On the coast nests with eggs have been found at Savannah on February 17, 1878 [Head, 1878], and February 22, 1892; at St. Marys on March 9, 1908; and at Pooler, in Chatham County, on February 8, 1917.

HABITS AND RECOGNITION: Among game birds the Woodcock ranks supreme. Flushing almost underfoot in the swampy undergrowth that it frequents, its swift flight requires quick and accurate shooting, but once secured, it affords a meal worthy of an epicure. The abundance of this species has fluctuated markedly over the years. Its numbers were reduced to a very low ebb by a severe cold spell in 1940, after which no hunting was permitted for a number of years until it became plentiful again.

It is a plump, long-billed bird, normally found in moist alder thickets fringing streams, the concealment afforded it there making it one of our least conspicuous birds. That it is largely nocturnal in its habits, its activities commencing at twilight and terminating with the first appearance of dawn, only promotes this inconspicuousness. Throughout the day it remains motionless on the ground, and so perfectly does its plumage blend with its surroundings that unless betrayed by some movement, it is practically invisible. Its food is largely earthworms, which it gets by probing in the soft ground with its long, sensitive bill, the borings thus produced being sufficiently characteristic to be readily recognized.

Because it is such a silent bird for much of the year, the mating song of the male comes as a distinct surprise. The bird then relinquishes its normal role of recluse of the alder thickets and for a brief interval in early spring performs in a manner worthy of our most inspired songsters. It begins as twilight approaches and so reveals its presence in an open stretch of marshy bottomland. The first intimation is a single, loud rasping note suggesting the "peent" of a Nighthawk. This may be repeated for several minutes before the bird suddenly flies from the ground. Circling then higher and higher in the night sky, and uttering a continuous musical twitter as it ascends, it abruptly drops back to the spot from which it flew, its fluttering descent being accompanied by a loud, musical, three-syllabled note, which, when first heard, is difficult to reconcile with one's idea of the nonsinging character of the Woodcock. This flight song is usually repeated until well after dark, and in Georgia can be heard from late January until early March.

The nest of a Woodcock is merely a depression in dead leaves large enough to hold the four eggs that are normally laid. It is usually in the open, for the incubating bird depends to a great extent on protective coloration for concealment. In this she is highly successful, for so well does she blend with her surroundings that, even when the location of a nest is known, it requires a close scrutiny to pick it out again.

Wilson's Common Snipe
Capella gallinago delicata (Ord)

GENERAL DISTRIBUTION: Breeds from northwestern Alaska, northern Mackenzie, northern Quebec, and Newfoundland south to southern California, Nevada, southern Colorado, eastern South Dakota, northern Iowa, northern Illinois, northern Indiana, and northern Pennsylvania. Winters from southern British Columbia, northern Idaho, Colorado, southern Missouri, and southern Virginia south through Central America and the West Indies to southern Brazil.

STATUS IN GEORGIA: A common transient and fairly common winter resident throughout the state.

At Athens [Burleigh, 1938], this species was a common transient in both the spring and the fall, small flocks being especially numerous in late February and early March. Relatively few birds remained through the winter, although it was always possible to flush several in December and January in the Sandy Creek bottoms. Normal dates for arrival and departure are October 5 (1924) and May 6 (1925); extreme dates of occurrence being September 11 (1926) and June 3 (1921). Griffin [MS] reports that it is a winter resident about Atlanta, occurring between the dates of August 25 (1932) and May 12 (1932). Jones [1944] found it a fairly common transient at Mt. Berry, near Rome, recording it in the spring from February 28 (1937) to April 23 (1936) and in the fall from October 22 (1939) until November 29 (1935). Murphey [1937] considers it an abundant winter resident at Augusta, being most numerous in late September and again in March. At Milledgeville, Tait [1946] reports it between the dates of December 26 (1936) and March 29 (1943). Johnston [MS] gives as extreme dates for Macon, September 10 (1955) and May 16 (1931).

In the southern part of the state it has been noted at Americus, Sumter County [Denton, 1942], from October 18, 1941 to April 22, 1942; at Tifton as early in the fall as September 8 (1932), and at Fitzgerald as late in the spring as May 6 (1940) [Norris and Hopkins, 1953]; in Grady County, from September 23 (1945) to May 5 (1945) [Stoddard, MS]; at Flemington, Liberty County, [Grimm, 1946] on February 8 and April 1, 1944; in the Okefenokee Swamp [Hebard, 1941] as a common winter resident,

Photograph by Brooke Meanley

Young Horned Owl in a coastal plain swamp.

Photograph by Brooke Meanley

Slash-pine bog with pitcher plants, habitat
of the Brown-headed Nuthatch and the Red-cockaded Woodpecker.

with the earliest date of arrival at Coleraine, October 6, 1940; and at Savannah [Tomkins, 1936] as an abundant winter resident from October until mid-May. There are years when it reaches the coast in September, for the distribution files of the Fish and Wildlife Service contain records of a bird seen at Savannah September 4, 1910, and of one striking the Tybee Light on September 17, 1930. Erichsen [MS] gives as his latest spring date for Chatham County, May 7 (1933).

HABITS AND RECOGNITION: With its wide distribution and abundance the Snipe was long a popular game bird. In January, 1940, there was a severe reduction in numbers resulting from unusually severe freezing weather throughout the South. After this the hunting season was discontinued, and since then the Snipe had not increased sufficiently in numbers to warrant opening the season again until 1953.

The Common Snipe, unlike the Woodcock, prefers open situations, and has no liking for swampy woodland or dense alder thickets. It should be looked for in wet meadows or along the edges of marshes where it probes with its long bill in the soft mud for the earthworms which comprise the bulk of its food. Although to some degree nocturnal in its habits, it feeds throughout much of the day and is noticeably more active when the sky is overcast or when foggy conditions prevail. When approached, it depends on its protective coloration for concealment, rarely flying until almost stepped on, and then darting off with a harsh "scaipe." In traveling any distance, its flight is straight and swift, but when first flushed, it indulges in erratic turns and twists that make it a very difficult target. If its whereabouts are known and due caution is used in approaching it, it can be seen crouching motionless on the ground, and under these conditions its long bill and conspicuously striped back leave no question of its identity. In former years it was much more abundant than it is now, but with suitable protection it should always be a fairly common bird in Georgia during the winter months.

Southern Long-billed Curlew
Numenius americanus americanus Bechstein

GENERAL DISTRIBUTION: Breeds in Utah, southern Idaho, and eastern Nevada; formerly in southern Wisconsin, Iowa, northern Illinois, eastern Nebraska, and eastern Kansas. Winters from central California and southern Arizona south to Guatemala, and formerly on the Atlantic Coast from South Carolina to Florida, Louisiana, and Texas.

STATUS IN GEORGIA: Formerly a common transient and winter resident; now rare and of casual occurrence on the coast.

Worthington reported this species common on the coast of McIntosh County in the winters of 1887–88 and 1889–90; he took ten or more specimens on Sapelo Island between November 19, 1887, and March 29, 1888.

Hoxie observed six birds on the coast near Savannah, April 10, 1910, and commented at the time that this curlew was now rarely seen. Tomkins [1936] states that he has seen a few birds in June, October, and November, but that "none were certainly seen since 1931." Tanner [1946] saw a single bird on Sea Island on November 21, 1943, and Woodward [1949] observed five on Sea Island, April 3 through April 11, 1947, and one on Little St. Simons Island on March 11, 1948. The most recent record is that of a single bird reported by Johnston and Major [1950] on Wolf Island, in Doboy Sound, March 22 and April 8, 1950.

HABITS AND RECOGNITION: The Long-billed Curlew, the largest and most impressive of our shore birds, was once an abundant bird on the Atlantic Coast, but excessive shooting and the gradual encroachment of civilization over much of its breeding range in the prairie states has materially reduced its numbers in recent years. Better protection has fortunately saved it from complete extermination, but it is improbable that it will ever again be of more than casual occurrence on the Georgia coast. Wary and ever on the alert, if seen, it will be at a distance, but its large size and long, down-curved bill, that in some individuals attains a length of seven inches, will at once distinguish it. In migration and in its winter quarters it is equally at home on the open beaches or on the mud flats exposed by the low tide. Unless disturbed, it is a quiet bird, but when flushed, it utters a loud, clear whistle as it puts a safe distance between itself and the intruder.

Northern Long-billed Curlew
Numenius americanus parvus   Bishop

GENERAL DISTRIBUTION: Breeds from eastern British Columbia, Alberta, Saskatchewan, and Manitoba south to Oregon, Montana, Wyoming, and South Dakota. Winters in southern California and northern Mexico.

STATUS IN GEORGIA: Of accidental occurrence on the coast.

There is only one definite record for the occurrence of this northern race in the state, that of a specimen taken May 9, 1885 on Sapelo Island, and identified by Oberholser [1918] as *parvus*.

HABITS AND RECOGNITION: This northern race of the Long-billed Curlew differs only in being smaller, so can be satisfactorily identified only on the basis of an actual specimen. Its habits are essentially the same as *americanus*, and if seen on the Georgia coast, it will be on the wider stretches of beach or exposed mud flats.

Hudsonian Whimbrel
Numenius phaeopus hudsonicus   Latham

GENERAL DISTRIBUTION: Breeds on the coast of Alaska north of the mouth of the Yukon and locally east to northern Mackenzie and northern Manitoba. Winters on the Pacific Coast from Lower California to southern Chile, and on the Atlantic Coast from British Guiana to the mouth of the Amazon.

STATUS IN GEORGIA: A fairly common spring and fall transient on the coast and of casual occurrence there throughout the rest of the year.

Hoxie reports small flocks seen near Savannah, April 10, 1910, and May 13, 1911, and I observed several birds there May 17, 1925. Pearson [1922] noted five on Cumberland Island, May 2, 1921, and two on May 6. Tomkins [1936] states that it is occasionally seen throughout the year at the mouth of the Savannah River, being fairly common in the spring and in the fall; he saw at least one hundred birds there on May 7, 1930. Woodward [1949] recorded it on St. Simons Island, March 25 through April 20, 1947, and again on March 11, 1948, when thirty were observed. Early fall transients were noted in Chatham County, July 27, 1917 (Rossignol), and July 26, 1934, and July 4, 1940 (Erichsen). Sprunt [1931] saw two birds near the mouth of the Savannah River, January 24, 1931, and Erichsen [MS] reports an occasional bird on Tybee Island in late December and January (January 10, 1915, January 7, 1923, January 1, 1929, December 27, 1931, December 24, 1940).

HABITS AND RECOGNITION: Despite its large size and its popularity with sportsmen in years gone by when it was legally hunted, this curlew has never had its numbers materially reduced. This is largely due to the fact that it has always been an extremely shy and wary bird. Another factor in its favor was its practice of making its long journeys to and from its breeding grounds in relatively small flocks, that were not subject to excessive slaughter at the hands of hunters, as was unfortunately the case with other shore birds. Although somewhat smaller than the Long-billed Curlew, it is nevertheless a striking bird when seen feeding on a stretch of open beach. The sandpipers with which it frequently associates seem dwarfed by comparison and, if close by, emphasize the large size of this curlew. Its movements are usually slow and deliberate, but it is capable of running rapidly if occasion demands, as may happen if it is pursuing a fiddler crab or a large insect.

On the Georgia coast it is not uncommon to see single birds, but if small flocks are encountered, the birds will be scattered out, and never in a compact group. Always alert, the Hudsonian Whimbrel will fly at the slightest hint of danger, its steady wing-beats, alternated by brief intervals of soaring, soon putting a safe distance between it and the intruder. When the tide is low, the edges of pools in the salt marsh are favorite feeding grounds, but at high tide these curlews will be found near the water's edge on the open beaches.

Upland Plover
Bartramia longicauda   (Bechstein)

GENERAL DISTRIBUTION: Breeds from northwestern Alaska east through southern Mackenzie, central Manitoba, and southern Ontario to southern Quebec, and south to southern Oregon, northern Utah, Colorado, southern Oklahoma, northern Texas, southern Illinois, southern Indiana, and northern Virginia. Winters on the *pampas* of South America from southern Brazil to Argentina and Chile.

STATUS IN GEORGIA: An uncommon spring transient and a rare fall transient throughout the state.

At Athens [Burleigh, 1938], I observed this species only in the spring, and it was irregular in its occurrence and only infrequently seen. There were years when none of these birds appeared and but once, in 1926, when they were at all plentiful. That year, small flocks, usually containing from two to four individuals, occasionally as many as eight, were frequently noted in the open fields from April 3 through April 23. My extreme dates of occurrence are April 3 (1926) and April 24 (1928). Johnston, however, [1954], noted a single bird at Athens as late as May 18 (1950).

At Atlanta, Greene [1933] reports a single bird seen April 9, 1932, and three, two days later. Griffin [1941] gives as migration extremes for the Atlanta area April 9 (1931) and April 20 (1930), but apparently overlooked in his summary a single fall record, a bird he personally observed on September 3, 1940 [Griffin, 1940]. There are also, in the collections at Emory University, two specimens taken in Newton County, one on April 16, 1908 (F. L. Bedingfield and W. H. LaPrade), and the other on July 15, 1909 (D. W. Travis). Meanley [1945] saw several on April 3–12, 1945, at Camp Wheeler, Bibb County, and Johnston [MS] cites as extreme spring records for Macon, March 18 (1924) and April 26 (1930), and for the fall migration one record, July 23, 1945.

At Mount Berry, near Rome, Jones [1944] found the Upland Plover a rare spring transient, extreme dates being March 10 (1937) and April 16 (1936). Murphey [1937] considers it a regular spring and fall transient at Augusta, while at Milledgeville [Tait, 1946] it has been noted but once, April 12, 1941.

In the southern part of the state it has been noted by Denton at Cochran, Bleckley County, on March 27, 1933; by Norris in Tift County, on April 2, 1934, and August 15 and 29, 1942; by Hopkins in Mitchell County, on August 23 and 30, 1950, and at Quitman, Brooks County, on September 21, 1952; by Erichsen in Chatham County, between the dates of March 29 (1924) and May 4 (1915) in the spring, and in the fall on August 18, 1918, August 20, 1922, and September 6, 1931.

HABITS AND RECOGNITION: This species is not well named, for it is actually a large sandpiper, not a plover. However, if one is watched as it feeds in an open field or pasture, its plover-like actions—a short run, a pause, and then another run—will soon reveal the reason for its being called a plover. It is probably less dependent on the proximity of water than any of the other shore birds, for both on its breeding grounds and in migration it is found in large open fields and never on beaches or in marshes. It likewise has the habit of alighting on the top of fence posts or even telephone poles, a trait distinctive enough to set it apart from its near relatives. It is a medium-sized bird slightly larger than a killdeer, with a slender appearance that is emphasized by its long neck and legs. Possibly because of its preference for open fields, it does not associate with the other shore birds, the small flocks seen in Georgia being invariably of their own kind. Except in its summer home it is normally a rather quiet bird, its rolling mellow whistle being only infrequently heard when it is flying by overhead.

It was at one time a much commoner bird than it is today, drastic reduction of its optimum breeding habitat, the midwestern prairie grasslands, in conjunction with hunting, reducing it to the point where it was feared it might be completely exterminated. Suitable laws protecting it have resulted in a slight increase in numbers, but it will probably never again be very plentiful. From an economic standpoint it is an extremely beneficial species and deserving of protection at all times, its food consisting largely of such injurious insects as grasshoppers, locusts, cutworms, and weevils.

Spotted Sandpiper
Actitis macularia (Linnaeus)

GENERAL DISTRIBUTION: Breeds from northwestern Alaska, northern Manitoba, northern Quebec, and Newfoundland south to southern California, central Arizona, southern New Mexico, Texas, the northern part of the Gulf states, western North Carolina, and Georgia. Winters from southern British Columbia, southern Arizona, Louisiana, and South Carolina south to southern Brazil and Argentina.

STATUS IN GEORGIA: A common spring and fall transient, and of casual occurrence throughout the state during the winter. There is one recent breeding record for Atlanta.

At Athens [Burleigh, 1938], I found this species a common transient, appearing at the edge of the river and about the scattered lakes and ponds from early April until the end of May, and again from the middle of July until the first of November. Extreme dates for occurrence in the spring are April 5 (1925) and May 31 (1925), and in the fall, July 15 (1926) and November 3 (1929). Griffin [1941] gives as migration extremes for the Atlanta area March 31 (1938) and May 30 (1941), and July 12 (1932) and October 29 (1931). Johnston [1945] cites as an earlier date of arrival in the spring, March 30 (1944). Jones [1944] considers it a fairly common transient at Mt. Berry, near Rome, giving as extreme dates in the spring April 15 (1941) and May 21 (1939). At Milledgeville [Tait, 1946], it has been noted in the spring from March 29 (1941) to April 25 (1943).

Other extreme dates of occurrence throughout the state, in the spring and in the fall, are: Young Harris, May 27 (1933); Macon, April 6 (1935) and May 28 (1925), and August 9 (1952) and October 30 (1924) [Johnston, MS]; Columbus, [Straw, 1947], April 30 (1946); Americus [Denton, 1942], May 6 (1942); Tifton, April 22 (1942) and October 7 (1941) (Norris); Fitzgerald, May 27 (1934) and July 18 (1941) (Hopkins); Grady County [Stoddard, MS], May 23 (1945) and July 21 (1946); Hinesville, Liberty County [Grimm, 1946], April 8 (1942) to May 2 (1943), and September 18 (1943); Okefenokee Swamp, June 5 (1912); Savannah, June 1 (1913) and July 15 (1910); Colonel's Island, November 1 (1931).

It has been recorded in winter at Atlanta on December 20 and 22, 1936 [Griffin, 1941], and December 21, 1947 [Branch Howe, Jr., 1948]; at St. Marys on January 5 and 22, 1902 (Helme); at Savannah on January 31, 1915 (Rossignol); at Darien on January 24, 1931 (Burleigh); on Sea Island, Glynn County, on December 29, 1948 [Sciple, 1949]; and on St. Simons Island, Glynn County, on December 31, 1929 [Greene, 1930], January 25, 1941 [Sciple and Griffin, 1941], and January 22, 1946 [Woodward, 1949].

HABITS AND RECOGNITION: This is one of the best known of our shore birds; with its wide distribution and relative abundance there are few streams or ponds throughout the country where it cannot be seen at one time or another during the year. It is one of the least gregarious of the sandpipers, for it is never seen in flocks, two or three birds scattered along the water's edge being the usual number observed at one spot. No bird is more easily recognized by its actions, for as it feeds, it teeters the posterior half of its body, almost without interruption, and if it flies, the rapid beat of its curved wings, alternated by brief intervals of sailing, readily distinguishes it. As seen in Georgia, it is a quiet bird, the only note commonly heard being a clear three-part whistle uttered as it takes flight, that has been aptly syllabled as "peet-weet-weet." In breeding plumage, its underparts, as its name implies, are heavily spotted, but in the fall and winter become a uniform dull white, so that at these seasons it is no longer "a spotted sandpiper."

In common with other shore birds a few individuals are found in the state so late in the spring as to suggest breeding. Of considerable interest, therefore, is the fact that in 1952 the Spotted Sandpiper was found breeding in the state for the first time by Griffin, who reports a nest with four eggs near Atlanta on June 1. He states [Griffin, 1952]:

In northern Georgia the species has been regarded as a transient only, late spring migrants remaining frequently until the end of May and fall migrants reappearing as early as the middle of July. On June 1, 1952, however, it was my good fortune to discover a nest of this species at the Intrenchment Creek Sewage Disposal Plant six miles southeast of the center of Atlanta in DeKalb County, Georgia. On that date the nest contained four eggs.

The nest itself was merely a depression in the ground lined with grasses. It was located under low weeds and tomato plants which were growing in the dry, pebbly base of one of the unused sludge pits at the Disposal Plant. Near by were other pits filled with sludge and water, a large rock spray bed, and the banks and sand bars of Intrenchment Creek, all of which offered attractive habitat for the species.

During the several trips made to the nesting site only one adult bird was seen. On June 1, the date of discovery of the nest, this adult remained always in close proximity to the nest but would not disclose its exact location while I remained in sight. The nest was finally discovered by leaving and then approaching the vicinity from the opposing direction, thereby flushing the incubating bird which had returned to the nest during my absence. Twice the bird flushed while I was still at a considerable distance, but on my third approach the bird sat closely, flushing only when nearly trodden on and thus enabling me definitely to spot the clump of weeds harboring the nest. I was unable to visit the nest again until June 15, but on that date it was found to be empty. The single adult was very much in evidence however, and its actions indicated the presence of young.

Later on during the summer, on July 5, Rufus Godwin was successful in finding the single adult and one young bird, fairly well feathered, at the edge of one of the near-by sludge pits. On several occasions subsequent to this date in July and early August, I, too, saw a single adult in company with one immature bird. Presumably this immature was hatched at the Disposal Plant. Possibly the other three eggs hatched and the young were unable to survive the intense, sustained heat which gripped the region during mid-June.

Eastern Solitary Sandpiper
Tringa solitaria solitaria   Wilson

GENERAL DISTRIBUTION: Breeds from central Alberta, northern Manitoba, and northern Quebec (Ungava) south to Nebraska, Iowa, Illinois, Indiana, Ohio, and northern Pennsylvania. Winters casually in Florida, and from the West Indies and southern Mexico south to Argentina, Peru, and Bolivia.

STATUS IN GEORGIA: A common spring and fall transient throughout the state.

At Athens [Burleigh, 1938], I found this species a common transient both in the spring and in the fall, being especially numerous early in May and again the latter part of July. Extreme dates of occurrence in the spring are March 28 (1926) and May 29 (1926), and in the fall July 12 (1925) and October 27 (1927). Griffin [MS] lists as migration extremes for the Atlanta region, March 16 (1933) and May 22 (1932), and July 8 (1932) and October 31 (1948). At Mt. Berry, near Rome, Jones [1944] cites but a single record of occurrence, three birds being seen May 11, 1936. At Augusta it is a regular spring and fall transient [Murphey, 1937]. I personally observed six birds there, July 23, 1929, and Howell reports three seen, May 7, 1933. At Macon it has been recorded between the dates of March 21 (1925) and May 21 (1925) and July 27 (1952) and October 1 (1927) [Johnston, MS]. Hopkins [in litt.] cites as extreme dates of occurrence for Fitzgerald, April 1 (1940) and May 16 (1940) and July 18 (1941) and October 18 (1941).

In Grady County, Stoddard [MS] noted the earliest fall transients on July 28 (1946) and July 22 (1950). One bird was seen there as late as the end of November (1947), and the fact that a Solitary Sandpiper was found on Sherwood Plantation on February 25, 1950, would indicate that this species occasionally winters in this part of the state. Grimm [1946] found it a common transient at Hinesville, in Liberty County, extreme dates of occurrence in the spring being April 21 (1943) and May 2 (1943), and in the fall, July 23 (1944) and September 26 (1943). Erichsen [MS] cites as extreme dates of occurrence for Chatham County, March 30 (1918) and May 26 (1929) and July 15 (1935) and October 24 (1926). It has likewise been noted at Columbus, April 28, 1946 [Straw, 1947]; at Americus, April 22, 1942 [Denton, 1942]; and at Cochran, Bleckley County, March 27, 1933 [Denton, 1945].

Family Scolopacidae: SNIPE & SANDPIPERS

HABITS AND RECOGNITION: The Solitary Sandpiper is never seen in flocks, usually single birds, infrequently two or three, being seen at a time. Stagnant woodland pools are preferred to open streams, and sandy beaches are shunned. While Spotted Sandpipers are commonly found along wooded streams, the only other sandpiper likely to be seen in such a situation is the Solitary. From my observations it has no liking for salt water, and while frequently observed about pools and sloughs in fresh-water swamps, it will rarely, if ever, be found in the salt-water marshes along the coast. It is a quiet and rather inconspicuous bird, and normally is easily approached as it feeds at the water's edge, where its slender shape and the bobbing motion of its body will readily distinguish it. If forced to fly, it usually utters a high-pitched "peet, weet" that is suggestive of the call of the Spotted Sandpiper, but its swift and rather erratic flight and conspicuous white tail should leave no question of its identity.

Eastern Willet
Catoptrophorus semipalmatus semipalmatus (Gmelin)

GENERAL DISTRIBUTION: Breeds in Nova Scotia and on Prince Edward Island, on the Atlantic Coast from southern New Jersey to the Bahamas, and on the Gulf Coast to Texas. Winters from the Bahamas and the West Indies south to Brazil and southern Peru.

STATUS IN GEORGIA: A common summer resident on the coast.

Where conditions are suitable, Willets can be found breeding in small colonies on the Georgia coast. Until recent years relatively few occurred on the mainland as conditions there made existence somewhat precarious for such a large, conspicuous bird. Fortunately adequate protection now enables this species to nest in the proximity of man. Practically all the islands have at least a few pairs, and where isolation affords sufficient protection, ten or more pairs can be found nesting together. Nests with eggs have been reported from Sapelo Island, Ossabaw Island, Cabbage Island, St. Catherine's Island, Jekyll Island, Folly Island, Myrtle Island, and Buck Hammock.

Although the majority of the birds nest in May, the breeding season extends from mid-April until well into July. Rossignol's egg catalog records seventy-five nests found on the islands from 1907 through 1937. Of this number, seventy-three held four eggs each, and two, five. His earliest nesting record is of four fresh eggs, April 24 (1937), and his latest, four slightly incubated eggs, June 18 (1923). Erichsen [1921] reports nests holding four eggs each, on Buck Hammock, June 14, 1914, and on Cabbage Island, July 4, 1915, and May 13, 1917. My own experience with this species has been rather limited, but I have found nests with eggs on Ossabaw Island, May 1, 1921; Folly Island, April 30, 1922; Myrtle Island, May 17, 1925; and Cabbage Island, May 10, 1933. Norris reports a nest with four eggs on Sea Island on April 16, 1939, and one with two eggs on St. Simons Island on June 15, 1939; and Hebard one with four eggs in the marsh opposite Jekyll Island, April 25, 1948, and another with four eggs on this same island, June 10, 1952.

The Eastern Willet has been said to winter in small numbers on the Georgia coast, but as no specimens have been taken to substantiate this claim, its status, for the time being, must be considered as that of a summer resident only. Tomkins [1936] states that "it arrives in mid-March and departs soon after the young are able to fly in July to late August."

HABITS AND RECOGNITION: This large, noisy shore bird is a conspicuous part of the bird life of the coastal islands, and one that can scarcely be overlooked. Anyone approaching the site where one or more pairs are nesting will be greeted with their loud, high-pitched notes as the birds fly overhead protesting without pause this intrusion on their breeding grounds. They seem singularly fearless then, and approach so close that the distinctive pattern of their black and white wings can be seen to good advantage. Their vocabulary is rather varied, but the note most commonly heard has been aptly translated as "pill-will-willet," and leaves no doubt in the mind of the observer as to the reason for their being known as willets.

Walter J. Erichsen has made a careful study of the habits of this large wader on the Georgia coast, and his comments are worth quoting in some detail. He writes [Erichsen, 1921]:

> The Willet's haunts are sand banks and mud flats adjacent to sounds and inlets, from which, during low tide, when they are exposed, the birds glean an abundant supply of food. This species breeds abundantly on most of the small coastal islands and hammocks between Tybee and Wassau Islands. The nesting environment is the shell strewn and grassy areas well above high-water mark. It is essential that there be an abundance of vegetation as protection for the eggs and young. The bare wind-swept sandy areas are never used as nesting sites, as their aspect is continually changing, on account of the absence of vegetation necessary to bind the sand to prevent its shifting. When placed among wild oats and other dense beach vegetation, Willets' nests are exceedingly hard to find if the birds are not incubating. The exact location of 90 per cent of the nests I have found was made known to me by flushing the sitting bird. Oftentimes this species makes no nest other than scooping out a shallow depression in the sand to prevent the eggs from rolling. On many occasions, however,

I have found really elaborate nests of soft fibrous grass gathered from localities some distance away. Quite frequently too I find eggs deposited in grassy spots in which situations the birds use the growing grass for nest material, simply bending it down and arranging it in a circular manner. The usual complement of eggs is four, and provided the first laying is hatched and the young successfully reared, the birds will not lay again that season. It is usually necessary, however, for a large percentage of the birds to lay two or three sets of eggs before they are finally successful in raising a brood. Numbers of eggs are destroyed by predatory animals, and unusually high tides wash many away. Willets appear to be greatly concerned when their breeding grounds are invaded. Whenever I visit Cabbage Island, the landing is usually made at a point near the northwestern side, in order to avoid dangerous breakers. Most of the Willets inhabiting the island breed close to this point, and a moment after I set foot upon land the air is filled with gyrating, vociferous birds. As long as a person remains in the vicinity of their nests the birds keep up a continual outcry, circling back and forth overhead, and often hovering on quivering wings. Frequently they alight on some near-by mud flat or sand bar, and gather in groups of three or four.

Western Willet
Catoptrophorus semipalmus inornatus (Brewster)

GENERAL DISTRIBUTION: Breeds from central Oregon, southern Alberta, southern Saskatchewan, and southern Manitoba south to northern California, Utah, Wyoming, Nebraska, and northern Iowa. Winters from northern California, the Gulf Coast, and South Carolina, south to Ecuador, Peru, and the Galápagos Islands.

STATUS IN GEORGIA: A fairly common winter resident on the coast; of accidental occurrence elsewhere in the state.

It has been long recognized that Willets winter regularly on the Georgia coast, but it was not until Tomkins collected a small series of these birds at this season that *inornatus* was definitely recorded in the state. He reports [Tomkins, 1933] that from 1930 through 1932 eight specimens were taken at the mouth of the Savannah River, both in Georgia and in South Carolina, and all of them were found to represent this western race. The earliest specimen was collected in October and the latest in February. On January 7, 1923, I spent the morning on Tybee Island and noted three birds there that day, feeding on a mud bar at the edge of a stretch of open salt marsh. The only record away from the coast is that of a single bird seen on Chase Prairie, in the Okefenokee Swamp, December 3, 1932 [Hebard, 1941].

HABITS AND RECOGNITION: The Western Willet resembles the eastern bird, but is larger, a characteristic impossible to be sure of in the field. It was for this reason that its presence in the state remained in doubt until specimens were taken and satisfactorily identified. In winter plumage it lacks the spotting of the underparts so noticeable in the breeding birds, and is uniformly dull-white beneath. Its haunts in Georgia are essentially the same as those of its eastern relative, which it apparently replaces in winter.

Greater Yellowlegs
Totanus melanoleucus (Gmelin)

GENERAL DISTRIBUTION: Breeds from southern Alaska, southern Mackenzie, and northern Ungava south to southern British Columbia, southern Manitoba, Newfoundland, and the Magdalen Islands. Winters from central California, southern Arizona, the Gulf Coast, and South Carolina south to Patagonia.

STATUS IN GEORGIA: A fairly common transient in the interior of the state and a common transient and winter resident on the coast.

At Athens [Burleigh, 1938], I found this species a fairly common spring transient, but rather scarce in the fall. Extreme dates for occurrence in the spring are March 19 (1928) and May 3 (1927); while in the fall it has been noted but twice, single birds, October 25, 1925, and August 16, 1928. Griffin [1941] lists it merely as a transient in the Atlanta region, giving as migration extremes March 16 (1933) and May 24 (1940) and August 18 (1939) and November 6 (1940). Greene [1933] records it as fairly common in the spring between the dates of March 30 (1930) and April 23 (1933). At Mt. Berry, near Rome, Jones [1944] considers it an uncommon transient, being seen in the spring on April 12, 1936 (a flock of 12), and in the fall on October 30–31, 1935, and October 25, 1940. Murphey [1937] records it as a regular transient at Augusta, his latest date in the spring being May 10 and his earliest date in the fall, August 7. Tait [1946] reports it at Milledgeville on April 19, 1942, and it has been noted at Macon [Johnston, MS] between the dates of March 21 (1933) and May 12 (1928), and July 27 (1952) and October 11 (1952). At Tifton, Norris [letter] reports it in the spring on April 21 and 26, 1932, and in the fall from September 12 through November 27, 1941. In Grady County, Stoddard [MS] noted this large shore bird from October 26 through November 17, 1944, and from March 23 through May 2, 1945.

Family Scolopacidae: SNIPE & SANDPIPERS

Hebard [1941] has one record for the Okefenokee Swamp, a flock of seven birds on Chase Prairie, November 2, 1932. On the coast, Worthington found this species common in winter at the mouth of the Altamaha River, and Helme observed an occasional individual at St. Marys, January 15 and February 8, 1902, and on Cumberland Island in March. Tomkins [1936] states that at the mouth of the Savannah River a few are present during the summer months, and that it is "abundant at other seasons." Erichsen [MS] cites as typical dates of occurrence in Chatham County during the summer months single birds seen June 19, 1915, June 24, 1917, July 11, 1920, June 19, 1926, and July 10, 1931.

HABITS AND RECOGNITION: This is a shore bird that is not easily overlooked. Always alert and on the lookout, it makes its presence known the minute an intruder appears. Its alarm notes are loud and ringing and serve as a warning to any other birds within hearing, one result being that duck hunting in a marsh where yellowlegs are feeding is not only impracticable, but almost impossible. As a consequence this species has acquired the name of "tattler," and is looked upon with considerable disfavor by the average hunter. It is one of the larger of the shore birds and is easily recognized by its slender appearance and long yellow legs. In flight, it displays a conspicuous white tail. It is seemingly less sociable than the sandpipers with which it associates, for it is not uncommon to see single birds feeding on a mud flat or at the edge of a pool in an open marsh, and flocks rarely exceed eight or ten individuals. With its long legs and relatively long bill it is able to feed in several inches of water, and shallow pools are favored spots both in migration and during the winter months. Its food consists of small fish, crustaceans, and the larger aquatic insects, and these it secures with apparent ease as it wades rapidly and nimbly in water often as deep as its legs are long. It is impartial concerning fresh-water or salt-water marshes, but has no liking for the open ocean beaches and is rarely seen there.

Lesser Yellowlegs
Totanus flavipes   (Gmelin)

GENERAL DISTRIBUTION: Breeds from the upper Yukon Valley in Alaska, northern Mackenzie, northern Manitoba, and northern Quebec (Ungava) south to northern British Columbia, southern Alberta, southern Saskatchewan, and central Quebec. Winters in Argentina, Patagonia, and Chile, and casually north to Louisiana, Georgia, and the Bahamas.

STATUS IN GEORGIA: A common spring transient and a local and uncommon fall transient in the interior of the state. A common spring and fall transient on the coast, of casual occurrence there during the winter and to a lesser extent throughout the summer.

At Athens [Burleigh, 1938], I found the Lesser Yellowlegs a common spring transient, but scarce and rarely observed in the fall. In the spring, it was most numerous in the latter part of April and the first week in May, flocks in which there were ten to twenty or more individuals being frequently noted. Extreme dates for occurrence at this time of year are March 21 (1928) and May 13 (1925). In the fall it was recorded but three times, single birds, October 16, 1927, and September 6 and 27, 1929. Griffin [1941] gives as migration extremes for the Atlanta region, March 15 (1931) and May 18 (1932), and July 23 (1939) and October 1 (1938), while Johnston [1945] reports this species at Atlanta on the unusually early date of March 4, 1944, and in the fall on October 15, 1944. At Mt. Berry, near Rome, Jones [1944] observed it only in the spring, and considered it a rather uncommon transient. His extreme dates of occurrence are April 8 (1936) and April 12 (1936). At Augusta it is reported by Murphey [1937] as a common transient both in the spring and in the fall. I personally observed two birds there on July 23, 1929.

Tait [1946] has one record for Milledgeville, April 19, 1942, while at Macon [Johnston, MS] extreme dates of occurrence are March 16 (1952) and May 12 (1928) and July 27 (1952) and October 11 (1952). There are records for Baker County, July 25, 1950 and April 17, 1951 [Hopkins, 1951]; Grady County, March 15 through May 5, 1945, and September 1, 1947 [Stoddard, MS]; and Chase Prairie, in the Okefenokee Swamp, November 2 and 25, 1932, and December 28, 1932 [Hebard, 1941]. On the coast, Hoxie recorded it at Savannah on August 18, 1908, and May 17 and 28, 1910. Tomkins [1936] reports it at the mouth of the Savannah River as "common in spring and fall, occasionally winters, a few seen in summer." He noted several there on January 10 and 27, 1933, and fully one hundred individuals on February 16, 1933. Pearson [1922] observed seventy on Cumberland Island on May 3 and 4, 1921. I saw three of these yellowlegs on Tybee Island, December 15, 1933.

HABITS AND RECOGNITION: The Lesser Yellowlegs is in almost every respect a miniature of the Greater Yellowlegs. In fact, so closely does it resemble that species in appearance and actions that it can easily be misidentified, for, in the field, size is often rather deceptive, and under certain conditions a bird will look larger than it really is. It is apparently more abundant, or possibly more gregarious, than the Greater Yellowlegs; since it is generally in flocks, it is exceptional to see single birds at any time. Its slender build and long yellow legs will readily distinguish it from the other shore birds, and its characteristic notes soon reveal its presence in any open marsh or mud flat where a flock is feeding. Although always alert and easily alarmed, it is not noticeably shy, and can usually be approached if a little caution is exercised, and watched as it wades in the shallow water where it prefers to feed. When standing quietly at the edge of a pool, it will bob its entire body in a manner unlike that of any other shore bird it associates with, a habit distinct enough to quickly identify it. Its food consists largely of insects which are picked up from the surface of the water. To a lesser degree small fish and crustaceans are eaten, and these seem to be procured with little effort.

American Knot
Calidris canutus rufa   (Wilson)

GENERAL DISTRIBUTION: Breeds from northern Ellesmere Island east to northern Greenland, and west to, possibly, Point Barrow, Alaska. Winters in South America south to Patagonia, and casually north to Georgia.

STATUS IN GEORGIA: A common spring transient and a fairly common fall transient on the coast, and of casual occurrence there during both summer and winter.

Worthington took specimens on Sapelo Island, November 23 and December 19, 1887, and at the mouth of the Altamaha River, January 15, February 18, and April 14, 1890. Another specimen was taken in Chatham County, May 16, 1907. Rossignol noted three birds near Savannah, May 29, 1911. There is a record of a bird striking the Tybee Light on September 24, 1924, and Howell reports several small flocks on Tybee Island, May 10, 1933. I saw two birds on Oysterbed Island, near the mouth of the Savannah River, on June 14, 1927. Tomkins [1936] states that at the Savannah River entrance this species is "common in spring migration, April last through June, less common in fall (October)." He has noted it on many dates in May, on October 31, 1931, and on July 15, 1933. Woodward [1949] found the knot on Sea Island February 25, through April 6, 1946–48, and notes "as many as 300 birds seen in a flock April 3, 1948." Occasional nonbreeding individuals are said to remain throughout the summer months.

HABITS AND RECOGNITION: Although a common transient in Georgia, the Knot is so restricted in its seasonal movements to the outer beaches that it is one of the less familiar of the shore birds occurring in the state. It is a medium-sized sandpiper with a chunky appearance that is emphasized by its short, yellowish-green legs and short, rather stout bill. In the spring it can be readily recognized by its reddish underparts, but in the fall and winter these are a dull white, so that the Knot is one of the least conspicuous of the shore birds. In migration it occurs in small flocks, which nor-

257

FLORIDA BARRED OWL

Strix varia georgica

Among the most enjoyable of woodland sounds in Georgia is the whooping
and hollering of Barred Owls. At Sherwood Plantation the birds lived
principally in the swamp woods, but I saw them occasionally in the pines.
One that I "squeaked up" into a big magnolia tree gave me the idea for
this painting. I had a living model, which I tethered at my end of the porch.
It was docile most of the time, but when Rip, the setter, sniffed at it,
or the children who were watching came too close, it puffed up, popped
its bill, and swayed menacingly from side to side.

mally feed on open beaches and exposed mud flats and remain compact without scattering over all the feeding grounds that are available. This habit, together with rather deliberate movements suggestive of a plover, separates the Knot from other shore birds with which it associates. Its food consists largely of small crustaceans and mollusks, which it procures by probing in the wet sand at the water's edge. Only infrequently does it seem to pick up morsels of food exposed on the surface.

Purple Sandpiper
Erolia maritima (Brunnich)

GENERAL DISTRIBUTION: Breeds from Melville Island, northern Elles-mere Island, and northern Greenland south to southern Baffin Island and southern Greenland; also in Spitzbergen, Franz Josef Land, Novaya Zem-lya, Norway, Russia, Siberia, Iceland, and the Faroë Islands. Winters from southern Greenland south to Long Island, and casually to the Bermudas, Georgia, and Florida; also in the British Isles, northern Azores, and the Mediterranean and Baltic seas.

STATUS IN GEORGIA: Apparently of regular occurrence on the coast during the winter months.

Tomkins [1950] reported this species for the first time in the state, noting that he had collected two females on Tybee Island, December 26, 1949. He saw a flock of five that day, eleven at the same spot on January 2, 1950, and ten on January 7, 1950.

A specimen in the Sennett Collection, American Museum of Natural History, labeled "Georgia, March 5, 1874," but otherwise with no definite locality, is now known to have been taken in New Brunswick, Canada [Amadon, 1949].

HABITS AND RECOGNITION: The Purple Sandpiper is the hardiest of the shore birds, wintering farther north than any other species, and occurring only casually during the winter months south of New England. Its ability to withstand the rigors of a northern winter is emphasized by its prefer-ence for large rocks and sloping rocky ledges and jetties that are constant-ly washed by the surf. Open, sandy beaches are not to its liking, and only rarely will it be found in such a prosaic situation. Tomkins' comments on the circumstances under which he found this species on Tybee Island illus-trate the habitat chosen by the Purple Sandpiper in Georgia, and are well worth quoting in detail:

It is a pleasure to report two females . . . collected on Tybee Is-land on December 26, 1949, from a group of five resting with other shore birds high on the sand over a high tide that completely covered the jetties at the mouth of the Savannah River a mile or so to the northward. On the following day three, possibly the remaining ones, were again resting in the same place.

Having considered the jetties the only likely place and planned for a long time to inspect them some time in mid-winter for this species, I was a little chagrined a week later (January 2, 1950) to find a group of ten feeding on one of the shore protection groins half-way down the front beach, and a single bird a mile farther down. Again on January 7, 1950 there were seven feeding on the first mentioned groin, and three on another one, though in neither case was it possible to inspect all the groins along the beach. The embarrassing thing about it was that these groins have not been looked over very carefully in other winters.

At any rate, we have a considerable number of these northern sandpipers staying and feeding over quite a period this winter. It is certainly not an accidental occurrence, and not caused by too cold weather in their usual range, for it would not be necessary for them to come clear to Georgia to find some relief from the New England climate. I am inclined to postulate a migration previously unnoticed, to suitable habitat, but only a great many observations will clear that up. It is definitely in order to examine all wave washed jetties and breakwaters in these South Atlantic States.

The birds feed with the turnstones, and resemble dark short-legged Red-backed Sandpipers, except that the purplish back and striping on the sides, the yellowish legs and yellowish basal half of the bill, clearly distinguish them. When feeding on the sides of the steel and timber groins, they often feed on the wing, butterfly-like.

That the Purple Sandpiper now apparently occurs regularly on the coast of Georgia during the winter months is suggested by Tomkins [1952]:

The first specimen of the Purple Sandpiper (*Erolia maritima*) for the state of Georgia was collected on December 26, 1949, and duly recorded in The Oriole (15:7,1950). During the rest of that winter I found some of these birds on five occasions up to February 22 (1950), eleven being the greatest number seen on any one day. The next winter the first ones were found on Christmas Day (1950), and I found from two to seventeen at a time on eight different days up to March 3 (1951). The species appeared again on November 3, and I saw them on eight different days to April 5 (1952). On December 17 a group estimated to contain thirty Purples was seen on one groin.

There were visits on which no birds were seen, perhaps because high tides covered the groins, or because the seas broke over them, driving the birds to more sheltered beaches. It was not always possible to examine all the groins along this beach, and some birds may have been missed. It is a forty-mile drive down and back, so it was not possible to make regular checks at low tide, but these data are considered sufficient to validate the species as a regular winter visitor to the locality.

Mr. Francis M. Uhler, of the Fish and Wildlife Service, has furnished an analysis of the contents of the stomachs of four birds collected on December 20, 1951. The birds had eaten small mussels, snails, one species of small cancroid crab, and considerable quantities of "tender green marine algae resembling Ulva." The algal contents of the four stomachs was 5, 42, 50, and 60% respectively.

The most recent record for this species in Georgia is that of a single bird seen on Tybee Island on the unusually early date of September 14, 1952, and two birds seen at the same spot two weeks later, on September 28 [Tomkins, letter].

Pectoral Sandpiper
Erolia melanotos (Vieillot)

GENERAL DISTRIBUTION: Breeds on the Arctic Coast from northern Siberia east to northeastern Mackenzie, and possibly to northern Ungava. Winters in South America from Peru and Bolivia south to Argentina and Chile.

STATUS IN GEORGIA: A fairly common spring and fall transient both on the coast and in the interior of the state.

At Athens [Burleigh, 1938], this species was noted only in the open Sandy Creek bottoms, but here it was fairly plentiful in both spring and fall. It was especially numerous in early April when small flocks were frequently observed. Extreme dates for occurrence in the spring are March 25 (1928) and April 15 (1928); and in the fall, July 26 (1926) and August 3 (1929). Griffin [1941] cites as migration extremes for the Atlanta region, March 15 (1931) and May 5 (1940), and July 23 (1939) and October 21 (1932). At Augusta, Murphey [1937] states that the Pectoral Sandpiper was formerly very abundant, "great flocks appearing in the wet grasslands about September 10th to 15th. These flocks persisted from 1891 to 1897 and rather abruptly disappeared." He noted small flocks in recent years and held the opinion that this species has gradually increased in numbers since 1929. Denton [1942] observed a flock of eight birds at Augusta on

November 1, 1942. At Macon [Johnston, MS] there is one spring record, March 28, 1931, while in the fall it has been seen between the dates of July 27 (1952) and October 11 (1952). Norris and Hopkins [1953] cite as extreme dates of occurrence in the fall July 29 (1940) (Fitzgerald) and September 2 (1946) (Tifton). In Grady County, Stoddard [MS] has noted this species but once, a single bird on August 16 and 17, 1945.

On the coast, Tomkins [1936] considers this species "a spring and fall migrant, more common in March-May, less common in August." It has been reported from St. Marys on April 21, 1904, and from Chatham County [Erichsen, MS], between the dates of March 16 (1919) and April 27 (1930), and July 19 (1914) and September 27 (1930). Specimens were taken by Worthington at Broro Neck, March 22 and 26, 1889, and by Helme on Cumberland Island, April 1 and 3, 1903.

HABITS AND RECOGNITION: The Pectoral Sandpiper is a bird of the marshy meadows rather than the open beaches, feeding preferably in short grass, or at the edges of open pools or sloughs, and well deserves the name of "grass snipe" by which it is commonly known. Its movements are rather deliberate as it probes in the mud, and when approached it is likely to crouch, motionless, depending upon its protective coloration for concealment. It frequently will not fly until almost stepped on, and then will flush suddenly and depart with a swift, erratic flight which suggests that of a snipe. On such occasions it utters a note that has been aptly compared to the syllables "kriek kriek," but as a rule it is a quiet and inconspicuous bird. In appearance, it is a medium-sized sandpiper, with a heavily streaked breast that contrasts sharply with the white of its other underparts; it has short greenish-yellow legs. Its food is almost entirely insects which are secured either from the marsh grass or by probing in soft mud.

White-rumped Sandpiper
Erolia fuscicollis (Vieillot)

GENERAL DISTRIBUTION: Breeds on the Arctic Coast from northern Alaska and Mackenzie east to Southampton and Baffin islands. Winters in South America from Paraguay and Argentina to the Falkland Islands.

STATUS IN GEORGIA: A rare transient in the interior of the state, and apparently an erratic but at times a not uncommon transient on the coast.

For the interior of the state there are at present seven records. At Atlanta a single bird was seen on the South River, May 21, 1932 [Eyles and Giles, 1935], and a flock of four was noted at the edge of DeKalb County, on May 17, 1952 [Griffin, 1952c]. At Augusta a specimen was taken May 25, 1935 [Murphey, 1937], six were seen June 12, 1942, and a single bird

May 7, 1945 [Thomas, 1945], three were observed and one collected September 1, 1946 [Denton, 1946], and one bird was seen and collected September 12, 1952 [Denton, letter].

On the coast, it was first noted on May 16, 1888, when Worthington took a specimen on Sapelo Island. In 1910, Hoxie observed two near Savannah on May 17 and four on October 9. Tomkins [1949] reports an unusual concentration of these small sandpipers on Hutchinsons Island, one and one-half miles from Savannah, in 1949. He recorded about one hundred on May 14; many on May 19, eight to ten on May 29, and one on August 14. On September 9, 1950, and again on November 12, 1951, he observed several near Savannah.

HABITS AND RECOGNITION: The White-rumped Sandpiper is one of several smaller sandpipers found on sandy beaches and exposed mud flats in the late spring and fall months. It is usually seen in small flocks that feed with characteristic restlessness near the water's edge, probing in the soft sand or mud for any marine life that is present. When quiet, it is not easy to identify, but in flight the white rump is a conspicuous field mark that will clearly distinguish it from the other species with which it associates. In breeding plumage, the upper parts are brown, but in the fall this is replaced by gray, which materially changes the appearance of the bird. It is normally quiet and unsuspicious and can be approached with little difficulty, but if alarmed, it displays a swift, undulating flight that soon takes it out of sight. In the air it utters a note which Nichols [1920] calls "a squeaky mouse-like jeet," and which is quite unlike that of any other shore bird.

Least Sandpiper
Erolia minutilla (Vieillot)

GENERAL DISTRIBUTION: Breeds from northwestern Alaska east through Mackenzie to Newfoundland, and south to southern Yukon, the Magdalen Islands, and Nova Scotia. Winters from Oregon, Texas, and North Carolina south through the West Indies and Central America to Brazil and Patagonia.

STATUS IN GEORGIA: A fairly common transient in the interior of the state and a common transient and winter resident on the coast. Non-breeding birds occur in small numbers on the coast throughout the summer.

At Athens [Burleigh, 1938], this species was a fairly common transient both in spring and in fall, being most frequently seen the first week in May and again the latter part of July. Extreme dates for its occurrence in the spring are April 1 (1927) and May 24 (1925), and in the fall, July

11 (1925) and September 27 (1929). Griffin cites as migration extremes for the Atlanta region, April 3 (1954) and May 28 (1932), and July 16 (1932) and September 18 (1938). At Augusta [Murphey, 1937], it was found to be a fairly common transient, frequently "the margins of grassy pools, flat marsh land, the margins of clay pits, and sand bars in the river, with equal impartiality." I myself observed a small flock of four birds there on July 23, 1929. At Macon, Johnston gives as extreme dates of occurrence April 15 (1950) and May 19 (1934), and August 13 (1933) and September 25 (1927); at Fitzgerald, it has been noted on August 27, 1940, and at Tifton, September 2, 1946 [Norris and Hopkins, 1953]; and in Grady County, [Stoddard, MS], September 2 and 17, 1945 and September 3, 1947.

On the coast, Tomkins [1936] considers it "a permanent resident, commonest in spring (April-May) and in fall (August-October)." It was reported from Cabbage Island, Wassaw Sound, on July 23, 1908, and I saw a flock of fifteen birds on Oysterbed Island on June 1, 1929. Specimens have been taken on Sapelo Island, April 27, 1888, and at the mouth of the Altamaha River, January 6, February 19, and April 19, 1890.

HABITS AND RECOGNITION: As its name implies, this is the smallest of our shore birds. It is often found on sandy beaches, but seems to prefer mud flats in the salt marshes and the edges of pools and stretches of short grass in the open fresh-water marshes. Here small flocks can be seen actively searching for the insect life that forms the bulk of their food, apparently so intent on what they are doing that it is often possible to approach within a few feet of them without causing them to fly. Under such circumstances they can be easily recognized, for they are the only very small sandpipers with noticeably greenish-yellow legs. Both the Semipalmated and Western Sandpipers are almost as small, and superficially are somewhat like the Least Sandpiper in appearance, but both have distinctly black legs. Few birds are more sociable by nature, for almost invariably they are found in flocks, single birds being rarely, if ever, noted. Such flocks scatter when feeding, but if forced to fly, all take wing at once and again become a compact group. In flight they utter a note they have in common with the other small sandpipers, and which gives them the name of "peeps."

Red-backed Dunlin
Erolia alpina pacifica   (Coues)

GENERAL DISTRIBUTION: Breeds on the northern coast of Siberia, and from the mouth of the Yukon east through northeastern Mackenzie to northeastern Ungava. Winters on the Pacific Coast from southern British Columbia to southern Lower California, and on the Atlantic and Gulf coasts from New Jersey to Florida and Texas.

264

Family *Scolopacidae:* SNIPE & SANDPIPERS

STATUS IN GEORGIA: A common transient and winter resident on the coast and of casual occurrence in the interior of the state.

Away from the coast, this species has to date been reported from but two localities. Hebard [1941] records two birds killed in the Okefenokee Swamp: one on Chase Prairie, November 2, 1932, and the other at Coffee Bay, November 30, 1936. Denton [1942] observed a single bird on a mud flat at Augusta on November 1 and 5, 1942, and three days later, on the eighth, found it dead at this same spot. Belger [1950] collected a female there on one of the local brickyard ponds, November 6, 1949.

On the coast, Worthington reported the Red-backed Dunlin on Sapelo Island, where two specimens were taken May 16, 1888, and at the mouth of the Altamaha River during the winter of 1889–90, specimens being collected January 12 and April 23.

Rossignol observed a small flock near Savannah, May 29, 1911, and I personally noted a flock of fifteen in the open salt marsh there on January 7, 1923. I also found the birds plentiful on the ocean beach of Blackbeard Island, January 25, 1931. Tomkins [1936] considers it "a common fall and spring transient, winters in smaller numbers." He recorded its arrival in the fall, at the mouth of the Savannah River, on October 12, 1929, October 21, 1930, October 8, 1933, and November 18, 1934; and noted it there in the spring as late as May 30, 1931. Erichsen [MS] cites as extreme dates of occurrence for Chatham County, September 10 (1924) and May 23 (1934).

HABITS AND RECOGNITION: The Red-backed Dunlin is one of the hardiest of the shore birds, appearing in Georgia in the late fall when most of the other species have come and gone, and remaining throughout the winter on the beaches and on the mud flats in the marshes. It is possibly the commonest sandpiper seen on the coast during the winter months, scattered flocks of varying size occurring wherever conditions are suitable. Its food consists largely of small mollusks and crustaceans and the adults and larvae of various aquatic insects, and these it secures by probing in the soft sand or mud with its long, curved bill. It is not averse to feeding in shallow water, and a flock nimbly wading in a pool left by the receding tide is a frequent sight.

The Red-back is rather unsuspicious and easily approached, so little difficulty is experienced in noting its characters. It is a medium-sized sandpiper, with a stout appearance that is emphasized by its rather short dark-colored legs and somewhat long and slightly down-curved bill. In breeding plumage it is unmistakable, for the upperparts are reddish, and the belly has a conspicuous black spot on each side. In the winter, it is grayish brown above and dull white beneath, but the length of its bill in comparison to its size should distinguish it from the other shore birds with which it will be found. In flight it utters a mellow note that most observers agree suggests the sound, "purre."

Interior Dowitcher
Limnodromus griseus hendersoni   (Rowan)

GENERAL DISTRIBUTION: Breeds from the west coast of Hudson Bay west to central Alberta, possibly east central British Columbia, and north to Great Slave Lake. Winters from Florida (casually North Carolina) and the West Indies south to central Brazil and Peru.

STATUS IN GEORGIA: A common transient and uncommon winter resident on the coast and of casual occurrence elsewhere in the state.

In the interior of the state it has been noted at but six localities. There is a record for Richmond County, September, 1894 [Murphey, 1937]; a number were observed on Chase Prairie, in the Okefenokee Swamp, February 3, 1931 [Hebard, 1941]; at Atlanta, in the South River section, one bird was seen August 25 and 27, 1932 [Greene, 1939], and two on August 19, 1939 [Griffin, 1939]; in Grady County, a single bird was noted April 2, 1945 [Stoddard, MS]; at Lake Arrowhead, twelve miles north of Rome, one bird was seen August 28, 1949 [Griffin, 1950]; and at Macon it was reported September 13 and 14, 1953 (Rohwer).

On the coast, this Dowitcher has been reported in the spring in McIntosh County, April 23, 1890; on Cumberland Island, March 12, 1903; and at Savannah, May 11, 1910. Hoxie first observed it in the fall at Savannah on August 1, 1908; and by August 5 numerous flocks were present. Tomkins [1936] states that at the mouth of the Savannah River it is "abundant in spring (April-June) and in fall (July-September). A few remain in winter and summer." Erichsen [MS] confirms the presence of this species in Chatham County during the winter, single birds or small flocks having been seen then at infrequent intervals. His dates of occurrence include the following: January 10, 1915; January 7, 1923; January 30, 1924; November 28, 1926; December 6, 1931; and December 24, 1940. Woodward [1949] reports it on Sea Island the first week in April (1946-48).

Some of the sight records here listed may refer to races other than *hendersoni*. However, since *hendersoni* has proved to be the only race as yet found in the state, it seems desirable, as well as logical, to cite them here. Johnston [1952] lists (Table 1) eight specimens of dowitchers collected in Georgia. Two of these, a juvenile male taken by Rossignol in Chatham County August 12, 1908, and an adult male taken by Denton on Sea Island, Glynn County, September 3, 1949, he identified as *hendersoni*, and this identification has been confirmed by Pitelka. The remaining six could not be determined subspecifically, their characters being intermediate and difficult to evaluate correctly. He further lists (Table 2) nine additional specimens of *griseus* from Georgia identified by Pitelka [1950]. Six of these—three from McIntosh County (April 7, 22, and 23, 1890) and three from Chatham County (May 16, 1907 and April 24, 1938)—are *hendersoni,* the remaining three being undetermined subspecifically. It is of interest to note that the nominate race, *griseus,* has yet to be found in the state.

HABITS AND RECOGNITION: The Dowitcher is essentially a bird of the mud flats and open salt marshes bordering the coast, rarely feeding on the sandy beaches favored by the other shore birds. Highly gregarious by nature, it is found in compact flocks throughout much of the year, and these are generally associated with other sandpipers. Its food consists largely of small mollusks and other invertebrates procured by probing with its long bill in the soft mud. In feeding, the bill is held perpendicularly and pushed with rapid motions to its full length, these actions then being quite distinct from those of other sandpipers. It is normally a quite tame and unsuspicious bird, and being easily approached, can be recognized with little difficulty. In appearance it is a stout, medium-sized sandpiper, with a bill that seems abnormally long for its size, and rather short greenish-yellow legs. When it is forced to fly, the conspicuous white rump and tail aid further in identifying it. In full breeding plumage it has conspicuously reddish underparts, but in the fall these are dull gray.

Long-billed Dowitcher
Limnodromus scolopaceus (Say)

GENERAL DISTRIBUTION: Breeds along the western and northern coasts of Alaska, from Hooper Bay and the Kashunik River north to Point Barrow, and east along the Arctic Coast to the Anderson River. Winters from central California and the Gulf Coast through Mexico to Chiapas and Guatemala.

STATUS IN GEORGIA: At present known only from two specimens.

There is a specimen in the U. S. National Museum, taken by Joseph LeConte, with merely "Georgia" on the label; and a male in the collection of the University of Georgia, taken by Hopkins at Newton, in Baker County, on April 17, 1951. The identification of both as *scolopaceus* has been confirmed by Pitelka [Johnston, 1952].

HABITS AND RECOGNITION: The Long-billed Dowitcher is slightly larger than the eastern bird, with a longer bill and more extensive reddish coloration of the underparts when in full breeding plumage. These characters are difficult to determine in the field, so further collecting will be necessary before the actual status of *scolopaceus* in the state can be determined. Its habits appear to differ in no way from other dowitchers, with which it can be found feeding on the mud flats.

Stilt Sandpiper
Micropalama himantopus   (Bonaparte)

GENERAL DISTRIBUTION: Breeds from the mouth of the Mackenzie River east to Hudson Bay. Winters in South America south to Uruguay and Chile, and casually north to Mexico and the Gulf Coast.

STATUS IN GEORGIA: A casual spring and fall transient on the coast, and of accidental occurrence in the interior of the state.

The first definite record for the state is that of a specimen taken by Helme on Cumberland Island, April 19, 1905. It apparently was not recorded again until September 3, 1941, when Tomkins [1941] took a specimen on Long Island, Chatham County.

That under favorable conditions this species may occur on the coast during migration in some numbers is shown by Tomkins' experience at Savannah in 1949 [Tomkins, 1949]:

> On Wednesday 11 May, 1949, I found an interesting group of shore birds, among which were one or two Stilt Sandpipers (*Micropalama himantopus*), in a new borrow pit on Hutchinsons Island, Georgia, across the river and one and a half miles from the City. On the following Saturday, 14 May, there were at least 34 Stilt Sandpipers. . . . A third visit to the locality on 19 May revealed only two Stilt Sandpipers. . . . In order to check on the occurrence of southward migrants, two visits were made to the locality in August, on the 14th and 27th. The first time there were 4 Stilt Sandpipers, and the second time I counted at least 11. . . . It was not possible to make other observations as dredging operations altered the habitat considerably. Probably this is the largest number of Stilt Sandpipers to be reported over quite a portion of the Southeast in many years. Apparently the species still migrates through here in some numbers, and will tarry if they find suitable habitat, which seems to be a brackish or fresh water pool of fairly constant level.

What is apparently the latest fall record for the state is that of three birds seen by Tomkins at Savannah on September 9, 1950. In 1952 [Tomkins, letter], a single bird was seen for the first time that fall at Savannah on August 26, and four birds on September 7. The only record away from the coast is that of a flock of five birds seen at Augusta on September 8, 1944 [Denton, 1944].

HABITS AND RECOGNITION: Superficially the Stilt Sandpiper resembles the Lesser Yellowlegs, for it is almost the same size, and has long legs and a slender body. However, the legs are dull olive-green rather than bright yellow, a character at once evident if the bird is seen within reasonable range. It is apparently not a common bird anywhere, but it is possible that, as it frequently associates with the Lesser Yellowlegs, it has been confused with this species and has been, to some extent at least, overlooked. It is essentially a bird of the open marshes and mud flats exposed by low tide, and in such spots feeds commonly in the shallow pools left by the receding water rather than on the soft mud. With its long legs it is able to wade in water up to three inches in depth, and as it feeds, its entire head and neck are frequently out of sight as it probes in the bottom of the pool. In contrast to the other shore birds with which it associates, its movements appear calm and unhurried, and any small flocks that are encountered will be found to remain in a rather compact group.

Semipalmated Sandpiper
Ereunetes pusillus   (Linnaeus)

GENERAL DISTRIBUTION: Breeds from northeastern Siberia and the Arctic Coast of North America south to the mouth of the Yukon and to Hudson Bay and east to southwestern Baffin Island and northern Labrador. Winters from South Carolina and the Gulf Coast through the West Indies and Central America to Patagonia.

STATUS IN GEORGIA: A common spring and fall transient and uncommon winter resident on the coast, and an uncommon transient in the interior of the state.

At Athens [Burleigh, 1938], I found this species a rather scarce transient. Single birds were noted in the spring on May 14, 1925; May 6 and May 22, 1926; May 14, 1927; and May 11, 1928; and but once during the fall migration, July 21, 1927. Griffin [1941] lists it as an uncommon spring and fall transient in the Atlanta region, giving as migration extremes May 5 (1929) and June 1 (1940), and August 12 (1939) and September 18 (1932). At Augusta, Murphey [1937] considers it a common transient; his latest spring record is May 29. A specimen in his collection was taken in Richmond County, May 25, 1935. It has been recorded at Macon, May 14, 1932, and May 6, 1934; at Fitzgerald, May 16, 1940, and in Irwin County, September 1, 1940, and May 4, 1941 [Norris and Hopkins, 1953]; in Grady

County, May 5, 1945 [Stoddard, MS]; and on Chase Prairie, in the Okefenokee Swamp, February 3, 1931 [Hebard, 1941].

On the coast, Pearson [1922] noted small flocks on Cumberland Is-
land, May 2 to 6, 1921; and Tomkins [1936] states that at the mouth of the
Savannah River the Semipalmated Sandpiper is "abundant in spring and
fall, some through the summer, an occasional specimen at least in winter."
It has been recorded at Savannah, May 22, 1910, and May 28, 1932, and
July 19, 1929; and there are specimens at the University of Georgia, at
Athens, taken in Chatham County, September 11, 1908, and October 9,
1909. Woodward [1949] reports this species common on Sea Island from
January through April, 1946–48.

HABITS AND RECOGNITION: The Semipalmated Sandpiper is unquestionably one of the commonest and most frequently observed sandpipers on
the Georgia coast. It normally occurs in flocks, and throughout much of the
year can be seen on open beaches or exposed mud flats, feeding close to
the water's edge. Here it follows the rise and fall of the surf, running seaward as the water recedes and retreating with equal speed as the waves
surge toward the shore, in the meantime probing rapidly in the sand with
its short stout bill. It gives the impression of being more energetic in its
actions than most of the other shore birds with which it associates and of
rarely hesitating in its pursuit of the marine crustaceans and small mollusks that form the bulk of its food.

If forced to fly, the flocks remain compact and show a uniformity of
movement that is approached by few other birds. Wheeling and turning
with surprising co-ordination, they show alternately their white breasts
and dark backs, creating the illusion of appearing and then disappearing
as they put a safe distance between themselves and the intruder. Being
usually tame and unsuspicious, flocks can be approached with little difficulty and readily identified. In size this species is hard to distinguish from
the Least Sandpiper, but differs in being grayer above, in having black
rather than greenish-yellow legs, and in having a distinctly stouter bill.

Western Sandpiper
Ereunetes mauri   Cabanis

GENERAL DISTRIBUTION: Breeds on the coast of Alaska from the Yukon
delta to Point Barrow. Winters on the Pacific Coast from Washington to
Venezuela and Peru, on the Gulf Coast, and on the Atlantic Coast from
North Carolina to Florida.

STATUS IN GEORGIA: A common spring and fall transient and winter resident on the coast and of casual occurrence elsewhere in the state during
the fall migration.

Apparently the first definite record for the state is that of a specimen, now in the U. S. National Museum, taken in Liberty County about 1859 by Professor Joseph LeConte. Another specimen was collected by Worthington on Egg Island, April 16, 1890, and two by Helme at St. Marys, February 16, 1903. It was reported at Savannah by Hoxie, September 11, 1908, and by Perry, October 3, 1909. Tomkins [1936] states that at the mouth of the Savannah River it is "abundant from September through May, perhaps at other seasons also." Woodward [1949] found it common on Sea Island from January through April, 1946–48.

In the interior of the state, it has been noted on but few occasions. A female was collected at Lake Kirota, on the State College of Agriculture campus on July 27, 1928 [Burleigh, 1938]; and Greene [1933] observed single birds at Atlanta, August 27 and September 5, 1932. Griffin [1951] reports ten at Atlanta, September 1, 1950, and a single bird collected there two days later. There is a single record for Macon, September 10, 1955 (Johnston).

HABITS AND RECOGNITION: The Western Sandpiper is so nearly like the Semipalmated Sandpiper in fall and winter plumage and in actions that it is extremely difficult to identify in the field. The most obvious character is the longer, stouter bill, but unless the two species are feeding together and a direct comparison is possible, it is not easy to determine this satisfactorily. A more brownish, less grayish wash to the upperparts of the Western Sandpiper is a more constant character, but only discernible by critical comparison of the birds in the hand. Furthermore, there is considerable overlap between the two species in this character. In breeding plumage, the Western Sandpiper is more rufous above and more heavily streaked on the breast, but here, again, direct comparison is desirable. Accordingly, although a common transient on the Georgia coast, this species has been largely overlooked and so has been recorded by few observers. Its actions are similar in every respect to those of the Semipalmated Sandpiper. It occurs in flocks that feed on the open beaches and exposed mud flats, following the surf as it recedes and nimbly picking up the small crustaceans and mollusks that can be found at the water's edge. It is a gentle, unsuspicious bird, and it is a source of satisfaction that with protection it has increased noticeably in recent years.

Buff-breasted Sandpiper
Tringites subruficollis (Vieillot)

GENERAL DISTRIBUTION: Breeds along the Arctic Coast from northern Alaska to northern Mackenzie. Winters in Argentina and Uruguay.

STATUS IN GEORGIA: At present known as a rare fall transient on the coast.

It was first recorded in the state on September 29, 1951, when a male was collected at Savannah by Ivan R. Tomkins as it fed with other shore birds at the edge of a shallow pool [Tomkins, 1951b]. The following year [Tomkins, 1952b] two additional specimens were collected at this same spot, a female on September 18 and a male on September 20.

HABITS AND RECOGNITION: This distinctive shore bird migrates to a large extent in the Mississippi Valley and occurs only casually on the Atlantic Coast. Consequently, it is doubtful that it is very often found in Georgia. It is a medium-sized sandpiper with buffy underparts that will, when seen at reasonable range, distinguish it from its associates. Its habits are much like those of the Pectoral Sandpiper, and it prefers to feed in open marshes where the grass is short, avoiding the mud flats and open beaches. It will usually permit a close approach and, if alarmed, will frequently attempt to escape by hiding in the grass rather than by taking flight.

Marbled Godwit
Limosa fedoa (Linnaeus)

GENERAL DISTRIBUTION: Breeds from southern Alberta and southern Manitoba south to South Dakota. Winters from California, the Gulf Coast, and Georgia south to Ecuador and Peru.

STATUS IN GEORGIA: A not uncommon transient and winter resident on the coast.

It has been observed between the dates of August 28 (1931) and June 27 (1943), but apparently is commonest from late November until the first of April. Record are as follows:

Sapelo Island: Worthington found this godwit numerous during the winter of 1887–88, taking specimens on various dates between November 21 and March 30. Jenkins [1949] saw a single bird, June 4, 1948.

Mouth of the Altamaha River: specimens were taken by Worthington on January 15 and February 17, 1890.

St. Simons Island: six birds were seen by Mrs. Bassett, May 4, 1929.

Mouth of the Savannah River: Sprunt [1931] noted a single bird, January 23, 1931. Tomkins [1936] reports this species an uncommon fall and winter resident, from one to six birds being seen on thirty-one different days from August 28, 1931 to February 20, 1932.

Sea Island: Thomas [1945] reports one, June 27, 1943, and a flock of eight, January 13, 1945. Tanner [1946] observed a flock of ten, November 21, 1943. Jenkins [1949] saw five on Pelican Spit, August 31, 1947. Woodward [1949] reports a flock of three on April 3, 1947, and another flock of four on March 11, 1948.

Wolf Island, Doboy Sound: Johnston and Major [1950] observed a flock of fifteen to twenty on March 22, 1950.

HABITS AND RECOGNITION: This large, handsome shore bird has decreased perceptibly in numbers in recent years, and it is doubtful if it will ever be very numerous again. It is no longer legally hunted, but its breeding grounds in the interior of the continent are gradually changing from open prairie to areas of intensive cultivation, and this means the ultimate disappearance of the godwit from much of its summer range. At the present time, small flocks can be found on open beaches and on mud flats in the marshes, feeding at the edge of the water where the wet sand or mud facilitates probing for small mollusks and crustaceans. Where shallow pools exist, they can be seen wading in several inches of water, their heads almost submerged at times as they search for food. Unless molested, they are normally easily approached, and there should never be any question of their identity. In size they are exceeded only by the Long-billed Curlew, and from this species they can be distinguished by the shorter bill that is distinctly upturned. Both the curlew and the godwit are uniformly rich brown in color, with conspicuous cinnamon in the wings that is revealed when the birds are in flight.

Sanderling
Crocethia alba   (Pallas)

GENERAL DISTRIBUTION: Breeds on the Arctic Coast from Point Barrow, Alaska, to Greenland, and in Iceland, Spitzbergen, and northern Siberia. Winters on the Pacific Coast from Washington and on the Atlantic Coast from Massachusetts south to Chile and Argentina.

STATUS IN GEORGIA: A common transient and winter resident on the coast and of casual occurrence in the interior of the state in the fall.

Specimens were taken by Worthington at the mouth of the Altamaha River February 24 and March 6, 1890; there are specimens at the University of Georgia collected in Chatham County, May 14, 1908, and October 3, 1909. Flocks were noted on Cumberland Island, March 10, 1902, and at the mouth of the Savannah River, September 24, 1908, and October 30, 1931. While on Blackbeard Island, January 25, 1931, I observed scattered flocks of sanderlings feeding on the stretches of open beach. Tomkins [1936] states that at the mouth of Savannah River this species was "an abundant permanent resident, nonbreeding." Woodward [1949] found it abundant on Sea Island from January through April, 1946–48.

Away from the coast, it has been recorded from but four localities. At Augusta, Murphey [1937] considers it "a regular but never abundant migrant, appearing on the sandbars and mud flats of the Savannah River, August 17th to September 15th." I noted it but once at Athens [Burleigh, 1938], two birds, one of which was collected, being seen on Lake Kirota

CHUCK-WILL'S-WIDOW

Caprimulgus carolinensis

In a thicketed part of Sherwood Plantation a Chuck-will's-widow sang
each evening just after nightfall. Its eyes glowed like live coals as they
reflected the rays of my flashlight. After a groan or two the bird fluttered
up and away, and weird flapping sounds told me the direction it had taken.
I found a nest not far from this place and made some pencil sketches
of the incubating bird. When I returned the following day, prepared
to make a direct-from-life study, all I could find were scattered bits of white
shell. Some wandering predator, an opossum perhaps, had eaten the two eggs.

September 16, 1924. There is likewise a single record for Macon, August 31, 1937 (Denton). Hebard [1941] found it present in numbers on Chase Prairie, in the Okefenokee Swamp, February 3, 1931, and reports it numerous there throughout the winter.

HABITS AND RECOGNITION: The Sanderling has been aptly called the beachcomber of the bird world, for there are few ocean beaches where at one time or another it cannot be seen. No other bird is more cosmopolitan in its distribution, for, after its nesting season in the far north, it departs for more temperate regions and can be found scattered over the entire globe. Europe, Asia, even Australia, are visited during part of the year by small flocks, which seem merely to require open sandy beaches in order to be content with their surroundings. Here they feed at the edge of the water, nimbly following the rise and fall of the surf as they glean minute forms of marine life from the surface of the wet sand. So dexterous are they in avoiding the incoming waves that only rarely is a bird taken unawares, and then it escapes by fluttering over the water until the waves recede again. Intent in searching for morsels of food, they show little concern for any dangers that might threaten, and if one stands quietly on the beach, small flocks will approach within a few feet before taking flight. Seen under these conditions, they are easily recognized, for they appear much whiter than any of the other small sandpipers. Compared with the Semipalmated Sandpiper, the Sanderling is noticeably larger and stouter in build, and in flight displays a prominent white wing-bar.

Avocets and Stilts: *Family Recurvirostridae*

Avocet
Recurvirostra americana Gmelin

GENERAL DISTRIBUTION: Breeds from eastern Washington, southern Alberta, and southern Manitoba south to southern California, southern New Mexico, southern Texas, and Iowa. Winters from central California and southern Texas to Guatemala, and occurs casually in migration on the Atlantic Coast, from New Brunswick to Florida.

STATUS IN GEORGIA: A scarce and irregular transient on the coast. There is a single record of this species for the interior of the state.

It was first recorded in Georgia by Arnow [1908], who collected a specimen at St. Marys, in Camden County, on October 8, 1903. Tomkins has noted it at infrequent intervals at the mouth of the Savannah River, single birds being seen there October 14, 1928, February 23 and March 4 and 7, 1929 [Tomkins, 1929], and November 9 and 10, 1929 [Tomkins, 1930]. The bird seen March 7, a female, was collected. It was again recorded in Chatham county by James B. Floyd on October 21, 1943 (Tomkins) and in 1951 [Tomkins, letter], when two birds were seen on October 21, five on November 3, nine on November 10, and three on November 11. There is a single record for Glynn County, two birds seen on St. Simons Island, October 12, 1951 [Rotchford, 1952].

The only record for the interior of the state is of a single bird seen at Albany on September 5, 1952 [Giffen, 1953].

HABITS AND RECOGNITION: Anyone fortunate enough to see an Avocet in Georgia will have no difficulty in recognizing this large, handsome bird. Its large size, striking black and white plumage, and long, upturned bill will distingiush it even at a distance from any of the other waders. Nesting as it does in the western part of the country, it is doubtful that it will ever be found more than casually in Georgia, and the sight of one will always be an outstanding event. With its long legs and bill, it is well adapted to feeding in shallow pools, where the larger part of its food is procured. Its manner of feeding is quite unlike that of the other shore birds, for, as it moves with quick steps through the water, its submerged and partly open bill is swung from side to side to intercept any aquatic larvae or small crustaceans that may be in its path. It is an adept swimmer, and on occasion does not hesitate to feed in pools where the water is several feet deep. On its breeding grounds it is a noisy and conspicuous bird, but during the fall and winter months it is quiet and unobtrusive.

Black-necked Stilt
Himantopus mexicanus (Müller)

GENERAL DISTRIBUTION: Breeds from central Oregon, northern Utah, and southern Colorado south to northern Lower California, southern New Mexico, southern Texas, the coast of Louisiana, Florida, the Bahamas, West Indies, Mexico, and northern South America. Winters from central California, southern Texas, and Louisiana south to Brazil and Peru.

STATUS IN GEORGIA: Now apparently of accidental occurrence on the coast.

White [1849] included this species in LeConte's list of the birds of Georgia, and it may have nested on the coast in former years, since Bailey [1883] records eggs in the collection of Dr. S. W. Wilson taken May 18, sometime between the years 1853 and 1865.

Hoxie reports one bird seen near Savannah in the fall of 1911, but there are no further records of its occurrence in the state until the spring of 1950. On June 21 of that year Tomkins found a pair of stilts on Hutchinsons Island, in Chatham County, and as there was a possibility of their breeding, they were kept under observation for several weeks. On July 2, a nest was found that held one egg, but a week later the egg had disappeared; and as there was no indication of further attempts at nesting, the male was finally collected on July 12 [Tomkins, 1950b]. On September 9, 1950, Tomkins observed three stilts at Savannah.

HABITS AND RECOGNITION: In some respects the Stilt suggests the Avocet, for it is a long-legged, long-billed shore bird that can be found feeding in shallow pools in open marshes. Its plumage is likewise black and white, but, as can be ascertained when it is seen within reasonable range, it is noticeably slimmer in appearance, and its very long slim legs are red, whereas the avocet's legs are light blue. Its food is secured by probing in the soft mud at the bottom of the pools, and although it is able to swim, it apparently has no liking for deep water and rarely ventures far from shore. Except on its breeding grounds, it is a quiet, unsuspicious bird and can be approached with little difficulty.

Phalaropes: *Family Phalaropodidae*

Wilson's Phalarope
Steganopus tricolor   Vieillot

GENERAL DISTRIBUTION: Breeds from southern British Columbia, Alberta, Saskatchewan, and Manitoba south to central California, Utah, Colorado, Nebraska, Iowa, northern Illinois, and northern Indiana. Winters in South America, from Chile and central Argentina south to the Falkland Islands.

STATUS IN GEORGIA: Of accidental occurrence on the coast.

What appears to be the only record for a specimen of this species being taken in the state is that of a female, mounted and at present in the State Museum at Atlanta, collected at Savannah, April 27, 1923. The name of the collector is not given, but there seems no reason to question the authenticity of this specimen. Tomkins [letter] noted two birds at Savannah on August 14, 1953.

HABITS AND RECOGNITION: It is unfortunate that so interesting a species as the Wilson's Phalarope is not found regularly in the state. In contrast to the other birds, the females of the several species of phalaropes are more highly plumaged than the males, and during the breeding season the responsibility of building the nest, incubating the eggs, and caring for the young is assumed by the male alone. One can only wonder how such a strange state of affairs ever originated and what reason there could be for such a reversal of domestic responsibilities. During the summer months this phalarope is found about pools in wet meadows or at the edges of prairie sloughs, and here it can be seen wading in the shallow water, gyrating on the surface in deeper places, or walking daintily about on the edge of the shore. Its food is largely insects, and as it seems especially fond of the larvae of mosquitoes, it can be considered highly beneficial in its feeding habits. If seen in Georgia in migration, it would suggest a Lesser Yellowlegs in appearance, but it is noticeably paler in color and can be distinguished by its rather small head and slender, needle-like bill.

Northern Phalarope
Lobipes lobatus (Linnaeus)

GENERAL DISTRIBUTION: Breeds from the Pribilof Islands, northern Alaska, Melville Island, and central Greenland south to the Aleutian Islands, northern Manitoba, northern Ontario, and northern Quebec (Ungava). Winters off the coasts of Peru and West Africa.

STATUS IN GEORGIA: A rare transient that is possibly of merely accidental occurrence in the state.

It was first recorded in Georgia on May 24, 1933, when Tomkins took a female at the mouth of the Savannah River, in Chatham County, [Tomkins, 1934].

It was next recorded in the state when a male was collected by Stoddard in Grady County on October 3, 1937 [Stoddard, 1939]. The third and most recent record is that of a male taken at Augusta on May 9, 1950 [Belger, 1950].

HABITS AND RECOGNITION: On the Atlantic Coast, this phalarope migrates so far offshore that it is only during severe storms that there is any possibility of its being found near land. For this reason it is doubtful that it will ever be seen with any frequency in Georgia. In size and general appearance, it suggests a Sanderling, but its slender neck, small head, and relatively long, needle-like bill will readily distinguish it. Despite its small size, it apparently experiences no difficulty in coping with all but the most severe storms in mid-ocean, and it is only far offshore that it will be seen in any numbers. Its food, largely minute forms of aquatic life, is secured from the surface of the water, and as it is a buoyant and graceful swimmer, its days are spent feeding or resting on the waves far from the sight of land.

Jaegers: *Family Stercorariidae*

Parasitic Jaeger
Stercorarius parasiticus   (Linnaeus)

GENERAL DISTRIBUTION: Breeds from northwestern Alaska east to northern Greenland and south to the Aleutian Islands, southern Mackenzie, Hudson Bay, and northern Labrador. Winters on the Pacific Coast from southern California to Argentina, and on the Atlantic Coast from Florida to the eastern coast of South America.

STATUS IN GEORGIA: Apparently of only casual occurrence.

There are at present three records of this species in Georgia. Murphey [1937] states that an immature female was collected by Dan Henderson on the Savannah River three miles below Augusta, November 7, 1936. Thomas [1945] reports a single bird seen twenty miles offshore from Brunswick January 18, 1945; while Johnston and Major [1950] report "two or three" two miles offshore opposite the south end of Sapelo Island on March 18, 1950; one, an immature male, was collected that day.

HABITS AND RECOGNITION: The Parasitic Jaeger is well named. It is capable of procuring food by its own efforts, but it prefers to rob the terns and gulls of the fish they have caught, and this is a common practice wherever it occurs. The victim protests vocally such high-handed actions and attempts to elude this bandit of the seas, but is rarely successful. This is not surprising, for the flight of a jaeger is swift, graceful, and suggestive of that of a falcon, its dexterity in the air enabling it to so confuse the bird it is pursuing that the outcome is seldom in doubt. It normally remains well offshore, and as under such circumstances it could easily be overlooked, it possibly occurs oftener in Georgia waters than is generally supposed. When seen on the coast, it should be easily recognized, for it is a dark, hawklike bird with a hooked bill, and with the middle tail feathers so elongated that they project several inches beyond the rest of the tail.

Gulls and Terns: *Family Laridae*

Eastern Glaucous Gull
Larus hyperboreus hyperboreus   Gunnerus

GENERAL DISTRIBUTION: Breeds from northwestern Alaska, Melville Island, Ellesmere Island, and northern Greenland south to the Pribilof Islands, northern Mackenzie, James Bay, and eastern Labrador. Winters south to California, the Great Lakes, and Long Island, and casually to Bermuda, Florida, and Texas.

STATUS IN GEORGIA: A rare straggler on the coast.

Tomkins [1931; 1941] collected three specimens near the Quarantine Station, below Savannah, on February 28, 1931, April 14, 1931, and February 14, 1935. Some years later, in 1951, he took another specimen at the south end of Tybee Island on the surprisingly late date of May 30 [Tomkins, 1951]. These are the only records of this species in the state.

HABITS AND RECOGNITION: The Glaucous Gull is a large, hardy bird that rarely comes far south in any numbers. Consequently, it will never occur more than casually on the Georgia coast, and it will be the exceptional winter when one is seen. During the winter months, it commonly associates with Herring Gulls, and can be distinguished then by its noticeably larger size and white-tipped wings. It is a notorious scavenger, feeding on any animal food that it can find regardless of its state of decomposition, and, having a voracious appetite, there is little which it can swallow that it will ignore. However, it is also probably the most predatory of any of the gulls, and on its breeding grounds is quite destructive to the eggs and young of other birds.

Eastern Iceland Gull
Larus glaucoides glaucoides Meyer

GENERAL DISTRIBUTION: Breeds from Victoria Land, Boothia Peninsula, and west central Greenland east to Jan Mayen Island. Winters from southern Greenland south to Long Island and the Great Lakes and casually to Florida and the Gulf of Mexico.

STATUS IN GEORGIA: Of accidental occurrence on the coast.

The only record of this species in the state is that of a specimen taken by Tomkins three miles east of Savannah, on the Savannah River, February 13, 1941 [Tomkins, 1941].

HABITS AND RECOGNITION: The Iceland Gull resembles closely the Glaucous Gull, but is smaller. If seen with Herring Gulls, it suggests the Ring-billed Gull in size, but its white-tipped wings clearly differentiate it from the other species. It is a hardy bird, wintering as far north as there is any open water, and rarely coming far south except in very severe winters. Like the Glaucous Gull, it is an efficient scavenger, with an insatiable appetite that overlooks nothing edible that can be picked up from the surface of the water or the ocean beaches. It apparently is not as predatory as its larger relative, but doubtless, as opportunity offers, takes its toll of eggs and small young of other sea birds.

Great Black-backed Gull
Larus marinus Linnaeus

GENERAL DISTRIBUTION: Breeds in North America from North Devon Island and western Greenland south to Newfoundland and Nova Scotia. Winters on the Atlantic Coast from southern Greenland to Delaware Bay and, rarely, farther south to Florida.

STATUS IN GEORGIA: Known only from one specimen taken in Chatham County by Hoxie and now at the University of Georgia at Athens. This bears no label giving information about where or when it was collected, but it was probably taken near Savannah about 1910, as it was mentioned in one of a series of articles published by Hoxie in the *Savannah Morning News* in 1911 [Fargo, 1934].

HABITS AND RECOGNITION: This is the largest of the gulls seen on the Atlantic Coast, its size and dark back making the adult birds unmistakable even at a distance. Young of the year are less distinct, but can be distinguished from young Herring Gulls by their size and whiter, less dusky, plumage. Although a hardy species, it winters south regularly as far as North Carolina, so it is rather surprising that it does not occur more frequently on the Georgia coast. At all times it is wary and suspicious, never permitting a close approach as it feeds on the ocean beach or flies high overhead. Seen in flight, it is a majestic bird, for it delights in soaring in wide circles at great heights, spiraling upward until almost out of sight. Like the other gulls, it is omnivorous in its feeding habits, eating practically anything that it can swallow and digest, and showing little concern for its degree of freshness.

American Herring Gull
Larus argentatus smithsonianus Coues

GENERAL DISTRIBUTION: Breeds from south-central Alaska and southern Baffin Island south to northern British Columbia, northern Alberta, northern North Dakota, central Wisconsin, southern Ontario, northern New York, and Maine. Winters on the Pacific Coast from southern Alaska south to Lower California, on the Great Lakes, and on the Atlantic Coast from the Gulf of St. Lawrence to the Bahamas, Cuba, and Yucatán.

STATUS IN GEORGIA: A transient and winter resident, common on the coast, and locally uncommon in the interior of the state.

Away from the coast, the Herring Gull has been recorded from the following localities:

Rome: An uncommon winter visitant, seen between the dates of November 7 (1935), and March 2 (1940) [Jones, 1944].

Dalton: Three seen March 5, 1944 [Hamilton, et al., 1944].

Atlanta: A scarce transient. Migration extremes: March 14 (1945) and April 6 (1937), and October 27 (1943) and December 21 (1947) [Griffin MS].

Athens: A scarce but regular transient, one or two being seen each spring and fall. Extreme dates of occurrence in the spring are March 31 (1926) and April 27 (1925), and in the fall August 16 (1928) and December 15 (1926). [Burleigh, 1938].

Augusta: A regular but uncommon winter resident, seen in December, January, and February [Murphey, 1937]. A specimen was taken January 16, 1903.

Macon: One record, March 20, 1944 [Johnston, MS].

Grady County: Fifty observed on November 28, 1942; another large flock on November 3, 1943; and a flock of fifteen on December 3, 1949 [Stoddard, MS].

Fitzgerald: Noted October 31, 1941, and December 23, 1942 (Hopkins).

Coffee County: One record, April 28, 1947 [Norris and Hopkins, 1953].

Okefenokee Swamp: Definitely recorded only in February, 1935, when three were seen on Chase Prairie [Hebard, 1941].

Charlton County: One in October, 1938; five flying south over Coleraine, November 26, 1940 (Robert Norris); and one at East Spring, east of Folkston on December 29, 1940 [Hebard, 1941].

On the coast, first arrivals in the fall were noted at Savannah on October 31, 1908, and October 28, 1910; the latest in the spring were seen on April 19, 1921. On Cumberland Island, the last were reported in the spring on April 16, 1902, and May 3, 1921. Tomkins observed a single bird at the mouth of the Savannah River in August, 1932. Woodward [1949] found this species common about Sea Island from January through April, 1946-48.

HABITS AND RECOGNITION: Because of its wide distribution and relative abundance, the Herring Gull is the best known and most frequently observed of all the so-called "sea gulls." On the Georgia coast, a large gull flying overhead or resting on a stretch of open beach is almost sure to be this species. Being a consistent scavenger and knowing from long experience the benefits to be derived from the proximity of man, it frequents harbors throughout the winter months and can be seen there daily in varying numbers. Fishing boats are apparently recognized as an unfailing source of food, as are also the larger vessels that ply the coast, and these are followed for miles for any bits of refuse thrown into the water. Although Herring Gulls are normally wary and suspicious, the protection afforded them in the harbors is soon recognized, and there these gulls become very tame and can be watched at close range. Little difficulty should be encountered in recognizing the species under these circumstances. Irrespective of age, no other gull approximating the large size of the Herring Gull and having black-tipped wings has such noticeably flesh-colored legs. In Georgia, young birds are far more numerous during the winter months than adults, and are characterized by their uniform, dark-brown coloration.

The usefulness of all gulls as scavengers may not be generally realized. However, with the tendency of modern civilization to use our tidal waters as a dumping ground for sewage, garbage, and other organic wastes, most of which are acceptable as food to gulls, our water fronts would be far less pleasant places if it were not for these feathered scavengers. Because of its abundance the Herring Gull is particularly valuable in this respect.

Ring-billed Gull
Larus delawarensis Ord

GENERAL DISTRIBUTION: Breeds from southern Alaska, Great Slave Lake, northern Manitoba, and James Bay south to southern Oregon, Utah, North Dakota, northern Wisconsin, and northern New York. Winters from British Columbia, Montana, Colorado, the Great Lakes, and Maine south to the Gulf Coast, Cuba, and southern Mexico.

STATUS IN GEORGIA: A common transient and winter resident on the coast and of local occurrence there during the summer months; a scarce transient in the interior of the state.

Except on the coast there are very few records of the Ring-billed Gull in Georgia. At Augusta, Murphey [1938] collected a female from a flock of four seen on the Savannah River, April 9, 1938, and Denton [letter] observed a single bird there April 25, 1943, collected a female in second-year plumage on May 3, 1945, and saw an adult June 4, 1949. He also reports four adults at the Clark Hill Reservoir, in Columbia County, on May 3, 1953. I noted it but once at Athens [Burleigh, 1938], one bird being seen October 24, 1925, circling over the Oconee River. Griffin [1941] considered it a rare transient in the Atlanta region, the only records being for the spring migration, May 1, 1932 (Greene), and April 11, 1936. It has since been noted there on May 24, 1954 (Mrs. Lewis Gordon), and June 2, 1954 (Parks). Jones [1944] cites two records for Mt. Berry, in Floyd County, two birds being seen March 27, 1941, and two October 26, 1941.

On the coast, the earliest date of arrival in the fall is that of a flock of thirty birds seen at Savannah, September 30, 1909. Departure in the spring is apparently in early May, the latest date given by Mrs. Bassett being May 3 (1924). Norris [1939] found these gulls abundant on St. Simons Island during all of June, 1939, 80 per cent of the birds observed being in immature plumage. Woodward [1949] found them equally abundant on Sea Island from January through April, 1946–48.

HABITS AND RECOGNITION: Seen at close range, the Ring-billed Gull is noticeably smaller than the Herring Gull, but otherwise its appearance is almost identical, and the same may be said of its actions. It is apparently, however, more gregarious, and normally is seen on the Georgia coast only in flocks. Anything edible being acceptable, the Ring-bill is to a large extent a scavenger during the winter months, and although found along the open beaches and on the mud flats in the salt marsh, it is most common in the harbors and about the docks. Its flight is strong and graceful, and when resting on the water, it rides the waves buoyantly. Its food is to a great extent taken from the surface of the water; it is exceptional to find this gull feeding on bits of refuse or small dead fish washed up on the shore. It is usually associated with the Herring Gull, but can be readily distinguished by its smaller size, the dark bar on its bill, and its distinctly yellowish-green legs, in contrast to the flesh-colored legs of the larger species.

Laughing Gull
Larus atricilla   Linnaeus

GENERAL DISTRIBUTION: Breeds from Maine and Massachusetts south to Florida, the Gulf Coast, the Lesser Antilles, and Venezuela. Winters from South Carolina and the Gulf Coast south to Brazil, Peru, and Chile.

STATUS IN GEORGIA: A common spring and fall transient on the coast and of casual occurrence there both in summer and winter; of accidental occurrence in the interior of the state.

Throughout much of the year the Laughing Gull is the common gull of the Georgia coast, but it has never been known to breed there. Relatively few are observed during the winter months. Crispin noted this species at Savannah January 27, 1912, but otherwise there appear to be no published records for this season of the year. On Cumberland Island, Helme noted many flocks from March 10 through April 17, 1902, and Pearson [1922] reported a flock of thirty birds there May 3, 1921. At Savannah, there are numerous records from March 18 through May 13. Norris [1939] observed an occasional bird at St. Simons Island throughout June, 1939, and Woodward [1949] found it common on Sea Island from the middle of March through April, 1948, the first birds appearing March 7.

Away from the coast, it has been observed on but few occasions. At Augusta, Murphey [1937] reports a female taken in August, 1909. Griffin [1941] considers it a rare transient at Atlanta, dates of occurrence being May 21, 1932 (Eyles); June 15, 1932 (Greene); and August 14, 1940

(Griffin). Milton Hopkins, Jr., saw a single bird in the Laura Walker State Park near Waycross on July 1 and 2, 1943.

HABITS AND RECOGNITION: The Laughing Gull is less of a scavenger than are the other larger gulls, its food consisting mostly of small fish and other marine life that it picks up from the surface of the water. As a result, it is not as numerous in harbors or about the docks, nor does it consistently follow boats for scraps of food that are thrown overboard. However, it is not averse to taking advantage of any bits of refuse that it may find, and on occasion will be found competing with other gulls for garbage dumped from the end of a wharf. It normally occurs in small, loose flocks that can be seen flying a short distance offshore searching for schools of small fish, or resting quietly on a stretch of open beach or on a mud flat exposed by low tide. Less wary than the larger species, the Laughing Gull is nevertheless usually suspicious of an intruder and will not permit close approach. Its small size—smaller than that of either the Herring Gull or the Ring-billed Gull—and the conspicuous black head will quickly identify adults seen during the spring and summer months. In immature birds and winter adults the head is white streaked with dark gray, but their size and dark backs should distinguish them even at a distance.

Bonaparte's Gull
Larus philadelphia (Ord)

GENERAL DISTRIBUTION: Breeds from northwestern Alaska and southern Mackenzie south to central British Columbia and central Alberta. Winters on the Atlantic Coast from Massachusetts to Florida, on the Gulf Coast and on the coast of Yucatán, and on the Pacific Coast from Washington to central Mexico and, rarely, to Peru.

STATUS IN GEORGIA: A common transient and winter resident on the coast and of casual occurrence in migration in the interior of the state.

On the coast, Worthington found this species common during the winter at the mouth of the Altamaha River, and Helme reports it common on Cumberland Island, March 16, 1902. At Savannah, the earliest transients in the fall were noted by Erichsen [MS] on September 21 (1918), and the latest in the spring, May 25 (1941). I found this little gull fairly plentiful at Savannah on January 30, 1924, occasional flocks of ten to fifteen birds being seen feeding about the larger pools or open channels in the wide stretches of salt marsh. Woodward [1949] recorded it at Sea Island from January through April, 1946–48, but states that it was "seen only in small numbers until 1948 when in March and April flocks of 12 or more were seen."

In the interior of the state Bonaparte's Gull has been reported from the following localities:

Augusta: Murphey [1937] considers it of accidental occurrence here. A single bird, in immature plumage, was taken at the mouth of Lake Olmstead on November 15, 1906.

Demorest: One flock of nine birds seen April 8, 1948 [Neal, 1948].

Athens: A rather scarce transient, observed at infrequent intervals. Records for the spring migration are a single bird April 5, 1925, on the city reservoir, and two, on Lake Kirota, April 9, 1927; for the fall migration a single bird November 3, 1926, on the city reservoir, and two on December 4, 1927, in the Sandy Creek bottoms [Burleigh, 1938].

Atlanta: Griffin [1941] states that it is an uncommon transient, extreme dates of occurrence being March 30 (1939) and April 22 (1932), and November 27 (1930) and December 11 (1932).

Rome: Noted, single birds each time, on March 24, 1941, and November 5, 1941 [Jones, 1944], and March 27, 1948 [Dorsey, letter].

Camp Wheeler, Bibb County: One seen November 10, 1943 [Meanley, 1944].

HABITS AND RECOGNITION: Bonaparte's Gull is the smallest of the gulls found in Georgia, its size and buoyant flight suggesting that of a tern. As with the Laughing Gull, adults in breeding plumage have a black head, but in any plumage this species can always be recognized by its small size, slender bill, and pale gray upperparts. During the winter it can be found in small flocks that seem to prefer the islands and the salt marsh, and are only infrequently seen in harbors or on the open beaches. Where available, insects form a large portion of its food, but small fish are eagerly sought after, as well as other forms of small marine life. It is less of a scavenger than are the other gulls, but bits of refuse floating on the surface of the water are not ignored. Usually it feeds as it flies, gracefully picking up with its bill any morsel that has attracted its attention.

Eastern Gull-billed Tern
Gelochelidon nilotica aranea (Wilson)

GENERAL DISTRIBUTION: Breeds on the Atlantic Coast from Virginia to Georgia, on the Gulf Coast, and in the Bahamas and Cuba. Winters in South America from Brazil to Patagonia, and casually to the Gulf Coast of Texas, Louisiana, and Florida.

STATUS IN GEORGIA: A scarce summer resident on the coast.

Worthington took three specimens on Sapelo Island May 8, 1888; and it has also been recorded as a transient on Cumberland Island, St. Simons Island, Wassaw Island, and at the mouth of the Savannah River. The only definite breeding record is that of a small colony found nesting on Oyster-bed Island in 1926 by W. J. Erichsen, three nests being found on May 23 and four on June 13 [Erichsen, 1926].

HABITS AND RECOGNITION: The Gull-billed Tern was at one time a common bird on the Atlantic Coast, but from 1890 until 1900 it was so relentlessly persecuted to meet the demands of the millinery trade for the adornment of women's hats that it almost disappeared. With adequate protection, it is now slowly increasing in numbers, but it is still far from common and is rather local in distribution. All of the terns are characterized by their slender build and agile flight, and this species is no exception. In the air it has the ease and skill of a swallow, its flight being strong and graceful as it feeds over an expanse of salt marsh. Its food apparently consists almost entirely of insects, and these are picked up from the surface of the water or from the marsh vegetation as the bird hovers momentarily in the air. Its bill is stouter than the bills of the other terns, suggesting that of a gull, and the bird can likewise be distinguished by its shorter, less deeply forked tail. The small breeding colony found on Oysterbed Island on May 23, 1926, has been well described by Walter J. Erichsen [1926] as follows:

Returning to the spot where I first encountered the windrows of marsh grass, I continued on down the beach examining the little elevations and searching the open sandy shell-encrusted area between the dead drift for nests of Wilson's Plover. As I reached this point several birds which I thought were Cabot's Terns began to circle overhead, uttering a peculiar laughing cackle. They were too wary and flew too high for satisfactory identification, but their actions were those of breeding birds, and I set about to find their nests. At each step the birds became more solicitous, and I soon became positive that whatever they were their eggs would soon be found. Taking a zigzag course, I searched now up on the shelly slope then back to the drift sprinkled sand, and had gone perhaps five hundred feet when my eyes rested on a nest containing three eggs, and a moment later I spied a second and a third, each containing two eggs. The nests were in windrows of dead marsh grass stems about fifty feet above high water mark. The three were in a direct line parallel with the shore line, the middle one, containing two eggs, being twenty-five feet from the other one with two eggs, and seven feet from the nest containing three eggs. All were substantial and well made, and each was almost an exact duplicate of the other. Into a hollow measuring about five inches across and an inch and a half deep, the birds had arranged a single layer of broken shells about the size of a ten cent piece. Upon this, but placed in a rather haphazard manner, was a close-set cluster of dead marsh grass stems, with numerous fragments trailing over the edge of the nest and extending in a little stream eight or nine inches beyond the rim, just as if some one had dragged the material into the hollow with a rake, leaving pieces along the way.

Concealing himself, Erichsen soon had the satisfaction of seeing the birds return to their nests, and had no difficulty in identifying them as Gull-billed Terns.

Forster's Tern
Sterna forsteri   Nuttall

GENERAL DISTRIBUTION: Breeds from central Alberta, southern Saskatchewan, and Manitoba south to California, Utah, Nevada, northern Colorado, northern Nebraska, Minnesota, Illinois, and southern Ontario, and on the coasts of Texas, Louisiana, and Virginia. Winters from central California, the Gulf Coast, and South Carolina to southern Guatemala.

STATUS IN GEORGIA: A common winter resident on the coast and of accidental occurrence in the interior.

The earliest date of arrival in the fall is September 2, 1903, in Camden County, a specimen taken then being at Emory University. However, these terns are usually not seen in numbers before November. Worthington reported them common in winter at the mouth of the Altamaha River. He took specimens on Sapelo Island in December, 1887, and February, 1888; at Broro Neck, McIntosh County, March 25, 1889; and on Egg Island, at the mouth of the Altamaha River, in January, 1890. Specimens have also been taken on Cumberland Island, April 10, 1902, April 7, 1903, and April 24, 1905. I found this species fairly plentiful at Savannah on January 30, 1924, an occasional small flock being noted. Woodward [1949] considered it abundant at Sea Island from January through April, 1946–48. Rossignol reported it at Savannah as late as May 29 (1911).

For the interior of the state there are but two records. It was noted at Macon on August 31, 1937 [Denton fide Johnston, MS], and Denton [1950] reports an immature male collected by Clarence Belger at Augusta on February 15, 1946.

HABITS AND RECOGNITION: During the summer this tern is a bird of the open marshes, but after it leaves its breeding grounds, it is found on the coast, and its actions are much the same then as the other terns. In Georgia, it is the medium-sized tern most frequently seen in small flocks during the winter, feeding a short distance offshore, or in the harbors. No bird is more graceful on the wing, its flight being light and buoyant, and so suggestive of that of a swallow that in many locations it is frequently called a sea swallow. Its food, aquatic insects and small fish, is picked up from the surface of the water, or, if necessary, by short plunges beneath the surface. Although only to a very small extent a scavenger in its feeding habits, it shows a decided preference for the harbors, and it is a common sight throughout the winter to see one or more of these terns resting on piling or at the end of the dock. In appearance and actions it is much like the Gull-billed Tern, but can be easily recognized by its long, slender bill and deeply forked tail. It can be distinguished from the Common Tern only with some difficulty, the main characters of the winter birds being the whiter appearance of the back and wings, the gray rather than white tail, and the lack of black on the back of the head, where the Common Tern has a noticeably black patch at that season of the year.

Northern Common Tern
Sterna hirundo hirundo   Linnaeus

GENERAL DISTRIBUTION: Breeds from Great Slave Lake, northern Manitoba, central Ontario, and the Gulf of St. Lawrence south to North Dakota, northern Ohio, and North Carolina; also locally in the Bahamas, on the Florida Keys, on the Gulf Coast of Louisiana and Texas, and in Venezuela. Winters casually in Florida and on the western coast of Mexico, and commonly on both coasts of South America, as well as in Africa and Asia.

STATUS IN GEORGIA: A fairly common spring and fall transient on the coast, and an uncommon transient in the interior of the state.

Possibly owing to the difficulty of distinguishing this species from the Forster's Tern, there are few published records for the state.

On the coast, the earliest date of arrival in the fall is September 12 (1909), at Savannah, while in the spring it has been recorded by Worthington at the mouth of the Altamaha River as early as February 1 (1890). Spring transients apparently linger well into May, for it has been taken on Egg Island on May 11, 1888, and in Chatham County on May 21, 1907, and has been reported on Cumberland Island on May 5, 1921 [Pearson, 1922].

Away from the coast, it has been most often noted at Augusta. Murphey [1937] states that it is "a constant but irregular visitant. Birds in full nuptial plumage have been taken in May; and in August and September, both the young of the year and adults occur. An immature bird was taken September 5, 1933, which was banded July 15, 1933, at Hennepin Island, Mille Lacs, Minnesota, by William I. Lyon."

At Athens, I observed this species only in the fall, and then at rather infrequent intervals. Dates of occurrence are November 1, 1925, (a single bird on the city reservoir); July 28, 1926 (four in the Sandy Creek bottoms); September 26 and 27, 1929 (one bird the first day, and eight the day following, in the Sandy Creek bottoms) [Burleigh, 1938]; and August 18, 1939 (a single bird in the Sandy Creek bottoms) [Burleigh, 1941].

FLORIDA COMMON NIGHTHAWK
Chordeiles minor minor

So many nighthawks lived among the big pines that I thought surely
I would find several nests, but I found only one. Nor would I have found
this one had I not, while walking across a barren stretch I usually drove
around, heard a nighthawk call "pee-yee" quite sharply, looked up,
seen the bird before it left its high perch, and known from its heated attack
that a nest must be close by. At last I found the nest—no nest at all,
of course; not even a depression; just two downy chicks side by side within
inches of tracks my car had made a day or so before. My painting
shows the male on guard above the nest.

Family Laridae: GULLS & TERNS

Norris recorded one bird at Fitzgerald on September 27, 1940 [Norris, 1940], and one at Tifton on September 12, 1941 [Norris, 1941].

HABITS AND RECOGNITION: This tern is a common bird on the Georgia coast during the late fall months and again in the spring, occurring in small flocks that can be seen resting on a stretch of open beach or feeding a short distance offshore. Unlike the Forster's Tern, which it closely resembles, it is a bird of the sandy beaches rather than of the open salt marsh, and its food consists almost entirely of small fish. These are secured beneath the surface of the water, the bird hovering momentarily when its prey is discovered and then plunging headlong with folded wings. Frequently, in its eagerness to get the fish it has sighted, it will disappear for a brief interval beneath the water and then emerge with the fish in its bill, shaking itself to dry its plumage as it flies off. It swims well, but apparently dislikes rough water, and only when the sea is calm can it be seen resting lightly on the water. In common with the other terns, its flight is light and graceful, its long wings giving it both speed and dexterity in the air.

Despite its wide distribution and relative abundance, it often escapes notice on the Georgia coast because its appearance is so similar to the equally common Forster's Tern. Seen within reasonable range, however, its white tail in contrast to a darker back, and dusky primaries in the wing, should distinguish it.

Arctic Tern
Sterna paradisaea Pontoppidan

GENERAL DISTRIBUTION: Breeds from northern Alaska east to Baffin Island and northern Greenland, south to northern British Columbia, northern Manitoba, Maine, and Massachusetts, and in the Arctic regions of Europe and Asia. Winters in the Antarctic Ocean, south to latitude 74 degrees.

STATUS IN GEORGIA: Of accidental occurrence.

The only record of this species in Georgia is that of an adult female taken by Francis Harper, May 22, 1921, in Ware County, on Suwannee Creek, two miles from the Okefenokee Swamp. This specimen is now at Cornell University, Ithaca, New York.

HABITS AND RECOGNITION: The presence of an Arctic Tern in southern Georgia is difficult to explain. It breeds in the Arctic and winters in the Antarctic, its migration route apparently well offshore, and while a few individuals have been noted along the coast south to Long Island, it is unknown farther south. It is doubtful, therefore, that this one record will ever be duplicated. The Arctic Tern has the unique distinction of experiencing more sunlight than any other living organism. Wells W. Cooke [1911] points this out so well that his comments are here quoted in full, as follows:

> The Arctic Terns have more hours of daylight and sunlight than any other animal on the globe. At their most northern nesting site the midnight sun has already appeared before their arrival, and it never sets during their entire stay at the breeding grounds. During two months of their sojourn in the Antarctic they do not see a sunset, and for the rest of the time the sun dips only a little way below the horizon and broad daylight continues all night. The birds therefore have 24 hours of daylight for at least eight months of the year, and during the other four months have considerably more daylight than darkness.

Eastern Sooty Tern
Sterna fuscata fuscata   Linnaeus

GENERAL DISTRIBUTION: Breeds from the Bahamas, West Indies, and the Dry Tortugas south to Venezuela and British Honduras. Winters south to Brazil and the Falkland Islands. Casual in the summer and fall months north to New England and Lake Ontario.

STATUS IN GEORGIA: Of casual occurrence both on the coast and in the interior during the summer and early fall months.

For the coast there are at present three records. At Savannah, a living bird was picked up by Mrs. V. H. Bassett on September 17, 1928, and a specimen was taken by Tomkins a mile west of the city on September 19, 1928 [Tomkins, 1932]. John Oney [letter] reports eight of these terns seen September 18, 1947, on the Frederica River near Brunswick.

For the interior of the state there are two records. Murphey [1937] records an adult female taken in Richmond County on July 31, 1926; and Greene [1935] states that "on or about September 6, 1933, a bird of this species was picked up, either dead or in a dying condition, near Milledgeville in Baldwin County."

HABITS AND RECOGNITION: The presence of the Sooty Tern in the state can be considered accidental, for it is only after severe tropical storms that an occasional bird appears. Apparently such birds are caught unawares and are forced by winds of hurricane strength far out of their normal range, and since the effect of such storms is seldom felt in Georgia, it is improbable that this tern will be often seen in the state. Its appearance is so unlike that of the other medium-sized terns, sooty black above and white beneath, that there should not be any difficulty in recognizing it, even at a distance. In common with the other tern, its flight is light and graceful, and it is so much at home in the air that only rarely is it said to rest during the daylight hours. As with the Common Tern, its food consists almost entirely of small fish, but instead of plunging into the water for them, it skillfully picks them up from the surface without wetting a feather.

Atlantic Bridled Tern
Sterna anaethetus melanoptera   Swainson

GENERAL DISTRIBUTION: Breeds from the Bahamas and the West Indies to British Honduras and Venezuela and on the west coast of Africa.

STATUS IN GEORGIA: Of accidental occurrence on the coast.

To Ivan Tomkins belongs the credit of adding this species to the state list. While on Tybee Island on October 1, 1950, he picked up two mummified terns on the beach at the north end of the island that have been identified by the Fish and Wildlife Service as *Sterna anaethetus melanoptera.* He thinks that "perhaps these birds were driven in by the four days of northeast wind about Labor Day at the edge of a hurricane that lingered near Tampa, Florida."

HABITS AND RECOGNITION: The Bridled Tern closely resembles the Sooty Tern, but can be distinguished by the white nape that separates the black crown from the dark gray back. It is an abundant bird throughout the West Indies and should be looked for on the Georgia coast whenever tropical hurricanes occur. Its appearance and actions are said to be similar to those of the Sooty Tern, the two species being so much alike that they are difficult to distinguish in life.

Eastern Least Tern
Sterna albifrons antillarum   (Lesson)

GENERAL DISTRIBUTION: Breeds on the Atlantic Coast from Massachusetts to Florida, on the Gulf Coast, in the Bahamas and the West Indies, and on the coasts of Venezuela and British Honduras. Winters south along the eastern coast of Central and South America to northeastern Brazil.

STATUS IN GEORGIA: A common summer resident on the coast and of casual occurrence during the summer in the interior of the state.

First arrivals in the spring were reported at Darien on April 23, 1890, and at Tybee Island on April 25, 1925. Woodward [1949] found this little tern common in April on Sea Island (from 1946 through 1948), the earliest date of arrival in the spring being April 7. It apparently departs in the fall some time in September.

It formerly nested in large numbers on Wassaw Island and to a limited extent on Folly Island [Erichsen, 1921], but breeding colonies are now known only on Oysterbed Island, near the mouth of the Savannah River, and on St. Simons Island. On Oysterbed Island, I found nests with the full complement of two or three eggs as early as May 16 (1925) and as late as June 14 (1927). Rossignol [letter] gives as extreme nesting dates for this island (193 occupied nests), two fresh eggs May 5 (1932) and two fresh eggs June 28 (1930). The breeding colony on St. Simons Island was found to have but a few nests with eggs on May 31, 1929, the majority of the hollows scraped in the sand being as yet empty. Troup D. Perry reports eggs as late as July 20.

In the interior of the state this species has been noted at Lake Rutledge, in Morgan County, on July 12, 13, and 14, 1939 [Bell, 1939], at Millen on August 11, 1940 [DeLoach, 1940], and at Fitzgerald on August 20, 1940 [Norris, 1940].

HABITS AND RECOGNITION: Because of its small size and handsome plumage the Least Tern was at one time so much in demand by the millinery trade that constant and unrelenting slaughter almost exterminated it on the Atlantic Coast. Fortunately suitable laws were passed in time to protect the remnant that remained, and today it is gradually regaining its former numbers throughout its breeding range in the eastern United States. This is graphically illustrated by what we know of its past and present status on the Georgia coast. Walter J. Erichsen, in 1921, stated that it formerly nested in large numbers on the isolated beaches of the larger coastal islands, but that since 1891 there was no record even of a single pair nesting in the state. On May 19, 1923, I visited Oysterbed Island, near the mouth of the Savannah River, and was highly gratified to find about 100 pairs nesting there. Two years later, on May 16, 1925, this breeding colony had practically doubled in size, while in 1927 I estimated that it contained approximately 500 pairs. My last visit was on June 1, 1929, and on that date I found that it had again more than doubled in size.

The nest of a Least Tern is merely a slight hollow in dry sand; rarely, one will be found with a slight lining of fragments of oyster shells. No attempt is made at concealment, the more open stretches of beach being selected that are well beyond the high-tide mark. Frequently suitable areas are rather circumscribed, and in this case the nests are close together. Either two or three eggs are laid, and, where the nests are undisturbed, it is doubtful that more than one brood is reared each year.

As its name implies, the Least Tern is the smallest of the terns, and, as such, is easily recognized. In most respects it is a miniature of its larger relatives, for its has pale-gray upperparts, a black cap, and a relatively long, forked tail. Its actions are essentially the same also, for its flight is light and graceful, and much of its time is spent in the air looking for the small fish that form the bulk of its food. These are usually obtained by a sudden plunge beneath the surface of the water, the bird hovering and then dropping with a splash that sends the spray flying in all directions.

As little is known of the longevity of these small terns, it is interesting to note that Tomkins [1934] reports that a bird banded by Rossignol on Oysterbed Island, June 17, 1923, was killed ten years later, on July 9, 1933, a few miles south of Savannah.

American Royal Tern
Thalasseus maximus maximus (Boddaert)

GENERAL DISTRIBUTION: Breeds on the Atlantic Coast from Virginia to Florida, on the Gulf Coast, in the Bahamas and the West Indies, and on the Pacific Coast of Lower California and Mexico. Winters from Georgia and the Gulf Coast south through the Bahamas and the West Indies to Patagonia.

STATUS IN GEORGIA: A common transient and winter resident and an uncommon summer resident on the coast; of accidental occurrence in the interior of the state.

Worthington reported this tern common in winter at the mouth of the Altamaha River, and Helme found it abundant on Cumberland Island in March, 1902. James Henry Rice, Jr., reported it abundant at the Isle of Hope and on Colonel's Island in December, 1916. Woodward [1949] records it as common at Sea Island from January through April, 1946–48. Specimens in the Dwight Collection (in the American Museum of Natural History) were taken on Cumberland Island, April 14, 1902; Ossabaw Island, November 29 and 30, 1904; and St. Simons Island, December 12 and 14, 1904.

Rice reported this species breeding on Blackbeard Island in 1914, and Rossignol [Tomkins, 1934] found a few birds nesting on Oysterbed Island, near the mouth of the Savannah River, on June 17, 1933—a nest found there that day held one fresh egg, which Rossignol collected. I noted six birds on Oysterbed Island on May 16, 1925, and twelve on the island on June 14, 1927, but saw no evidence of breeding.

Away from the coast, the Royal Tern has been noted only at Augusta. Denton [1944] saw a single bird, October 28, 1944, and was advised that another had been killed there by a hunter on October 21 and that four were seen on October 23 at the Fifth Street bridge.

HABITS AND RECOGNITION: The Royal Tern approaches the larger gulls in size, but can readily be recognized as a tern by its forked tail. Since it is a large, heavy-bodied bird, its flight is not as light as that of the smaller terns. When not engaged in searching for the small fish that form the bulk of its diet, it spends much of its time resting in small groups on open beaches or on mud flats exposed by low tide. On the Georgia coast it is commonly found in the harbors throughout the winter months, and can be seen then resting on the tops of pilings and at the ends of the less frequented docks. It usually occurs in small flocks, although single birds are not infrequently seen. Fish are captured by plunging into the water, but otherwise this large tern avoids alighting on the surface of the water and is never known to swim in even the calmest seas. Its nest is merely a slight hollow in the sand, unlined, and in the southern part of its range but a single egg is normally laid. Farther north, two, or rarely three, eggs are laid. Because of its size it can be confused only with the Caspian Tern, from which it may be differentiated by its orange rather than red bill, its more deeply forked tail, and the limited amount of black in the primaries.

Cabot's Sandwich Tern
Thalasseus sandvicensis acuflavidus (Cabot)

GENERAL DISTRIBUTION: Breeds locally on the Atlantic Coast from Virginia to Florida, on the Gulf Coast, in the Bahamas and West Indies, and on the coast of British Honduras. Winters from Florida and the Bahamas south to Brazil, and on the Pacific coasts of Oaxaca and Guatemala.

STATUS IN GEORGIA: Apparently a scarce transient on the coast, although as it breeds as far north as Virginia, it should occur oftener than the few records would indicate.

Worthington took specimens at Egg Bank, at the mouth of the Altamaha River, on May 10, 20, 25, 1888, and Dr. Murphey had a male in his collection that was taken on Wolf Island, September 27, 1892. Helme reports approximately twenty-five birds seen and three collected on Cumberland Island, April 14, 1902. Tomkins saw three in Buttermilk Sound and St. Simons Sound, August 25 and 27, 1942. What is apparently the most recent record is that of five birds seen and a male collected by Sciple on St. Andrews Sound, Glynn County, September 4, 1949 [Sciple, 1950].

HABITS AND RECOGNITION: To me the most interesting thing about the Cabot's Sandwich Tern, a characteristic that sets it apart from the other terns, is its close association with the Royal Tern. My experience has been rather limited, but it agrees with that of other observers, so apparently this trait is the same everywhere. On its breeding grounds the nests are placed in close proximity to those of the Royal Tern, and if that species is not present in a breeding colony of terns, then the Cabot's Sandwich Tern is likewise absent. The same is true to a large extent during the winter months, for where the Royal Terns concentrate on a sand bar or open beach, there the Cabot's Sandwich Terns will be found. In size Cabot's Sandwich Tern is intermediate between such species as the Common Tern and the Royal Tern, and in any plumage has a long, slender, black bill, tipped with yellow, that will clearly identify it.

Its habits are much the same as those of the other terns, although it apparently prefers the open ocean to the harbors and more protected bays, and can usually be seen feeding well offshore. Its food is largely small fish, which it seizes in characteristic fashion, plunging headlong into the water and frequently submerging its entire body before it appears with the fish in its bill. Its slender body and long, pointed wings make it a swift and agile flier, and even in strong gales it demonstrates complete mastery of the air.

Caspian Tern
Hydroprogne caspia (Pallas)

GENERAL DISTRIBUTION: A cosmopolitan species; in North America it breeds in widely scattered localities from Great Slave Lake east to southeastern Quebec and south to California, Oregon, the Great Lakes, the Gulf Coast of Texas and Louisiana, and South Carolina. Winters on the Pacific Coast from San Francisco Bay to western Mexico (Colima), on the Gulf Coast, and on the Atlantic Coast from South Carolina to Mexico.

STATUS IN GEORGIA: A fairly common transient and winter resident on the coast and of casual occurrence there during the summer.

Worthington took two specimens on Sapelo Island, December 16, 1887, and reported this species uncommon at the mouth of the Altamaha River during the winter of 1889-90. I noted an occasional bird near the mouth of the Savannah River on January 27, 1924. Mrs. Bassett observed one at Tybee Island, May 11, 1930, and eight at Belfast, August 24 and 25, 1930. Woodward [1949] found this large tern fairly common at Sea Island from January through April 1946-48.

HABITS AND RECOGNITION: The Caspian Tern is the largest of the terns, and because of its size, almost that of a Herring Gull, and wide expanse of wing, it is more suggestive in appearance of a gull than of a tern. However, like all the terns, it flies with its conspicuous red bill pointed down, and this characteristic, together with its forked tail, should readily distinguish it. Being rather heavy-bodied, it does not give the impression of buoyancy in the air that the smaller terns do, but its flight is, nevertheless, strong and graceful. Like the gulls, it seems to delight in soaring high in the air, circling until almost out of sight overhead. Although possibly gregarious by nature, it is rarely observed in flocks of any size, and so far as my own experience on the Georgia coast is concerned, it is exceptional to see more than one or two birds at a time. It is at all times a wary and suspicious bird, and so, unlike the other terns, has suffered little in past years from the depredations of man. Its food, largely small fish, is secured well off-shore, and once its appetite is satisfied, it rests for long intervals on an isolated sand spit, or a wide stretch of open beach where it can readily detect any real or fancied danger.

American Black Tern
Chlidonias niger surinamensis   (Gmelin)

GENERAL DISTRIBUTION: Breeds from central eastern Alaska and Great Slave Lake, and locally in Nova Scotia, south to southern California, Nevada, Colorado, Kansas, northern Missouri, and Tennessee. Winters from the West Coast of Mexico south to Dutch Guiana, Peru, and Chile.

STATUS IN GEORGIA: An uncommon spring transient and a common fall transient throughout the state and of casual occurrence on the coast during the summer months.

In the interior, the Black Tern has been reported from the following localities:

Augusta: A regular spring, late summer, and early autumn transient. Adults in full breeding plumage taken May 4. Autumnal birds are nearly all young of the year [Murphey, 1937].

Athens: A regular and at times fairly common transient in the fall. Its abundance was influenced to a certain extent by the weather, for heavy rains in August and September, which invariably flooded such spots as the Sandy Creek bottoms, usually resulted in the appearance of scattered flocks of these terns. Extreme dates of occurrence in the fall are July 29 (1926) and September 16 (1929). The only record for the spring migration is that of a single bird seen May 25, 1929, at Lake Kirota [Burleigh, 1938].

Lake Rabun, Rabun County: A flock of thirty seen September 4, 1939 [Giles, 1940].

Dalton, Whitfield County: Single birds seen May 18 and September 5, 1943 [Hamilton et al., 1944].

Lake Rutledge, Morgan County: Two birds seen October 12 and 13, 1940 [Griffin, 1940].

Atlanta: Observed only in the fall, extreme dates of occurrence being August 5 (1928) and September 15 (1923) [Greene, 1933, and Griffin, 1941].

Macon: Noted May 11, 1952, and September 21–24, 1955 [Cater, fide Johnston, MS].

Waynesboro: A single bird seen September 5, 1935 [Stevenson, 1936].

Tifton: Seen September 15, 1941 (Norris).

Irwin County: One bird seen at Crystal

Lake, September 1, 1940 [Norris, 1940].

Grady County: A flock of fifteen seen August 16, 1947 [Stoddard, MS].

Okefenokee Swamp: Five birds seen on Chase Prairie, August 6, 1940 [Hebard, letter].

On the coast, it has been reported at Savannah in the fall between the dates of August 15 (1912) and October 20 (1922), and in the spring on March 30, 1918, and April 11, 1922. I observed a single bird still in winter plumage on Oysterbed Island, June 14, 1927, and Norris [letter] reports "6 immatures and 2 adults on St. Simons Island June 10, 1942."

HABITS AND RECOGNITION: The Black Tern is the only Georgia tern that can be seen commonly in migration away from the coast. It is found during the breeding season in fresh-water marshes, and in its long journeys to and from its winter quarters takes advantage of any such marshes it finds en route. Its food consists almost entirely of small insects, and these it secures as it flies, picking them up from the tops of the vegetation or catching them in the air. This method of feeding doubtless accounts for its erratic flight, for in the air its course is apt to take almost any direction, and may be swift or leisurely as the occasion demands. In common with the other smaller terns, its flight suggests lightness and buoyancy, and even in bad weather it apparently experiences little difficulty in aerial feeding. In migration it occurs commonly on the coast, and can be seen then in harbors and inlets, pursuing its erratic flight low over the water. It is an easy bird to recognize as it is intermediate in size between the Least Tern and the Common Tern, and in breeding plumage has a conspicuous black head and underparts. Young birds and adults in winter plumage have this black largely replaced by white, but black markings remain on the head, and this character, together with the rather short, forked tail, should readily identify it.

Atlantic Noddy Tern
Anoüs stolidus stolidus (Linnaeus)

GENERAL DISTRIBUTION: Breeds, and is to a large extent resident, on the Dry Tortugas, in the Bahamas and West Indies, and from British Honduras to Margarita Island, Venezuela; also on St. Helena, Tristan da Cunha, and Ascension Island, in the South Atlantic Ocean.

STATUS IN GEORGIA: Of accidental occurrence on the coast.

On the same day, October 1, 1950, that Ivan Tomkins picked up two mummified Bridled Terns on the beach at the north end of Tybee Island, he also found another mummified tern that has been identified by the Fish and Wildlife Service as an adult *Anoüs stolidus stolidus.* This is the only record for the state. Like the Bridled Terns it was, as Tomkins suggests, very probably blown in by the tropical hurricane in early September.

HABITS AND RECOGNITION: The Noddy Tern is a tropical species that may be looked for in Georgia after the infrequent hurricanes that strike the coast in the fall months. It apparently rarely wanders north of its breeding range, and accordingly will always be of accidental occurrence in the state. It is an easy bird to identify, for with the exception of the dull white crown, its plumage is uniformly brown, and it is the only tern with a rounded tail. It is said to be reluctant to alight on water at any time, and its food, small fish, is picked from the surface of the ocean. It has never been known to dive for its prey, nor does it attempt to swim in even the calmest seas.

Skimmers: *Family Rynchopidae*

Northern Black Skimmer
Rynchops nigra nigra Linnaeus

GENERAL DISTRIBUTION: Breeds on the Atlantic Coast from New Jersey to Florida, and on the Gulf Coast from Texas to Florida. Winters from Georgia and the Gulf Coast south to northern Brazil.

STATUS IN GEORGIA: A common resident on the coast and of accidental occurrence in the interior of the state.

Worthington reported it common during the winter at the mouth of the Altamaha River, and he took specimens on Sapelo Island, November 21, 1887. Helme noted a flock on Cumberland Island, January 13, 1902, and estimated that there were approximately 2,500 birds there on March 10. I observed a flock of fully 1,000 skimmers on Blackbeard Island, January 21, 1932. Woodward [1949] reported this species common on Sea Island from January through April, 1946–48.

It formerly nested on Pelican Point, a key lying some distance off the south end of Tybee Island [Erichsen, 1921], but is now known to breed only on Oysterbed Island, lying near the mouth of the Savannah River. Here it has increased noticeably in recent years. In June, 1923, I estimated that approximately 200 pairs were nesting on the island, while four years later, in June, 1927, this breeding colony was found to contain between 800 and 1,000 pairs of these birds. Rossignol's egg catalog records 102 occupied nests found here from 1922 through 1934, 86 holding four eggs and 16 but three. His earliest breeding record is June 9 (1928), four fresh eggs; his latest July 6 (1930), four slightly incubated eggs.

Family Rynchopidae: SKIMMERS

For the interior of the state there is but a single record. Murphey [1937] reports a pair taken at Sandbar Ferry on the Savannah River just below Augusta, in 1888.

HABITS AND RECOGNITION: In many respects the Black Skimmer is unique. As its name implies, it secures its food, largely small fish, by skimming low over the surface of the water and scooping up any tempting morsel that it encounters. For this purpose, its conspicuously red (tipped with black) bill is highly modified, being compressed laterally, with the lower mandible much longer than the upper. The process of feeding consists of flying close to the water with the lower mandible slicing the surface until some edible morsel is contacted and secured by a quick motion of the bill. By this incredible process even active small fish are captured as food for the skimmer and its young. Much of its feeding is done at night, but by personal observation I have found that it is also active in daylight.

No bird is more gregarious by nature, for it not only nests in large compact colonies, but during the fall and winter months large flocks can be seen resting much of the day on a sand bar or stretch of open beach. Such flocks are not scattered out, but invariably occupy the smallest possible area, the birds being so close together that at a distance a large flock suggests a black patch on the sand. The skimmer's slender build and conspicuous black and white plumage, combined with its unusual beak and method of feeding, distinguish it and make identification very simple.

On June 16, 1923, I found approximately 200 pairs of skimmers breeding on Oysterbed Island, nesting activities, despite the seemingly late date, having just begun. The nests were well-defined hollows in the sand, with no lining of any kind, and were segregated on an open stretch of beach in the middle of the island. They were an inch or an inch and one-half deep, and ten to twelve inches across. There were as yet comparatively few hollows in proportion to the number of birds seen, and fully half the nests were empty. Forty held eggs, two with full sets of four, and the rest with incomplete sets of one, two, or three eggs, eleven holding three eggs each, twelve with two eggs, and the remainder but one each. The nests averaged but three feet apart, although many were closer than that. The birds were noisy when first flushed, but later gathered at the edge of the water in a long black line, and were then fairly quiet.

I returned to this colony on June 14, 1927, and found that it had more than doubled in size. Four hundred and thirteen nests with eggs were counted, while fully as many were as yet empty. The eggs varied in number from one to five, two-thirds of the nests holding four; but three held five. The nests, as before, were well-defined hollows in the sand, and as they were within a few feet of each other, the colony as a whole covered but a small part of the island. On my first leaving the boat, the birds left their nests and literally charged at me with quite an uproar, turning aside when possibly a hundred feet away and then circling overhead. They later gathered at the water's edge in large compact groups that flew with apparent reluctance at my approach.

Auks, Murres, and Puffins: *Family Alcidae*

Common Dovekie
Plautus alle alle (Linnaeus)

GENERAL DISTRIBUTION: Breeds on the north coasts and islands of Greenland, Iceland, Spitzbergen, and Novaya Zemlya. Winters from Greenland south to Long Island, and casually to South Carolina.

STATUS IN GEORGIA: Largely of accidental occurrence on the coast. It was recorded for the first time during the unprecedented invasion of 1932, when countless numbers of Dovekies appeared as far south as the Florida Keys and Cuba.

Murphey and Vogt [1933] quote Alexander Sprunt, Jr., as follows: "Captain T. Danielson, of Lightship 94, stationed off Tybee Beach, Georgia, brought three birds to the Charleston Museum in fluid, on December 12th. He stated that 'thousands' of them had passed his ship in late November, all flying southward. Some stopped about the ship and he succeeded in catching several with a dip-net from the deck." Greene [1935] records a specimen taken on St. Simons Island by George Stevens on November 23 and another bird seen the same day. Still another specimen was taken by Tomkins at the Savannah lightship and sent to the Charleston Museum. After an interval of eighteen years, the Dovekie again appeared on the Georgia coast, two dead birds being reported by Tomkins as having been picked up on Tybee Island on December 14, 1950.

HABITS AND RECOGNITION: The Dovekie exists in enormous numbers on its far northern breeding grounds, but being a hardy bird, is of only casual occurrence south of New England. Much of its life is spent in mid-ocean where it survives successfully the violent storms it encounters, so it must have been an unusual combination of circumstances that resulted in its being driven as far south as Cuba in the early winter of 1932. It is a plump little bird about the size of a robin, and, with its black back and white underparts, is so unlike any other species occurring on the coast that it should be easily recognized. It is a strong flier, but is equally at home on the water, riding the waves buoyantly, and is adept at diving and swimming beneath the surface.

ORDER COLUMBIFORMES

Pigeons and Doves: *Family Columbidae*

Eastern White-winged Dove
Zenaida asiatica asiatica (Linnaeus)

GENERAL DISTRIBUTION: Resident from the lower Río Grande Valley, Texas, south through eastern Mexico to Costa Rica, and in the Bahamas, Cuba, Haiti, and Jamaica. Casual in Florida and Louisiana.

STATUS IN GEORGIA: Of accidental occurrence.

There is but a single record for this species in Georgia, a bird shot by Harrison Lee near Hoboken, in Brantley County, on January 6, 1917 [Harper, 1918].

HABITS AND RECOGNITION: Anyone fortunate enough to see a White-winged Dove in Georgia should have no difficulty in recognizing it, for while about the size of a Mourning Dove, it has a conspicuous white wing patch, and a short, rounded tail. It is apparently more gregarious than the other doves, for it usually nests in large compact colonies and occurs in flocks throughout the year. On its breeding grounds, it is a noisy bird, its cooing notes being heard at all hours of the day and often well into the night. It apparently has a tendency to wander some distance from its normal range, for, although noted but once in Georgia, there are numerous records for Florida and the Gulf Coast in the late fall and early winter.

Eastern Mourning Dove
Zenaidura macroura carolinensis (Linnaeus)

GENERAL DISTRIBUTION: Breeds from Ontario, New Brunswick, and Nova Scotia south to the Florida Keys and the Gulf Coast. Winters from Iowa, southern Michigan, and Massachusetts south to the east coast of Mexico, Central America, and Panama.

STATUS IN GEORGIA: A common resident throughout the state, being especially numerous during the winter months when its numbers are materially increased by migrants from the north.

At Athens [Burleigh, 1938], I found it most abundant from the latter part of October through the middle of March, flocks in which there were 100 or more birds being seen feeding in open fields. Scattered pairs were noted each year in late February, but the first nests were not found until late March.

Murphey (1937) states that at Augusta "the numbers of this species are vastly augmented in autumn and winter by migrant birds which arrive in October and remain until March. Great numbers are killed annually for sport—in years gone by I have known of 1,500 to 2,000 to be slaughtered in a single day."

Grimm (1946) found the Mourning Dove common throughout the year on the Camp Stewart reservation. He noted large flocks in the vicinity of Gliscom's Pond on October 25, 1942, and flocks totaling several hundred birds near Flemington between February 16 and March 30, 1944.

Taber (1930) reports that a detailed study of available banding records showed that northern breeding doves concentrated in large numbers during the winter months in southeastern Georgia.

Nelson (1952), reporting the results of a Mourning Dove Study in Georgia from April, 1949, to January, 1953, under the Federal Aid to Wildlife Program, states that nesting occurs from February through October with the bulk from mid-May until late July. The Georgia population is lowest in May, gradually increasing through the summer and fall, when a peak is reached in September, with a higher peak in early December. The population is relatively stable until the northern migration begins in April. Doves move out of the state until migration ceases about May 20.

HABITS AND RECOGNITION: (Contributed by Harold S. Peters.) The Mourning Dove is second only to the Bobwhite as a game bird in Georgia. Apart from its importance to hunters, it has an esthetic appeal to many persons, and is well known to rural and urban folk alike. While actual figures are lacking before 1949, the dove population appears to be slowly declining in the eastern United States and, therefore, in Georgia. Certainly the fantastically large kills of past years are now impossible as well as illegal. The total kill for the state was estimated (Nelson, *loc. cit.*) to be nearly two million per year from 1949 to 1952. Three thousand doves have been banded in Georgia during the past thirty-five years. Three per cent have been recovered, ninety-two inside the state and seven from other states (Alabama, Florida, Illinois, Mississippi, and South Carolina). This may appear to indicate that Georgia shoots many of the birds produced in the state, but since these doves were usually banded as flying birds, they may have originated in other states. Nearly 200 doves have been shot in Georgia that were banded in other states (Alabama, 12; Arkansas, 1; Florida, 18; Illinois, 18; Indiana, 7; Louisiana, 1; Massachusetts, 37; Michigan, 19; Missouri, 3; New Jersey, 4; New York, 11; North Carolina, 5; Ohio, 23; Ontario, 2; Pennsylvania, 10; South Carolina, 7; Tennessee, 2; Texas, 1; Virginia, 3; and Wisconsin, 6). In fact, Georgia has recovered more banded doves from other states than any other southeastern state. These recoveries prove that doves migrate to Georgia from practically every state to the northward, from Massachusetts westward to Wisconsin.

The Mourning Dove is common to abundant throughout the year. Nesting begins in late February in extreme southern Georgia, and by early May it is under way in all sections of the state. The peak of nesting is from mid-May through July, and most pairs raise three broods of young. Most of the nesting is over by early September, but late nests have been found until mid-October. Occasionally a pair will utilize an old nest of a robin, cardinal, blue jay, or some other species. The two eggs are otherwise laid in flimsy platform-like nests; the earliest ones almost invariably are built in pines. As the deciduous trees leaf out, some nests may be found in them, although the species seems to prefer evergreens. Nesting failures are frequent; only half of the attempts are successful. Strong winds and cool, rainy weather cause many nest failures, while squirrels, blue jays, and similar predators account for some destruction.

The eggs hatch in fourteen days and the nestlings at first are fed a "dove milk," then small seeds, and finally larger seeds and grains. They leave the nest in twelve to fourteen days, but are partially dependent upon the parents for a week or two afterwards, even during part of the succeeding brood cycle. The juveniles tend to flock together and feed upon waste grain and weed seeds while gradually trying out their wings and moving southward. But the bulk of the juveniles raised in northern states seem to move southward into Georgia and other southeastern states during late summer and early fall. By September many northern-raised birds have reached the state, and others continue to arrive through October, November, and even early December. Some which arrive early in the fall will pass on into Florida, only to return in mid- or late winter and not leave until early spring for northern nesting grounds.

Although sociable by nature and seeming to prefer nesting around farmsteads and in small towns or in the suburbs of cities, doves scatter out during the nesting season to farms and edges of woodlands and even to mountain valleys. The dove eats only seeds and grains which can be secured from the ground. The weak feet and bill preclude scratching for food and plucking grain from ears of corn or plant stalks. They seem to prefer the seeds of grasses and waste grains like wheat and corn so that no damage results to agricultural crops.

Western Mourning Dove
Zenaidura macroura marginella (Woodhouse)

GENERAL DISTRIBUTION: Breeds in western and interior North America from eastern Texas, Oklahoma, western Iowa, and Minnesota to the Pacif-

SOUTHERN PILEATED WOODPECKERS

Dryocopus pileatus pileatus

This handsome bird was common throughout the heavily wooded bottomlands.
If I wanted to see one at close range, all I had to do was go to a certain
fallen log shortly after daybreak. Here, following the same route
morning after morning, a male bird flew in low and set to work hacking
the rotten wood to pieces in its search for grubs and ants. After it had fed
awhile, it flew to a standing dead tree not far away and rapped sharply.
The sound was very different from the dull, methodical *chop, chop*
produced while hunting food. The bird in the foreground is a male,
the other a female.

ic Coast, north to Manitoba, Saskatchewan, and British Columbia, and south throughout Mexico. Winters south to western Panama and apparently east regularly to the southeastern United States.

STATUS IN GEORGIA: Apparently a fairly common winter resident throughout the state.

Allen J. Duvall, of the Fish and Wildlife Service, makes the following comments about these doves in Georgia [MS]:

Recent studies have indicated that racial components of fall and winter Mourning Dove populations can be determined by identifying wing samples obtained during hunter bag checks. This is done by careful comparisons with museum reference collections. To interpret these identifications properly, it was necessary to establish the breeding limits of the two currently accepted forms in the United States as well as to determine the amount of variation within these two (*carolinensis* and *marginella*). In so doing it was learned that the eastern mourning dove (*carolinensis*) has a much more restricted breeding range than heretofore known and that there is a relatively broad area east and west of the Mississippi River in which doves are intermediate in characters, and in which some resemble *carolinensis* while others resemble *marginella*. This population, therefore, is referred to below as "intermediate."

Examination of more than 1,000 wing samples received from Georgia hunters during the split dove season (September 1951 and January 1952) gave the following results: On a statewide basis 62.9 per cent of doves bagged by hunters represented the Eastern Mourning Dove (*carolinensis*); 27.4 per cent represented the "intermediate" population of the midwest; and 9.7 per cent represented the Western Mourning Dove (*marginella*). However, to get a clear picture of the varying racial composition of the dove bag in Georgia during the fall and winter, the large sample of wings was grouped according to the season they were shot as well as to the part of the state (north or south Georgia) where taken.

A most striking difference was noted between the September half of the season when 80 per cent of the wings were of the eastern race as opposed to only 19.2 per cent in January. The western subspecies, *marginella,* composed only 2 per cent of the bag in September, but jumped to 29.6 in January. In addition the intermediate population made up half of the doves bagged by Georgia hunters in January.

From the above analysis of wing samples, it appears that during the fall and winter of 1951–52 there was a large influx of migrants into the state of Georgia, largely from areas west of the Appalachians, and that these migrants were not present in appreciable numbers until after the close of the fall portion of the split hunting season.

Samples considered to be *marginella* were from Catoosa County, in the extreme northwestern part of the state, to Echols County in central southern Georgia. A total of 99 wings (out of the 1,022) were determined as the western form.

In addition to the above, a female collected by H. L. Stoddard, Sr., at Birdsong Plantation, Grady County, on December 31, 1950, is typical of the western subspecies, *marginella*.

HABITS AND RECOGNITION: Like most subspecies, the Western Mourning Dove has little to distinguish it, as far as general appearance or actions go; it is paler above and below, but specimens are necessary to determine this.

Passenger Pigeon
Ectopistes migratorius   (Linnaeus)

GENERAL DISTRIBUTION: Now extinct; formerly bred from western Mackenzie, central Keewatin, central Ontario, central Quebec, and Nova Scotia south to Kansas, Mississippi, Kentucky, Pennsylvania, and New York, and wintered from Arkansas and North Carolina south to central Texas, Louisiana, and Florida.

STATUS IN GEORGIA: Formerly a common winter resident, but not recorded since 1893.

Very little is known about the occurrence of this species in the state in former years. The first specimen taken in the state, a male, was collected by John Abbot at Savannah about 1812, and is now in the Zoological Museum of Berlin University, Germany [Streseman, 1953]. In LeConte's list of Georgia birds [White, 1849], it is mentioned, but without comment. However, there is a specimen in the United States National Museum taken by LeConte, with the locality on the label given as Georgia, which is probably the basis for the inclusion of the species in this list. Neither date nor specific locality is given, but there seems no reason to question the fact that this bird was actually taken in the state.

Murphey [1937] has given us the most complete account of the presence of the Passenger Pigeon in Georgia:

Formerly a regular winter resident. Since 1895 I have made diligent inquiry whenever and wherever possible of older residents of this section as to what they knew or had observed concerning the Passenger Pigeon in the days of its abundance. The late Messrs. Albert and George Twiggs, who spent a large part of their boyhood in the western portion of Aiken County above the fall line, informed me that during the years immediately before the Civil War and immediately thereafter, that there had been great flights of pigeons passing from West to East and that some of these flocks required an hour or more to pass a given point and that their formation was so compact that they cast a shadow upon the ground like a moving cloud but that the last of these great flights which was witnessed was in the winter of 1869. My father, who was born in 1822, informed me that while it was common at times during every winter, it never occurred in the country around Hephzibah in great flocks, such as have been described from the West, and that the largest flocks which he ever saw could not have contained more than 3,000 birds. Whenever the pigeons arrived, every lad who was old enough to fire the family fowling piece was excused from school and sent to the woods to shoot, and pigeon-pot-pie was a highly prized dish throughout the countryside for days thereafter. Richmond County was heavily wooded at that time (1836), much of the original hardwood timber was still standing and it was along the ridges covered with deciduous trees that the birds congregated. They never remained in one locality more than a few days at a time, but passed on as suddenly as they had appeared. The concensus of opinion derived from the sources above referred to was that the pigeons continued to come in fair but steadily diminishing numbers until the winter of 1884–85 when a sharp drop in their numbers was observed, and in a few years, they had entirely disappeared.

Following are the last records of its appearance in this vicinity:

1888: Dr. Robert H. Land shot one from a large oak in his farm yard seven miles from Augusta.

1887: I saw and handled a bunch of about eight birds exposed for sale at the "Fish, Game and Ice Shop" of Mr. Adolphus Bignon, Augusta.

1887: Two were hanging with other game on exhibition in the window of Lexius Henson's restaurant, Augusta.

1887: One was shot by Mr. George Leitner in Davison's woods, which is now within the city limits of Augusta.

1888: Two killed while feeding on hack berries in "Lover's Lane," three miles below Augusta, by Lawrence McMurphey.

1893: September 12th, a male, young of the year, killed in the same woodland referred to in the Leitner record, 1887, by the late George Jackson and presented by him to Mr. Henry Hillyer, a promising young ornithologist of Augusta. I saw this bird in the flesh and after Mr. Hillyer's untimely death, I packed and sent the skin along with the rest of his collection to the Department of Biology, University of Georgia, in Athens, where it was destroyed by fire occurring a few years later which consumed Science Hall with all its contents.

HABITS AND RECOGNITION: When one reads of the incredible number of Passenger Pigeons that existed in this country at one time, it is difficult to understand how this species could have been exterminated in such a relatively few years. Extremely gregarious by nature, these pigeons nested in compact rookeries that frequently covered many square miles, and migrated in flocks so large as to be almost unbelievable. Probably the outstanding account of such a migratory movement is that given by Alexander Wilson (1832), who estimated that the number of pigeons passing overhead in a single afternoon exceeded two and one-quarter billion birds. Apparently, however, no species can long stand up against man's cupidity and greed unless accorded at least a minimum of protection, and the profit to be derived from the sale of both squabs and adult birds was the factor that doomed this splendid bird to rapid extinction. No wild birds have been seen alive since 1898, and the last Passenger Pigeon died of old age in the Cincinnati Zoo in September, 1914.

Eastern Ground Dove
Columbigallina passerina passerina (Linnaeus)

GENERAL DISTRIBUTION: Resident on the Atlantic Coast from North Carolina to Florida, and locally on the Gulf Coast west to eastern Texas.

STATUS IN GEORGIA: Resident and fairly common south of the fall line, but largely of accidental occurrence in the northern half of the state.

Worthington found this little dove common on Sapelo Island in the winter of 1887–88. I noted it in small numbers at Savannah on April 29, 1922, January 7, 1923, and February 28, 1929; at Cuthbert, Randolph County, on March 27, 1923; at Newton, Baker County, on December 26, 1924, November 19, 1929, and September 27, 1930; at Darien, McIntosh County, on May 29, 1929; at Smithville, Lee County, on July 9, 1929; and at Banks Lake, Lanier County, on November 21, 1929. It has also been reported from Augusta [Murphey, 1937], Monroe County, [Griffin, 1936], Stewart County, [Eyles, 1936], Grady County, (Stoddard), and has been recorded as breeding on Blackbeard, Cumberland, and Ossabaw Islands.

Erichsen [MS] reports finding fifty-one occupied nests of this little dove in Chatham County from 1914 through 1947. The majority held eggs or young from the middle of April until early June, extreme nesting dates being two fresh eggs on March 16 (1940) and two small young on September 5 (1935). At Fitzgerald, Norris and Hopkins [MS] report a nest with two eggs on June 22, 1941, and another, also with two eggs, on July 29, 1947. The earliest breeding record for the state is that of a nest found in Baker County that held two eggs on January 23, 1950 [Hopkins, 1951]. What is apparently the latest breeding record is reported by Norris [letter], who collected a male fledgling, still pin-feathered and with traces of natal down on the head, at Tifton on October 31, 1941.

North of the fall line the Ground Dove has been reported at Rising Fawn on May 9, 1885 (Howell), and at Atlanta on April 1, 1954 (Mrs. J. M. Smith); and specimens have been taken in Newton County on December 28, 1909, and August 4 and 21, 1911; and at Roswell, Fulton County, on February 20, 1920 [Greene, 1933].

HABITS AND RECOGNITION: Although nowhere very common, the little Ground Dove is a familiar bird to the rural population of southern Georgia, for it is fond of the proximity of man and is found about farm yards, in open cultivated fields, and not infrequently at the edges of the smaller towns. Usually single birds or pairs are seen, and it is possible that these birds remain mated for life. They seem to lead a very sedentary existence, staying throughout the year within a rather circumscribed area, and never, even in midwinter, gathering into flocks. They are well named, for much of their life is spent on the ground, walking rapidly about with a characteristic nodding motion of the head. If forced to fly, they go but a short distance before dropping to the ground again.

Nesting activities are carried on from late January until October, and it is probable that two or more broods are reared each year. The nests are frequently on the ground, but have been found in bushes or on the horizontal limb of a tree at a height varying from a foot or so to, in several instances, thirty feet. They are frail platforms of rootlets and grasses, with a slight hollow in the center to hold the two white eggs that are normally laid. Erichsen [1920] mentions a nest, found on Ossabaw Island on May 13, 1915, that was a slight hollow in the sand, unlined, and another that was merely an old cardinal's nest to which nothing had been added.

No difficulty should be experienced in recognizing the Ground Dove wherever seen, for it is much smaller than the Mourning Dove, and when it flies, the reddish under surface of the wings is quite noticeable.

Mexican Ground Dove
Columbigallina passerina pallescens   (Baird)

GENERAL DISTRIBUTION: Lower California, southeastern California, southern Arizona, and western Texas south to Guatemala.

STATUS IN GEORGIA: Of accidental occurrence.

There is but a single record of this well-marked race in Georgia, a male taken by Robert C. McClanahan at Rockledge, in Laurens County, on March 26, 1938 [Burleigh, 1948].

HABITS AND RECOGNITION: This race of the ground dove is noticeably paler than are birds of the Southeastern states, but otherwise is similar in appearance and actions. It possibly occurs more often in the state than this one record would indicate, for in recent years it has been found that *pallescens* is a regular and not uncommon transient on the Gulf Coast [Burleigh, 1944].

ORDER PSITTACIFORMES

Parrots and Parakeets: *Family Psittacidae*

Eastern Carolina Parakeet
Conuropsis carolinensis carolinensis (Linnaeus)

GENERAL DISTRIBUTION: Now extinct. Formerly found throughout Florida, north along the Atlantic Coast to southern Virginia and west to Alabama. Casual farther north to Pennsylvania and New York.

STATUS IN GEORGIA: Formerly common, now extinct.

Little is known of the occurrence of the parakeet in Georgia. LeConte [White, 1849], writing in 1849, said, "It is a remarkable fact that our paroquets are very rapidly diminishing in number. Along our maritime districts, where 15 or 20 years ago they were plentiful, scarcely any are now to be found; and it is probable that in a short time they will entirely disappear from our State."

Bailey [1883], writing of a collection of eggs made by S. W. Wilson, chiefly on St. Simons Island and in Wayne and McIntosh counties, records a set of two eggs taken April 26, 1855, from a hollow tree. One egg was sent to Robert Ridgway at the United States National Museum, who confirmed the identification.

HABITS AND RECOGNITION: It is unfortunate that such a spectacular bird as the parakeet was so completely and so rapidly wiped out as a part of the indigenous bird life of the eastern United States. Once abundant throughout its range, its brilliantly colored flocks were a conspicuous part of the wildlife of the Southeastern states, and their disappearance is a sad commentary on the destructiveness of man. It must be admitted, however, that in the case of the parakeets there was some justification for their slaughter. Originally their food consisted of the seeds of the pines and such deciduous hardwoods as the maples and elms, as well as those of such weeds as the thistle and the cocklebur. Had they remained satisfied with this fare, the story might have been quite different. Unfortunately, they developed a fondness for corn and for cultivated fruits, and the large flocks caused so much damage to crops that the birds were killed at every opportunity.

The Carolina Parakeet is approximately the size of a Mourning Dove, with a long pointed tail, a bright green body, and a yellow head becoming orange about the base of the bill. These birds invariably occurred in flocks and were said to be rather unsuspicious and easy to approach. If frightened, their flight was swift and straight, accompanied by discordant cries that were audible for a long distance. It has been many years now since the last living bird was seen, although there are unconfirmed reports of small flocks being observed in southern Florida as late as 1920.

ORDER CUCULIFORMES

Cuckoos, Roadrunners, and Anis:
Family Cuculidae

Eastern Yellow-billed Cuckoo
Coccyzus americanus americanus   (Linnaeus)

GENERAL DISTRIBUTION: Breeds from North Dakota, Minnesota, southern Ontario, Quebec, and New Brunswick south to northern Mexico, the Gulf Coast, and southern Florida. Winters in small numbers in southern Florida and in northern South America (Venezuela, Colombia, Ecuador, and Uruguay).

STATUS IN GEORGIA: A common summer resident throughout the state.

The Yellow-billed Cuckoo is generally distributed over all of Georgia, usually appearing in the spring in April and being only infrequently seen after the middle of October.

Earliest arrivals in the spring were reported at St. Marys, April 3 (1902); Hinesville, April 22 (1945); Savannah, March 24; Okefenokee Swamp, April 11 (1944); Grady County, April 9 (1929); Fitzgerald, May 8 (1952); Americus, May 6 (1942); Kestler, Early County, April 6; Macon, April 5 (1953); Atlanta, April 7 (1906); Athens, April 23 (1923); and Augusta, April 26 (1945).

The latest in the fall were recorded at Athens, October 29 (1920); Atlanta, October 25 (1946); Macon, October 16 (1954); Fitzgerald, October 7 (1939); Grady County, October 28 (1924); Okefenokee Swamp, October 17 (1947); Savannah, November 4 (1915).

It has been reported as breeding at Allenhurst, Okefenokee Swamp, Grady County, Athens, Atlanta, East Point, Augusta, Columbia County, Dahlonega, Toccoa, Young Harris, Margret, Chatsworth, Rome, and Cloudland. At Savannah, Rossignol [letter], gives as nesting extremes (ten nests): four slightly incubated eggs, April 25 (1906); and two fresh eggs, June 1 (1913). Erichsen [MS] cites as his latest breeding record for Chatham County a nest with two young, June 28 (1933). He likewise reports a nest with three young at Midway, Liberty County, May 17, 1913. Hebard [1948] records nests for the Coleraine Plantation, near the St. Marys River: one on July 18, 1943, with two small young; the second on May 9, 1945, with two eggs; and the third on June 10, 1945, with four eggs.

In Grady County, Stoddard [MS] reports a nest with one egg, June 23, 1924, and two "bob-tailed young" just out of the nest on May 16, 1946.

The latest breeding record for the state is that of a nest found in Baker County that held three eggs on September 8, 1940 [Hopkins, letter]. Denton [letter] found a nest at Augusta, June 13, 1945, with two incubated eggs, and another at Appling, in Columbia County, that held three eggs June 10, 1950. Griffin [1940] cites as nesting extremes for the Atlanta region May 10 (1939), one egg (Griffin), and July 26 (1903), two eggs (Mills). Jones [1947] records a nest found at Rome on May 23, 1946, that held four young. A nest that I found at Young Harris on June 21, 1922, contained three incubated eggs.

HABITS AND RECOGNITION: To many a casual observer the Yellow-billed Cuckoo is a voice rather than a bird. Shy and secretive by nature, it spends its days in the denser-foliaged trees where its quiet, stealthy movements usually go unobserved. Its characteristic notes, however, reveal its presence, and actually render it more conspicuous (at least to the ear) than other less retiring species. These guttural notes are loud, prolonged, and uttered in a gradually decreasing tempo; Aretas A. Saunders describes them by syllables as "KaKaKaKaKaKaKaKa Ka Ka Ka Ka Ka Ka Kow Kow Kow Kow Kow Kow Kow Kow." If the author of this strange "song" is searched for, the reward is a glimpse of a slender brown bird with a long tail sitting motionless where the foliage is thickest or disappearing in the nearest underbrush with swift, silent flight.

Breeding activities begin in early May, but it is usually the latter part of the month before many of the birds are nesting, and it is not uncommon to find an occasional pair rearing their young in late June or July. The nest is built in a thick bush or tree, usually from four to twelve feet from the ground, and is a rather flimsy structure of twigs and dead leaves, the slight cavity, holding the three or four light blue eggs, being lined with gray moss, dry pine needles, or grasses. Eggs are apparently not infrequently laid at irregular intervals, for young of different ages can often be found in a nest.

Economically no bird is more valuable to the farmer, the horticulturist, or the forester, than is the cuckoo. Unlike most other species, it is very fond of caterpillars, and is especially destructive to those that are hairy or spiny, and for that reason distasteful to the average bird. Tent caterpillars are eaten wherever found, and this fact alone should accord the cuckoo protection at all times. Other insects and various fruits are also eaten, but there is little question that caterpillars comprise fully half of its diet. Denton [letter] states that "with unprecedented numbers of Georgians fishing, the catalpa caterpillars (Catawba worms), a prime bream and red breast bait, bring a premium price as fish bait. The Yellow-bill's liking for these caterpillars causes some to be shot by collectors of these 'worms.' Once a Yellow-bill finds an infested tree, he will not leave it alone until the last caterpillar is eaten." This "crime" seems slight reason for shooting a cuckoo, and the collectors should remember that the bird is fully protected by law.

Black-billed Cuckoo
Coccyzus erythropthalmus (Wilson)

GENERAL DISTRIBUTION: Breeds from southeastern Alberta, southern Manitoba, southern Quebec, and Prince Edward Island south to Kansas, Arkansas, North Carolina, and northern Georgia. Winters in South America from Colombia to Peru.

STATUS IN GEORGIA: A regular but uncommon spring and fall transient and a scarce and local summer resident in the northern part of the state.

Earliest arrivals in the spring were reported at Sapelo Island, April 25 (1888); Savannah, April 9 (1911) and April 13 (1915); Macon, April 23 (1938); Atlanta, April 24 (1916); and Athens, April 27 (1929). Late spring transients were noted in the Okefenokee Swamp, May 8, 1912; Grady County, May 7 and 16, 1940; Fitzgerald, May 27, 1940; Macon, May 18, 1924; and Athens, May 31 and June 5, 1926.

In the fall the Black-billed Cuckoo was reported at Atlanta as late as October 14 (1923); at Athens, between the dates of September 15 (1926 and 1931) and October 13 (1926); Macon, October 9, 1937; Thomasville, October 21, 1925; and in Grady County, September 21, 1938, and September 30, 1940.

Breeding records are few in number. Baird, Brewer, and Ridgway [1847] state that the nest and eggs of this species were taken at Varnell Station by Alexander Gerhardt. Greene [1933] reports two eggs collected at Roswell, Fulton County, May 14, 1911; and a nest containing one young bird and one egg, photographed by Wallace Rogers at Atlanta on May 5, 1920. Bell [1940] found a nest at Fairburn, in southern Fulton County, that held two half-grown young on September 7, 1940. Arthur H. Howell collected a male at Margret, in Fannin County, on June 8, 1927, that apparently was breeding, but a search for the nest proved unsuccessful. Johnston [1947] reports two birds seen near Lake Rabun, in Rabun County, on May 10, 1947. One was collected and found to have a large brood patch, indicating an occupied nest somewhere in the vicinity, which, however, was not found.

HABITS AND RECOGNITION: So similar in appearance and actions is this species to the Yellow-billed Cuckoo that it must be seen at close range to be recognized. As its name indicates, its bill is entirely black, and it can be further distinguished by the lesser amount of white on the tail feathers and the lack of russet in the wings. Its days are spent skulking in dense underbrush, and were it not for its loud guttural notes, it could easily be overlooked by the casual observer. Not infrequently one will be found in an orchard or a village shade tree infested by tent caterpillars, and seen under such circumstances, it is revealed as a slender brown bird with a conspicuously long tail and quiet, stealthy movements.

It is apparently a scarce transient in the state, and likewise breeds in rather limited numbers in the more northern counties. The few nests that have been found were built in saplings within ten feet of the ground and were rather shabby structures of twigs and dead leaves, the slight hollow in the top being lined with fragments of dead leaves and grasses. Two bluish-green eggs are laid, and, as is characteristic with the cuckoos, at irregular intervals rather than on successive days. Like the Yellow-billed Cuckoo, this species prefers caterpillars to any other insect food and is so beneficial from an economic standpoint that it deserves protection at all times.

ORDER STRIGIFORMES

Barn Owls: *Family Tytonidae*

North American Barn Owl
Tyto alba pratincola   (Bonaparte)

GENERAL DISTRIBUTION: Resident from northern California, Colorado, Nebraska, Illinois, southern Wisconsin, Ohio, New York, and Connecticut south to Florida, the Gulf Coast, and southern Mexico.

STATUS IN GEORGIA: Of local occurrence throughout the state.

Audubon [1834] was the first to note its occurrence in the state, recording two specimens taken on St. Simons Island. Other specimens have been taken at Dahlonega, June 4, 1927 (Howell); Clayton County, October 1, 1906, and DeKalb County, September 21, 1933 [Greene, 1933]; Athens, in 1947 [Odum, 1947]; Tifton, July 6, 1945 [Gaulding, 1945]; and western Camden County, January, 1938, and February 26, 1941 [Hebard, 1941]. Stoddard [MS] reports a specimen taken in Grady County in 1924 or 1925, and a bird dead possibly about a week when found, on Sherwood Plantation, December 10, 1938. Murphey [1937] considers it a common resident at Augusta, and Denton collected a specimen there on March 20, 1951. Griffin [1940] reports a single bird seen at Decatur, June 14, 21, and 29, 1940.

Breeding records are few in number. Tomkins [1946] reports four nests found near Savannah in 1932, one with two eggs on March 21, another with six eggs on March 17, a third with six eggs on September 23, and the fourth with two eggs on December 24. Rossignol's egg catalog lists a set of five incubated eggs taken at the Long Island Beacon in Chatham County, on July 25, 1935, and Erichsen [MS] cites three additional breeding records for the coast region, five eggs March 30, 1929, three eggs September 10, 1933, and five eggs March 20, 1942. Jones [1947] reports a nest found by Glenn W. Bell at Rome on May 7, 1929, that held young birds. The most recent record is that of a nest found at Bogart on March 19, 1949 [Hunter et al., 1949], with two young birds and one egg. The adult birds failed to rear these nestlings, and made another attempt that spring, there being six eggs in this nest when it was visited on May 2.

HABITS AND RECOGNITION: Entirely nocturnal in its habits and even more shy and retiring than the other owls, the Barn Owl is rarely seen and is possibly much commoner in Georgia than available records indicate. Its days are spent in a hollow tree, less frequently in an abandoned building, and it is only at dusk that it emerges to hunt its rodent prey in the fields and more open woodlands. Its flight is swift and noiseless, and its pale plumage makes it appear almost white. Owls have always been the object of superstitious dread, and the ghostlike appearance and weird screams of the Barn Owl make it an especially feared species. Actually, it is a harmless, inoffensive bird, and one whose food habits are extremely beneficial from an economic standpoint. There are instances known where small birds have been molested, but to a very large extent its food consists of destructive rodents. It unquestionably is an extremely valuable bird about a farm and should be protected.

Not much is known concerning the nesting habits of this owl in Georgia. Tomkins made a detailed study of some nests found near the mouth of the Savannah River. He states:

On each side of the river, which is about 1,800 feet wide, there are low islands of sand floated on the salt marsh from dredging operations. On the south side is Cockspur Island, on which is located Fort Pulaski and the Quarantine Station. On the eastern tip is an old round lighthouse, of masonry, and long abandoned. Along the marsh islands to the westward, as well as in the shallow South Channel to the southward, are several steel towers with range lights on the top; and directly under the light is a steel box with a sliding door. On the north side of the river is Oysterbed Island, with an old brick tower, used as a lighthouse long ago, located on it. In a radius of one and a half miles Barn Owls nested seven times in five different locations during the years 1927 to 1938, and there are a few other places that may have been used. A rectangular plot taking in all these nesting sites was roughly 6.88 square miles in area. Of this 34% was salt marsh, 6% land above tidal reach, and the remaining 60% was water at high tide and partly exposed mudflat at low water. The area near the nests varied greatly. In one case there was open water all around for at least 200 yards, in another good hunting ground close at hand. The nesting places were of two types: (1) the "old house" or "belfry" type and (2) the steel boxes under the range lights, of about six cubic feet capacity. The old stone and brick towers on Cockspur and Oysterbed and the flue in Fort Pulaski come under the first type. The others all were practically identical. Of the four nests found in 1932, one was in Fort Pulaski, one in the Old Tower on Oysterbed Island, and two in the Range Lights.

The pair found breeding at Bogart in 1949 had selected the belfry of a church, the "nest" consisting of "a few scraps of debris on a wooden floor directly under and within three feet of the church bell."

Typical Owls: *Family Strigidae*

Eastern Screech Owl
Otus asio naevius (Gmelin)

GENERAL DISTRIBUTION: Largely resident from southern Manitoba, Minnesota, Ontario, and New Brunswick south to northern Arkansas, Alabama, and probably northern Georgia.

STATUS IN GEORGIA: This northern race is possibly resident in the extreme northern part of the state, but as no breeding specimens have been taken there, this can only be conjecture at the present time.

It has been recorded at Young Harris on August 11, 1918, at Margret on June 8, 1927, and at Cloudland; thus is probably generally distributed throughout the mountain counties. Specimens identified as *naevius* have been taken in Newton County, December 17, 1910, and at Oxford, February 5, 1919; they are at present in the Emory University Museum. They may represent the breeding form in the mountains of the northern part of the state, but it is equally possible that they wandered south from well within the area occupied by this northern race.

HABITS AND RECOGNITION: The race of Screech Owl of the northeastern United States is slightly larger than that commonly breeding in Georgia, but otherwise is similar in both appearance and actions. Having a wide distribution and being generally common throughout its range, it is a well-known bird. Where cavities are available, old apple orchards are preferred spots during much of the year, and its tremulous cries are familiar night sounds on many farms.

Southern Screech Owl
Otus asio asio (Linnaeus)

GENERAL DISTRIBUTION: Resident in the Lower Austral Zone from Virginia to Georgia and the Gulf States west to Louisiana, north to western Tennessee, southern Illinois, southeastern Kansas, Oklahoma, and Arkansas.

STATUS IN GEORGIA: A permanent resident, fairly common and generally distributed throughout the state except the extreme southeastern corner and possibly the mountains.

EASTERN RED-BELLIED WOODPECKER
Centurus carolinus carolinus

While I was working at the Carolina Wren painting, a Red-bellied
Woodpecker, obsessed by curiosity because I stayed in one place so long
and kept so quiet, hitched down the fire-scarred trunk of an old bay tree
and began calling "chiv, chiv" at me, obviously in annoyance or excitement.
Two Tufted Titmice and some Carolina Chickadees responded almost
instantly. When they, too, began scolding, all the little birds of the
neighborhood gathered—along with some fox squirrels.

Specimens identified as this race have been taken at Riceboro (April 14, 1892), East Point (May 17, 1903), Oxford (March 11, 1908, April 5, 1909), and Athens (April 16, 1924, November 17, 1929, December 30, 1930). Specimens from Grady County (September 20, 1946, and January 20, 1949) are intermediate between this race and *floridanus* (Stoddard).

Definite breeding records are as follows: Rossignol [letter] states that he has found five occupied nests at Savannah, the earliest on April 4, (1907) with three fresh eggs, the latest on May 5, (1907) with three small young. Erichsen [MS] cites as his nesting extremes for Chatham County (nineteen occupied nests): three fresh eggs, March 9 (1924), and four well-grown young, May 17 (1918). Stoddard [MS] records a brood of nearly grown young in Grady County, September 1, 1939, and three downy young in a nest in Thomas County, May 3, 1943. Norris [1940] reports a nest at Fitzgerald on April 30, 1940, that held three eggs. Griffin [1940] cites as nesting extremes for the Atlanta region a nest with one fresh egg, April 15, 1920 (Hembree), and another with one egg, May 18, 1932 (Barkalow). At Athens [Burleigh, 1938], I succeeded in finding four nests: one on March 31, 1922, with three partially incubated eggs; another on April 16, 1924, with three well-incubated eggs; the third on April 5, 1925 with four eggs, possibly one-third incubated; and the fourth on March 21, 1926 with one fresh egg—this nest was later found deserted.

HABITS AND RECOGNITION: This little owl is unfortunately named, for in no sense of the word can it be said to screech. The note most commonly heard, especially in the early spring when it is nesting, is a tremulous, melodious cry that can be confused with no other sound heard after nightfall. It is strictly nocturnal in its habits, remaining hidden during the day in a hollow tree or not infrequently in thick foliage, where its presence is rarely suspected. As night falls, it emerges and on silent wings searches for insects or a mouse or small bird with which to assuage its hunger. On occasion one may be found during the daytime in a relatively open situation, and then it will be revealed as a small owl not much larger than a robin, with conspicuous ear tufts, and, oddly enough, it may be either brownish-gray in color or a bright rusty red. Not many birds are characterized by two distinct color phases, so it comes as rather a surprise that two individuals of the same species can be so different in appearance.

The nest is either in a natural cavity or in an old flicker's hole, the three or four white eggs that are normally laid in Georgia resting on fragments of rotten wood a foot or two below the entrance. The four nests that I found at Athens varied in height from eight to twenty feet from the ground; two were in red gums, one in a willow, and one in a river birch.

In each case the female was incubating and refused to leave her eggs, so that it was necessary to remove her by hand in order to ascertain the contents of the nest.

Although it does eat an occasional small bird, the Screech Owl is very largely beneficial in its food habits and deserves protection. Small rodents form the bulk of its diet, although it is also known to eat large insects, spiders, crawfish, small fish, snails, lizards, and snakes. In one nest I found that there were fresh blue jay feathers, and in another the hind quarters of a large frog. I examined the stomach contents of a male collected at Athens on November 17, 1929, and found included a number of large black beetles and the remains of a pipit.

Florida Screech Owl
Otus asio floridanus   (Ridgway)

GENERAL DISTRIBUTION: Extreme southeastern Georgia, Florida, and the Gulf Coast of Alabama, Mississippi, and Louisiana.

STATUS IN GEORGIA: Resident and apparently not uncommon in the extreme southeastern corner of the state.

Six Screech Owls taken by Isaac F. Arnow in Camden County have been critically examined by Allen J. Duvall, and five, all from St. Marys, were found to represent this Florida race. Three were females, collected in December—year not given on label—March 16, 1903, and April 4, 1904; one a male, collected on March 18, 1904; and a fifth that was unsexed and undated. The sixth specimen, taken at Griffin's Neck, June 6, 1905, was intermediate in characters, indicating that the range of *floridanus* in Georgia is limited to the extreme southern edge of the state. This supposition was further confirmed by two specimens from Broro Neck and Sapelo Island examined by Bangs [1930] and found to be intermediate between *asio* and *floridanus* [Hebard and Johnston, 1951]. A female taken by Fleetwood at Camp Cornelia, at the edge of the Okefenokee Swamp, on January 12, 1948, was found to be typical of *floridanus*, extending the range of this race as far west as Charlton County.

HABITS AND RECOGNITION: This is the smallest of the eastern screech owls, although otherwise it differs little from the others either in appearance or actions. Both color phases are said to occur, but so far as my own experience is concerned, the red phase is rare, for all the specimens I have seen have been brownish-gray. It is found both in open pine woods and in deciduous timber bordering the streams, and is fairly common and generally distributed throughout its range.

324

Family Strigidae: TYPICAL OWLS

Eastern Horned Owl
Bubo virginianus virginianus   (Gmelin)

GENERAL DISTRIBUTION: Resident from Ontario, Quebec, and New Brunswick south to the Gulf states, and west to South Dakota, Kansas, Oklahoma, and eastern Texas.

STATUS IN GEORGIA: Uncommon and of local distribution in the larger stretches of timber throughout the state.

It has been reported from: Young Harris, Rome, Augusta, Athens, Atlanta, Macon, Columbus, the Piedmont National Wildlife Refuge, Miller County, Baker County, Fitzgerald, Grady County, Savannah, Darien, Cumberland Island, Blackbeard Island, Wilmington Island, and Sea Island and other smaller islands off the coast. It is apparently more numerous in the Okefenokee Swamp than elsewhere in the state, for Hebard [1941] states that "from December 1 to 7, 1934, Herbert L. Stoddard, Lucien Harris, Jr., and I noted at least twenty different individuals scattered along the canal, over Chase Prairie and on Floyd's Island."

Definite breeding records are not numerous. Hoxie saw well-grown young on Wilmington Island, May 18, 1907; and Rossignol [letter] reports four nests found near Savannah by himself: one on Wilson Island on January 21, 1912, with two slightly incubated eggs; another on Cavanaugh's Island on January 10, 1915, with two slightly incubated eggs; and two on Wilmington Island, the first with two slightly incubated eggs on January 17, 1915, and the second with two well-incubated eggs on January 31, 1915. Erichsen [MS] cites as his earliest breeding record for Chatham County a nest found on Little Tybee Island, January 1, 1929, that held two well-incubated eggs. I found a nest with two partially incubated eggs on Wilson Island, January 30, 1924, and another with two half-grown young on Spring Island, also near Savannah, February 27, 1933. Griffin [letter] states that, "although no nests have been found in the Atlanta region, two young were found on May 10, 1939, by a farmer and sold to Athos Menaboni." Odum [1947] reports two nests found at Athens in 1947; the female was incubating on one of these nests when it was shown to him on February 23.

HABITS AND RECOGNITION: The Eastern Horned Owl has been called "the winged tiger of the woods," and to one familiar with its savage strength and ferocity, the title is quite apt. Its size is such that no birds and only the larger mammals are immune from its attacks, and as it is capable of tireless hunting over wide areas, it has little difficulty satisfying its voracious appetite. A list of its prey includes not only such small mammals as mice, rats, and rabbits, but also woodchucks, skunks, and even porcupines, and it has been known to kill birds as large as geese and turkeys. Poultry and game birds unquestionably suffer from its nightly forays, and it is not surprising, therefore, that there are few persons who will say a good word in its behalf. Its fondness for skunks, however, is definitely in its favor, for skunks are notorious predators upon ground nesting birds and, except for the Great Horned Owl, have almost no enemies.

Chiefly nocturnal in its habits, this large owl usually spends the daylight hours in a hollow tree, but not infrequently one will be seen resting quietly in the upper branches of a thickly foliaged tree. Seen thus, its large size and conspicuous ear tufts will readily identify it. Wary and suspicious of close approach, it will gaze at the intruder for a moment with its big yellow eyes and then depart with swift, noiseless flight.

In Georgia, the breeding season varies according to the part of the state in which the birds occur. On the coast the eggs are laid in early January, while north of the fall line it is usually the latter part of February before these owls are incubating the two dull-white eggs that form the normal clutch. Nest building consists merely of pre-empting an old hawk's nest that is sufficiently high from the ground to be reasonably safe from intrusion. A nest that I found on Wilson Island was a long-deserted nest of a Bald Eagle, forty-five feet from the ground in a tall slash pine. It was two feet in height, and two and one-half feet across, the eggs lying on decomposed wood that formed the lining of the rather shallow cavity. The female was incubating and was conspicuous for some distance, her large ear tufts especially revealing her presence long before the tree was reached. She would not flush when the trunk was rapped with a stick, nor in fact while the tree was being slowly climbed, only leaving her two eggs very reluctantly before being actually touched. On Spring Island, an old dilapidated Osprey's nest, sixty feet from the ground in a slash pine, had been selected, the two half-grown young crouching on the decomposed fragments of wood that formed the lining. In Grady County, Stoddard [MS] found this owl commonly utilizing old squirrel nests for rearing its young. In some instances, when heavy winds had dislodged the nest, the young birds, if unable to fly, would be reared at the base of the nesting tree. He cites as a typical instance two young found April 6, 1940, "reared at the base of a pine tree, the remains of their nest being near by. They were on burned-over ground, and very conspicuous. Judging from the evidence all about they had been there two or three weeks at least."

Snowy Owl
Nyctea scandiaca (Linnaeus)

GENERAL DISTRIBUTION: Breeds in North America on the barren grounds from the islands of Bering Sea, the Yukon Delta, Melville Island, and northern Greenland south to central Mackenzie, central Keewatin, and northern Ungava. Winters from the Arctic Coast south to the southern Canadian provinces, and irregularly to California, Texas, Louisiana, and Georgia; also in Bermuda.

STATUS IN GEORGIA: Of casual occurrence in the state in the winter months of "invasion" years.

There are at present but two records of this Arctic owl in Georgia. Greene [1931] reports a specimen taken near Gainesville, in Hall County, December 31, 1930; and Tomkins [1931] states that he collected a female at Fort Pulaski, on Cockspur Island, February 8, 1931.

HABITS AND RECOGNITION: The Snowy Owl is found regularly during the winter months as far south as the New England states, but it is only in years when its food becomes scarce in the far north that it appears in such numbers as to deserve the name "invasion." In its normal range, its food consists to a large extent of mice and lemmings, and when, as periodically happens, these small mammals become scarce, it must migrate or starve. Accordingly, there are winters when it appears in the northern states in great numbers, and it is then that an occasional individual comes as far south as Georgia. Spending the summer months as it does in a land where the days are twenty-four hours long, it is far less nocturnal in its habits than are the other owls, and hunts its prey as much by day as by night. Always shy and suspicious of a close approach, it is usually seen at a distance as it perches on a fence post or hillock, flying at once if it senses any undue interest in its presence. No difficulty will ever be experienced in recognizing it, for it is as large as the Great Horned Owl, and almost completely white, the upperparts being irregularly marked with dark grayish-brown bars.

Florida Barred Owl
Strix varia georgica   Latham

GENERAL DISTRIBUTION: Resident from Arkansas, northern Alabama, and North Carolina south to eastern Texas, the Gulf Coast, and Florida.

STATUS IN GEORGIA: Resident and of general distribution throughout the state, being most numerous in the swamps and stream bottoms south of the fall line.

Although it is a common bird, little has been published concerning its occurrence in Georgia. It has been reported from Augusta, Woodville, Athens, Atlanta, Rome, the Piedmont National Wildlife Refuge, Americus,

Cuthbert, Ben Hill County, Tift County, Baker County, Okefenokee Swamp, Grady County, Hinesville, Darien, Brunswick, Riceboro, Savannah, Cumberland Island, and Blackbeard Island. Specimens have been taken in Newton County, February 26 and November 25, 1909, and at Atlanta, December 23, 1943.

There are few definite breeding records for the state. Erichsen [MS] reports a nest at Savannah that held two slightly incubated eggs March 3, 1940. A nest found at Rome March 12, 1939, likewise held two eggs [Jones, 1947]. Hebard reports two well-grown young at Coleraine, in Camden County, June 14, 1948, and two young along the canal in the Okefenokee Swamp, February 23, 1950.

HABITS AND RECOGNITION: The Barred Owl is the best-known and most frequently observed owl of the Southeast. In Georgia there are few stream bottoms or wooded swamps in which a pair cannot be found throughout the year, and as it is normally a noisy bird, its presence soon is made known to even the casual observer. Largely nocturnal, it is nevertheless active to some extent during the daylight hours, and if seen then, will be found alert and well aware of what is going on in its vicinity. In appearance, it is smaller than the Great Horned Owl, grayish-brown, with a large round head lacking ear tufts. These characters are easily observed, for it is usually unsuspicious and easily approached, only flying when it has satisfied its curiosity or has become alarmed by too abrupt a movement on the part of the intruder.

In the southern part of the state, breeding activities are apparently well under way by the latter part of January, but farther north it is late February or early March before the female is incubating the two dull-white eggs that are normally laid. The nest is usually in the cavity of a tree, either in the trunk or in one of the larger limbs, but if such a site cannot be found, an old nest of a hawk or crow is utilized. No attempt is made at nest building, the eggs being laid on the fragments of rotten wood, dead leaves, or other debris lining the bottom of the cavity. Always a loquacious bird, it is during the period of courtship that the loud hoots of this owl are most frequently heard from the wooded stream bottoms. The effect of this close at hand, and unexpectedly, is rather startling, the deep-toned hoots being interspersed with catlike squalls and notes too suggestive of demoniac laughter to be at all comforting.

This owl's food is rather varied, and consists of large insects, crawfish, frogs, snakes, lizards, an occasional small bird, rabbits, squirrels, and rodents. Since poultry is rarely bothered, it can be considered a highly beneficial species, one that well deserves protection.

American Long-eared Owl
Asio otus wilsonianus (Lesson)

GENERAL DISTRIBUTION: Breeds from central British Columbia, southern Mackenzie, and southern Quebec south to southern California, northern Texas, Arkansas, and Virginia. Winters from southern Canada to Florida, Louisiana, and central Mexico.

STATUS IN GEORGIA: An uncommon winter resident throughout the state.

Apparently the first specimen known from Georgia is one taken by Helme on Cumberland Island, December 22, 1904. Greene [1933] reports three taken by D. V. Hembree at Roswell, in Fulton County, on February 25, 1918, February 8, 1926, and May 1, 1928. Murphey [1937] states that specimens have been taken in Richmond, Burke, and Columbia counties; two in his collection were from Richmond County, January 26, 1923, and Burke County, November 26, 1930. Gaulding [1945] collected one at Tifton, March 5, 1945, and saw another there that same day.

It has been noted at Coleraine on November 25 and December 3 and 5, 1941 [Hebard, 1942], and at Athens, November 21, 1943 [Odum, 1943].

HABITS AND RECOGNITION: The Long-eared Owl is so consistently nocturnal in its activities that it is rarely seen, and consequently is largely overlooked. Its days are spent concealed in the densest thicket it can find, and here it remains until dusk, when it quietly emerges and with light, buoyant flight searches for its rodent prey. On rare occasions it will be encountered at close range, and instead of seeking safety in flight, it will draw itself erect, contract its body, and remain so rigid that it suggests to a remarkable degree the dead limb of a tree. Seen thus, its ear tufts are conspicuous, although otherwise they are not always noticeable. In appearance it is a medium-sized owl, intermediate between the Screech Owl and the Barred Owl, and dark grayish-brown in color. Since its food consists to a very great extent of injurious rodents, it is one of our most beneficial birds of prey and should be protected at all times. As it is so adept at concealing itself during the daylight hours, it is possibly commoner in Georgia during winter than the infrequent records would indicate.

Northern Short-eared Owl
Asio flammeus flammeus (Pontoppidan)

GENERAL DISTRIBUTION: Breeds in North America from northern Alaska, northern Mackenzie, northern Quebec, and Greenland south to California, Colorado, Kansas, Missouri, Indiana, and New Jersey; also in Europe and northern Asia. Winters from British Columbia, Wyoming, Minnesota, Indiana, Ohio, and Massachusetts south to Cuba and Guatemala.

STATUS IN GEORGIA: A locally common winter resident on the coast and of irregular occurrence elsewhere in the state in winter.

On the coast, specimens have been taken on Sapelo Island, January 10, 1888; Jacks Bank (mouth of the Altamaha River), January 27, 1890; Cumberland Island, March 18, 1902, and December 14 and 28, 1904; and St. Marys, February 10, 1903. Tomkins [1931] states that one or two can always be seen throughout the winter in the marshes at the mouth of the Savannah River, and that in November and December, 1930, this owl was unusually plentiful there, eight and possibly nine being observed on November 24, and five on December 14.

At Augusta, Murphey [1937] considers this species a common winter resident; specimens have been taken in Richmond County in January, 1895, February, 1896, and on December 10, 1902. Elsewhere in the interior of the state, Greene [1933] reports a specimen taken in Fulton County, November 15, 1930, and Werner [1944] a single bird seen at Atlanta, December 19, 1943. Johnston [MS] gives two records for Macon, December 26, 1952, and January 25, 1953. Stoddard [MS] has found it a rare winter resident in Grady County.

HABITS AND RECOGNITION: The Short-eared Owl is unique among owls of the state in that it prefers open country and is never seen in wooded areas. To see one, it is necessary to go to the open fields and marshes, where it will be found perched on a fence post or on the top of a dead snag or, if such a convenience is wanting, on the ground itself. Being almost as active in the daytime as it is after dark, it is not uncommon to encounter one flying low over the ground much in the manner of a Marsh Hawk, alternately flapping its long wings and then gliding or circling for a short distance. These habits result in its being more frequently seen than are the other owls, and were it more common in the state, it would be a well-known bird. In appearance it resembles very closely the Long-eared Owl, but as the latter species will never be found in open country, there should be little chance of confusing the two.

An analysis of its food habits has shown that the Short-eared Owl feeds to a very large extent on small rodents. Small birds are taken on relatively few occasions, and I know of no instance when poultry was molested. Tomkins succeeded in getting a number of pellets near Savannah during the winter months, and of these he says: "The 50 pellets collected during January and February contained remains of 34 birds, of 14 identifiable species, and 54 mammals, of two or more species. The 18 pellets collected in the same places during late February and March contained remains of 4 birds and 45 house mice." [Bent, 1938]. In this case the number of birds eaten was unusually large; under ordinary circumstances this owl is a beneficial species, the wanton destruction of which should never be permitted.

Acadian Saw-whet Owl
Aegolius acadicus acadicus   (Gmelin)

GENERAL DISTRIBUTION: Breeds from southern Alaska and central British Columbia east through Alberta, Manitoba, and Quebec to Nova Scotia south to California, eastern Mexico, Nebraska, Illinois, and Maryland. Winters south to southern California, Louisiana, Virginia, and casually to the Carolinas and Georgia.

STATUS IN GEORGIA: A casual winter resident throughout the state.

Six specimens are known to have been taken in Georgia. Hoxie [1911] recorded this owl apparently for the first time when he collected a female at Buck Hammock, a small island near the mouth of the Savannah River, on January 1, 1911. Murphey [1937] reports three specimens taken in Richmond County, one in 1912, another on January 4, 1913, and the third in 1920. At Atlanta, Griffin [1940] collected a male on January 20, 1940, and Parks [1948] reports picking up a recently killed bird there on March 14, 1948. Denton [in litt.] states that "Paul Davis saw a bird on Wilmington Island, January 17, 1953," getting a perfect view at almost arm's length before dark.

HABITS AND RECOGNITION: So secretive is this little owl, and so largely by accident is it usually found, that it may be commoner in Georgia in winter than the few records indicate. Its daylight hours are spent concealed in a dense thicket, whence it emerges at dusk to feed. Anyone fortunate enough to see one in the daytime will find it so reluctant to fly that it can be approached within a few feet without causing it much concern, and there are instances known when it has actually been caught in the hand. Smaller than the Screech Owl and with a round head lacking any ear tufts, it is easily recognized. During the winter months it is a quiet bird, but on its breeding ground it can be heard uttering metallic notes so suggestive of filing a saw that the aptness of its common name is soon apparent. Its food consists to a great extent of mice, although, if pressed by hunger, it eats an occasional small bird.

ORDER CAPRIMULGIFORMES

Goatsuckers: *Family Caprimulgidae*

Chuck-will's-widow
Caprimulgus carolinensis   Gmelin

GENERAL DISTRIBUTION: Breeds from southeastern Kansas, southern Missouri, southern Ohio, and southern Virginia south to central Texas, the Gulf states, and Florida. Winters from Florida to the Greater Antilles, Central America, and Colombia.

STATUS IN GEORGIA: A common summer resident in all parts of the state except the mountains.

This large goatsucker arrives in Georgia from its winter quarters in March or early April, and is rarely seen in the fall after the middle of September. Earliest arrivals in the spring were reported at Savannah, March 5 (1910) and March 15 (1913); Sea Island, April 1 (1947) and March 24 (1948); Hinesville, March 30 (1945); eastern Charlton County, February 28 (1945); Okefenokee Swamp, March 26 (1936); Grady County, March 6 (1937); Tifton, April 3 (1952); Macon, April 2 (1953); Milledgeville, April 3 (1936); Augusta, March 15; Athens, April 9 (1922) and April 5 (1929); Atlanta, April 12 (1955); and Rising Fawn, April 22 (1885). In the fall it was last seen at Athens on September 6 (1925); in Grady County, September 29 (1949); and at Savannah on September 23 (1916) and September 25 (1926).

It has been noted in the breeding season at all the above localities, and also at Chatsworth, Trenton, Canton, the Piedmont National Wildlife Refuge, Columbus, Americus, Woodbine, and Darien. At Rome, Jones [1947] reports a nest with two eggs on May 15, 1946. At Athens [Burleigh, 1938], I succeeded once, June 6, 1923, in flushing a female from her two eggs. Stoddard [MS] reports a nest in Grady County that held two fresh eggs on April 12, 1928, and Norris and Hopkins [letter] report a nest at Fitzgerald with two eggs on May 10, 1941, and another at Tifton on May 2, 1942, that likewise held two eggs. Harper [1938] found two downy young near Camp Cornelia, at the edge of the Okefenokee Swamp, on May 24, 1929. Rossignol [letter] reports finding twenty nests in Chatham County, the earliest on April 30 (1916) with two fresh eggs, the latest on June 10 (1922), also with two fresh eggs. Erichsen [MS] gives approximately the same nesting extremes for eighty nests that he found near Savannah from 1912 through 1949, his earliest record being two fresh eggs on April 27 (1919), his latest, two incubated eggs on June 13 (1916). Bent [1940] cites as nesting extremes for Georgia: "28 records, April 25 to June 18; 14 records, May 7 to 24."

HABITS AND RECOGNITION: To the average person the Chuck-will's-widow is merely a voice. It spends the daylight hours quietly, concealed in dense underbrush or resting motionless on the horizontal limb of a large tree. In such a situation its variegated brown and gray plumage blends perfectly with its surroundings, and it seems well aware of this protective coloration, for only a very close approach will cause it to fly. If forced to seek safety in flight, it rises silently from the spot where it had been dozing and hunts the seclusion of the nearest thicket, where again it must almost be walked on before flushing. At dusk, however, it becomes active, and its clear vigorous notes can be heard from then until daylight. Considering the effort that it must expend in uttering this "song," one cannot but be impressed with the energy displayed by this bird in repeating its "chuck-will's-widow" literally hundreds of times. At a distance the call gives the impression of being three-syllabled, for only close at hand is the first note, the low toned "chuck," noticeable.

Its food consists of the various large night-flying insects, and these it captures as it flies low over the ground in open woodland or at the edges of fields and pastures. Its open mouth is enormous for the size of the bird, and this enables it to prey upon the larger moths, but also, unfortunately, upon small birds, notably warblers.

Nesting is a simple matter for this species, two eggs being deposited in a slight hollow among dead leaves on the ground. The site selected is always in a rather open spot in the woods instead of in dense underbrush, the female depending on her protective coloration for concealment and rarely flushing until almost stepped upon. The nest that I found at Athens was in the middle of a stretch of thick woods and was typical in all respects. The larger trees were all shortleaf pine, but there was a dense understory of hardwoods, broken at intervals by small openings, and it was in one of these that the female was flushed, on June 6, from her two fresh eggs.

Eastern Whip-poor-will
Caprimulgus vociferus vociferus Wilson

GENERAL DISTRIBUTION: Breeds from Manitoba, southern Quebec, New Brunswick, and Nova Scotia south to the northern parts of Louisiana, Alabama, and Georgia, and west to Kansas, Nebraska, and North Dakota.

Winters from South Carolina and the Gulf Coast south to British Honduras and Salvador.

STATUS IN GEORGIA: A fairly common summer resident in the extreme northern part of the state and an uncommon transient south of the mountain counties. A locally scarce to uncommon winter resident in extreme southern Georgia.

At Athens [Burleigh, 1938], I found the Whip-poor-will a somewhat scarce transient, extreme dates of occurrence in the spring being March 29 (1929) and April 17 (1926), and in the fall, September 30 (1925) and October 22 (1922). Griffin gives as migration extremes for the Atlanta region March 19 (1922) and September 12 (1953). At Rising Fawn its arrival in the spring was noted on April 15, 1885. Murphey [1937] considers it an uncommon transient at Augusta. Johnston [MS] reports it at Macon in the spring from March 30 (1934) to April 30 (1943). In Grady County, Stoddard states [MS] that it appears in September (earliest record September 1, 1939) and is last noted in late March (March 28, 1950).

In the breeding season it has been reported at Dahlonega, Margret, (Fannin County), Young Harris, Canton, Trenton, Toccoa, Sullivan Creek (sixteen miles north of Atlanta), and Marietta. Actual breeding records, however, are limited to three localities. On July 7, 1922, at Young Harris, Towns County, I succeeded in flushing a female from two well-incubated eggs [Burleigh, 1925]. Barkalow [1940] reports two eggs found a quarter of a mile south of Kennesaw Mountain, in Cobb County, the middle of May, 1932, by T. Lawrence; and Stevenson [1944] reports one nestling at Cloudland, June 10, 1943.

During the winter, it has been recorded in McIntosh County, February 19, 1889; at Savannah, January 14, 1905, February 11 and 24, 1908, and January 17, 1913; Okefenokee Swamp, January 9, 1930, and November 25, 1932; on the Camden-Charlton County line, November 24, 1937; in Camden County, December 10, 1940 (Mill Creek), and December 31, 1940 (Silco); and in Grady County, December 26, 1927 and January 30, 1940.

HABITS AND RECOGNITION: Because of its wide distribution and relative abundance throughout its range, the Whip-poor-will is a well-known bird. Nevertheless, to all but the more ardent bird students, it is merely a voice heard in the night. Its days are spent resting quietly on the ground in thick underbrush, and so protective is its brown coloration that it is rare to see one before it becomes active at dusk. With the setting of the sun its vigorous notes, so aptly interpreted as "whip-poor-will," are soon heard, and throughout the night they are repeated at frequent intervals as the bird pauses in its quest for the moths and other nocturnal insects on which it

334

feeds. On nights when the moon is full, it is possible to catch a glimpse of it as it flies by close to the ground, and its noiseless flight and broad wings are then very suggestive of those of an owl. On the rare occasions when one is flushed from the ground during the daytime, it can be readily distinguished from the Chuck-will's-widow, for it is much smaller, and its long, rounded tail is noticeably tipped with white.

In common with the other goatsuckers, it makes no attempt at nest building, the two eggs being incubated in a slight depression in the dead leaves covering the ground. The few nests found in Georgia have been in rather open woods, the birds depending for protection on their remarkable resemblance to their surroundings, this rendering them practically invisible except at close range.

A species as inconspicuous in migration as is the Whip-poor-will is not easily observed, though more often heard, and it is probably a more common transient over much of the state than is generally supposed. In the spring, I have frequently heard one singing after dark at Athens, where it is not known to breed, and this has enabled me to record its presence when otherwise it would have gone undetected. On April 15, 1925, three individuals were heard at dusk in stretches of open pine woods at Lexington, in Oglethorpe County. The fact that I had been in those areas throughout that day without suspecting the presence of these birds demonstrates how easily this species is overlooked. In the fall it is quiet and even more retiring, and this undoubtedly accounts for the few records of its occurrence in the northern part of the state after late summer.

Eastern Common Nighthawk
Chordeiles minor minor (Forster)

GENERAL DISTRIBUTION: Breeds from southern Yukon, central Mackenzie, and northern Quebec south to northern Arkansas, southern Missouri, Illinois, eastern Tennessee, and northern Georgia. Winters in South America from Colombia to Argentina.

STATUS IN GEORGIA: An uncommon summer resident in the extreme northern counties and a common transient over the entire state, being more numerous in the fall than in the spring.

A breeding bird, representing this northern race, was taken at Chatsworth on June 22, 1927; and individuals seen during late June and early July at Young Harris, Towns County, and Margret, Fannin County, were probably likewise *minor*. Bell [1938] reports a nest with eggs in Union County, May 29, 1938. A male whose actions indicated that it was a breeding bird was collected at Athens on July 14, 1941 [Burleigh, 1941], and this possibly marks the extreme southern limit for this race in the state.

At Athens, I found the Nighthawk as a transient rather scarce in the spring, but abundant in the fall, when, for a month or more, from the latter part of August through September, many small flocks were seen overhead in the late afternoon. The earliest date of arrival in the spring is April 17 (1921), then April 26 (1922), and April 23 (1928); while in the fall, transient flocks have been noted as early as July 31 (1929) and as late as October 17 (1924) and October 19 (1928).

At Augusta, Murphey [1937] states that this species is "abundant during migration, but especially so in autumn, when the number visible at one time is truly amazing. In September, 1934, I counted over 2,200 in the course of a thirty-seven-mile ride, and several observers informed me that their numbers were equalled by those seen over a distance of thirty miles in the opposite direction—a zone of migrating nighthawks sixty-seven miles in breadth."

Transients representing this northern race have been taken at Savannah, April 23, 1939; in Grady County, August 17, 1940; at Fitzgerald, May 7, 1941; in Fulton County, August 8, 1906, and September 8, 1949; at Athens, September 15, 1931; and at Blairsville, September 29, 1945.

HABITS AND RECOGNITION: Unlike the other Georgia goatsuckers, the Nighthawk is a bird of the open country. Heavily wooded areas are consistently avoided, and probably for that reason it is an uncommon bird in the northern part of the state. In the mountains, scattered pairs can be found in open spots on the higher ridges, while in the upper Piedmont the few I have seen have been in slashings where logging operations had left suitable open areas. Although the Nighthawk is active to some extent throughout the night, it commonly feeds in the early morning hours and in the late afternoon, and on occasion can be seen flying during the middle of the day. Consequently it is a familiar bird to many who have the opportunity of watching it as it follows its erratic course high overhead in pursuit of the insects on which it feeds.

The note most commonly heard then is a loud nasal "peent," which once learned will always identify this species. During the nesting season, the male has a spectacular courtship flight that is well worth witnessing. At frequent intervals a sudden swoop will be made from high in the air down to the spot where the female is resting quietly on the ground, the speed of the descent being abruptly checked just before reaching her, and, as the upward turn is made, a loud, booming sound is created, apparently by the air rushing through the quills of the wings.

Florida Common Nighthawk
Chordeiles minor chapmani Coues

GENERAL DISTRIBUTION: Breeds from Arkansas, southern Illinois, central Alabama, and eastern North Carolina, south to eastern Texas, the Gulf Coast, and Florida. Winters in South America from Colombia to Argentina.

STATUS IN GEORGIA: A fairly common summer resident in all parts of the state except the northeastern counties; especially numerous on the coast.

Specimens of this race have been taken in Burke County, July 29, 1902; Armuchee, Floyd County, August 30, 1949; Roswell, Fulton County, May 25, 1933; Newton, Baker County, July 9, 1929; and Savannah, Chatham County, June 1, 1929. Eyles and Giles [1935] report a dead bird found on a road in Rabun County, August 27, 1933, that was identified by H. C. Oberholser as *chapmani*. Being within the breeding range of *minor*, it is probable that this was a straggler and not a representative of the breeding population of Rabun County.

Earliest migrants in the spring were noted at St. Marys, April 14 (1902); Darien, April 15 (1890); Cumberland Island, April 10 (1902); Sea Island, April 10 (1946) and April 15 (1947); Hinesville, April 11 (1944); Savannah, April 8 (1934); Grady County, April 6 (1938); Fitzgerald, March 20 (1942); Macon, April 10 (1944); Milledgeville, April 14 (1941); and Atlanta, April 15 (1946). In the fall, latest dates of occurrence are for Decatur, October 27 (1946); Milledgeville, October 11 (1943); Macon, October 22 (1922); Americus, September 27 (1941); Fitzgerald, October 24 (1941); Grady County, September 27 (1941); and Savannah, October 17 (1925). Because *chapmani* is the breeding bird over the larger part of the state, arrival and departure dates as given above are credited to this form; it is entirely possible, however, that some of these records refer to *minor*.

Eggs have been found at St. Marys, May 7, 1905, and at Savannah. Rossignol [letter] gives as nesting extremes (twenty-one nests): two fresh eggs, May 8 (1915), and two fresh eggs, June 18 (1915). In Grady County, Stoddard [MS] reports a nest with two fresh eggs, May 2, 1924; another with eggs just hatching, May 16, 1941; and a third with nearly hatched young, June 14, 1941. Hopkins [letter] reports finding two nests at Fitzgerald in 1941, one with two eggs on May 22, the other with one egg on July 12. At Atlanta, Griffin [1940] reports a nest with two eggs on June 8, 1939. Bent [1940] gives as nesting extremes for Georgia: "16 records, May 17 to July 13; 8 records, May 24 to June 10."

HABITS AND RECOGNITON: This southern race of the Nighthawk differs from the Eastern subspecies in being smaller and darker both above and below. The open nature of the country in the southern part of the state is well suited to the requirements of this race, and it is a fairly common bird. This is especially true on the coast, where one or more pairs can be found on all the islands. In appearance and actions it is similar in every respect to its more northern relative. Away from the coast its two eggs are laid on the bare ground in the open pine woods, while on the islands they can be found on the beaches or among the dunes well back from the water's edge. In many parts of the country the Nighthawk has acquired the habit of nesting on the flat gravel roof of a building, and while this may be the case in Georgia, no actual instance has yet been reported. For many years migrating flocks of Nighthawks in the fall were eagerly watched for by hunters, and killed in large numbers either for food or merely for the sport of shooting them. Murphey [1937] states that about Augusta hundreds were killed in the course of an afternoon, and this was likely what happened over much of the state. Fortunately such wanton destruction has been abolished through enactment of suitable laws, and this highly beneficial species is now accorded the protection it well deserves.

ORDER APODIFORMES

Swifts: *Family Apodidae*

Chimney Swift
Chaetura pelagica (Linnaeus)

GENERAL DISTRIBUTION: Breeds from central Alberta, Saskatchewan, Manitoba, and southern Quebec south to Florida and the Gulf Coast and west to eastern Montana and eastern Texas. Winters south of the United States and possibly entirely in South America, as the only definite winter record to date is for Peru.

STATUS IN GEORGIA: A common summer resident over the entire state.

Earliest dates of arrival in the spring are, for Sea Island, April 1 (1947); Savannah, March 19 (1909); Hinesville, March 29 (1945); Grady County, March 25 (1937); Baxley, March 26 (1924); Tifton, March 20 (1944); Americus, April 2 (1942); Marshallville, April 1 (1888); Macon, March 21 (1945); Milledgeville, March 24 (1929); Atlanta, March 22 (1944); and Athens, March 24 (1949). The last were observed in the fall at Athens, October 20 (1926); Atlanta, October 24 (1947); Milledgeville, October 15 (1943); Macon, October 27 (1954); Americus, October 23 (1941); Fitzgerald, October 29 (1941); Grady County, October 24 (1940); and Savannah, October 26 (1908).

Actual breeding records for the state are not numerous and are limited to the following localities: Margret, Fannin County (five slightly incubated eggs, June 12, 1921, Burleigh); Marietta (four eggs, July 2, 1932, Barkalow); Atlanta (four partially incubated eggs, June 20, 1930, Mills; incubated eggs June 6, 1939, Bell); Athens (four well-fledged young, June 28, 1925; five fresh eggs, May 30, 1926, Burleigh); and Chatham County (five fresh eggs, May 30, 1923; five eggs June 12, 1933, Erichsen).

HABITS AND RECOGNITION: Originally the Chimney Swift nested in hollow trees, and as such nesting sites were probably rather limited in number, this species, despite its wide distribution, was only locally a common bird. As the country became settled, however, farms and towns replaced the primitive wilderness, and the swifts found the new environment exactly suited to their needs. Chimneys proved ideal nesting sites, equal to, if not actually better than, hollow trees, and the birds were not long in accepting them. As a result the Chimney Swift is an abundant bird today. In Georgia

339

there are few, if any, towns or cities throughout the state where one or more pairs cannot be found throughout the summer months, and, as the "chimney swallow," it is familiar to everybody. Its food, entirely insects, is taken in flight, and there is unquestionably no species to which the adjective "tireless" can be applied more appropriately. From daylight until dark it pursues its swift, erratic course overhead, never alighting in a tree, and only under adverse weather conditions resting in a chimney in the daytime. During much of the day it feeds so high in the sky that it is inconspicuous and rarely seen, but during the early morning hours and again in late afternoon, it is a familiar sight overhead. Seen then it is easily recognized, its appearance being that of a small dark-gray bird with long, narrow wings and almost no tail. In the hand, its feet will be found to be short and stout, suggestive of the strength necessary to cling for hours against the side of a chimney or hollow tree.

Its nest is distinct from that of any other of our birds, being a shallow half-saucer composed entirely of dead twigs held together by a cement formed from the bird's saliva. Once this hardens, the nest remains firmly attached to the side of the chimney, only the heaviest rains sometimes dislodging it. The nest that I found in the chimney of a farmhouse in Fannin County had dry pine needles mixed with the twigs, but normally only the latter are used. These are secured in flight, and it is interesting to watch the bird break the twig from the branch with its feet by applying sudden pressure as it momentarily hesitates in the air. Often this attempt is not successful, but the bird will persist until the desired twig is secured. Four or five white eggs are laid, and the young are reared in a nest that would appear to offer few comforts during the period of their infancy.

It is in the fall that the Chimney Swift is most noticeable. Large numbers gather then to roost in a big chimney preparatory to their departure for their winter quarters. At Athens, from two to four hundred were present each fall from September until well into October, different chimneys being used each year. The birds would appear shortly before dusk and, after an interval of darting swiftly overhead, would gather in a swirling mass over the top of the chimney, and in a remarkably short time the last bird would have dropped into it and out of sight.

In recent years, large numbers of swifts have been banded in the state, notably at Rome, Atlanta, Milledgeville, and Thomasville, and returns have shown that the birds occurring in Georgia in the fall have come from localities representing almost the entire range of this species. Possibly the most interesting return was that of a swift banded at Thomasville by Herbert L. Stoddard and Charles O. Handley on September 14, 1928, that was picked up dead on Vancouver Island, British Columbia, on April 7, 1934. As Vaux's Swift is now known to occur in small numbers in Louisiana during the winter months and as British Columbia is fully one thousand miles west of the present known range of the Chimney Swift, it is logical to assume that this bird was actually a Vaux's Swift, heretofore unrecorded from the state. Unfortunately only the band was preserved, so that, for the time being, one can only surmise as to whether this assumption is correct, or whether the Chimney Swift did wander so far west of its normal haunts. Banding has also revealed another interesting and noteworthy fact in connection with this species. Until 1944 nothing definite was known about where it spent the winter months. In May of that year, however, thirteen bands were recovered that had been removed from the legs of swifts killed by natives of Peru on the Yenayaco River the previous December. Of this number, one was a swift banded at Macon by Raymond J. Fleetwood on September 17, 1939. It has long been suspected that the majority of the Chimney Swifts wintered in South America, but this is the first tangible proof that has appeared.

Hummingbirds: *Family Trochilidae*

Ruby-throated Hummingbird
Archilochus colubris (Linnaeus)

GENERAL DISTRIBUTION: Breeds from Alberta, central Saskatchewan, Manitoba, and Cape Breton Island south to the Gulf Coast and Florida, and west to North Dakota, Nebraska, Kansas, and central Texas. Winters from Florida and Louisiana south to Panama.

STATUS IN GEORGIA: A common summer resident throughout the state, arriving in March and early April and lingering in the fall until well into October.

Earliest dates of arrival in the spring are, for Cumberland Island, March 17 (1902); Sea Island, March 31 (1947); Hinesville, March 26 (1944); Savannah, March 12 (1916); Grady County, March 9 (1929); Tifton, March 7 (1945); Macon, March 24 (1945); Milledgeville, April 4 (1943); Atlanta, April 2 (1922); Athens, April 8 (1922) and April 5 (1929); August, April 10 (1884); and Canton, April 11 (1905). The last in the fall were observed at Athens, October 20 (1925); Atlanta, October 20 (1954); Macon, October 19 (1954); Americus, October 18 (1941); Fitzgerald, October 22 (1940); Grady County, November 5 (1925); and Savannah, October 30 (1931).

It would appear that in Georgia two broods are reared each year, for nests with eggs can be found in late April and May and again in late June, July, and early August. At Athens [Burleigh, 1938], my earliest breeding record is that of a nest discovered April 28, 1927, with two fresh eggs; and my latest a nest with one young bird almost fully fledged on August 6, 1927. Nests with eggs have also been found at Athens on the following dates: May 7, 19, and 29, 1921; May 1, 1922; May 10, 1924; June 21, 1925; June 1, July 1 and 18, 1927. Griffin [1940] cites as nesting extremes for the Atlanta region, May 10, 1913 and 1922 (two eggs); and August 12, 1939 (one egg). Definite breeding records for other localities are as follows:

Margret, Fannin County: June 14, 1921, one incubated egg (Burleigh).

Young Harris, Towns County: May 23, 1923, two slightly incubated eggs; and July 25, 1923, two well-incubated eggs (Burleigh).

Marietta, Cobb County: May 9, 1933, one egg (Barkalow).

Ben Hill County: nesting extremes—five nests—May 3 (1941), two young, and June 1 (1940), two eggs (Norris).

Savannah, Chatham County: May 10, 1906, two fresh eggs; May 22, 1908, two fresh eggs; May 3, 1914, two incubated eggs (Rossignol). May 13, 1920, two fresh eggs; June 4, 1945, two fresh eggs (Erichsen).

HABITS AND RECOGNITION: The Ruby-throated Hummingbird is a well-known species throughout its range, its extremely small size and brilliant plumage attracting attention wherever it appears. Eighteen species of hummingbirds—justifiably considered the jewels of the bird world—occur in the United States, but of this number only the Ruby-throat is normally found east of the Mississippi River. Fortunately it is common and generally distributed during the summer. In both sexes of our species the upperparts are bright iridescent bronze-green, and the males have a ruby throat, which, if seen in the right light, gleams like a live coal. It is certainly one of the most remarkable birds found in Georgia, and one that invariably arouses interest wherever seen.

Not only in appearance, but in actions as well, does it differ from any other bird found in the state. Its food is composed of both nectar and minute insects that it finds in flowers, and these are obtained in a manner all its own. Hovering before a flower, its wings moving so rapidly that they are almost invisible, it probes with its long bill and deftly extracts the food it is seeking. At intervals it will rest on a convenient twig, and when it is seen thus, its diminutive size is strikingly apparent.

Male hummingbirds have a rather uncommon trait. Ardent during courtship, once the eggs are laid they lose all interest in family affairs and are never seen about the nest. Of necessity the females assume entire responsibility for rearing the young. The males also depart for their winter quarters much earlier than the females or young of the year. Hummingbirds can usually be seen in Georgia until late October, but I personally have never noted an adult male later than the latter part of July.

The nest of a hummingbird is a dainty and very attractive structure, being made up of soft plant down, covered on the outside with gray lichens. An inch across, and deeply cupped, it is usually saddled on a limb and is so inconspicuous that, except for the actions of the female, it would only be discovered by accident. Almost invariably the female will leave the nest if anyone approaches the tree in which it is located, and her uneasiness soon reveals its presence. No preference is shown for any special tree, for the fourteen nests that I have found in Georgia were in water oak, blackjack oak, Spanish oak, post oak, blue beech, dogwood, black gum, scrub pine, beech, and red oak. The height of the nests from the ground varied from five to thirty feet, the majority, however, being from fifteen to twenty feet above the ground.

ORDER CORACIIFORMES

Kingfishers: *Family Alcedinidae*

Eastern Belted Kingfisher
Megaceryle alcyon alcyon   (Linnaeus)

GENERAL DISTRIBUTION: Breeds from Mackenzie, central Quebec, and Newfoundland, south to the Gulf Coast and Florida, and west to the Rocky Mountains. Winters from British Columbia, Nebraska, Illinois, Ohio, and Virginia (casually Ontario and the New England states) to the West Indies, Colombia, and British Guiana.

STATUS IN GEORGIA: A fairly common permanent resident throughout the state.

All local lists that have been published (for Augusta, Athens, Atlanta, Rome, Columbus, Fitzgerald, Tifton, Okefenokee Swamp, Hinesville, and Savannah) list this species. While it has been reported as breeding at Young Harris, Winston, Athens, Kirkwood, the Okefenokee Swamp, and Savannah, there are but two actual records of a nest's being found. Griffin [1940] records a nest with young at Atlanta, June 19, 1937, and Hopkins [letter] one at Crystal Lake, Irwin County, that held six young on May 5, 1951.

HABITS AND RECOGNITION: The kingfisher is nowhere common, but is generally distributed throughout the state, and there are few streams or bodies of water of any size where it cannot, at times, be seen. It is a solitary bird, shunning even its own kind except during the breeding season; thus, usually a single bird will be seen perched on a branch overhanging the water or flying by overhead uttering its loud, rattling cry. Noisy, and vigorous in its actions, it is conspicuous wherever it is found, and soon makes its presence known. As its food is largely fish, it is not a popular bird with the average sportsman, and being accorded no legal protection, it has been shot at so often that it is at all times wary and difficult to approach.

Rarely an incautious bird will be seen close at hand, and then its large crested head and long, heavy bill, oddly out of proportion to the rest of its body, leave no doubt of its identity. Though an expert fisherman and preferring small fish to any other food, the kingfisher is known to vary its diet by eating crawfish, lizards, small snakes, frogs, and the larger insects such as grasshoppers, locusts, crickets, and beetles. On many occasions, while

Family *Alcedinidae:* KINGFISHERS

driving through open pine woods in the southern part of the state, I have observed a kingfisher perched on a telephone wire that paralleled a roadside ditch partially filled with water. In such instances it must have been a crawfish, or perhaps a frog, in which it was interested, for there was no possibility of even minnows being found in such a spot.

In nesting, the birds excavate a burrow in a sand or clay bank, preferably close to water, but which may be some distance away if a suitable site is not otherwise available. This burrow is never less than three feet in length, not infrequently as much as six feet, and, unless an obstruction is encountered, goes straight to the enlarged chamber at the end in which the eggs are laid. These vary in number from five to eight, are glossy white and oval in shape. When fresh, they can be found lying on the bare ground, but as incubation progresses, there is a gradual accumulation of fish scales and bones that, whether intentional or not, forms a rough nest lining. An occupied burrow is not too hard to find, but as the most isolated sites are selected and the birds are extremely cautious about entering or leaving the nest, they are usually successful in rearing their young undisturbed.

ORDER PICIFORMES

Woodpeckers: *Family Picidae*

Southern Yellow-shafted Flicker
Colaptes auratus auratus (Linnaeus)

GENERAL DISTRIBUTION: Resident in the Lower Austral Zone of the South Atlantic and Gulf states from southern Illinois and Indiana east to North Carolina, south to central Texas, the Gulf Coast, and Florida.

STATUS IN GEORGIA: A common resident throughout the state, with the exception of the extreme northern counties.

Specimens verifying the presence of this southern race as breeding and probably resident were taken at Roswell (October 15, 1920), Atlanta (May 12, 1942, December 4, 1946, December 11, 1949), Decatur (November 30, 1946, July 1 and November 2, 1947), Stone Mountain (May 24, 1933), and Athens (June 13, 1936, July 18, 1939, May 23, 1945, October 5, 1947).

Although it is a common bird and reported as nesting throughout Georgia, not many definite breeding records are available. Rossignol [letter] states that he has found thirteen nests at Savannah, the earliest on April 18 (1914) with five fresh eggs; the latest on June 6 (1915) also with five fresh eggs. Five eggs make the set usually laid in the southern part of the state, for of these thirteen nests one held four, four held six, and eight held five eggs. Erichsen reports a nest at Allenhurst, in Liberty County, that held six eggs on May 6, 1913; and Norris two in Ben Hill County in 1940, one with two eggs on April 27 and the other with five eggs on June 14. At Athens, [Burleigh, 1938], I found that while apparently but one brood is reared each year, there is considerable irregularity in the time that individual pairs nest, fresh eggs being found from the latter part of April through the middle of June. My extreme breeding records there are a nest that held six fresh eggs, April 21 (1922), and one with newly hatched young examined June 30 (1926). Griffin [1940] cites as nesting extremes for the Atlanta region six fresh eggs April 25 (1903) (Mills), and seven young, June 5 (1937) (Griffin). A nest I found at Woodville, in Greene County, May 23, 1922, held six fresh eggs.

HABITS AND RECOGNITION: Commonly known as the "Yellowhammer," the flicker is a familiar bird to the rural population of the state. Its distribution being limited only by an available food supply, and, during the summer months, by suitable nesting sites, it is found practically everywhere much of the year. A confiding and sociable bird, it customarily occurs about farms and even in the smaller towns, but it is equally at home in the forested areas of the state. Unlike the other woodpeckers, it feeds mostly on the ground, moving about with short hops as it searches for the ants that it seems to prefer to any other food. If approached, it departs with the bounding flight that is characteristic of all the woodpeckers, revealing the bright yellow primaries of its wings and conspicuous white rump that readily identify it. It is a noisy bird with a rather varied vocabulary, but the note most often heard is a loud call, repeated many times, that to me, suggests the syllables "wick-a, wick-a, wick-a." These are usually uttered as it perches in the upper branches of a tree and have a penetrating quality that carries a long distance.

In nesting, it excavates a cavity a foot and a half in depth in a dead limb or trunk of a tree, the six or seven glossy white eggs normally laid in Georgia lying on the bits of decayed wood covering the bottom. The tree or stub selected may be in the open or in woods, and no attempt is made at concealment, more often than not the chips removed in the process of digging the cavity lying on the ground at the base of the tree. So far as my own experience goes, the height of the nest varies from eight to thirty-five feet from the ground, and practically any tree that is sufficiently decayed may be used. At Athens, occupied nests were found to be in loblolly pines, sycamores, black willows, red gums, yellow poplars, river birches, and red oaks.

Northern Yellow-shafted Flicker
Colaptes auratus luteus Bangs

GENERAL DISTRIBUTION: Breeds from Ontario, Nova Scotia, and Newfoundland south through the northern and central United States, east of the Rocky Mountains, to northern Alabama and northern Georgia. Winters south to southern Texas, the Gulf Coast, and Florida.

STATUS IN GEORGIA: A fairly common breeding bird in the mountain counties and a transient and winter resident elsewhere in the state.

This northern race of the flicker breeds in the northern part of the state, as shown by specimens taken in 1927 at Margret, Fannin County, (June 9), Chatsworth (June 23), and Chickamauga (June 25); in 1929 at Toccoa (May 29) and Blood Mountain (June 18); and in 1939 at Brasstown Bald (July 22). A female taken at Decatur on June 8, 1947, was clearly referable to *luteus*, but showed no signs of breeding, and was probably a straggler from the mountains.

This flicker apparently winters regularly over the entire state, specimens having been taken at the following localities: Athens, January 13 and 20, April 12, and September 15, 1929, November 14, 1938, February 18 and 23, 1946, and October 13 and November 5, 1947; Decatur, December 5, 1946, and February 16, 1947; Calhoun, December 18, 1946; and Grady County, January 21, 1940.

HABITS AND RECOGNITION: Only in size does the Northern Yellow-shafted Flicker differ from its southern relative. It is a larger bird, but as far as its plumage is concerned, it is indistinguishable, even in the hand. In the mountains of northern Georgia it occurs in the valleys and in the more open woods on the ridges. It has the same vigorous, noisy traits characteristic of its species wherever found. In the Northern states, apple orchards are favored spots for the flicker during the summer months, and such orchards in northern Georgia are almost sure to have a pair of these familiar woodpeckers.

Boreal Yellow-shafted Flicker
Colaptes auratus borealis   Ridgway

GENERAL DISTRIBUTION: Breeds from Alaska, Mackenzie, and northern Quebec (Ungava) south through Alberta, Saskatchewan, and Newfoundland and Labrador. Winters in the northern United States, south irregularly to California, Texas, and the Gulf Coast.

STATUS IN GEORGIA: Probably of casual occurrence in the state during the winter months.

Up to the present time, this far northern race of the flicker has been recorded four times in Georgia. A male was taken at Athens, November 27, 1945; another male at Atlanta, December 6, 1945 [Burleigh, 1947], and two specimens in Grady County, October 5, 1950, and January 20, 1952 (Stoddard). Further collecting, however, should reveal its presence in at least small numbers in other parts of the state.

HABITS AND RECOGNITION: This race differs from *luteus* in the same way that *luteus* differs from *auratus,* being larger but otherwise similar in appearance and actions. Living during the summer months in the far north, almost to the limit of tree growth, it is a hardy bird, and it is doubtful that it ever reaches the Southern states in any numbers.

Southern Pileated Woodpecker
Dryocopus pileatus pileatus   (Linnaeus)

GENERAL DISTRIBUTION: Resident in the Lower Austral Zone of the southeastern United States, from Florida north to North Carolina, and west to middle Texas and western Oklahoma.

STATUS IN GEORGIA: Resident and fairly common, but of local distribution throughout the state.

Both in the mountains and in the southern part of Georgia the Pileated Woodpecker is a common bird, but the cutting away of much of the larger timber between the fall line and the foothills of the mountains has materially reduced its numbers in that section of the state. It is reported abundant in the Okefenokee Swamp and at Coleraine, [Hebard, 1943]. I found it fairly common in woods bordering the Satilla River north of Folkston, and observed it in small numbers along the Flint River near Newton, in Baker County. Norris [letter] reports it present in suitable habitat in Ben Hill County and Irwin County. Woodward [1949] noted one pair on St. Simons Island and one pair on Sea Island, and Denton [1942] states that he found four pairs in the Muckalee Swamp near Americus. Greene [1933] considers it fairly common in the Atlanta region, while at Athens it was found in rather small numbers because of the cutting away of much of the heavy timber [Burleigh, 1938]. At Augusta, Murphey [1937] reports it still common in the cypress swamps along the Savannah River. In the mountains, it has been reported from Young Harris, Margret, and Cowpen Mountain (Fannin County).

Actual breeding records are few in number. Griffin [1940] cites as nesting extremes for the Atlanta region, four eggs on April 26 (1932) (Barkalow), and one young bird on June 6 (1939) (Griffin). Stoddard reports adults feeding large young in a nest on Sherwood Plantation in Grady County, May 12, 1924. In western Camden County, Hebard [1943] observed both birds of a pair working on the nest cavity on April 20, 1942. Erichsen reports a nest on Ossabaw Island, in Chatham County, that held four half-grown young on May 10, 1915; and Grimm [1946] reports a nest at Flemington, in Liberty County, on May 13, 1943.

HABITS AND RECOGNITION: To my mind no bird is more symbolical of the primitive wilderness areas than is the Pileated Woodpecker. Its large size, conspicuous red crest, and wild, vigorous notes cannot fail to impress even those having but a casual interest in bird life. Always wary and alert, it has the habit of keeping the trunk of a tree between it and the intruder, and, more often than not, one merely glimpses its long slender neck and large head with its scarlet crest as it momentarily appears in view. If it is forced to fly, its black body and large wings suggest a crow, but the wing-beats are slower, and before it is out of sight, it displays the undulating flight characteristic of all the woodpeckers. Being adept at keeping out of sight, it is more often heard than seen, but its presence is frequently revealed, even at a considerable distance, as it hammers vigorously on a dead tree in quest of wood-boring beetles and their larvae. The strength of its heavy wedge-shaped bill enables it to excavate large cavities in the trunk of a tree as it feeds, and these indications of its work are usually much in evidence wherever it occurs. Its ordinary call note resembles to some extent that of a flicker, but it has a wild, ringing quality that quickly distinguishes it.

Hebard [1943] devoted considerable time to a study of this magnificent bird in the southeastern corner of the state, and makes the following comments:

> The great Pileated Woodpecker is an abundant bird in southeastern Georgia . . . its affinity for the deep woods is clearly marked, but it often can be seen swinging from pine head to pine head, crossing a prairie within the Okefenokee, crossing the lawn at Coleraine, or calling from the woods between the rice fields and the plantation house. The daily rounds of the Pileated are quite regular, and their movements seem guided by their quest for food. Both in the Okefenokee and at Coleraine they are late risers. About sunrise or somewhat later, they leave their roost and sally forth across a prairie or through a bay in the Okefenokee or across a field or road or through a branch at Coleraine. Not so long thereafter they return by almost exactly the same route they came. Then they sally forth again in the same manner when the sun is high and again towards evening. Generally one will see but one or two traverse the same route, but more than one pair may feed on the berries of the same batch of black gums. This I observed on January 1, 1941, when I noted at least 17 different individuals feeding on black gum berries in Gum Pond in eastern Charlton County. When not feeding or travelling, Pileateds may remain comparatively motionless near the top of a tall tree. The Pileateds' flight seems not as undulating as that of a Flicker or of a Red-bellied Woodpecker but it is much less direct than that of a Crow. Its flight is more undulating if the terrain is more open. The only nest I have seen was about 40 feet up in a dead slash pine. It opened toward the northeast. The parents were seen digging on this nest on April 20, 1942. The surrounding woods were mostly black gums and other deciduous trees and the nesting hole faced the most open part of the forest canopy.

In Grady County, Stoddard [MS] has frequently watched this large woodpecker feeding on mulberries in the late spring, and later in the year on the fleshy fruit of the magnolia, dogwood, and sassafras. Hebard [letter] says that "their fondness for carpenter ants is extraordinary. These

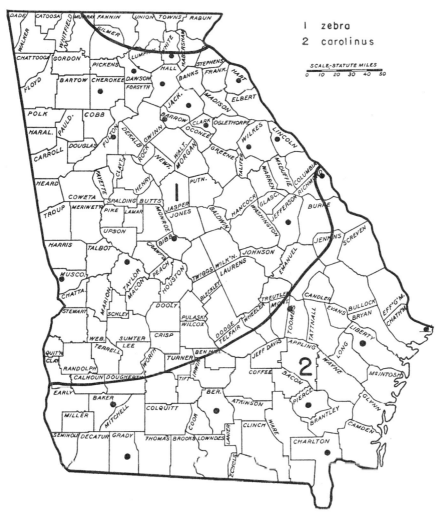

BREEDING DISTRIBUTION OF THE RED-BELLIED WOODPECKER

ants had invaded a number of shutters on the house at Coleraine. In July, 1949, pileated woodpeckers almost completely destroyed one of these shutters."

Eastern Red-bellied Woodpecker
Centurus carolinus carolinus (Linnaeus)

GENERAL DISTRIBUTION: Resident on the Atlantic Coast from Virginia to northern Florida and on the Gulf Coast west to Louisiana.

STATUS IN GEORGIA: Resident and common on the coast, in the southern part of the state, and on the Savannah River as far north as Augusta.

A critical examination of a large series of Red-bellied Woodpeckers taken throughout the state shows that the race, *carolinus,* is rather limited in its distribution in Georgia. Specimens typical of this form were taken at Hinesville, Yellow Bluff, Savannah, Vidalia, Blackshear, Banks Lake, Nashville, Grady County, and Newton. Augusta specimens proved referable to *carolinus* but approaching *zebra* in the more extensive white of the upperparts.

Within its range, it is common and widely distributed, but definite breeding records are largely limited to Chatham County. Here Rossignol [letter] reports finding four nests: three holding four fresh eggs on April 23, 1907, and May 8 and 26, 1914; and one, five slightly incubated eggs on May 10, 1915. Erichsen [MS] cites as breeding records for Savannah a nest with four fresh eggs on April 23, 1921, and another with four eggs on April 30, 1944. Norris [letter] reports nests "with both parents feeding young" in Baker County, June 23, 1947, and at Tifton, July 26, 1951.

HABITS AND RECOGNITION: No bird is more characteristic of the stream bottoms and wooded swamps of the southern part of the state than the Red-bellied Woodpecker. It is noisy and conspicuous throughout much of the day, and its presence is soon made known if one is within hearing of its loud, scolding notes; indeed, in time one comes to associate this sound with the timbered bottom lands. Unless molested, it is not especially shy and can be watched at a reasonably close distance as it works up the trunk of a swamp oak or black gum searching for wood-boring beetles and other insects. If frightened, it will go but a short distance, its undulating flight taking it to a near-by tree, where it calmly resumes its scrutiny of the bark.

A medium-sized woodpecker, its upperparts conspicuously barred with black and white, it can hardly be confused with any other species, especially if a male with the bright scarlet crown and nape is seen. In the female only the back of the head and the nape is scarlet. The note most commonly heard from both sexes is much like that of the Red-headed Woodpecker, but is harsher and has a scolding quality, which, to my ear, definitely sets it apart. It has been variously described as "chuh-chuh," "chawh-chawh," and "churr-churr." Although its food is largely insects, Norris [letter] reports that an adult female collected six miles north of Sylvester, Worth County, on August 6, 1951, "had eaten many drupes of pokeweed (*Phytolacca americana*), this being the main item (which, interestingly, had stained gizzard, intestine, and surrounding viscera a purplish red color)."

Like the other woodpeckers, it normally excavates a new nest cavity each year, and in most instances selects a dead limb of a hardwood. Hebard, however, states [letter] that in southeastern Georgia pines are used almost exclusively, and that an occasional pair will appropriate the nest cavity of a pair of Red-cockaded Woodpeckers, regardless of the protests of the rightful owners.

Western Red-bellied Woodpecker
Centurus carolinus zebra (Boddaert)

GENERAL DISTRIBUTION: Resident from southeastern South Dakota, southeastern Minnesota, southern Ontario, western New York, and Delaware south to central Texas, the northern part of the Gulf states, and Virginia.

STATUS IN GEORGIA: Resident and common over the entire state, with the exception of the mountains and the southern and easternmost counties.

Specimens typical of this northern and western race and representing the breeding population were taken at Canton, Atlanta, Roswell, Athens, Royston, Jefferson, Lexington, Commerce, Auburn, Gratis (Walton County), Dawsonville, and Lincolnton. The northern part of the state would appear to represent the area of intergradation between the two races of *Centurus carolinus,* for specimens having the characters of *zebra* but approaching *carolinus* in the less extensive white of the upperparts and the suggestion of gray on the underparts were taken at Yonah Mountain (White County), Atlanta, Decatur, Athens, Hull, Monroe, Carsonville, Washington, and Louisville. Birds from the northern part of the range of this species are apparently migratory to some extent, for specimens characteristic of *zebra* have been taken at Thomasville, Yellow Bluff, in Liberty County, and in the Okefenokee Swamp.

HABITS AND RECOGNITION: In appearance and actions this race of the Red-bellied Woodpecker differs little from its more southern relative. A bird of the wooded stream bottoms, it is common and widely distributed over much of the state. So far as available records go, it has not yet been seen in any of the mountain counties.

At Athens, I found one or more pairs in practically all the scattered stretches of open woods and succeeded in locating three occupied nests. The first held small young on May 2, 1922, and was fifty feet from the ground in a dead limb of a large white oak. The second held four slightly incubated eggs on April 17, 1923, and was also fifty feet from the ground in the dead top of a sycamore in woods bordering the Oconee River. Another nest investigated that same day held but a single fresh egg and was sixty feet from the ground in a dead limb of a large black oak. In each case the cavity was approximately a foot and a half in depth, with an opening so inconspicuous that it was only by watching the bird enter that the nest

353

Northern Red-cockaded Woodpeckers
Dendrocopos borealis borealis

This woodpecker lived in the pines. It had the interesting habit of tearing
the outer bark away near the nest opening and slashing the inner bark in
such a way as to cause the pitch to flow freely. By the time this pitch
hardened it became tallow-white, and a nesting-tree was recognizable
from afar because of its broad white band. Nest trees invariably were
infected by the fungus-disease known as red-heart. The woodpeckers
did not cause the disease or help to spread it; they merely took advantage
of the softness of the rotted heartwood. They never nested in a sound tree.
The nest I painted was about thirty feet from the ground. I used a
binocular while working in the details. In my painting a young bird is
sticking its head out of the nest.

GEORGE
MIKSCH
SUTTON
1952

was, after long search, finally found. Griffin [1940] records nesting extremes at Atlanta, four eggs April 16 (1938) and young June 8 (1937).

The races of the Red-bellied Woodpecker are well marked and easily recognized from specimens, *zebra* differing from *carolinus* in being decidedly whiter above (the white interspaces being equal to, or wider than, the black bars), with the gray of the underparts paler and tinged with yellow.

Eastern Red-headed Woodpecker
Melanerpes erythrocephalus erythrocephalus   (Linnaeus)

GENERAL DISTRIBUTION: Breeds from southern Manitoba east to southern New Brunswick, south to Texas, the Gulf Coast, and southern Florida. Winters irregularly over much of its breeding range north to South Dakota, Wisconsin, and Ontario.

STATUS IN GEORGIA: Resident and locally common over the entire state, although less numerous in the mountains. During the winter months there is a noticeable fluctuation in numbers, few of these birds being seen some years and as many as in the summer in others.

At Athens [Burleigh, 1938], I found that although these woodpeckers were resident and common throughout the summer months, the number seen during the winter was influenced to a large extent by the acorn crop. Normally there was no scarcity, but there was an occasional year when this source of food was almost totally lacking, and then only one or two of these birds would be noted from the latter part of September until the following April.

It is doubtful that more than one brood is reared each year, for while fresh eggs have been found in July, this species usually does not nest until the latter part of May or the first of June. My earliest breeding record, by fully a month, is that of a nest which, on May 7, 1927, held young possibly three or four days old. My latest breeding record is of a nest found July 9, 1925, with three slightly incubated eggs. Griffin [1940] gives as nesting extremes for the Atlanta region, young on the early date of April 16 (1937) and four young July 21 (1937), while Bell [1947] reports that four "fledglings" were found in a nest at Rome on April 20, 1942. At Savannah, Erichsen [MS] cites as nesting extremes (among twenty nests) three with fresh eggs, May 15 (1927), and four with incubated eggs, July 13 (1946). He also reports a nest at Allenhurst, Liberty County, that held five eggs on May 28, 1913. Denton found a nest at Macon with four apparently fresh eggs on May 27, 1931, and another in Richmond County with young, July 20, 1947. Stoddard [MS] reports an "occupied nest" on Sherwood Plantation in Grady County, June 14, 1941.

Although no nests have been reported, this species is said to breed also at St. Marys, Darien, Hinesville, Cumberland Island, Okefenokee Swamp, Columbus, Kirkwood, Mimsville, Chatsworth, and Cloudland. In the mountains, it has been noted during the summer months at Young Harris and on Cowpen Mountain (Fannin County).

HABITS AND RECOGNITION: The Red-headed Woodpecker is beyond question the handsomest of the various species of woodpeckers found in Georgia. With its bright red head, black back, and white underparts, it attracts attention and is a well-known bird throughout the state. As it has no liking for thick woods, it has benefited by the clearing activities of man; and being of a social disposition, it is found not only about farms but in towns and even in the larger cities. The widespread use of water oaks as shade trees in the northern and central parts of the state and of live oaks below the fall line undoubtedly has contributed to luring this woodpecker into the towns and cities, for it depends on acorns for food in the fall and winter. However, there are other urban inducements, among them telephone poles as ideal nesting sites. In addition to the usual method of securing food, this woodpecker is adept at catching flying insects, and in summer it is a common sight to see one of these birds making repeated sallies from the top of a telephone pole or dead tree much in the manner of a flycatcher. Unfortunately, this habit sometimes proves its undoing, for in swooping across a street or highway, it may misjudge the speed of passing traffic and be killed. There has been a noticeable decrease in the number of these woodpeckers in Georgia in recent years, and it is suspected that this highway mortality is largely responsible.

The note of the redhead most often heard has been well described as a loud "tchur-tchur," usually uttered as the bird perches in the dead top of a tree standing well out in the open.

All the nests of this species that I have seen were in and about Athens, and were either in telephone poles or in the trunks of dead trees; I have never known a living tree to be used. The height from the ground varied from eighteen to thirty feet, with the nest cavity twelve to fifteen inches in depth. In the northern part of its range from four to seven glossy white eggs are laid, five being the usual number. In Georgia, however, I have never found more than four, and as far as my experience goes, it is equally common to find three eggs to a complete clutch.

Eastern Yellow-bellied Sapsucker
Sphyrapicus varius varius (Linnaeus)

GENERAL DISTRIBUTION: Breeds from central Mackenzie, central Alberta, southern Quebec, and Newfoundland south to central Missouri, northern

Ohio, and Massachusetts. Winters from Iowa, Wisconsin, Michigan, and Massachusetts south to the Gulf Coast, the West Indies, western Mexico, and Panama.

STATUS IN GEORGIA: A fairly common winter resident throughout the state.

Earliest arrivals in the fall were recorded at Athens, October 5 (1920); Atlanta, September 1 (1902) and October 4 (1938); Milledgeville, October 26 (1940); Macon, October 5 (1929); Cochran, October 8 (1933); Fitzgerald, October 15 (1939); Grady County, October 8 (1944); Savannah, October 9 (1926); and St. Marys, September 30 (1905).

The last birds seen in the spring were noted at Cumberland Island, April 14 (1902); Savannah, April 14 (1935); Fitzgerald, March 22 (1940); Americus, April 2 (1942); Macon, April 16 (1934); Milledgeville, April 21 (1944); Atlanta, May 5 (1940); and Athens, April 21 (1929).

HABITS AND RECOGNITION: The Yellow-bellied Sapsucker is a handsome bird, but unfortunately certain of its actions make it rather unpopular with tree owners. As its name implies, sap forms part of its food, and at times a favored tree is so riddled with small holes made in procuring the sap as to be almost girdled, thus being killed or seriously weakened, and naturally arousing resentment toward the sapsucker. Stoddard [MS] comments on the destructiveness of this woodpecker in Grady County: "About half the locally grown hickory is not marketable commercially on account of 'bird peck,' while the basswood of the area is mostly pecked. Sometimes the birds work so heavily on isolated longleaf saplings that the trunk becomes a mass of exuding pitch. Such trees are often severely burned, the pitch igniting from grass fires, and the flames traveling up the trees. Such trees, in spite of the normally high fire resistance of the species, are injured so severely that they become stunted or die."

It must be admitted that this species is economically less beneficial than are the other woodpeckers found in Georgia. It would almost seem as if the sapsucker realizes that it is not behaving as it should, for during its winter sojourn in the state it is a quiet and elusive bird. Rarely will more than a single bird be seen at any one spot, and since it is rather deliberate in its movements and has a tendency to remain on the opposite side of the tree from the intruder, its presence frequently goes undetected. The only note heard at this season of the year is a peculiar whining call that will at once identify it. In addition to sap, it eats the inner cambium of the tree and also various insects, especially those that are attracted by the sap. During periods of cold weather it supplements these foods with varieties of fruits such as those of the dogwood, black gum, and poison ivy.

Southern Yellow-bellied Sapsucker
Sphyrapicus varius appalachiensis Ganier

GENERAL DISTRIBUTION: Breeds from the mountains of extreme northern Georgia, extreme eastern Tennessee, and western North Carolina north to include southwestern Virginia.

STATUS IN GEORGIA: A rare summer resident in the extreme northeastern corner of the state. Possibly winters, at least in small numbers, south of the mountain counties, but specimens have yet to be taken after the breeding season anywhere in Georgia.

There is but a single breeding record for the state. Neal [1947] found a nest with small young at an altitude of 3,850 feet on Tray Mountain, on the Towns-White county line, June 14, 1947. A breeding male, taken in White County on June 23, 1947, has been identified by Ganier as *appalachiensis.*

HABITS AND RECOGNITION: As with most subspecies the breeding sapsuckers of the southern Appalachians can be recognized only when in the hand—when actual measurements can be taken and color differences noted. In common with most southern races, *appalachiensis* is smaller, and is also characterized by being "nearly black dorsally, while the northern birds display a great deal of white thus giving a white-spotted appearance to the back" (Ganier, 1954).

To Mrs. Charles Neal goes the credit for finding this species breeding in the state for the first time. Describing the circumstances under which this interesting discovery was made, she says:

> I was standing on the Appalachian Trail at the beginning of the climb up Tray Mountain trying to locate the source of the sound of young birds fussing when I heard the familiar 'cat-note' of the Yellow-bellied Sapsucker. I looked up and saw the male with a small moth in its bill. He eyed me with disfavor and flew a short distance away but returned almost immediately and entered a hole about eighteen feet from the ground in a Black Locust (*Robinia pseudoacacia*). The voices of the young birds became so loud at the approach of food that they were noticeable to my companions fifty feet away.

Eastern Hairy Woodpecker
Dendrocopos villosus villosus (Linnaeus)

GENERAL DISTRIBUTION: Resident in the Transition and Upper Austral zones from Manitoba, central North Dakota, Ontario, southern Quebec, and the Magdalen Islands south to eastern Colorado, central Texas, northern Georgia, and northwestern South Carolina.

Family Picidae: WOODPECKERS

STATUS IN GEORGIA: Resident and fairly common in the extreme northern part of the state.

A breeding male taken May 24, 1929, at Young Harris, on the slopes of Brasstown Bald, was found to represent this northern race. It apparently is strictly nonmigratory, for there are no records south of the mountains.

HABITS AND RECOGNITION: As one follows a trail up a wooded ridge in the mountains of northern Georgia, a high, sharp note will call attention to a medium-sized, black and white woodpecker feeding in a near-by tree. Inching its way up the trunk or digging vigorously for a wood-borer it has discovered, it nevertheless is alert to its surroundings and rarely will permit a close approach. Its appearance and actions, however, will under such circumstances readily identify it as a Hairy Woodpecker. Solitary by nature and living by choice in the heavier timber, it is less often seen than are the other woodpeckers, and for this reason is not as well known. In the course of a day spent in the mountains it is usually possible to see one or more of these birds, but it is nowhere common, and there have been times when I have been unsuccessful in locating a single individual. A nest that I found on the slopes of Brasstown Bald, at Young Harris, held noisy young on May 12, 1922, and was sixty-five feet from the ground in a partially dead limb of a large red oak.

Southern Hairy Woodpecker
Dendrocopos villosus audubonii (Swainson)

GENERAL DISTRIBUTION: Resident in the Lower Austral Zone of the South Atlantic and Gulf states from southeastern Missouri, southern Illinois, southeastern Virginia, and northern Alabama to southeastern Texas and southern Florida.

STATUS IN GEORGIA: Resident and fairly common in all of the state but the extreme northern portion.

Specimens typical of this southern race have been examined from Marietta, Atlanta, Gainesville, Bogart, Center (Jackson County), Athens, Ila (Madison County), Woodville (Greene County), Franklin County, Okefenokee Swamp, Riceboro, and Midway (Liberty County).

Rossignol [letter] reports finding a nest at Savannah, which on April 7, 1908, held four slightly incubated eggs. Erichsen [MS] cites as nesting extremes for Chatham County (nine nests): three fresh eggs, April 3 (1917), and three incubated eggs, May 5 (1923). Stoddard [MS] states that young nearly ready to leave the nest were seen on Sherwood Plantation in Grady County, May 9, 1924. At Athens, I found a nest with three fresh eggs on April 4, 1924, and three others with noisy young on April 15 and 16, 1923, and April 12, 1924. Griffin [1940] gives as nesting extremes for the Atlanta region nests with young, April 9 and June 4, 1939.

HABITS AND RECOGNITION: South of the mountains the Hairy Woodpecker is fairly common and well distributed wherever conditions are suitable. While not particularly shy, it shows a decided preference for the larger stretches of woods and rarely, if ever, ventures into towns, or, for that matter, even into small woodlots near farms. The larger deciduous timber in the stream bottoms is favored, and not infrequently this bird can be found in the open pine woods that cover such extensive areas in the southern part of the state. Except during the breeding season, it is exceptional to see more than a single individual at any one spot.

The flight of all woodpeckers is more or less undulating, and in my experience this trait is especially pronounced in the Hairy Woodpecker if its destination is any distance away. In leaving the tree in which it has been feeding, it drops toward the ground and then bounds, as it were, through the air, rising and falling in long arcs. As it flies, it can be heard uttering its sharp, metallic notes, which suggest those of the Downy Woodpecker but have a wilder, more robust quality that even at a distance clearly identifies this species.

In my experience, the nest is always in the trunk of a dead, or partially dead, tree, and excavated at heights from twenty to forty-five feet from the ground. At Athens, I have found this woodpecker nesting in a sycamore, a red gum, and a black oak, and doubtless other species are used. Three or four glossy white eggs are laid in late March or early April, and but a single brood is reared each year. The entrance hole seems small for the size of the bird and is so inconspicuous that it can easily escape notice. Once the young are well grown, however, finding the nest is an entirely different story. If one of the parents appears at the opening with food, there is an immediate uproar that is audible for some distance and cannot help but attract the attention of anyone in the vicinity. This would appear to be a hazard where the rearing of the young is concerned, but as a rule no harm befalls them.

This southern race of the Hairy Woodpecker differs from *villosus* in being decidedly smaller, with the underparts dull white rather than clear white. The white markings on the back and wings are also less extensive.

Northern Downy Woodpecker
Dendrocopos pubescens medianus   (Swainson)

GENERAL DISTRIBUTION: Resident in the Canadian and Transition zones of eastern North America from southeastern Alberta, Manitoba, southern

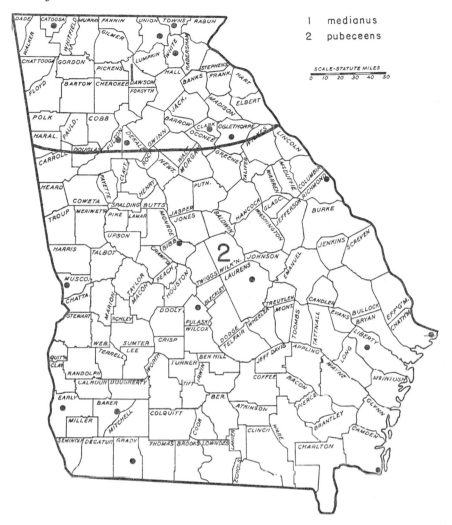

1 medianus
2 pubeceens

SCALE-STATUTE MILES

0 10 20 30 40 50

BREEDING DISTRIBUTION OF THE DOWNY WOODPECKER

Ungava, and Newfoundland south to eastern Nebraska, Kansas, Tennessee, and northern Georgia.

STATUS IN GEORGIA: Resident and common in the northern part of the state.

A series of twenty-four Downy Woodpeckers, of both sexes, taken in northern Georgia showed clearly that the northern form, *medianus,* is the race occurring in the mountains and in the upper Piedmont. Specimens typical of this northern race have been examined from Young Harris, Neel's Gap (Union County), Yonah Mountain (White County), Ringgold, Atlanta, Decatur, Athens, Princeton, Watkinsville, and Lexington.

Athens would appear to represent the part of the state where the two races meet, for of eight specimens taken there (five males and three females), only one is typical of *medianus.* The others, while intermediate in their characters, approach *pubescens* both in respect to measurements and plumage [Burleigh, 1948]. Although there is no recognized migration among Downy Woodpeckers, an occasional individual apparently goes farther south during the winter, for a specimen taken at Thomasville, March 30, 1904, is clearly referable to *medianus.*

HABITS AND RECOGNITION: In appearance and actions the Northern Downy Woodpecker differs little from the typical southern *pubescens.* It is a slightly larger bird, with whiter underparts, but to the casual observer this is hardly noticeable. It is the same sociable little woodpecker, frequenting wooded stream bottoms during much of the year and associating with restless flocks of chickadees, kinglets, and nuthatches throughout the winter. A common habit in the late fall is the excavating of a cavity in an old stub, where during periods of cold weather it spends each night snug and warm. On more than one occasion I have seen a bird slip unobtrusively into such a roosting cavity just at dusk, reappearing momentarily at the entrance to be sure that all was well.

Because of its preference for stream bottoms, the nest is usually near water, and the few nests that I have found in Georgia have been without exception in willows. They varied from twelve to twenty-five feet above the ground, the four or five glossy white eggs lying on fragments of decayed wood at the bottom of a cavity from ten to twelve inches in depth. Only one brood is reared each year, and with few exceptions the young have left the nest by the middle of May. At Athens, my earliest breeding record is of a nest that held four fresh eggs on April 5 (1927); my latest one, also with four fresh eggs, on April 21 (1924). Griffin [1940] cites as nesting extremes for the Atlanta region five incubated eggs on April 12 (1921) and young on June 4 (1939).

Southern Downy Woodpecker
Dendrocopos pubescens pubescens (Linnaeus)

GENERAL DISTRIBUTION: Resident in the Lower Austral Zone of the South Atlantic and Gulf states from Florida to eastern Texas, north to Oklahoma and North Carolina.

STATUS IN GEORGIA: Resident and common in the lower Piedmont and the coastal plain.

Specimens typical of this southern race have been examined from: Allenhurst, Hinesville, Hawkinsville, Blakely, Louisville, Dublin, and Columbus. It intergrades with the northern race, *medianus,* in the upper

Piedmont, for specimens representing *medianus* but approaching *pubescens* in size were taken at Washington, Jefferson, Center (Jackson County), Athens, and Canton.

Rossignol [letter] gives as nesting extremes for Savannah (seven nests) five fresh eggs on April 28 (1905) and four well-incubated eggs on May 28 (1914). Erichsen [MS] states that his earliest breeding record for Chatham County is a nest found April 16, 1927, with four eggs. Norris [letter] reports two nests with young found at Fitzgerald by Hopkins, one on May 27, 1940, the other on May 3, 1941. Straw [1947] reports a nest at Columbus that on April 28, 1946, held small young.

HABITS AND RECOGNITION: In appearance the Downy Woodpecker is a miniature of the Hairy Woodpecker. In temperament, however, it is very different. It is a sociable little bird, and this characteristic is especially noticeable during the winter months when it is commonly seen associating with roving flocks of chickadees, kinglets, and nuthatches. It is the smallest of the woodpeckers, and in Georgia one of the best known, for it is unsuspicious and readily accepts the presence of man. During the spring months, when it is occupied with domestic responsibilities, it can usually be found in the wooded stream bottoms, for it is partial to deciduous timber. An occasional pair will nest in a pecan orchard, and elsewhere in its range there are instances when fence posts at the edge of pine woods are used. In the fall and winter it appears in farmyards, in roadside hedges, and in the shade trees in the towns, where it is soon a familiar sight. In no sense of the word is it a noisy bird, but it can frequently be heard uttering a high, sharp note, either in flight or as it momentarily pauses in its industrious search for food, that is somewhat similar to that of the Hairy Woodpecker but lacks the wild, ringing quality of the cry of the larger bird.

Northern Red-cockaded Woodpecker
Dendrocopos borealis borealis (Vieillot)

GENERAL DISTRIBUTION: Resident in the Lower Austral Zone of the South Atlantic and Gulf states from southern Missouri, western Kentucky, Tennessee, and southeastern Virginia south to the Gulf Coast and northern Florida.

STATUS IN GEORGIA: Resident and locally common in the southern half of the state, north casually to Rome, Macon, Milledgeville, and Augusta.

It has been reported as breeding at St. Marys, Hinesville, Blackbeard Island, Reidsville, Okefenokee Swamp, Grady County, Newton, Surrency (Appling County), Cochran (Bleckly County), Columbus, Tarversville (Twiggs County), Macon, Piedmont National Wildlife Refuge, Milledgeville, Woodville (Greene County), Augusta, Rome, and Chickamauga Park. Erichsen [MS] reports three nests found in Chatham County on April 17, 1929, and April 4 and 11, 1931, each holding four fresh eggs; Norris [1951] reports a nest with young in Baker County on May 24, 1948; and Hebard [letter] one with well-grown young near Kingsland on May 29, 1949.

Considered resident within its range, it appears to wander to some extent in the fall and late winter months, for, although it is not known to breed in the vicinity of Atlanta, two specimens were taken there by W. H. LaPrade on March 6, 1906; and single birds were seen at Vinings, in Cobb County, February 26, 1928 [Greene, 1933], and at Atlanta, September 12, 1944 [Johnston, 1945].

HABITS AND RECOGNITION: In some respects the Red-cockaded Woodpeckers are unique among Georgia woodpeckers. An outstanding characteristic is their gregariousness, for, except during the breeding season, they are found in small flocks that feed in the upper branches of the larger pines. Their actions then suggest nuthatches as they work over the outer ends of the limbs, and this impression is emphasized by their subdued chatter, as one bird calls to another close by. They are among the most vocal of the woodpeckers, and one is seldom in doubt about their presence. The note most commonly heard suggests to my ear a high-pitched squeal, although at times it is lower in tone and could then be called a grunt. As they feed, they move restlessly from one tree to another, and in the course of a day visit widely separated areas. Their breeding habits likewise set them apart from the other woodpeckers. The nest is always in the trunk of a living pine and can be recognized even at a distance by the pitch that covers the bark for a foot or more below the entrance. This results from the actions of the birds in deliberately drilling many small holes into the cambium until the exuding resin has spread into a large, conspicuous white patch. The reason for this odd departure from the normal nesting activities of its tribe has yet to be explained, but the trait has been noticed for all pairs of Red-cockaded Woodpeckers that have been watched during the breeding season.

This species has suffered from changed environment resulting from the activities of man. It prefers open stands of fairly mature pine timber, and with the cutting over of much of the extensive stretches of pine forest in the southern part of the state, the Red-cockaded Woodpecker has disappeared from many areas where once it was common. It now occurs locally in rather limited numbers only where the pine timber is large enough to provide suitable nesting sites and food. In Georgia there are sufficient tracts of such timber still in existence to eliminate the possibility of the complete disappearance of this species, but it is doubtful that it will ever be very plentiful again. No difficulty should be experienced in recognizing this woodpecker, which is usually tame and easily approached. Slightly smaller than the Hairy Woodpecker, it differs in that the top of the head is black, the cheeks conspicuously white, and the sides spotted with black. The males have a bright red streak above each ear, but it is rather inconspicuous even at close range.

Ivory-billed Woodpecker
Campephilus principalis (Linnaeus)

GENERAL DISTRIBUTION: Formerly resident in the South Atlantic and Gulf states from eastern Texas to North Carolina, north in the Mississippi Valley to Oklahoma, Missouri, southern Illinois, and southern Indiana, now extirpated over most of its range. It has been reported in recent years only from Louisiana, Mississippi, southern Georgia, South Carolina, and Florida.

STATUS IN GEORGIA: Formerly fairly common in the southern part of the state, now apparently completely gone.

Wilson [1811] wrote concerning this species: "Along the borders of the Savannah River . . . between Savannah and Augusta, I found them very frequently." H. B. Bailey [1883] records a set of four eggs taken by S. W. Wilson in the Altamaha Swamp, on April 10, some year prior to 1865. Murphey [1937] credits George N. Bailie with seeing a single bird in September, 1907, in the Savannah River swamp below Augusta. Wright and Harper [1913] reported this woodpecker still existing in small numbers in the Okefenokee Swamp in 1912, and Hebard [1941] states that one was shot there in March of that year and given to his father, who had it mounted. Under date of February 19, 1949, Mr. Hebard has written me: "Ivory-bills were not noted in the swamp between March, 1912, and the great fire of April, 1932. Since then there have been a number of records I am inclined to accept. Phillips B. Street and I saw a pair of Ivory-bills at the Gap o'Grand Prairie in the Okefenokee on November 30, 1948. There's another recent report from the west end of the south fork of the Canal. Our Coleraine birds were last recorded late in April, 1946."

HABITS AND RECOGNITION: This magnificent woodpecker may possibly still exist in extremely small numbers in the southeastern corner of the state, but probably before many more years have passed it will have joined the ranks of the ill-fated Passenger Pigeon and the Carolina Parokeet. From what little is known of its early history, existence for the Ivory-billed Woodpecker was always precarious. The Indians coveted its large, so-called ivory bill as an ornament, and killed the bird at every opportunity.

Its flesh was said to be quite palatable, and since it was a large bird, it was consistently shot for food. It remained, however, for the cutting of the virgin forests in which it found suitable habitat to add the final factor that meant its ultimate extinction, for unlike most birds, it seems unable to adapt itself to a changed environment, and requires large, mature timber that furnishes an unfailing supply of the insect larvae on which it feeds almost exclusively. These insects are obtained by scaling off the bark under which they live, rather than by drilling into the wood as other woodpeckers do, and the smaller trees left after logging fail to provide its essential food.

As it is slightly larger than the Pileated Woodpecker and somewhat similar in appearance, there is little question but that it could be easily confused with this latter species by the casual observer, and that many recent records actually are of this relatively common bird rather than of the extremely rare Ivory-bill. If seen within reasonably close range, however, it should be easily recognized, for its large, stout, light-colored bill and the conspicuous white in the wings clearly differentiate it from the Pileated Woodpecker. In addition, it has a steady flight that does not have the pronounced undulations characteristic of the Pileated Woodpecker; and its note, strangely weak for so large a bird and inaudible at even a short distance, is a nasal, high-pitched call that some observers have compared to the sound produced by a tin trumpet. The contrast between this sound and the loud, strident cackle of the Pileated Woodpecker is so striking that once a person has noted the difference, it will never be forgotten.

Almost nothing is known concerning the breeding habits of this species in Georgia. Elsewhere within its range the nesting cavity has been found in the trunk of a living or partially dead tree, from twenty-five to forty-five feet from the ground, the depth varying from eighteen to twenty inches. Normally but two or three glossy white eggs are laid, and one or more are so frequently infertile that the average brood studied rarely exceeded two young. Possibly this is another factor that has limited the numbers of these birds within their present restricted range.

ORDER PASSERIFORMES

Tyrant Flycatchers: *Family Tyrannidae*

Eastern Kingbird
Tyrannus tyrannus   (Linnaeus)

GENERAL DISTRIBUTION: Breeds from southern British Columbia, southern Mackenzie, central Manitoba, northern Ontario, southern Quebec, and Nova Scotia south to central Oregon, northern New Mexico, central Texas, the Gulf Coast, and Florida. Winters from southern Mexico to Colombia, Peru, and Bolivia.

STATUS IN GEORGIA: A common summer resident throughout the state.

The Eastern Kingbird appears in the spring in late March or early April, is soon plentiful, and remains so until late August. The first part of September sees a noticeable decrease in numbers, and only rarely is this species recorded in the state after the middle of the month.

Earliest arrivals in the spring were noted at:

St. Marys: March 28 (1902).
Darien: March 29 (1890).
Sea Island: April 7 (1946).
Hinesville: April 4 (1945).
Savannah: March 24 (1929).
Grady County: March 23 (1937 and
   1945).
Fitzgerald: April 5 (1941).
Americus: April 2 (1942).

Columbus: April 4 (1945).
Macon: March 28 (1944).
Mimsville: March 31 (1902).
Milledgeville: March 27 (1936).
Augusta: April 9 (1945).
Athens: April 5 (1929).
Atlanta: April 4 (1931).
Dillard, Rabun County: April 13 (1933).

The last in the fall were seen at Athens, September 14 (1926); Atlanta, September 19 (1929); Augusta, October 1 (1944); Milledgeville, October 3 (1942); Americus, September 24 (1941); Fitzgerald, September 17 (1941); Grady County, September 24 (1947); Savannah, October 16 (1910); Hinesville, September 11 (1944); and Camden County, October 6 (1945).

Definite breeding records for the state include the following localities:

Margret, Fannin County: Nest with well-grown young, June 26, 1921 (Burleigh).
Young Harris, Towns County: Four slightly incubated eggs, May 27, 1925 (Burleigh).

Athens: Earliest breeding record, May 27 (1927), three slightly incubated eggs; latest, two fresh eggs, July 28 (1926) (Burleigh).
Atlanta: Nesting extremes, May 25 (1918), four partially incubated eggs

(L. Harris); and July 29 (1938), four eggs (Griffin).

Richmond County: Nest with well-fledged young, June 16, 1947 (Denton).

Fitzgerald: Three eggs, May 3, 1941; three young, June 17, 1941 (Hopkins).

Grady County: Nest with three fully grown young, June 13, 1940 (Stoddard).

Savannah: Nesting extremes (nine nests), May 10 (1914); four fresh eggs, June 10 (1906); four fresh eggs (Rossignol).

HABITS AND RECOGNITION: Commonly known as the Bee Martin in Georgia, the Eastern Kingbird is a familiar and well-known bird. Shunning the deep woods, it inhabits the open country, favorite spots being the top of a tree in a field or pasture or a telephone wire at the side of a road. From such a vantage point it makes frequent sallies for passing insects, meanwhile maintaining a constant vigilance for trespass on its territory. No bird is more fearless or aggressive in defending its nest, and the appearance of a crow or a hawk during the summer months is the signal for a spirited pursuit that persists until the intruder is driven out of sight. That the Kingbird is not bluffing in its determination to protect its young or eggs is soon apparent, and regardless of the size of the bird attacked, it is merely a question of moments before the threatened danger has ceased to exist.

It is more than a month after the birds arrive in the spring before nesting activities are well under way, but, despite this late start, two broods are frequently reared. The first young are on the wing in late June, and a month later many pairs are again engrossed in domestic duties. The nest is usually at the outer end of a limb on a tree standing well out in the open and from twenty to fifty feet from the ground. It is compactly built of weed stems, rootlets, grasses, and dry pine needles, deeply cupped, and lined with fine rootlets and, at times, bits of cotton and wool.

A rather suprising association that I have observed is the tolerance of this normally intolerant flycatcher toward the Orchard Oriole. On three occasions at Athens I have found both the Kingbird and the Orchard Oriole nesting in the same tree. The first time was on June 11, 1924, when in a large persimmon tree standing a short distance out in an open field I found a Kingbird's nest with three incubated eggs and on the opposite side of the tree an Orchard Oriole's with four slightly incubated eggs. The second instance was much the same, while the third emphasized to an even greater degree the seeming friendliness existing between these two species. On June 20, 1926, when I was in the open Sandy Creek bottoms, I came across a small wild plum tree in which, within six feet of each other, were the nests of a Kingbird and an Orchard Oriole, both containing half-grown young.

As a general rule the flycatchers are rather solitary so far as their normal existence is concerned, but the Kingbird is exceptional in this respect. In migration it occurs in flocks that are especially noticeable in the fall when compact groups will be seen feeding on the fruit of the pokeberry or scattered along a barb-wire fence separating open fields. They are silent then, in contrast to their noisy exuberance during the summer months, and, for kingbirds, relatively inconspicuous.

Northern Gray Kingbird
Tyrannus dominicensis dominicensis   (Gmelin)

GENERAL DISTRIBUTION: Breeds from the coast of southeastern South Carolina south through Florida, the Bahamas, Cuba, Puerto Rico, the Virgin Islands, Haiti, and Jamaica. Winters from Jamaica and Haiti south to northern South America.

STATUS IN GEORGIA: A rare summer resident on the coast.

The Gray Kingbird was first recorded for the state by John Krider, who collected a specimen (now in the Academy of Natural Sciences at Philadelphia) on St. Simons Island, September 1, 1859. Many years later it was again reported from this island by Robert Norris, who observed two birds there on June 4, 16, and 20, 1939 [Norris, 1939], and collected a male, in breeding condition, on June 9, 1942 [Norris, 1944]. In his journal for 1877, [Oriole, September, 1950, p. 27], William Brewster states that he collected a Gray Kingbird at St. Marys on April 26.

In recent years it has occurred casually on Cockspur Island, near the mouth of the Savannah River, being noted by Gilbert R. Rossignol on June 8, 1933; by Ivan Tomkins and Don Eyles in July, 1938, and June, 1939; and by William Griffin on September 4, 1939 [Eyles, 1941]. In 1939 it was observed by Tomkins also at Lazaretto, on Tybee Island, on April 29, and on Long Island May 30 [Eyles, 1941]. The most recent records are those of a single bird seen on Sea Island by Clay and Thomas, June 27, 1943 [Thomas, 1945]; and one bird at St. Marys by Richard Kuerzi on July 14, 1950 [Denton, letter].

Definite breeding records are limited to two localities: H. B. Bailey [1883] states that eggs were taken by Dr. S. W. Wilson on St. Simons Island between 1853 and 1865 (a little uncertainty exists, however, concerning the reliability of this identification), and Eyles [1938] reports a nest with three eggs on Cockspur Island, July 3, 1938, and another nest [Eyles, 1941] at the same spot (later destroyed by dredging operations) on June 24, 1939.

HABITS AND RECOGNITION: Anyone familiar with the Eastern Kingbird will have no difficulty in recognizing the Gray Kingbird. It is typically a kingbird in appearance and actions, but is larger, is noticeably gray above, and lacks the conspicuous white band at the end of the tail. Its partiality for open country in the vicinity of water is apparently the limiting factor in

FISH CROW

Corvus ossifragus

The Fish Crow is much like the Common Crow but is smaller and glossier.
It is fond of circling high in air above its nesting grounds. Its
characteristic call note is not a "caw" but rather a "cahr." Its fondness
for ripe mulberries led me to paint it in an old mulberry tree, several of
which grew near the main house on Sherwood Plantation. I had so much
trouble with the highlights of the glossy plumage that I might never
have finished the painting had not Herbert Stoddard helped out
by mounting a model for me.

its distribution on the coast, for as yet it has been noted nowhere but on the islands that are separated from the mainland by extensive stretches of salt marsh. Georgia being at the northern limit of its range on the Atlantic Coast, it is doubtful that the bird will ever be of more than casual occurrence in the state, but it is probable that a few pairs nest each year where suitable conditions are found. It is a noisy, aggressive bird, its common call note, aptly described as "pe-cheer-y," being heard throughout the day as it perches in the top of a live oak or on a telephone wire. From such an exposed situation, it takes its toll of passing insects, meanwhile keeping an alert watch over its territory and never hesitating in attacking such a potential threat to its welfare as a passing Crow or Boat-tailed Grackle.

Little is known of the breeding habits of this kingbird in Georgia. The two nests that were found on Cockspur Island were in Chinaberry trees, but no details are given of their construction or height from the ground. Elsewhere within the range of this species, nests found have been as low as three feet from the ground, rarely over twelve feet, and they have been described as distinct from those of the Eastern Kingbird in being flimsy in construction, never compact or at all bulky.

Western Kingbird
Tyrannus verticalis Say

GENERAL DISTRIBUTION: Breeds from southern British Columbia, southern Alberta, and southern Manitoba south to northern Lower California and Chihuahua, east to western Texas and western Iowa. Winters from western Mexico to Nicaragua. Casual in migration and during the winter months east of the Mississippi River, from Maine to southern Florida.

STATUS IN GEORGIA: Of casual occurrence throughout the state.

The Western Kingbird was first recorded in Georgia by Robert Norris, who took a specimen at Waycross in January, 1938. This specimen was not preserved, but a sketch was made that satisfactorily identified it. On October 9, 1938, one bird was seen on Billy's Island in the Okefenokee Swamp by various members of the Georgia Ornithological Society [Griffin and Sciple, 1938]. It was next recorded in the state on November 13, 1941, when a specimen was taken at Montezuma, in Macon County [Burleigh, 1942]. The most recent records are those of a bird seen in the South River section near Atlanta on May 9, 1949 [Gordon, 1949], and two seen, and one collected, at Fort Screven, Tybee Island, on November 29, 1953 [Tomkins, 1954].

HABITS AND RECOGNITION: Even at a distance, this Western Kingbird can be readily recognized for what it is, a large flycatcher of the genus *Tyrannus*. Like the preceding two species, it is a bird of the open country, and when seen it will be in a conspicuous position, perched in the top of a tree or bush or on a telephone wire at the side of a road. Under such circumstances, its relatively long tail, gray breast, and yellow belly will at once distinguish it from the other kingbirds. During the summer, it is typically noisy and pugnacious, but once the breeding season is over, this attitude gradually changes, and the few individuals seen in Georgia have been quiet, almost subdued, in their demeanor. In recent years this species has been extending its range eastward, and it is possible that in time it may occur regularly in the state as a spring and fall transient.

Scissor-tailed Flycatcher
Muscivora forficata (Gmelin)

GENERAL DISTRIBUTION: Breeds from southern Nebraska to southern Kansas and southern Texas, casually to southwestern Missouri, western Arkansas, and western Louisiana. Winters from southern Mexico to Panama.

STATUS IN GEORGIA: Of accidental occurrence in the southern part of the state.

Hoxie, in a series of articles published in the *Savannah Morning News* in 1911, records a bird seen by him on Wassaw Island, but gives no date [Fargo, 1934]. Tomkins [1934] reports a male taken by Gilbert R. Rossignol on Cockspur Island, near the mouth of the Savannah River, June 5, 1933. The most recent record is that of a bird that appeared at Tifton in 1943. It was first seen on January 2, and at intervals thereafter until February 9, when it was collected [Norris and Gaulding, 1944].

HABITS AND RECOGNITION: It is unfortunate that the Scissor-tailed Flycatcher is not a commoner bird in Georgia, for it is one of the handsomest and most attractive members of its family. Its prevailing colors are pearl-gray and white, offset by a pink wash on the back and deep salmon flanks that border the white of the underparts. What cannot fail to catch the eye, however, is its long, deeply forked tail, considerably longer in both sexes than the rest of the body. When it is perched in the top of a bush or on the upper strand of a barb-wire fence, its unique appearance gives it a distinction which in flight is further emphasized as, long tail streaming behind it, it darts high into the air after a passing insect. An inhabitant of the open prairie country, it has no liking for timbered areas, and in migration can be looked for at the edges of fields and pastures.

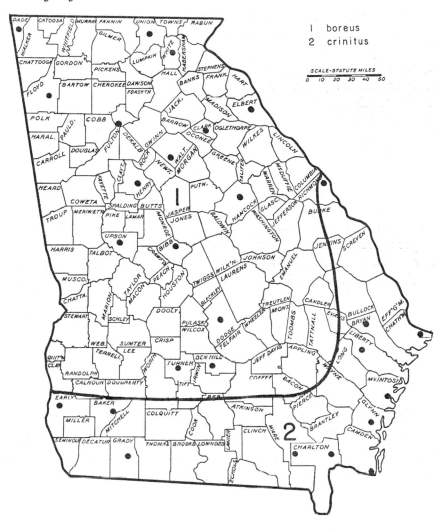

BREEDING DISTRIBUTION OF THE CRESTED FLYCATCHER

Northern Great-crested Flycatcher
Myiarchus crinitus boreus　Bangs

GENERAL DISTRIBUTION:　Breeds from southern Manitoba, central Ontario, southern Quebec, and New Brunswick south to southern Texas, the northern edge of the Gulf states, and central Georgia. Winters from eastern and southern Mexico to Panama and Colombia.

STATUS IN GEORGIA:　A common summer resident over the larger part of the state.

A small series of breeding birds taken in 1946 as far south as Carrollton and McDonough proved to be referable to this northern race. *Boreus* is readily distinguished from *crinitus* by its much smaller bill, this character being constant in the specimens taken at Yonah Mountain (White County), June 28; Athens (Clarke County), May 24, May 26, and August 28; Princeton (Clarke County), June 8; Social Circle (Walton County), June 13; Atlanta (Fulton County), August 1; Stone Mountain (DeKalb County), July 26; Smyrna (Cobb County), June 17; Carrollton (Carroll County), July 18; and McDonough (Henry County), June 19. In addition to these breeding birds, specimens that were apparently transients were taken at Yellow Bluff (Liberty County), April 16; Savannah (Chatham County), April 18; Nahunta (Brantley County), April 30; and Alma (Bacon County), May 4 [Burleigh, 1947].

Further field work in June, 1947, in the southern part of the state, materially extending the breeding range of *boreus*. Males from Thomaston (Upson County) and Ashburn (Turner County) proved to be typical of this northern race, while males from Eastman (Dodge County) and Fitzgerald (Ben Hill County) approached *crinitus* in their characters but were closer to *boreus*. It would appear, therefore, that typical *crinitus* is limited in its distribution during the summer months to the extreme southern edge of the state and to the vicinity of the Savannah River as far north as Augusta, and that *boreus* is the form occupying the larger part of Georgia north of this relatively narrow belt [Burleigh, 1948]. Norris [1951] further verifies this extensive breeding range of *boreus* in the state, specimens taken by him in Baker County proving referable to the northern race.

Earliest arrivals in the spring were noted at Irwin County, March 22 (1952); Fitzgerald, April 13 (1940); Americus, April 12 (1942); Columbus, April 14 (1946); Macon, March 30 (1945); Milledgeville, April 9 (1929); Athens, April 6 (1929); and Atlanta, March 20 (1948).

The last in the fall were seen at Atlanta, September 29 (1951); Athens, September 25 (1921); Macon, September 26 (1934); Americus, September 15 (1941); and Fitzgerald, September 23 (1940).

Following are definite breeding records:

Athens: July 5, 1925, four well-incubated eggs; May 31, 1926, five slightly incubated eggs [Burleigh, 1938].
Atlanta: May 20, 1902, two fresh eggs (Mills); July 3, 1939, five eggs [Griffin, 1940].
Fitzgerald: May 24, 1941, five eggs; June 21, 1941, one egg (Hopkins).

HABITS AND RECOGNITION: During much of its sojourn in Georgia, the Northern Great-crested Flycatcher is a noisy bird, but occurring as it does in wooded areas, it is more often heard than seen. It is common and well distributed throughout most of the state, and anyone within hearing distance of this flycatcher will soon be aware of its presence, for it has a loud, harsh note that is frequently uttered and at once attracts attention to it. It must be searched for to be seen, however, for it spends much of its time

374

on a favorite perch in some tall tree where it is far from conspicuous. It is a slender, medium-sized flycatcher, olive-brown above, pale gray on the throat and breast, and bright yellow on the belly, with a relatively long reddish tail that is especially noticeable in flight. Except during the breeding season, it is rather solitary by nature, so when seen it will usually be alone. No other birds are tolerated in the vicinity of its nest, but unlike the Kingbird, it shows no concern about hawks or crows and has never been seen to pursue or attack one.

The nest is by preference built in the natural cavity of a tree, and according to my experience, the site chosen is in the open. The few nests that I succeeded in finding at Athens were in each case in trees in fields or pastures, the nearest woods being some distance away. At the time, this somewhat surprised me, but a possible explanation is that these nests were less apt to be bothered by the flying squirrels that are found in goodly number in this part of the state. These small squirrels are known to molest birds that nest in natural cavities or old woodpecker holes, eating both their eggs and their young and not infrequently the parent birds themselves, and are unquestionably a real hazard during the breeding season. Gaulding [1944] states that at Tifton he has found the Crested Flycatcher nesting year after year in a gourd put up for the Purple Martins, and birdhouses are said to be readily accepted if they are large enough both in capacity and in size of opening. The foundation of the nest, sometimes to a depth of several inches, is composed of dry pine needles, bits of dead leaves, weed stems, and rootlets. The hollow in the top is lined with horse or mule hair, bunches of rabbit fur, a few feathers, and, without exception, fragments of a cast-off snakeskin. Much has been written regarding this odd custom of using an old snakeskin, and while it possibly serves a useful purpose in protecting the nest from many natural enemies, this has yet to be proved. Only one brood is reared each year, and in Georgia four or five eggs usually constitute the complete clutch. Nesting activities begin in May, but as there is some irregularity in the time that individual pairs nest, it is late July before the last young are fully fledged and on the wing.

Southern Great-crested Flycatcher
Myiarchus crinitus crinitus   (Linnaeus)

GENERAL DISTRIBUTION: Breeds on the Atlantic Coast from southern South Carolina to southern Florida, and on the Gulf Coast west to eastern Louisiana. Winters in southern Florida and probably also in Central America.

STATUS IN GEORGIA: A common summer resident in the southern part of the state and on the Savannah River as far north as Augusta.

Specimens typical of *crinitus* have been taken at Hinesville (Liberty County), April 16 and 26, 1946; Pembroke (Bryan County), April 19, 1946; Metter (Candler County), May 7, 1946; Gibson (Glascock County), June 29, 1946; and Augusta (Richmond County), May 7, 1933 [Burleigh, 1947].

Earliest arrivals in the spring were noted at Camden County, March 22 (1946); Sea Island, April 6 (1948); Savannah, April 4 (1920); Grady County, March 25 (1945); and Augusta, April 8 (1945). The latest record in the fall at Augusta is September 19 (1944); in Grady County, September 17 (1944); and Savannah, October 2 (1927). As no specimens were taken, these records refer to either of the two recognized forms, but being within the breeding range of *crinitus,* they are listed under this southern race.

Definite breeding records are largely limited to Chatham County, where Rossignol [letter] reports twenty-one nests found from 1906 through 1928, the earliest on May 10 (1914) with six slightly incubated eggs; the latest, on June 22 (1906) with four slightly incubated eggs. Erichsen [MS] found a nest on St. Catherine's Island, in Liberty County, that held five eggs on May 24, 1913; and another in Effingham County, May 18, 1927, with four eggs.

HABITS AND RECOGNITION: In appearance and actions the Southern Great-crested Flycatcher differs in no way from its more northern relative. It is a common bird within its rather restricted range, scattered pairs occurring both in the deciduous hardwoods in the stream bottoms and in the open pine woods. Murphey [1937] states that it is found in the city limits of Augusta and commonly nests there in cavities in large Chinaberry trees.

Eastern Phoebe
Sayornis phoebe (Latham)

GENERAL DISTRIBUTION: Breeds from western Mackenzie, Manitoba, Ontario, southern Quebec, and Nova Scotia south to central Texas, northern Mississippi, northern Alabama, and northern Georgia. Winters in the southeastern United States (casually to Pennsylvania) south to southeastern Mexico.

STATUS IN GEORGIA: Resident and common in the more northern counties and a common transient and winter resident throughout the rest of the state.

The Eastern Phoebe is a common breeding bird in the mountains and occurs casually in summer as far south as Atlanta and Athens. There is some evidence that it is gradually extending its breeding range southward into the lower Piedmont, and in time it may reach the fall line. Its status in Clarke County was for many years that of a winter resident, but in 1933 it was found nesting at Athens for the first time, and it is now fairly common there as a breeding bird. Actual breeding records for Georgia include at the present time the following localities:

Margret, Fannin County: Seventeen nests found in 1921 between the dates of April 21 (small young) and June 18 (four incubated eggs) (Burleigh).

Young Harris, Towns County: June 20, 1923, four incubated eggs; May 2, 1924, five incubated eggs (Burleigh).

Gainesville, Hall County: June 6, 1927, well-grown young (Burleigh).

Cornelia, Habersham County: April 14, 1933, five fresh eggs (Burleigh).

Athens, Clarke County: April 17, 1933, two fresh eggs; April 6, 1935, five fresh eggs (Burleigh).

Eatonton, Putnam County: Female incubating on nest under bridge May 14, 1953 (Denton).

Atlanta, Fulton County: April 10, 1922, five eggs; June 23, 1936, three young (Griffin).

Rome, Floyd County: March 25, 1945, four eggs (Jones).

South of its breeding range, extreme dates of arrival and departure are as follows:

Milledgeville: October 14 (1944) and March 12 (1941).

Macon: September 27 (1924) and April 21 (1923).

Augusta: March 22 (1945).

Cochran: October 8 (1943).

Americus: October 11 (1941) and March 10 (1942).

Fitzgerald: October 7 (1939) and April 13 (1940).

Grady County: September 28 (1950) and April 2 (1941).

Savannah: September 24 (1931) and April 29 (1912).

St. Marys: October 3 (1905).

HABITS AND RECOGNITION: Originally the Eastern Phoebe nested on ledges of cliffs and in crevices of banks. It still does to some extent, but, like the Chimney Swift, it found that man had unwittingly furnished it with an inexhaustible supply of suitable nesting sites, and it showed no hesitation in accepting them. As a result, today the Phoebe is commonly found about farms and even in the smaller towns, nesting on beams and rafters in barns and sheds and not infrequently under eaves or porches of houses. This has made it a familiar bird, and known as the pewee, it is accepted and tolerated wherever it occurs during the summer months. In the southern part of the state, where it is common and widely distributed throughout the winter, it shows an equal liking for farms, but at this season of the year it is apt to be found in any open spot where there is a food supply.

This is the only flycatcher sufficiently hardy to survive even the relatively mild winters experienced in Georgia. Its ability to withstand brief intervals when the temperature drops below freezing can probably be attributed to its varied diet. Insects are preferred, but if none are found, it is not averse to filling its stomach with dried fruits and berries. On more than one bleak day in January, I have seen this flycatcher feeding on the fruit of the dwarf sumac or competing with a flock of Myrtle Warblers for poison ivy berries.

Denton [1946] has given us an interesting picture of how the Phoebe takes advantage of man's habitations even during the winter months. He writes:

> Our knowledge of the roosting habits of birds, particularly migrants in winter, is far from complete. Therefore, this note describing an incident which made the observers aware that the Phoebe (*Sayornis phoebe*), when such is available, uses the same sort of sheltered site for roosting in winter as it does for nesting in summer should be of interest to others. At dusk on December 30, 1945, Thomas D. Burleigh and the writer were resting, waiting for supper, on a bench in the clearing before the cabin on Floyd's Island in the heart of the great Okefenokee Swamp. Suddenly our attention was attracted to a Phoebe as it flew in and lit on the bare floor near one end of the porch. After hesitating a moment on the floor to glance about, the bird flew up to a point just inside the eave and settled down to roost. Later, before we had a chance to observe the exact location in which the bird was roosting, the guide entered the cabin and frightened it out into the night. Subsequent examination of the place where the bird apparently went to roost and the position of the pile of droppings on the floor indicated that the bird was not roosting on the rafter as we supposed but on a nail driven into the side of the rafter just inside the eave. Judging from the size of the pile of droppings the bird had used this roosting perch for a number of nights.

Although it is normally quiet and inconspicuous during the winter months, the first warm days of early spring find it uttering its cheery "phoebe," and as the nesting season approaches, this familiar note is constantly heard throughout much of the day. Few birds are easier to recognize, even at a distance, for although it has no conspicuous colors, it continually jerks its tail in a manner that, once seen, will in the future always identify it.

The nest of a Phoebe is a handsome structure, substantially built of green moss intermixed with mud and fine grasses, the well-defined hollow in the top being lined with soft grasses and shreds of inner bark. The usual situations are on a beam in a barn or shed, under a bridge, on a ledge of a cliff, or among the upturned roots of a fallen tree at the top of a bank. Occasional pairs show some originality in choosing the nest site; the most unusual, that I found at Athens, was in the side of an old, unused well in an open field, ten feet below the surface of the ground. Four or five plain white eggs are laid, and at least two broods are reared each year in Georgia, fresh eggs being found in late March and April, and again in June.

Yellow-bellied Flycatcher
Empidonax flaviventris (Baird and Baird)

GENERAL DISTRIBUTION: Breeds from northern Alberta, Manitoba, Quebec, and Newfoundland south to North Dakota, northern Minnesota, northern Michigan, and northern Pennsylvania. Winters from southern Mexico to Panama.

STATUS IN GEORGIA: A scarce fall transient.

The similarity in the appearance of the small flycatchers of the genus *Empidonax*, when seen in migration, makes it impracticable to attempt to identify them unless they are collected. Consequently, although there are few records of the Yellow-bellied Flycatcher in Georgia, further collecting might change its present status as a scarce transient. To date, five specimens have been taken, as follows: Athens, September 15, 1929 [Burleigh, 1938]; September 16, 1948 [Johnston, 1949]; Center, Jackson County, September 11, 1945 [Burleigh, 1946]; Decatur, August 26, 1946 [Burleigh, 1947]; Atlanta, September 13, 1954 [Griffin, 1955].

HABITS AND RECOGNITION: As its name implies, this small flycatcher is noticeably yellow-bellied, and to the uninitiated this would seem to be a characteristic that would readily identify it. Unfortunately, the other small flycatchers have, in varying degrees, yellow underparts in the fall, so that it is extremely difficult, if not impossible, satisfactorily to identify one then unless actually in hand. In its breeding range in the far north, this species is commonly found in spruce and tamarack bogs, and as it consistently remains in the densest thickets, it could be easily overlooked were it not for its characteristic notes. This retiring disposition is equally evident in migration, the few birds definitely recorded in Georgia being found in dense alder thickets bordering streams. They are silent then, and far from conspicuous, and were it not for their frequent sallies after passing insects and their characteristic nervous jerk of the tail, they would be very difficult to detect.

Acadian Flycatcher
Empidonax virescens (Vieillot)

GENERAL DISTRIBUTION: Breeds from northeastern Nebraska, central Iowa, southern Michigan, Ontario, and Connecticut south to southern

Texas, the Gulf Coast, and central Florida. Winters in Colombia and Ecuador.

STATUS IN GEORGIA: A common summer resident throughout the state.

In the southern part of the state the Acadian Flycatcher appears in the spring in early April, but apparently it is almost a month later before it reaches northern Georgia. In the fall there is a definite southward movement in August, but an occasional bird can be seen throughout September and rarely in October.

Earliest arrivals in the spring were at St. Marys, April 3 (1904); Savannah, April 4 (1912); Grady County, April 7 (1938); Columbus, April 29 (1946); Americus, May 3 (1942); Macon, March 28 (1954); Milledgeville, April 28 (1943); Atlanta, April 16 (1941); Athens, April 17 (1927); and Augusta, April 26 (1945).

The last in the fall were noted at Atlanta, October 9 (1948); Athens, October 9 (1947); Macon, October 17 (1954); Fitzgerald, October 5 (1940); Grady County, October 23 (1949); and Savannah, September 28 (1931).

Although reported as breeding at many localities throughout the state, definite nesting records are not numerous. Summarized briefly they are as follows:

Margret, Fannin County: Nine nests found in 1921 between the dates of June 7 (three well-incubated eggs) and June 28 (three fresh eggs) (Burleigh).

Young Harris, Towns County: June 13, 1922, three slightly incubated eggs; July 20, 1923, one young bird, newly hatched, and two pipped eggs (Burleigh).

Athens, Clarke County: May 25, 1922, three fresh eggs; June 4, 1924, three well-incubated eggs (Burleigh).

Atlanta, Fulton County: May 12, 1918, three fresh eggs (L. Harris); June 28, 1904, three fresh eggs (Mills).

Augusta: June 2, 1952, two small young (Denton).

Macon: June 4, 1931, three eggs (Denton).

Fitzgerald: Ben Hill County: May 21, 1940, three eggs; July 1, 1941, three young (Hopkins).

Grady County: May 24, 1938, three eggs (Stoddard).

Savannah, Chatham County: Nesting extremes (thirteen nests), May 11 (1909), three fresh eggs; June 19 (1908), two fresh eggs (Rossignol).

HABITS AND RECOGNITION: Except during the breeding season the Acadian Flycatcher is as hard to identify as are the other small flycatchers of the genus *Empidonax*. As a transient, when it is quiet and inconspicuous, it is extremely difficult to identify, and sight records, especially in the fall, must be regarded with suspicion. Fortunately, when first observed in the spring, it is usually on its breeding grounds and uttering its distinctive call, "ika-zeep," and then it is readily recognized. It is common and generally distributed throughout the state and is the best known of this puzzling group of small flycatchers. During the summer, it shows a decided preference for the vicinity of water, and it is never seen then in dry woodlands. In the northern part of the state, it can be found in wooded ravines and along the edges of streams and lakes, while farther south it is one of the characteristic birds of the tupelo and cypress swamps. While not especially shy, it spends much of its time in heavily foliaged trees, and its olive-green plumage blends so well with its surroundings that were it not for its short, explosive little song, it would go largely undetected. This song, if such it can be called, soon attracts attention to its presence, and search will reveal it perched on a lower limb of a near-by tree, motionless except for the frequent nervous jerks of its tail typical of this genus. From time to time it will make a sudden sally for a passing insect, but otherwise it appears content to remain quietly in the thickest shade that it can find.

Its nest is usually built over water, and has the questionable distinction of being more poorly constructed and more fragile than that of any other small bird known to nest in Georgia. While normally from ten to twenty feet above the ground, the nest may sometimes be no more than three feet over the water, and the suggestion it then gives of debris caught at the end of a branch during high water is so noticeable that, it seems to me, such protective camouflage might explain the reason for this bird's seeming inability, or disinclination, to do a more creditable job of construction. The average nest is built of grasses, weed stems, and fine twigs, with a lining of fine grasses and vine tendrils which is frequently so meager that the eggs can be seen through the bottom. In the southern part of the state, Spanish moss (*Tillandsia usneoides*) is used at times to the exclusion of any other material. In the northern part of its range, the Acadian Flycatcher frequently lays four eggs, but in Georgia three appears to be the maximum number. It is doubtful that more than one brood is reared each year, despite the fact that the nesting season extends from late May into July.

Alder Traill's Flycatcher
Empidonax traillii traillii (Audubon)

GENERAL DISTRIBUTION: Breeds from central Alaska, northwestern Mackenzie, and central Quebec south to east-central British Columbia, eastern Montana, central Arkansas, New York, and New Jersey, and in the mountains of Pennsylvania, western Maryland, and West Virginia. Winters from Yucatán, Nicaragua, and Costa Rica to Colombia and Ecuador.

STATUS IN GEORGIA: Apparently a scarce fall transient in the northern part of the state.

Until recently the Traill's Flycatcher had been definitely recorded in the state but once, a specimen having been taken at Athens, September

24, 1930 [Burleigh, 1938]. It now appears probable, however, that, in the fall at least, it is a not uncommon transient in the northern part of Georgia. In addition to several birds which there is every reason to believe represented the species but which were not collected, two specimens were also taken in the fall of 1945. Both were females, collected at Young Harris, Towns County, on September 12, and at Gainesville, Hall County, on September 14 [Burleigh, 1946]. Johnston (1955) reports a specimen from Macon, October 8, 1954.

HABITS AND RECOGNITION: Unless its characteristic notes are heard, the Traill's Flycatcher is almost impossible to recognize in the field, for its appearance in life is very like that of the other small flycatchers in this genus. As far as my experiences goes, it is invariably silent in migration, so unfortunately it is necessary to collect any birds suspected of being of this species in order to identify them satisfactorily. Consequently, while it apparently is a scarce fall transient in Georgia, the Traill's Flycatcher may actually be commoner than the few specimens would indicate. On its breeding grounds it is found in alder thickets in the vicinity of water, and it was in similar situations that three of the specimens taken in the state were found.

Least Flycatcher
Empidonax minimus   (Baird and Baird)

GENERAL DISTRIBUTION: Breeds from Mackenzie, central Manitoba, southern Quebec, and Cape Breton Island south to central Montana, eastern Wyoming, western Oklahoma, Missouri, Indiana, northern Pennsylvania, and northern New Jersey, and in the Alleghenies to northern Georgia. Winters from northeastern Mexico and Yucatán to Panama.

STATUS IN GEORGIA: A fairly common summer resident in the extreme northeastern corner of the state and a rare transient south of the mountains.

As a transient, the Least Flycatcher is an extremely scarce bird in Georgia, there being but three definite records. At Athens, specimens were taken October 12, 1927 [Burleigh, 1938], and October 3, 1945 [Burleigh, 1946], while at Roswell a male was taken by Hembree, April 11, 1932 [Greene, 1933].

Odum [1947] has discussed in some detail the discovery of the breeding of this little flycatcher in Rabun County:

On June 2, 1946, I was driving south on Route 23 when I heard the unmistakable "chebec" call of the Least Flycatcher coming from a little strip of white pine-hardwood second growth just within the city limits of Clayton, Georgia. I spent about three-quarters of an hour watching this bird as it appeared to be patrolling a territory within the small strip of trees between the highway and the railroad, but no nest or mate was evident. Later, on reaching Lakemont I located another "singing" male, this time back of a tourist cabin along the bank of a stream, but did not have time to observe it.

On June 9, Mr. Thomas D. Burleigh, Dr. Fred Denton and I organized a "Least Flycatcher expedition" with the object of locating a nest or other conclusive breeding evidence. Driving along on Route 23 we had barely left Tallulah Gorge and entered Rabun County when vigorous "chebecs" brought our car to a halt at Wade's tourist camp, 3 miles south of Lakemont. Here, in a group of white pines a single bird was observed, but no sign of mate or nest. At Lakemont, a bird was calling at the same place as observed a week before, but again no nest or mate. At one time during our search here our hopes were raised high when Dr. Denton spied a nest with a small flycatcher sitting on it. However, when the bird was flushed and the eggs examined it turned out to be an Acadian Flycatcher (*Empidonax virescens*). This experience illustrated how easily a mistake could be made, since the Least Flycatcher was constantly singing nearby and we had not heard or seen any previous sign of the Acadian Flycatcher.

At the Clayton location, first discovered on June 2, we had no trouble finding the singing bird and also its mate, but again no nest. After some time Burleigh and Denton decided they would explore the vicinity for other birds while I tried again to locate the nest by attempting to follow the elusive female. As often happens, Burleigh and Denton "stumbled" upon another pair of Least Flycatchers nearby while chasing Song Sparrows and soon came back with the adult bird, the nest and four nestlings, all the evidence that would ever be needed to convince the most skeptical that Georgia does have nesting Least Flycatchers. The nest was about 15 feet up on a horizontal limb of a small short-leaved pine.

In summary, the short trip disclosed four locations where the Least Flycatcher was holding territory and probably nesting, all locations a few feet from the highway and near habitations. The one nest found was within the city limits of the town of Clayton. Since the Least Flycatcher is a very noisy bird during the breeding season it is not difficult to find (especially since it seems to prefer tourist camps!) provided one is familiar with its distinctive call. As with all *Empidonax* flycatchers, the voice is by far the best recognition aid. Whether birds have recently invaded Rabun County or whether they have always been here is a matter of conjecture.

HABITS AND RECOGNITION: The Least Flycatcher is well named, for it is the smallest of the species of flycatchers found in the eastern United States. On its breeding grounds, it is a noisy, aggressive little bird, its emphatic "chebec" soon attracting attention to its presence. Unlike the other small flycatchers, it prefers open woods, orchards, and even trees bordering highways rather than thickets and thick woods, so is conspicuous and much in evidence throughout the daylight hours. Its nest is equally distinctive, for it is a compactly built structure of grasses, gray plant fibers, and soft shreds of inner bark, well cupped and lined with fine grasses and plant down.

In late summer the bird becomes silent, and individuals seen in migration during the fall months are merely small flycatchers so closely resembling in appearance and actions the other species of this genus that it is largely guesswork to attempt to identify one as a Least Flycatcher. For this reason, although the Least has been rarely recorded in Georgia south of its limited breeding range in the northeastern corner of the state, it may actually be much commoner in migration than the few records would indicate.

Eastern Wood Pewee
Contopus virens (Linnaeus)

GENERAL DISTRIBUTION: Breeds from southern Manitoba, southern Ontario, southern Quebec, and Prince Edward Island to southern Texas and central Florida, and west to central Nebraska. Winters from Nicaragua to Colombia and Peru.

STATUS IN GEORGIA: A common summer resident throughout the state.

In the spring, the Wood Pewee appears in southern Georgia in early April, but it is usually two weeks later in reaching the northern part of the state. In the fall, it is October before there is any noticeable decrease in the number of birds seen, and an occasional hardy individual may linger until early November.

Earliest arrivals in the spring were seen at St. Marys, April 1 (1904); Savannah, April 5 (1916); Grady County, April 4 (1945); Fitzgerald, March 20 (1942); Americus, April 20 (1942); Macon, April 11 (1925); Atlanta, March 21 (1899); Athens, April 11 (1947); and Augusta, April 15 (1945).

The last in the fall were noted at Atlanta, October 26 (1947); Athens, November 1 (1925); Macon, November 11 (1925); Americus, October 19 (1941); Tifton, October 22 (1941); Grady County, October 20 (1940); and Savannah, October 30 (1927).

The Eastern Wood Pewee is reported as breeding in many localities throughout the state, but actual nesting records are largely limited to the more northern counties. They include the following:

Margret, Fannin County: Four nests found in 1921, one on June 10, three on June 11, all containing three eggs (Burleigh).

Young Harris, Towns County: June 24, 1922, three slightly incubated eggs; July 20, 1922, two slightly incubated eggs (Burleigh).

Athens, Clarke County: Five nests found between the dates of May 20 (1926), two fresh eggs, and July 25 (1926), two fresh eggs (Burleigh).

Atlanta, Fulton County: Nesting ex-tremes, May 15 (1921), three par-tially incubated eggs (Hembree), and July 29 (1939), four eggs (Griffin).

Tifton, Tift County: Female incubating on nest, May 10. 1952 (Norris).

Grady County: Female incubating on nest May 25, 1937 (Stoddard).

Savannah, Chatham County: Nesting ex-tremes (thirteen nests), May 9 (1914), three fresh eggs; and June 18 (1911), two slightly incubated eggs (Rossignol).

HABITS AND RECOGNITION: So far as appearance goes, the Wood Pewee bears a superficial resemblance to the small flycatchers of the genus *Empidonax*. In disposition and actions, however, it is a totally different bird. Quiet and unobtrusive, it spends its time perched on a dead limb well up from the ground in one of the larger trees of the open woodland that is its preferred habitat. From time to time it will depart momentarily in pursuit of an insect, but if undisturbed will usually return to the same spot. Under such circumstances it displays none of the restlessness characteristic of the Least Flycatcher or the Acadian Flycatcher. The nervous jerk of the tail is absent, and it appears content to wait for insect prey to appear rather than to move from tree to tree in search of it. Its note emphasizes further its gentle nature, being a soft "pee-a-wee" that is frequently repeated throughout the day. Few birds sing in late summer, but the Wood Pewee can be heard uttering its plaintive song during all of July and the early part of August, and in time one comes to associate this note with the hot, languid days characteristic of Georgia at that season.

Few birds build a more attractive nest than the Wood Pewee. It is a shallow but compactly built cup of grasses, shreds of bark, and bits of moss, lined with fine grasses and well covered on the outside with gray lichens. Placed in a fork at the outer end of a limb, usually from twenty to thirty feet from the ground, it is far from conspicuous and is usually found only by watching the birds. Apparently two broods are reared each year, the first in late May and early June, the second in July. In Georgia, three eggs are almost invariably laid, although exceptionally late nests have been found to hold but two.

Olive-sided Flycatcher
Nuttallornis borealis (Swainson)

GENERAL DISTRIBUTION: Breeds from central Alaska, southern Macken-

NORTHERN BROWN-HEADED NUTHATCHES

Sitta pusilla pusilla

When I made this painting, the nuthatches were not moving through
the pine tops in noisy family groups, as they so often do, but nesting quietly.
This pair had a nest in a small hollowed-out cypress knee placed
for them on a fence post. I looked a long while before finding exactly
the right shortleaf pine branch for the picture. I wanted the branch,
as well as the birds, to be interesting.

zie, northern Ontario, southern Quebec, and Newfoundland south in the western United States to southern California, New Mexico, Arizona, and western Texas, and in the east to northern Michigan, New York, northern New Jersey, and Massachusetts; also in the Alleghenies south to Tennessee and North Carolina. Winters in northern South America from Colombia to Peru.

STATUS IN GEORGIA: A rare transient.

Audubon [1839, V, 422] mentions having seen this flycatcher in Georgia, but only in recent years has it been definitely recorded in the state and a specimen taken.

It was seen at Athens, April 27, 1924 [Burleigh, 1938], and in Lumpkin County June 10, 1939 [Dorsey, 1939]; and a specimen was collected by Stoddard on Sherwood Plantation, Grady County, September 11, 1944.

HABITS AND RECOGNITION: On its breeding grounds the Olive-sided Flycatcher is a noisy and conspicuous bird, but it is largely silent in migration and can be easily overlooked. At all times, however, it remains in the tops of the tallest trees, preferably well out in the open, and it is there that it should be watched for in Georgia. The only bird that I was fortunate enough to see at Athens was perched in the very top of a large dead tree on a wooded bluff overlooking the Oconee River, and as I was able to walk directly beneath it without alarming it, I had no difficulty in identifying it. In appearance, this flycatcher suggests a large Wood Pewee, but is noticeably stouter in build, with a short neck and a rather large head.

Northeastern Vermilion Flycatcher
Pyrocephalus rubinus mexicanus   Sclater

GENERAL DISTRIBUTION: Largely resident in the Lower Austral Zone from southeastern California, southern Nevada, southwestern Utah, southern Arizona, southern New Mexico, and southern Texas south to Lower California, Guatemala, and Honduras. Of casual occurrence in recent years on the Gulf Coast during the winter.

STATUS IN GEORGIA: Apparently of accidental occurrence during the winter in the southern part of the state.

The Vermilion Flycatcher was first recorded in Georgia on December 28, 1949, when an adult was seen near Albany, Dougherty County, by Charles Jones, Sr., and his brother Joe Jones. Odum [1950] has discussed in detail the circumstances in connection with this most interesting discovery:

On December 28, 1949, Charles Jones, Sr., and his brother Joe

Jones, visiting from Chapel Hill, North Carolina, were observing birds near a small, partly dried-up pond when they saw a strange, bright-colored bird flycatching out over the water. It soon dawned upon them that it was a Vermilion Flycatcher. It was not until later that they were to discover that this was the first record for Georgia. On December 30 and January 1, it was observed again by several of the Albany bird students. On January 11, Milton Hopkins came up from the Emory Field Station near Newton and saw the bird, while on January 20, Dan Nelson and the writer in company with the Joneses, Mrs. Giffen and Mr. Dann, were fortunate in finding the bird in the same tree where first discovered. From its favorite tree, a willow, and from other perches over and near the water it made frequent forays after insects in typical flycatcher manner and often allowed a very close approach. It was a full-plumaged male with brilliant vermilion underparts and crown, and brown upperparts—nothing else like it in the notoriously dull flycatcher family in North America. It was last seen on the spot on January 22, 1950.

William Gaulding recorded the second bird for the state, which he collected near Tifton on December 31, 1949. He describes his experience as follows [Odum, 1950]:

> On December 31, 1949, while observing birds around the edge of one of the lily ponds west of Tifton the writer collected a Vermilion Flycatcher (*Pyrocephalus rubinus*). The bird was first observed perched on the top of the highest of a small group of bare trees. When flushed, it flew to a nearby telephone wire and then to a fence from whence it was collected. The sex remained undetermined (shot injury), but the plumage resembled that of a young male. This is the first specimen collected in the state and thus places this species on our Georgia bird list. I wish to thank Mr. Herbert L. Stoddard for confirming the identification.

HABITS AND RECOGNITION: Throughout its range in the Southwest, the Vermilion Flycatcher is found in willows and cottonwoods fringing streams and irrigation ditches; and, apparently, it is the vicinity of water that attracts this spectacular little flycatcher during its winter sojourns in the southeastern United States. It has in recent years appeared with increasing regularity on the Gulf Coast, and the individuals observed have, as was the case with the two found in southern Georgia, been almost invariably in willows or other deciduous growth bordering ponds or streams. The adult male is unquestionably one of the handsomest of our smaller birds, and the first sight of one with its bright scarlet plumage will long remain a vivid memory.

Family Alaudidae: LARKS

Larks: *Family Alaudidae*

Northern Horned Lark
Eremophila alpestris alpestris (Linnaeus)

GENERAL DISTRIBUTION: Breeds from Hudson Strait south to the head of James Bay, Labrador, southeastern Quebec (Gaspé), and Newfoundland. Winters south to the Ohio Valley and Georgia and west to Manitoba.

STATUS IN GEORGIA: Known from a single record.
Cooke [1908] records a specimen taken by R. W. Smith at Kirkwood, January 20, 1893, now in the Emory University Museum.

HABITS AND RECOGNITION: A bird that spends the summer months in the far north is sufficiently hardy to withstand ordinary winters in the Northern states. Consequently, it is probably only when the weather is unusually severe that this northern race of the Horned Lark comes as far south as Georgia. Although there is but a single record for its occurrence in the state, undetected stragglers may have been present in other years, for its close similarity to the Prairie Horned Lark makes it extremely difficult to identify unless collected. In Georgia, the Northern Horned Lark is a bird of the open fields and seems to delight in the most exposed situations.

Prairie Horned Lark
Eremophila alpestris praticola (Henshaw)

GENERAL DISTRIBUTION: Breeds from southern Manitoba and southern Quebec south to eastern Kansas, southern Missouri, Ohio, northern Georgia, and Connecticut. Winters south to Texas, Alabama, and Florida.

STATUS IN GEORGIA: A fairly common winter resident in the northern part of the state and a summer resident near Rome and Augusta.
At Athens, small flocks are frequently seen in open fields and pastures from the latter part of October through the first week of February, extreme dates of occurrence being October 20 (1948) and February 25 (1929). Specimens taken February 5, 1928, November 12 and December 26, 1929, December 9 and 12, 1945, and January 4 and 31 and February 10, 1946, were all typical of this race (Burleigh). At Atlanta, Griffin [1941] cites as extreme dates of occurrence November 12 (1940) and March 4 (1939). It has also been recorded at Augusta (Murphey); at Hartwell, Hart County, December 13, 1945 (Burleigh); Covington, Newton County, January 3, 1942 (Griffin); Round Oak, Jones County (Fleetwood); Macon, December 25, 1944, through January 26, 1945; and August 11, 1955 (John-

ston, MS); and in Wilcox County, January 13, 1946 (Hopkins). Specimens verifying the identification of this race were taken at Hartwell, Athens, and Covington, and there are also six specimens in the Emory University Museum, including one taken by W. H. LaPrade in Clayton County, November 30, 1907.

To William W. Griffin goes the credit for first recording the Prairie Horned Lark as breeding in the state. He says [Griffin, 1951]:

A few years ago Eugene P. Odum and Thomas D. Burleigh (*Auk,* 63:388–401, 1946) suggested that the Horned Lark (*Eremophila alpestris*) might one day become a breeding bird in Georgia, inasmuch as this species appeared to be extending its range southward and eastward through Tennessee and into Alabama and North Carolina. Early realization of their prediction was indicated when the writer discovered a family group of these birds in August, 1949, at Russell Field, an airport located seven miles north of Rome in Floyd County, Georgia (see Griffin, *Oriole,* 15:10–11, 1950).

It is gratifying, therefore, to report now that the Horned Lark was definitely added to the list of breeding birds of Georgia on April 9, 1950. On that date the writer, accompanied by George W. Sciple, succeeded in finding a nest of this species at Russell Field, the identical spot where the observations of the previous year were made. The nest, consisting of finely woven grasses lining a cup-shaped depression in the ground, contained three well-incubated eggs. It was located in a sparse tuft of grasses in the center of a bare clay and gravel area adjoining one of the runways of the airport. Both nest and eggs were collected and are now deposited in the Museum of Zoology, University of Georgia, in Athens.

During several hours of observation on April 9, and on later dates during the spring and summer of 1950, it was determined that at least two pairs of larks and probably three were occupying the airfield. Approximately 25 acres of open grassy fields with a large amount of bare ground interspersed throughout apparently provided ideal conditions for an open-country species such as the Horned Lark.

Little opportunity to observe the behavior of adult larks at the nest was afforded. It was noticed, however, that the female always remained in the general vicinity of the nest as long as anyone was near. She would leave the nest before close approach could be made and then feed nonchalantly within several hundred feet of it. As a matter of fact, the nest was discovered by noticing that she refused to leave one particular area and by then conducting a careful, inch by inch, search of the ground within that area.

Away from the nesting area single adult birds were observed

feeding, generally in bare spots on the airfield. They occasionally foraged on the asphalt runways and on the walks about the buildings, where they allowed close approach.

A further extension of the breeding range of this species in Georgia was noted by Denton in 1953 who states [letter]:

> Horned Larks were detected nesting for the first time at Augusta this spring (1953). Birds were present all spring and apparently nesting on three different areas in Richmond County: Daniel Field Airport, Municipal Airport (Bush Field), and the parade ground at Camp Gordon. The single pair nesting at Daniel Field had their two newly fledged, speckled young out of the nest on April 20. This pair is apparently nesting again now (June 29) as the female seems to be incubating. At the Municipal Airport, where I was not allowed on the field, there were at least two singing males. Whether there is more than one pair at Camp Gordon, I do not know.

HABITS AND RECOGNITION: It is probable that at one time the range of the Prairie Horned Lark was confined to the extensive prairies of the Middle West. However, with the settlement of the eastern United States, as pastures replaced virgin forests, the horned lark invaded this new favorable environment. In the last fifty years it has not only penetrated, but become a common bird in the northeastern states, and its recent appearance as a breeding bird in Georgia would indicate that it is now extending its range into the Southeast.

A bird of the open country, the horned lark seeks by preference the most barren and apparently inhospitable sites. Regardless of season, it is useless to look for it where the grass is tall and thick. The sparser the vegetation the more desirable a field becomes for this hardy bird. In Georgia, it can be looked for during the winter months on open hillsides or in plowed fields, where it apparently finds an ample food supply of dormant insects and weed seeds.

Except during the breeding season it can be found in small flocks, which in my experience are characterized by a very noticeable restlessness. Watched for any length of time, a flock will suddenly, for no apparent reason, take flight, remain in the air for a short interval, and then drop to the ground near the spot so abruptly left. With caution, it is possible to approach within fairly close range of such a flock, and it will be noted then that the birds scatter as they feed, and never remain in a compact group. Most small birds hop as they move about on the ground, but horned larks walk or run. The Prairie Horned Lark is so similar in appearance to the Northern Horned Lark that it can be identified satisfactorily only when in the hand. It differs in being smaller and somewhat paler, with the forehead and line over the eye white instead of yellow and the throat less extensively yellow in males and sometimes white in females.

Swallows: *Family Hirundinidae*

Tree Swallow
Iridoprocne bicolor (Vieillot)

GENERAL DISTRIBUTION: Breeds from northwestern Alaska, southern Mackenzie, and northern Quebec south to southern California, Colorado, Kansas, Louisiana, and Virginia. Winters from central California, southern Texas, the Gulf Coast, and eastern North Carolina south to Guatemala and Cuba.

STATUS IN GEORGIA: A common transient and winter resident on the coast, more rarely in the southern edge of the state, and a scarce transient elsewhere.

At Athens, this species was a rather scarce migrant both in spring and fall, being usually seen feeding with other swallows over the open fields. Extreme dates of occurrence in the spring are March 18 (1928) and May 16 (1926), and in the fall, August 19 (1929) and October 26 (1926) [Burleigh, 1938]. Griffin gives as migration extremes for the Atlanta region March 18 (1946) and May 27 (1954), and July 10 (1932) and September 13 (1930).

At Augusta, Murphey [1937] states that the Tree Swallow is "abundant during migration but particularly so on its southward flight. The spring migration occurs in large flocks usually from May 23rd to the 4th of June, but in 1926, they remained as late as June 18th, and reappeared on July 17th. Great flocks appear about July 20, and remain for a month or more." At Rising Fawn, the earliest spring transient was noted, April 3 (1885); at Dalton, March 30 (1944); at Cartersville, March 4 (1951); at Milledgeville, April 6 (1943); and at Macon, March 25 (1933). Stoddard [MS] reports this species an uncommon winter resident in Grady County, although it is a common transient both in the spring and in the fall. His extreme dates of occurrence are August 6 (1947) and May 15 (1949).

On the coast, this swallow has been noted at Savannah as late in the spring as May 26 (1909) and May 29 (1911), and as early in the fall as July 18 (1931) and July 23 (1908). I found it already plentiful there on August 6, 1929, hundreds being seen on telephone wires at the side of the road through a stretch of open salt marsh. It was equally interesting to me to note how late it remained plentiful in the spring; on Tybee Island, I observed numerous flocks on May 10, 1933. It apparently winters commonly on the coast. I saw an occasional bird on Tybee Island, January 6, 1923, and a flock of possibly one hundred in the open salt marsh near the mouth of the Savannah River, January 30, 1924. Woodward [1949] reported it common on Sea Island from January through April, 1946–48.

Hebard [1941] noted a flock on Floyd's Island Prairie, Okefenokee Swamp, on January 8, 1930, and numerous flocks at Coleraine, December 23, 1935, to January 4, 1936. Murphey [1937] considered it occasional in winter at Augusta.

HABITS AND RECOGNITION: In view of the extensive breeding range of the Tree Swallow in the northern United States and Canada, it is rather surprising that it is such a scarce and irregular transient over much of Georgia. Except on the coast and on the Savannah River at Augusta, it is seen only at infrequent intervals and then in rather small numbers. At Athens, I usually saw one or two birds, rarely as many as eight or ten, with other swallows.

The Tree Swallow in adult plumage can be easily recognized, the upperparts being uniform glossy steel-blue or steel-green and the underparts pure white. In the fall, immature birds are to some extent brown above, but the white throat and dingy-white belly distinguish them from either the Bank Swallow or the Rough-winged Swallow. In flight, the Tree Swallow does not appear as swift or as agile as the other swallows, a characteristic noticeable when it is seen feeding with Barn Swallows or Bank Swallows.

It is apparently a hardy bird, for it winters regularly and in fairly large numbers on the Georgia coast. During much of each winter it probably experiences little difficulty in obtaining sufficient insect food for its survival, but when this is lacking, it finds a ready source of food in the myrtle thickets that border the salt marsh. The ability to subsist during intervals of cold weather on the berries of the wax-myrtle makes it possible for this species to winter much farther north than it could if dependent entirely on insects. To one familiar with swallows feeding overhead, the first sight of a flock of Tree Swallows feeding in a myrtle thicket comes as a surprise. The individuals in a flock concentrate on those bushes having the most berries, and each branch and twig will have a swallow eagerly eating those within reach.

Common Bank Swallow
Riparia riparia riparia   (Linnaeus)

GENERAL DISTRIBUTION: Breeds from northern Alaska, northern Quebec, and Newfoundland south to southern California, Arizona, Texas, central Alabama, and Virginia. Winters in Brazil and Peru.

393

STATUS IN GEORGIA: An uncommon spring and fall transient over the entire state.

Earliest arrivals in the spring were recorded at Savannah, April 15 (1923); Macon, April 13 (1929); Athens, April 25 (1927); Atlanta, April 23 (1933); and Dalton, April 19 (1944). The last in the spring were noted at Savannah, May 4 (1941); Macon, May 18 (1924); Athens, May 20 (1928); and Atlanta, May 16 (1931).

In the fall, the first birds were seen at Atlanta, July 10 (1932); Athens, July 31 (1929); Macon, August 31 (1936); and Savannah, August 14 (1912). The latest recorded were noted at Atlanta, September 15 (1946); Athens, September 25 (1929); Macon, September 5 (1934); and Savannah, October 17 (1913). Stoddard [MS] reports one fall record for Grady County, September 10, 1950.

HABITS AND RECOGNITION: This is the smallest swallow found in Georgia, but as size in the field is rather deceptive, a close look is necessary to distinguish it from the Rough-winged Swallow when it is feeding overhead. Both species are brown backed, with a relatively short, slightly forked tail, but the Bank Swallow can be recognized by the dark band across the breast that stands out in contrast to the white throat and belly. As far as my experience goes, it is not a common bird in either spring or fall, one or two individuals, rarely as many as ten, being seen feeding with other swallows over the open fields or larger ponds. Considering its wide distribution and its abundance over much of its breeding range, the Bank Swallow is strangely scarce as a transient in Georgia, even on the coast. It is possible, on the coast at least, that it has been largely overlooked, for large flocks have been reported on the coasts of both South Carolina and Florida. Few species have a wider range, for the Bank Swallow is circumpolar in its distribution, breeding over the entire Northern Hemisphere and wintering in South America, Africa, and India.

Northern Rough-winged Swallow
Stelgidopteryx ruficollis serripennis   (Audubon)

GENERAL DISTRIBUTION: Breeds from southern British Columbia, Montana, North Dakota, Minnesota, Wisconsin, southern Ontario, southern New York, and Massachusetts south to central Florida, the Gulf Coast, Veracruz, and Jalisco, Mexico. Winters from southern Arizona and Mexico (casually to Louisiana and South Carolina) south to Costa Rica.

STATUS IN GEORGIA: A locally common summer resident throughout the state, except in the south-central and extreme southwestern parts of the coastal plain.

Family *Hirundinidae:* SWALLOWS

Earliest transients in the spring were noted at Savannah, March 10 (1912); McIntosh County, March 16 (1889); Americus, April 2 (1942); Columbus, March 21 (1945); Milledgeville, March 14 (1937); Macon, March 26 (1932); Atlanta, March 18 (1933); Athens, March 20 (1929); and Dalton, March 20 (1944).

The last in the fall were seen at Athens, August 28 (1929); Atlanta, August 23 (1936); Macon, October 12 (1955); Tifton, August 15 (1942); and Savannah, October 29, 1927. Grimm [1946] reports few seen in 1945 after the middle of September at Hinesville, in Liberty County. Stoddard [MS] considers it a rather scarce spring transient and a common fall migrant in Grady County. His only spring records are for April 13, 1947 and April 22, 1951; while in the fall it has been noted as early as July 8 (1950) and as late as October 24 (1950).

It is said to occur during the summer months at many localities throughout the state (St. Marys, Savannah, Americus, Augusta, Atlanta, Athens, Canton, Toccoa, and Eton, in Murray County), but actual breeding records are not numerous. At Savannah, Rossignol [letter] gives as nesting extremes for eleven nests, six fresh eggs, April 27 (1919), and five fresh eggs, May 15 (1921). Erichsen gives as his latest breeding record a nest that held five slightly incubated eggs, May 27, 1945. My only breeding record for Athens [Burleigh, 1938] is that of a nest found, May 15, 1921, that held six fresh eggs. Griffin [1940] cites as nesting extremes for the Atlanta region, three eggs, April 9 (1939), and five eggs June 19 (1939). Peters [letter] reports a nest at Rome that held young on July 8, 1953.

HABITS AND RECOGNITION: The Rough-winged Swallow is a less sociable bird than are the other swallows. Flocks are rarely seen in the spring, and the first individuals noted in March are usually not associated with any of their relatives. As a usual thing, one or two birds appear in the vicinity of the site where they will later nest, and gradually as the days go by, scattered pairs will be found in the more open country.

Like the Bank Swallow, this species commonly nests in burrows in banks, but differs in that it rarely, if ever, colonizes to any extent. If the site is exceptionally favorable, several pairs may nest in close proximity, but ordinarily only a single pair will be found at any one site. In most cases, the birds excavate the burrow themselves, although on occasion a kingfisher's old burrow, a natural cavity in a bank, or a crevice in a wall may be used. Railroad embankments are favored spots, as are also bluffs along streams, but it is not uncommon to find occupied burrows in low banks at the side of country roads. The nest is rather loosely built of rootlets, weed stems, and grasses, the cavity in the top being lined with finer grasses and fragments of dead leaves. Six or seven plain white eggs are laid, and but a single brood is reared each year.

Despite the fact that the Rough-winged Swallow is one of the earlier migrants to appear in the spring, it never lingers late in the fall except on or near the coast. At Athens, I found it to be one of the first birds to disappear in the late summer. By early July the broods of young were fully fledged and strong on the wing, and it was not long afterward that this swallow was scarce and rarely observed. In August, an occasional bird, apparently a transient from farther north, was seen at infrequent intervals, but this was so exceptional that such occurrences were emphasized in my field notes.

Superficially this brown-backed swallow resembles the Bank Swallow, but its slightly larger size and the pale underparts without the dark band across the breast should readily distinguish it.

American Barn Swallow
Hirundo rustica erythrogaster Boddaert

GENERAL DISTRIBUTION: Breeds from northwestern Alaska, northern Mackenzie, central Quebec, and Newfoundland south to southern California, southern Texas, northern Arkansas, Tennessee, and North Carolina; on the islands off the coast of Louisiana, Mississippi, and Alabama; and in Mexico south to Jalisco and Nayarit. Winters from southern Mexico to Brazil, northern Argentina, and central Chile.

STATUS IN GEORGIA: A common spring and fall transient throughout the state; reported to have nested prior to 1904 on Wassaw Island, in Chatham County. Pindar [1926] reports it "a rare summer habitant" at Chickamauga Park, and Jones [1947] as "present all summer" at Rome, so it is possible that it nests sparingly in the northwestern part of the state.

Earliest transients in the spring appeared at Darien, April 5 (1890); Cumberland Island, April 10 (1902); Hinesville, April 13 (1944); Savannah, March 26 (1905) and March 30 (1909); Grady County, April 10 (1945); Fitzgerald, April 17 (1941); Macon, April 4 (1936); Milledgeville, April 9 (1938); Athens, April 9 (1927) and April 12 (1928); Atlanta, April 9 (1937); and Dalton, April 17 (1944). The spring migration is rather prolonged, the last birds being reported from Brunswick, May 31 (1929); Chatham County, May 25 (1929); St. Simons Island, June 10 (1942); Fitzgerald, May 14 (1940); Macon, May 27 (1955); Atlanta, May 31 (1941); Athens, May 24 (1928); and Augusta, May 24 (1945).

The fall migration begins in late July, the earliest transients being seen at Athens, July 27 (1926); Atlanta, July 23 (1933); Tifton, July 13

(1942); Grady County, August 1 (1943); Chatham County, July 17 (1931); Hinesville, August 7 (1945); and St. Marys, August 7 (1905). The latest in the fall were recorded at Athens, October 1 (1929) and November 14 (1945); Atlanta, October 25 (1947); Macon, October 12 (1955); Fitzgerald, October 25 (1942); Grady County, October 10 (1946); and Savannah, October 26 (1908) and October 27 (1910).

HABITS AND RECOGNITION: The Barn Swallow is well named, for within its breeding range it is commonly found about farms, and nests by preference on the beams in barns. It is a friendly, sociable little bird, and its value in destroying injurious insects is so well recognized that it is seldom molested. As with so many of our smaller birds, it has readily accepted the advantages accompanying man's presence, and is undoubtedly far commoner today than it originally was. When this country was first settled, Barn Swallows were found nesting in caves and on rocky cliffs, and there were not enough of such natural sites to accommodate a very large population. Today the situation is quite different, with the many man-made nesting sites, and this swallow is now a common bird throughout much of its wide range. In Georgia, it is a common transient both in spring and fall, and is most frequently seen in early May and again in mid-August.

Under normal conditions, it feeds low over the open fields and pastures, but if the weather is cold and rainy, it seeks the vicinity of water, where apparently insects are then more easily obtained. Its mastery of the air enables it to remain on the wing throughout the larger part of the day, but in late afternoon flocks gather on convenient telephone wires to rest, preen their feathers, and indulge in what would appear to be a social hour with their fellow travelers. In migration, it is frequently found with other swallows, and can be easily distinguished, as it flies overhead, by its long, forked tail and cinnamon-buff underparts.

Years ago, prior to 1904, a small colony of Barn Swallows nested in an open pavilion on Wassaw Island, in Chatham County, but for some unknown reason ceased to come to this site. Gilbert R. Rossignol, a recognized authority on the bird life of the Georgia coast, remembers distinctly as a boy seeing Barn Swallows nesting on Wassaw Island. In a letter dated July 3, 1951, he writes: "Glad you asked about the Barn Swallows. I remember them well darting in and out of the old pavilion; the red-breasted, forked-tailed birds; and as a boy I climbed among the rafters and got their eggs. They were *speckled.* What became of them I don't know, but it was prior to 1904 and there is no entry in my book."

The nest is quite distinctive, being built of pellets of mud intermixed with grass, the hollow in the top being lined with finer grasses, feathers, and, where available, horsehair.

Eastern Cliff Swallow
Petrochelidon pyrrhonota pyrrhonota (Vieillot)

GENERAL DISTRIBUTION: Breeds from central Alaska, Mackenzie, northern Ontario, and southern Quebec south to southern Texas, Arkansas, Kentucky, Virginia, and northern Alabama. Winters, so far as is now known, in Brazil and Argentina.

STATUS IN GEORGIA: A regular but somewhat scarce transient throughout the state in both spring and fall.

At Athens, the Cliff Swallow was a somewhat scarce transient in the spring, and was even less frequently seen in the fall. Usually one or two would be noted feeding over the open fields with other swallows, the few exceptions being a flock of 16 seen May 8, 1925, resting on a barb-wire fence at the side of the road, and a flock in which there were fully 150 of these birds found September 10, 1926, feeding over the Sandy Creek bottoms. Extreme dates of occurrence for the spring migration in this area are April 18 (1929) and May 20 (1928); and for the fall migration, August 14 (1925) and September 21 (1924) [Burleigh, 1938]. Griffin [1941] gives as migration extremes for the Atlanta region, April 17 (1900) and May 17 (1923), and June 28 (1936) and September 4 (1938). This swallow has also been reported from Macon between the dates of March 30 (1924) and May 18 (1924), and August 31 (1935) and September 4 (1955); in Grady County, September 12, 1946; and at Savannah, August 20 and September 1, 1911, and August 12, 1912.

HABITS AND RECOGNITION: Apparently the Cliff Swallow, in its long journeys to and from its summer home, follows a route that causes it largely to bypass Georgia. Otherwise, considering its abundance throughout its wide breeding range, it would be seen more frequently and in larger numbers. Usually small flocks are noted at rather infrequent intervals, and, more often than not, one or two birds will appear with flocks of other swallows. Under the latter circumstances they may be readily recognized, the light-brown rump and pale-buff forehead being good field characters that will at once separate them from their associates.

Like the other swallows observed in migration, this species will be found feeding over the open fields, or resting for brief intervals on a convenient telephone wire. Watched as it flies overhead it does not appear as graceful as the Barn Swallow, its short, slightly forked tail seeming to give it less agility in the air. It is, nevertheless, a swift and skillful flier and capable of spending the larger part of the daylight hours on the wing.

Northern Purple Martin
Progne subis subis (Linnaeus)

GENERAL DISTRIBUTION: Breeds from central Alberta, Saskatchewan, southern Manitoba, Ontario, New Brunswick, and Nova Scotia west to Vancouver Island, British Columbia, and south to the Mexican boundary, the Gulf Coast, Florida, Veracruz, and Jalisco. Winters in Brazil.

STATUS IN GEORGIA: A common summer resident throughout the state.

Earliest transients in the spring appeared at Sea Island, February 25 (1947); Savannah, February 21 (1917); Coleraine, January 28 (1948); Grady County, February 4 (1939); Smithville, February 12 (1889); Fitzgerald, February 16 (1946); Coffee County, February 12 (1947); Jones County, February 27 (1944) and February 28 (1943 and 1945); Macon, March 16 (1946); Milledgeville, March 16 (1945); Augusta, March 20 (1890); Athens, February 13 (1956); Atlanta, January 19 (1950); and Dalton, March 26 (1944).

Bulk departure in the fall takes place in late July and August, usually only an occasional bird being recorded in the state after the first of September, the last in the fall being seen at Augusta, August 30 (1944); Athens, August 30 (1929); Atlanta, September 23 (1933); Macon, September 10 (1934); Savannah, September 14 (1931); and St. Marys, September 5 (1905). In Grady County, however, Stoddard [MS] has found the martin common throughout September, and reports that "a heavy migration through the region was noted September 21–23, 1943, and this is about the usual time of the heaviest flights." His latest record in the fall is October 3 (1924).

While it is known to nest throughout the state, there are few definite breeding records. At Athens, two nests that I examined on May 25, 1921, held fresh eggs: in one, four, and in the other, three. A pair of Martins nesting in a gourd near Margret, in Fannin County, were feeding four half-grown young on June 10, 1927. Griffin [1940] gives as nesting extremes for the Atlanta region, four young, May 7 (1938), and five young, July 1 (1937).

HABITS AND RECOGNITION: Many birds have found living in the vicinity of man advantageous, and have prospered accordingly, but none more so than the Purple Martin. Originally this large, handsome swallow nested in old woodpecker holes and in natural cavities of trees, but in Georgia it seldom if ever now rears its young in any places other than gourds or birdhouses provided for it. History tells that even before the advent of the early colonists, the Indian encampments had their martin colonies, and the Indian practice of putting up hollow gourds for the use of these birds is still followed by the rural population of Georgia. In the Northern states large and often ornate birdhouses are popularly used, but so far as my experience goes, the hollow gourd is universally provided in the South as nesting site for martins. It is possible that some birdhouses have been erected for their use in Georgia, but all the nesting colonies that I have personally seen have been in gourds suspended from cross-arms nailed to the tops of poles.

The poplarity of these birds is not difficult to understand. The males are singularly attractive with their glossy, blue-black plumage; their notes are mellow and pleasing, and, what is probably even more important, martins have the reputation of driving away any hawks that appear in the vicinity of their nests. Consequently their presence is encouraged. They are rarely, if ever, molested, and they enjoy an immunity from man few other birds have attained.

The Purple Martin is one of the earliest migrants to arrive in the spring, the first males appearing in the southern part of the state in early February. As their food is entirely insects, they are dependent to some extent on the weather, and it is several weeks later before they venture farther north. At Athens, it was invariably the middle of March before they were first seen, and not infrequently the females appeared at the same time as the males.

The few nests which I had the opportunity to examine were built in early May, the bottom of a hollow gourd being well filled with a substantial bed of twigs, weed stems, dead leaves, and coarse grasses. So far as is known but a single brood is reared each year. By late June the young are, with few exceptions, fully grown and capable of caring for themselves, and old and young gather then in large roosts each night for a period before starting on their long journey to their winter quarters in South America. Such roosts are established in the larger shade trees in the cities and, because of the great number of birds that use them, are conspicuous and well known. Greene [1933] describes a summer concentration of martins in Atlanta as follows:

> A well-known roosting place in Atlanta was on Capitol Avenue near Ormond Street where it is said they had been gathering for a number of years. On July 21, 1927, between 6 and 7 P.M. I estimated the number of birds at this place between 3,000 and 5,000 individuals, and on July 22, 1928, between the same hours my estimate was 2,000 birds. The tops of the elm trees along the street were literally filled with birds. Again on August 3, 1930, between 6 and 7 P.M. in the same section I estimated the number of birds at 5,000.

At Athens, the martins for years gathered each night during July and early August in large water oaks in the center of the city. Quoting from my field notes written at the time:

> July 4, 1922—Fully 2,000 birds now roosting in several large water oaks in the center of town; about 7:30 the first birds appeared, feeding overhead, and they gradually increased then until dusk when they sudden dropped down low over the trees and after swirling in a confused mass for a few minutes disappeared in a remarkably short time in the tops of the trees; for a few minutes small parties flew out and shifted about, but by dark all was quiet; after the birds had settled down, small flocks appeared at intervals, flying rapidly and seemingly having come some distance. . . .

> July 8, 1927—Fully 5,000 birds found gathering for the night in the upper branches of six large water oaks bordering a street in the center of town; the afternoon had been gloomy and dark, with an intermittent light rain, so the first small flock appeared early, at a quarter to seven, and by twenty minutes to eight all were settled for the night; during that hour, it was only at intervals that many birds were in sight at one time, the small flocks of eight or ten birds that appeared from all directions going by overhead together in one large flock, and for a few minutes before the first few dropped down into the trees, the sky was black with them, swirling in a seemingly confused mass over their roost; once started, it was remarkable how rapidly they disappeared into the tops of the trees, although the ensuing uproar left no doubt as to where they were.

Jays, Magpies, and Crows: *Family Corvidae*

Northern Blue Jay
Cyanocitta cristata bromia Oberholser

GENERAL DISTRIBUTION: Breeds from southern Alberta, northern Manitoba, Quebec, and Newfoundland south to central Illinois, Tennessee, Virginia, and northern Georgia, and west to western Nebraska, central Colorado, and central Texas. Casual farther south in winter.

STATUS IN GEORGIA: Resident and fairly common in the extreme northeastern corner of the state, and of casual occurrence during the winter months in the upper Piedmont.

A male taken on Rabun Bald, June 1, 1933, and another male taken on Brasstown Bald, November 24, 1945, are clearly referable to this north-

Southern Carolina Wrens

Thryothorus ludovicianus ludovicianus

A pair of Carolina Wrens had a nest in the garage at Sherwood Plantation,
but the birds I painted lived in a thicket at the edge of a little swamp.
I pencilled the birds and the fallen-pine branch in, then worked a whole
morning on the flowers. We accept the fact that birds are hard to
draw direct from life because they so rarely stay still, but I found that
flowers are anything but motionless—their petals curl back, their stamens
spread, each blossom of the clump moves up and down. The flowers
are those of the azalea.

ern race [Burleigh, 1948]. A female from Tray Mountain, White County (June 23, 1947), is intermediate in its characters, but closer in measurements to *bromia.*

South of the mountains specimens have been collected in Floyd County [Harold Jones, MS]; Hall County (Gainesville, March 27, 1947) [Burleigh, 1948]; Clarke County (Athens, November 10 and November 21, 1945); Winterville (November 30, 1945) [Burleigh, 1948]; and Columbia County [Murphey, 1937].

HABITS AND RECOGNITION: The northern race of the Blue Jay differs from typical *cristata* in being larger and in having the upperparts bluer and less purplish. Within its limited range in the state, it is a fairly common bird, and during most of the year can be found in small, noisy flocks on the mountain ridges. Unlike its more southern relative, it is suspicious of the proximity of man, and while rearing its young in the spring, retires to the deeper woods where it is inconspicuous and rarely seen.

Southern Blue Jay
Cyanocitta cristata cristata   (Linnaeus)

GENERAL DISTRIBUTION: Resident from southern Illinois, Indiana, northern Alabama, and central North Carolina south to central Texas, the Gulf Coast, and central Florida.

STATUS IN GEORGIA: Resident and common throughout all of the state except the extreme northeastern corner.

Specimens typical of this southern race have been examined from Franklin County (Red Hill), Clarke County (Athens), Forsyth County (Cumming), DeKalb County (Decatur), Fulton County (Atlanta), Cobb County (Kennesaw), Chattahoochee County (Cusseta), Wilkinson County (Irwinton), Baker County (Newton), Liberty County (Hinesville), and Glynn County (Brunswick).

It has been reported as nesting throughout the state, but definite breeding records are not numerous. At Savannah, Rossignol [letter] reports fourteen nests found from 1907 through 1916, the earliest on April 25 (1907) with three fresh eggs, and the latest on May 17 (1914) with four incubated eggs. Erichsen's extreme nesting dates for Savannah are April 18 (1931), four fresh eggs, and June 20 (1934), four incubated eggs. Stoddard [MS] reports a nest in Grady County with four eggs on May 11, 1940, and young already out of the nest in early May. A nest found by Norris at Tifton on May 8, 1952, held three eggs and one newly hatched young, while at Fitzgerald [Hopkins, letter] nesting extremes (ten nests) are March 18 (1940), four eggs, and May 31 (1940), "eggs." At Augusta,

Denton found nests with fully fledged young, May 22, 1945, and May 14, 1950. At Athens [Burleigh, 1938], two broods are apparently reared each year, as fresh eggs have been found in early April and again in the latter part of June and the first week of July. Extreme breeding records are a nest found April 2 (1923) with six fresh eggs, and one, which on July 1 (1926) held three slightly incubated eggs. Griffin [1940] cites as nesting extremes for the Atlanta region, five fresh eggs April 3 (1918) (L. Harris), and four eggs July 19 (1939) (Griffin). Jones [1947] reports a nest at Rome, March 29, 1945, with four eggs, and another, May 14, 1945, that held four young.

HABITS AND RECOGNITION: To one familiar with the Blue Jay in the Northern states, the confiding disposition of this jay in Georgia comes as a distinct surprise. As a boy in Pennsylvania, I knew the Blue Jay as a bird of the deep woods, always suspicious of man and never venturing into the cities or towns. Consequently it was interesting, to say the least, to find it throughout the year in the residential sections of towns in Georgia, nesting in the shade trees along the streets and in the yards, and apparently well accustomed to civilization. Prior to 1920, the Robin had not nested in Georgia south of the mountain counties, and the jay appeared to have taken its place in the South as a semidomesticated bird of the towns and villages. Noisy and inquisitive, curious about everything in its vicinity, it is constantly in evidence and familiar to everybody.

Much has been written and said concerning the bad habits of the Blue Jay, and it must be admitted that in some respects its actions, from man's point of view, leave much to be desired. During the spring, it varies its fare with the eggs and small young of other birds, and this dietary habit has aroused the wrath of many a bird lover. How destructive it actually is in this respect is open to question, but it certainly is not innocent. One spring morning at Athens, I watched a jay kill and eat a young but fully grown English Sparrow that it had carried to the ground from the lower limb of a water oak. It apparently required quite an effort to do this, but although mobbed by the distracted parents and their kin that had been attracted by the cries of the young bird, the jay hammered away and tore at the struggling body until it succeeded in at last gulping it down. Such a sight is apt to prejudice the casual observer, but the jay does some good through its food habits and lends color and action to a landscape which, especially in the winter months, would be rather drab; for these reasons and for its entertaining individuality its sins should be generally condoned.

It is during the spring months that the Southern Blue Jay is least in evidence. Busy then rearing its young, it is relatively inconspicuous, its movements being quiet and even stealthy as it goes about its daily affairs. Its nest is built in the crotch of one of the larger trees, rarely more than

404

twenty feet from the ground and, while rather bulky, is usually fairly well concealed by the surrounding foliage. It is constructed of twigs, weed stems, coarse rootlets, dead leaves, grasses, and considerable mud, the well-defined hollow in the top being lined with fine rootlets. Normally four or five eggs are laid for the first brood and but three for the second.

Northern Common Raven
Corvus corax principalis   Ridgway

GENERAL DISTRIBUTION: Northwestern Alaska, Melville Island, northern Ellesmere Island, and northern Greenland south to Washington, central Minnesota, Michigan, and Virginia, and in the southern Appalachians to northern Georgia.

STATUS IN GEORGIA: Resident in the extreme northeastern corner of the state.

There are definite breeding records for Brasstown Bald, in Towns County (five fresh eggs, March 14, 1934; three half-grown young May 4, 1934, Burleigh), and it has been noted on Blood Mountain, Union County, and Rabun Bald, Rabun County, where it possibly nests. Odum [1943] reports this species on Hawk Mountain, July 12, 1942.

HABITS AND RECOGNITION: To see a raven in Georgia, one must invade the higher mountain ridges, for this is one bird that insists on the primitive wilderness for its home. As a result, it has gradually disappeared as the virgin forests have been cleared and farms and settlements have taken their place, so that at the present time relatively few remain in the eastern United States. As far back as the oldest inhabitants can remember, a pair of ravens have nested each year on the upper slopes of Brasstown Bald, and today this is one of the few spots in the state where the bird can be looked for with a reasonable assurance of success.

The first intimation of its presence will be a hoarse, guttural croak, as it protests the intrusion into its domain, and then, if the observer is fortunate, he may see it for a brief interval, circling over the top of a ridge before disappearing from view. Seen thus, it suggests a large crow, but its notes and its characteristic flight should readily identify it. The raven has a mastery of the air that is not possessed by the crow. It delights in soaring high overhead and will often drop from a great height in a spectacular dive that no crow could ever achieve. Normally its flight is swift and has a buoyancy that is apparent even at a distance.

In other parts of the country, the raven is known to build its nest in the tops of tall trees, but in Georgia the nesting site is invariably the ledge of a cliff. The few nests that have been found on the slopes of Brasstown

Bald have been within thirty feet of the ground and have been on ledges chosen because of their inaccessibility. The wisdom of such a choice is apparent when one considers that the bobcat is equally fond of these cliffs and that it would destroy the raven broods if it could reach the nest. The nest is built in late winter when vegetation is still dormant, and no attempt is made at concealment, the large mass of sticks and twigs being in plain view from the ground. The eggs and young must be well protected from the snowstorms and low temperatures of late February and early March, so the hollow in the top is deep and well lined with soft material, such as bits of rabbit fur and shreds of bark. The nest that held five eggs on March 14, 1934, was found to be thickly lined with bunches of hog hair, and it is possible that in the southern Appalachians this material is commonly used.

One brood only is reared each year, and by early June the young are fully grown and able to care for themselves. They remain for a time with their parents, but eventually disappear, and the following year but a single pair can again be found on the upper slopes of Brasstown Bald.

Eastern Common Crow
Corvus brachyrhynchos brachyrhynchos   Brehm

GENERAL DISTRIBUTION: Breeds from Mackenzie, northern Manitoba, southern Quebec, and Newfoundland south to northern Texas, the northern part of the Gulf states, and Maryland. Winters casually south of its breeding range.

STATUS IN GEORGIA: Apparently of casual occurrence in the eastern part of the state.

Murphey [1937] states that specimens taken at Augusta in January and February represent the northern race; there are no other records.

HABITS AND RECOGNITION: The Crow of the Northern states differs from its more southern relative only in size; it is somewhat larger and has a stouter bill. So far as appearance and actions go, there is nothing to distinguish it, specimens being necessary for satisfactory identification.

Southern Common Crow
Corvus brachyrhynchos paulus   Howell

GENERAL DISTRIBUTION: Southern Illinois east to the District of Columbia, south to southeastern Texas, the Gulf Coast, Georgia, and western Florida.

Family Corvidae: JAYS, MAGPIES, & CROWS

STATUS IN GEORGIA: Resident and common throughout the state.

Specimens typical of this southern race have been examined from Fannin County (Margret), Cherokee County, Clarke County (Athens), Clayton County, Grady County (Beachton), Miller County (Colquitt), and Clinch County (Fargo).

It has been reported as breeding at various localities, but definite records are not numerous. At Athens, seven nests were found from 1921 through 1926. The earliest held five fresh eggs on March 17 (1923); the latest, four incubated eggs on April 13 (1926) (Burleigh). Barkalow [1940] gives as nesting extremes for the Atlanta region, five fresh eggs, March 9 (1935) (Barkalow), and three eggs, May 4 (1931) (T. Lawrence). Denton [1942] reports a nest with fully grown young at Americus, April 29, 1942. At Savannah, Erichsen reports a nest found on March 11, 1918, with four fresh eggs; another, March 23, 1924, that held four well-incubated eggs; and a third, March 13, 1934, with three fresh eggs.

HABITS AND RECOGNITION: The Crow is one bird that needs no description. Familiar to practically everybody because of its wide range and general abundance, it needs merely to be seen or heard to be instantly recognized. Omnivorous to a high degree, it eats everything that the changing seasons make available, and it has long been held in disrepute by farmers and sportsmen everywhere. There is little question that at times it is rather destructive to farm crops and that it takes an annual toll of bird eggs and fledglings. So bad is its reputation, in fact, that it is shot at every opportunity, and were it not for its ability to take care of itself, its existence would be seriously jeopardized. The Crow, however, is a very sagacious bird. Constantly persecuted, it has developed a wisdom that enables it to survive, and today it is probably much more common than it was when this country was originally settled. In reality, it does about as much good as harm through its feeding habits.

Being a hardy bird, it winters over much of its breeding range, and in Georgia there is little fluctuation in its numbers throughout the year. Farther north it gathers in large roosts during the winter months, countless thousands assembling each night at certain favored spots from November until early February, but in the Southeast this habit has never been noted. Except during the nesting season, small flocks can be observed in the open fields and scattered stretches of woods, and it is probable that such flocks are family parties, which remain together until mating occurs in early spring.

Over much of the state, breeding activities of the Crow begin in late February, and by the middle of March many of the birds are incubating clutches of four, five, or, rarely, six eggs. It is doubtful that more than one brood is reared each year, the few nests found in April and early May probably representing second attempts by pairs whose first nests were destroyed. At Athens, nests found were invariably built in the tops of short-leaf pines, varying in height from fifty to eighty feet from the ground, and despite their bulk were far from conspicuous. Materials used included sticks, twigs, grasses, rootlets, pine needles, bits of rotten wood, and, at times, mud, the deep hollow in the top being lined with shreds of bark, horse hair, and sometimes wool.

Fish Crow
Corvus ossifragus Wilson

GENERAL DISTRIBUTION: The coast region of the Atlantic and Gulf states, from southern Massachusetts to southern Florida, and west to eastern Texas.

STATUS IN GEORGIA: A common resident on the coast and of local occurrence in the interior of the state near the larger streams and bodies of water.

On or near the coast it has been reported from Brunswick, Darien, Hinesville, Sea Island, Cumberland Island, and Savannah. Inland, it is largely limited in its distribution to the river valleys, which are apparently followed up from the point where they reach salt water. On the Savannah River, it has been noted near Sylvania [Howell, 1936]; and Murphey [1937] considers it uncommon at Augusta. Denton [1950] extended its breeding range inland from Augusta when he found a pair nesting twelve miles north of Thomson, in McDuffie County, in 1949. On the Oconee River, it has been seen at Athens [Johnston, 1947] and at Milledgeville [Tait, 1946]; on the Ocmulgee River, at Macon [Denton, 1950]; on the Flint River, at Lake Blackshear, in Crisp and Sumter counties [Denton, 1950]; and on the Chattahoochee River, north of Chattahoochee, Florida [Howell, 1936]; and at Fort Gaines, Clay County (Norris). It is also reported by Hebard [1941] from Floyd's Island in the Okefenokee Swamp, in Grady and Thomas counties by Stoddard [1945], and at Tifton, in Tift County, by Norris [1942].

There are definite breeding records for only a few localities. On Cabbage Island, in Chatham County, I found a nest on May 17, 1925, that was fully built but still empty. Erichsen [MS] reports four nests on Little Tybee Island, May 10, 1938, two with four well-incubated eggs and two with four nearly hatched young; and five on Skidaway Island on May 4, 1941, that held fresh eggs—in two, three eggs each; and in three, four eggs. Denton [1950] reports an occupied nest at Augusta, June 24, 1947, and one at Thomson, June 22, 1949.

408

HABITS AND RECOGNITION: The Fish Crow is so called because of its preference for the vicinity of water, where, as a scavenger, it undoubtedly includes dead fish as a part of its regular diet. However, like the other crows it is omnivorous, and nothing digestible or of interest from a gastronomic standpoint is ignored. Its limited distribution in Georgia makes it relatively unimportant from an economic standpoint, and since its haunts are largely marshes and seacoast, it is not so much subject to the persecution accorded its more common relative. Nevertheless, it possesses all the attributes of a crow, and is at all times alert and difficult to take unaware. When it is seen at reasonably close range, its small size is apparent, but at a distance it is merely a crow, and then its notes are the best means of identification. The note most commonly uttered is short and hoarse, and once heard will in the future always distinguish this species from the Common Crow.

Sociable by nature, it occurs in small flocks throughout much of the year, and where suitable nesting sites are available, two or more pairs will nest in close proximity to one another. An interesting fact in connection with the breeding habits of this small crow is the late dates that it nests. Despite the mild winters on the Georgia coast and the early advent of warm weather in the spring, it is the middle of May before the majority of the Fish Crows are fully occupied in rearing their young. This is almost two months later than the average date for nests of the Common Crow. On the coast, the nest is frequently built in a live oak within ten or twelve feet of the ground, less frequently in a pine. Both the nest found at Augusta and that near Thomson were, however, in the tops of loblolly pines, each fully fifty feet from the ground; and Denton states that he was unable to determine the contents of either one. In construction they vary little from nests of the Common Crow.

Titmice, Chickadees, and Bush-Tits: *Family Paridae*

Southern Carolina Chickadee
Parus carolinensis carolinensis Audubon

GENERAL DISTRIBUTION: Northern Mississippi east to North Carolina and south to southern Alabama and southern Georgia.

STATUS IN GEORGIA: A common resident over all the state except the extreme southern counties.

Specimens have been examined from all parts of the state, including the following localities: Young Harris, Blue Ridge, Dalton, Atlanta, Athens, Augusta, Columbus, Louisville, Blakely, Newton, Savannah, Hinesville. All were found to represent this race.

It probably breeds wherever found, but definite breeding records are not numerous. Rossignol [letter] reports as nesting extremes for Savannah (thirteen nests), six fresh eggs on April 3 (1921) and five incubated eggs on May 1 (1914). Erichsen [MS] cites as his earliest breeding record for Chatham County, six fresh eggs on March 30 (1917). At Athens, fresh eggs were found between the dates of March 30 (1925) and May 1 (1926) [Burleigh, 1938]. Griffin gives as nesting extremes for the Atlanta region, five fresh eggs, April 12 (1903) (Mills), and one young May 22 (1932) (Greene).

HABITS AND RECOGNITION: Few birds are easier to get acquainted with than is the Carolina Chickadee. Confiding and inquisitive, it soon appears if its woodland haunts are entered; and if its curiosity is aroused, it may come so close that it can almost be touched. There is a temptation at times to attribute human qualities to familiar birds, and in the case of the chickadee, optimism and contentment seem to be its outstanding characteristics. Regardless of the time of year or of the weather, it energetically searches for its insect food in the woodland it inhabits, uttering at frequent intervals its cheery "chick-a-dee-dee" note and showing an instant interest in events about it. Other birds would appear to recognize and appreciate this cheerful disposition, for during the short, bleak days of winter, roving flocks of chickadees are almost invariably accompanied by titmice, creepers, nuthatches, kinglets, and pine warblers, and not infrequently by downy woodpeckers and bluebirds.

With the approach of spring, mated pairs replace the small flocks, and it is then that the male can be heard uttering his simple little song, four-syllabled, and suggesting the syllables "o-phee-o-bee." The nest is built in a cavity in a rotten stub or old fence post, usually within four or five feet of the ground, and with few exceptions the site is excavated by the birds themselves. A pair of chickadees at Athens used a Downy Woodpecker's old hole, and were incubating six almost fresh eggs in this cavity on May 1, 1926, but I know of no other instance of this kind in Georgia. The average cavity is four inches in depth, and the nest itself is a soft, matted bed of soft shreds of inner bark, green moss, plant down, and, where available, bits of cotton, rabbit fur, and feathers. Normally six or seven eggs are laid, and but a single brood is reared each year. An occasional pair will be found incubating by the latter part of March, but it is usually the first week in April before many are so engaged.

Since it is so tame and easily approached, no difficulty should be experienced in recognizing the Carolina Chickadee. A small bird with a gray back, black crown and throat, and white cheeks, it will almost at once confirm its identity by uttering its "chick-a-dee-dee" note.

Peninsular Carolina Chickadee
Parus carolinensis impiger Bangs

GENERAL DISTRIBUTION: Florida and southern Georgia.

STATUS IN GEORGIA: Resident and fairly common in the southern part of the state.

Specimens of this race have been examined from Baxley, Appling County (November 24, 1929); Grady County (November 3, 1939); Tifton, Tift County (February 20, 1942); Camden County (November 6, 1941); Statensville, Echols County (March 22, 1947); and the Okefenokee Swamp (Cowhouse Island, January 1, 1946).

Hebard [letter] states that his earliest breeding record for Camden County is a nest that held five fresh eggs on March 31, 1944. In Grady County, Stoddard [MS] reports broods of young "almost fully feathered and ready to leave the nest" as early as April 23 (1927) and as late as May 24 (1926). Another nest found in 1947 held three or more eggs on April 16. Norris and Hopkins [letter] cite as nesting extremes for Fitzgerald, two eggs and three newly hatched young on April 27 (1940) and young on May 24 (1939).

HABITS AND RECOGNITION: This extreme southern race of the Carolina Chickadee differs in being smaller and having distinctly darker upperparts. In appearance and actions, it resembles in every way the birds in the northern part of the state, and only actual specimens can be satisfactorily identified. So far as my personal experience goes, it is not as common as are the chickadees farther north in the state, and it is rather local in its distribution, being confined to deciduous timber in stream bottoms.

Tufted Titmouse
Parus bicolor Linnaeus

GENERAL DISTRIBUTION: Nebraska, Iowa, Illinois, Indiana, Ohio, southern Pennsylvania, and New Jersey south to central Texas, the Gulf Coast, and southern Florida.

STATUS IN GEORGIA: Resident and common throughout the state.

It has been reported from the mountain counties south to the Florida line, and specimens have been examined from the following localities: Brasstown Bald (Towns County), Decatur, Atlanta, Athens, Banks Lake

(Lanier County), Newton, Camilla, the Okefenokee Swamp (Minne's Lake), Beachton (Grady County), and Hinesville.

At Savannah, Rossignol [letter] gives as nesting extremes (ten nests), April 3 (1908), two fresh eggs, and May 25 (1919), three incubated eggs. Hebard [letter] reports a nest with young in Charlton County on May 13, 1942; and Stoddard [MS], one on Sherwood Plantation in Grady County that held six well-grown young on April 25, 1927. Norris [letter] says that two occupied nests were found by Hopkins at Fitzgerald in 1940, one with five eggs on April 27, the other with young on May 25. At Athens, a nest was found May 7, 1921, with newly hatched young; another on May 30, 1922, with five fresh eggs; and a third on May 6, 1923, with six slightly incubated eggs (Burleigh). Griffin [1940] cites as nesting extremes for the Atlanta region, seven incubated eggs, April 26 (1903) (Mills), and three young, June 9 (1937) (Griffin). Jones [1947] reports a nest with four newly hatched young at Rome, May 13, 1942. Murphey [1937] states that it breeds very early at Augusta, "a full set of eggs having been taken March 23."

HABITS AND RECOGNITION: No bird is more typical of the wooded areas of the Southern states than is the Tufted Titmouse. Noisy and normally restless and active, it is a conspicuous part of the bird life wherever found. Enter almost any extensive stretch of woodland in Georgia, and soon you will be greeted with a loud, clear whistle that has been aptly translated as "peto, peto." Investigate the source of this note and you will have little difficulty in at once becoming acquainted with the Tufted Titmouse. It is a close relative of the chickadee and, like it, is a friendly and inquisitive little bird, interested in everything happening in its vicinity. Arouse its interest and it will approach almost to within arm's length, scolding the intruder if at all alarmed, but otherwise merely satisfying its inherent curiosity.

Except during the breeding season, it occurs in small flocks that are probably family groups, and throughout the winter months these groups are commonly associated with Chickadees, Nuthatches, and Kinglets. Restless and active, the Titmouse roves over a considerable area in the course of a day, its feeding activities taking it from the underbrush to the upper branches of the larger trees, where foliage, twigs, and even the outer bark are carefully examined for insect life. Its appearance is radically different from that of a Chickadee, for while predominantly gray, it is much larger, and it has a prominent crest that is noticeable even when flattened against the head.

In early April, mated pairs replace the small flocks that have roamed so widely through the wooded areas, and by the end of the month most of the Titmice are fully occupied with domestic responsibilities. The nest is built in a natural cavity of a tree, usually within thirty feet of the ground, and is a substantial bed of soft shreds of inner bark, green moss, and fragments of dead leaves. On several occasions I have known an old snakeskin to be used in the construction of the nest, but apparently this is not as invariable a habit as it is with the Crested Flycatcher. A single brood only is reared each year, and five or six, rarely seven, eggs are laid. Both birds take turns in incubating, and they sit so closely that, unless they are seen entering the cavity, the nest is extremely difficult to find. A unique occurrence was noted on Sherwood Plantation in Grady County where Stoddard found a pair of Tufted Titmice and a pair of Crested Flycatchers using the same nest cavity. Each female laid four eggs in the nest, but the Flycatchers soon disappeared, and the Titmice succeeded in rearing their four young and two of the Crested Flycatcher!

Nuthatches: *Family Sittidae*

Florida White-breasted Nuthatch
Sitta carolinensis carolinensis Latham

GENERAL DISTRIBUTION: Missouri, southern Illinois, Kentucky, Tennessee, and North Carolina south to southeastern Texas, the Gulf Coast, and central Florida.

STATUS IN GEORGIA: Locally a scarce to fairly common resident throughout the state.

In the mountain counties the White-breasted Nuthatch is common and generally distributed. Throughout the Piedmont and coastal plain, however, it is noticeably scarcer and of local occurrence, being absent from many localities apparently well suited to its needs. At Athens, it proved to be a scarce and somewhat irregular winter resident, appearing the latter part of October and being rarely seen after the first week in March. With the exception of one rather unexpected record, that of a single bird seen July 22, 1924, extreme dates of occurrence were October 15 (1929) and April 14 (1924) [Burleigh, 1938]. Fleetwood [1946] reports a single bird seen in Jones County on June 21, 1946, the only record in seven years. Norris and Hopkins [1953] consider this species rare at Fitzgerald, Ben Hill County; their few records for this area being December 22, 1939, May 17, 1940, and October 11, 1941.

In the mountains it has been reported from numerous localities, including Brasstown Bald, Rabun Bald, Cowpen Mountain, Neels Gap, and Rich Mountain; and in the coastal plain from Tarversville (Twiggs County), Columbus, Americus, Cuthbert, Waycross, Hinesville, and Camden County (St. Marys and Coleraine).

Definite breeding records are available for the following localities:

Atlanta: Five young, April 17, 1937 [Griffin, 1940]; six small young, April 8, 1945 [Werner, 1945].

Covington: Two young and three infertile eggs April 18, 1926 (Burleigh).

Grady County: Fully grown young out of the nest May 2, 1944 [Stoddard].

Homerville: Well-grown young March 13, 1932 [Grimes, 1944].

Specimens identified as the southern race, *carolinensis,* have been taken at Young Harris, Rabun Bald, Atlanta, Athens, Augusta, Lincolnton, Baker County, Waycross, and St. Marys.

HABITS AND RECOGNITION: Watching a nuthatch for the first time, one is impressed by its lack of concern for the laws of gravity. If it is searching the trunk for insects, their larvae, or eggs, it commonly comes down toward the ground head first, doing so with as much ease as climbing by the more orthodox method. While feeding among the branches, it is just as apt to be seen on the under surface as on top. No part of a tree escapes its close scrutiny. This nuthatch has frequently been referred to as the acrobat of the bird world, and the agility it displays at all times makes this a rather apt title. Normally tame and unsuspicious, it can be watched at fairly close range, and its unique actions alone will readily identify it. From the other nuthatches, however, the White-breasted can be distinguished by its larger size and by its distinct pattern—gray back, glossy black crown, and white underparts. During the summer, family groups remain together, but during the greater part of the year single birds or pairs will be seen. As it feeds, it continually utters a nasal note for which the syllables "quank, quank, quank" have been suggested. It also has a loud, mellow whistle that can be heard throughout much of the year, and which will at once attract attention to its presence.

In Georgia, nesting activities begin early, and by the first of April the average pair of White-breasted Nuthatches will be busily occupied in feeding a brood of incessantly hungry young. Under normal circumstances, the nest is built in a natural cavity in the trunk of a tree, from twenty to sixty feet from the ground, but occasional pairs display individuality in this respect. At Atlanta, they were reported by Werner and Lucien Harris [1927] as using bird boxes, and the nest found by Grimes at Homerville was in a Red-cockaded Woodpecker's old hole. I know of no instance of this species' excavating a cavity of its own. The nest itself is a compact bed of soft shreds of inner bark intermixed with bits of green moss and, where available, bits of fur and feathers. Four or five eggs are usually laid, and, once the female begins to incubate, she rarely leaves the nest until the eggs are hatched. The male feeds her at frequent intervals throughout the day, bringing food to her at the entrance of the cavity.

Red-breasted Nuthatch
Sitta canadensis Linnaeus

GENERAL DISTRIBUTION: Breeds from the upper Yukon Valley, southern Mackenzie, northern Manitoba, southern Quebec, and Newfoundland south to northern Minnesota, Michigan, and Massachusetts, and in the mountains to California, Arizona, New Mexico, and North Carolina; also on Guadalupe Island, Lower California. Winters from southern Canada south to southern California, New Mexico, Arizona, the Gulf Coast, and northern Florida.

STATUS IN GEORGIA: An irregular transient and winter resident throughout the state, although rarely observed below the fall line.

The occurrence of the Red-breasted Nuthatch at Athens is typical of the unpredictable southward movements of this species. There it was found to be a rather irregular winter resident, fairly common in some years, scarce or totally lacking in others. During the winter of 1923–24 it was frequently seen from October 20 through April 23, was absent the following year, and scarce during the winter of 1925–26, when it was noted at infrequent intervals from October 11 through March 30. In 1927 it was reported but once, a single bird on October 28; it was not seen at all in 1928, and in 1929 was noted once in the spring, a single bird, March 12, and at infrequent intervals in the fall from October 9 through December 27. In 1933, three were seen November 30 [Burleigh, 1938]. Odum [1942] states that during the winter of 1941–42 this species "was observed four times between October 15 and January 25 and three times between March 28 and April 23. On November 29, twenty individuals were observed during a four-hour census of a three-hundred-acre area."

Elsewhere in the state it has been reported from the following localities:

Camden County: One seen February 2, 1942 [Hebard, letter].

Fitzgerald: One specimen taken December 30, 1940 [Norris, 1941b].

Osierfield, Irwin County: Four seen and one collected February 13, 1952 [Hopkins, 1953b].

Macon: March 23, 1944; October 22, 1949.

Augusta: Rare; three specimens taken in the months of November and December [Murphey, 1937].

Atlanta: September 24, 1903 [Greene, 1933]; December 24, 1927, January 11, 1940 [Griffin, 1941]; October 11, 1941, through February 5, 1942 [Griffin, 1942]; March 26, 1944 [Johnston, 1944]; September 24, 1949 [Parks, 1950].

Stone Mountain: November 12, 1941 (Burleigh).

Lake Rabun: May 11, 1947 [Johnston, 1947].

Lookout Mountain: April 4, 1944 [Hamilton, 1944].

Dalton: November and December 26, 1941 [Hamilton, 1942]; November 27, 1943, through February 6, 1944 [Mitchell et al., 1944].

HABITS AND RECOGNITION: In many respects the Red-breasted Nuthatch is a miniature of the White-breasted Nuthatch. It has the same stout, short-tailed appearance, and displays equal agility as from every conceivable angle it explores the trunk and branches of a tree for insects. In my experience it seems to prefer the outer ends of the branches, casually hanging from the ends of the smaller twigs as it searches the terminal buds for insects. In its summer home it is closely associated with the conifers, and as a transient and winter resident in Georgia it can be looked for in woodlands where pines predominate. Only at rare intervals will one be found in the deciduous hardwoods in the stream bottoms. At Athens the short-leaf pine (*Pinus echinata*) appeared to be its favorite tree; the numerous small cones supplied it with an unfailing store of seeds that it devoted much of its time to extracting from beneath the scales. As more seeds were usually available than it could possibly eat, it frequently stored many of these seeds in cracks in the bark of other trees close by.

Friendly and inquisitive, its curiosity is easily aroused, and it will approach almost to within arms length. Its small size, reddish underparts, and black line through the eye will leave no doubt of its identity. All of the nuthatches are characterized by their loquaciousness, and the Red-breasted Nuthatch is no exception. The note most commonly heard is high pitched and nasal, and might be expressed as "yna, yna, yna."

Northern Brown-headed Nuthatch
Sitta pusilla pusilla (Latham)

GENERAL DISTRIBUTION: Resident in the Lower Austral Zone from eastern Arkansas, southern Missouri, and southern Delaware south to eastern Texas, the Gulf Coast, and southern Georgia.

STATUS IN GEORGIA: Resident and common in all parts of the state except the mountain counties and the extreme southeastern corner.

The Brown-headed Nuthatch has been reported in the eastern part of the state north to Toccoa and in western Georgia to Rome. In the Piedmont and coastal plain it occurs locally wherever conditions are suitable, but is commoner and more widely distributed south of the fall line.

Definite breeding records are limited to the following localities:

Athens: Extreme dates of nesting, March 24 (1925), five slightly incubated eggs; and April 26 (1923), four fresh eggs [Burleigh, 1938].

Atlanta: Nesting extremes, March 13 (1938), three eggs (Griffin); and May 21 (1932), four eggs (Eyles, Giles) [Griffin, 1940].

Fitzgerald: Tifton region nesting extremes (twenty-five nests), March 13 (1952), four fresh eggs (Ty Ty, Tift County); and May 10 (1941), four young (Fitzgerald) [Norris and Hopkins].

Grady County: Five eggs, March 25, 1939 (Stoddard).

Family *Sittidae:* NUTHATCHES

Savannah: Nesting extremes, March 12 (1911), six fresh eggs; and May 8 (1911), four fresh eggs (Rossignol); March 8 (1925), six slightly incubated eggs (Erichsen).

Bent (1948) cites as "egg dates" for Georgia "22 records, March 11 to July 20; 11 records March 24 to April 11, indicating the height of the season." Specimens representing this race have been examined from: Athens, Dewy Rose (Elbert County), Stone Mountain, Atlanta, and Newton (Baker County).

HABITS AND RECOGNITION: No bird is more typical of the stretches of open pine woods in Georgia than is the Brown-headed Nuthatch. An occasional individual may feed briefly in a post oak or a sweet gum, but it is in the upper branches of the larger pines that these little nuthatches spend most of their time. So closely associated are they with this preferred environment that if logging operations remove the pine timber in any locality, the Brown-headed Nuthatches either disappear or greatly decrease. I personally saw this happen at Athens. At one time common and widely distributed, this species gradually decreased as the pine woods were cut over, and at the present time it is rather scarce and found at only a few widely separated spots.

It is an extremely sociable bird, occurring throughout much of the year in small flocks that only the breeding season temporarily breaks up. Restless and apparently full of boundless energy, the individuals comprising a flock pause for only a brief interval in the top of a pine, searching the branches and terminal twigs for insects, then one after another troop to another tree close by. Agile, and with the characteristic nuthatch disregard for orthodox tree climbing, they hang head downward from a cone or cluster of needles, casually explore the under surface of a limb, or work up or down the trunk as the mood strikes them. In the meantime, they keep up a continual chatter, calling to each other with a rapid, high-pitched "cha, cha, cha," that is quite unlike any note of the other nuthatches and that once heard will in the future readily identify them. If seen at reasonably close range, which is not difficult as their curiosity is easily aroused and they have little fear of man, they will be revealed as the smallest of their family, with gray back, white underparts, and a dark-brown crown.

Their breeding activities begin early, for by the latter part of February many pairs are busy excavating a nesting cavity in an old fence post, telephone pole, or rotten pine stub. This is usually within three or four feet from the ground, although at Athens one nest I found was but a foot and a half from the ground, while another was up fully twenty feet in a dead branch of a shortleaf pine. The cavity varies in depth from five to ten inches, the bottom being lined with pine seed wings, shreds of inner bark, and, not infrequently, wool. Occasional pairs show some originality

417

EASTERN BROWN THRASHER

Toxostoma rufum rufum

This strong-footed, somewhat terrestrial songster is Georgia's state bird.
It was common in thickets along roadsides and forest edges.
I was tempted to show it singing high in a tree, or scratching vigorously
among the dry leaves, but when the crossvine came into bloom,
and I noticed how much time the thrashers spent in it, I decided the
beautiful plant would have to become part of the painting.

in choice of nesting site. One nest that I saw at Savannah was in the side of a three-inch plank, leaning against a tree in open pine woods, the birds having discovered a rotten spot that made it possible to dig a cavity in it. A nest found by Hopkins at Fitzgerald was even more unusual, being three feet from the ground in a small burned-out depression (actually a fire scar) in the trunk of a longleaf pine. This is the only instance I know where the birds did not excavate a cavity themselves. It is possible that more than one brood is occasionally reared each year, but there is no direct evidence to that effect. Normally four or five, rarely six or seven, eggs are laid.

Southern Brown-headed Nuthatch
Sitta pusilla caniceps   Bangs

GENERAL DISTRIBUTION: The peninsula of Florida, north to extreme southeastern Georgia.

STATUS IN GEORGIA: Resident and common in the extreme southeastern corner of the state.

Specimens taken at the edge of the Okefenokee Swamp south of Folkston on December 31, 1945 (two males and a female), are typical of this Florida race. Other specimens taken slightly farther north—at Valdosta (November 20, 1929), Brunswick (October 19, 1931), Savannah (October 20, 1931), and Richmond Hill (January 25, 1946)—are intermediate in their characters, the color of the crown being variable and the measurements those of *pusilla* rather than of *caniceps*. Peet [1947] states that a mated pair were collected at Bainbridge, February 25, 1943, and the male found to be intermediate in size but the color of *caniceps*, and the female typical of the Florida race. However, Norris [1950] casts doubt on the possibility of *caniceps* occupying southwestern Georgia.

Apparently the only definite breeding records are three nests reported by Hebard [Bent, 1948]. All were found in 1942: the first in Camden County on April 12 with one fresh egg; the second, also in Camden County, on April 14 with young; and the third in Charlton County on April 23 with young almost ready to fly.

HABITS AND RECOGNITION: This Florida race of the Brown-headed Nuthatch is characterized by being smaller, in having the top of the head noticeably lighter brown and the gray of the back darker. In appearance and actions it differs little from its more northern relative. Except during the breeding season, restless, noisy flocks can be found feeding in the upper branches of the larger pines; within its range it is probably as common and as widely distributed as any other species. The three nests reported by Hebard were all within four feet of the ground, one being in a fence post and two in old pine stumps. One was built of shreds of cypress bark, pine seed wings, and a little Spanish moss.

Creepers: *Family Certhiidae*

Eastern Brown Creeper
Certhia familiaris americana   Bonaparte

GENERAL DISTRIBUTION: Breeds from southern Manitoba, central Ontario, and southern Quebec south to eastern Nebraska, northern Indiana, and New Jersey. Winters over much of its breeding range and south to central Texas, the Gulf Coast, and Florida.

STATUS IN GEORGIA: A fairly common transient and winter resident throughout the state.

The Brown Creeper appears in Georgia in the fall in early October, and is in evidence daily thereafter until late March. By the first of April, there is a noticeable decrease in the numbers seen, but an occasional individual lingers until the middle of that month.

Earliest arrivals in the fall were noted at Atlanta, October 12 (1930); Athens, October 2 (1925); Milledgeville, October 26 (1944); Macon, October 14 (1934); Americus, November 22 (1941); Tifton, October 28 (1941); Grady County, October 18 (1942); Savannah, October 8 (1920); and Hinesville, November 1 (1944).

In the spring the last were seen at Hinesville, March 17 (1942); Savannah, April 16 (1904); Fitzgerald, April 7 (1941); Americus, March 7 (1942); Columbus, March 24 (1946); Macon, April 5 (1924); Milledgeville, March 16 (1946); Athens, April 16 (1947); and Atlanta, April 17, (1936).

Specimens representing this race were taken on dates varying from October 14 (1945) (Athens) to March 16 (1946) (Atlanta), and were from the following localities: Elbert County (Dewy Rose); Clarke County (Athens, Princeton); Hall County (Lula); DeKalb County (Decatur, Stone Mountain); Fulton County (Atlanta); Cherokee County (Canton); and Whitfield County (Dalton) [Burleigh, 1948]. Stoddard [MS] also reports taking specimens of *americana* in Grady County on November 17, 1947, January 2, 1949, and February 27, 1950.

HABITS AND RECOGNITION: One watching a Brown Creeper for the first time is impressed both with its industriousness and by the monotony of its existence. Starting at the base of a tree it carefully works up the trunk, examining as it goes the crevices in the bark for the minute insect life on

420

which it feeds. Approaching the top, it suddenly drops to the base of another tree close by, and once more continues its unending scrutiny of the bark up which it creeps. Throughout each day it varies little from this means of obtaining a livelihood. An occasional venturesome individual will disappear briefly in the crown of a tree as it explores the larger branches, but it soon reappears and resumes its patient journeys up the trunks. Its dull-brown plumage and small size make it inconspicuous and difficult to detect, as does its habit of remaining on the opposite side of the tree from the observer if at all alarmed. Largely silent, it utters at intervals a high, thin note that is inaudible at any distance. Although it is rather solitary by nature and never seen in flocks, two birds can frequently be found together during the winter months, and at this season of the year creepers are customarily associated with restless, roving flocks of chickadees and kinglets.

Appalachian Brown Creeper
Certhia familiaris nigrescens Burleigh

GENERAL DISTRIBUTION: Breeds in the Canadian Zone of the southern Appalachians from West Virginia to the Great Smoky Mountains in western North Carolina and eastern Tennessee. Winters at a lower altitude in this same region, and casually south to the Gulf Coast.

STATUS IN GEORGIA: A fairly common transient and winter resident throughout the state.

Specimens representing this southern Appalachian race were taken in Georgia between the dates of November 11 (1945) (Athens) and April 4 (1947) (Decatur), and were from the following localities: Clarke County (Athens), DeKalb County (Decatur, Stone Mountain), Fulton County (Atlanta), Cobb County (Kennesaw), and McIntosh County (Blackbeard Island) (Burleigh, 1948). Stoddard [MS] also reports taking specimens of *nigrescens* in Grady County on November 17, 1947, and January 2, 1949.

HABITS AND RECOGNITION: The Brown Creeper of the southern Appalachians is characterized by having the upperparts distinctly darker, and the underparts grayer than in the preceding race. Its general appearance and actions differ in no way from *americana,* and it cannot be identified unless in the hand.

Anticosti Brown Creeper
Certhia familiaris anticostiensis Braund and McCullagh

GENERAL DISTRIBUTION: Breeds on Anticosti Island and Newfoundland.

Winters south at least to northern Georgia, although at present its winter range is imperfectly known.

STATUS IN GEORGIA: A casual winter resident in the northern part of the state.

Specimens representing this northern race were taken as follows: Stone Mountain, December 10, 1944; Bogart, November 16, 1945; Winterville, November 30, 1945; Whitehall, December 5, 1945; and Athens, March 25, 1946.

HABITS AND RECOGNITION: This recently described race from Anticosti Island is suggestive in coloration of *nigrescens* but is less gray above and lighter brown on the rump, with the nape noticeably darker brown. Its general appearance and actions are similar to those of the other creepers.

Wrens: *Family Troglodytidae*

Eastern House Wren
Troglodytes aedon aedon   Vieillot

GENERAL DISTRIBUTION: Breeds from southern Quebec and New Brunswick south to Virginia. Winters from the Gulf Coast and the coast of South Carolina to southern Florida, and in eastern Mexico.

STATUS IN GEORGIA: A scarce transient in the northern part of the state and an equally scarce winter resident south of the fall line.

Specimens representing this race were taken at Roswell, April 27, 1922; Athens, April 10 and September 15 and 22, 1929; Okefenokee Swamp (Floyd's Island), December 2, 1934; Savannah, February 26, 1933; and Colonel's Island, Liberty County, February 16, 1907.

HABITS AND RECOGNITION: The Eastern House Wren was at one time considered the house wren commonly found in the state, but recent studies have shown that the race described from Ohio is far more common. As it can be identified only by actual specimens, it is possibly more abundant as a transient and winter resident than the few records would indicate.

Ohio House Wren
Troglodytes aedon baldwini   Oberholser

GENERAL DISTRIBUTION: Breeds from Michigan east to southwestern Quebec, south to northern Georgia and eastern North Carolina. Winters in southeastern Texas, southern Louisiana, the Gulf Coast, Georgia, and South Carolina.

STATUS IN GEORGIA: An uncommon transient and winter resident over most of the state. In 1950, it was reported as breeding in Georgia for the first time, on the Agricultural Campus of the University of Georgia at Athens.

Earliest arrivals in the fall were noted at Athens, September 15 (1929); Atlanta, September 14 (1953); Macon, September 28 (1940); Americus, October 11 (1941); Fitzgerald, October 6 (1939); Grady County, September 25 (1949); Hinesville, October 10 (1943); Savannah, September 23 (1934); and St. Marys, October 20 (1905).

In the spring the last were seen at Hinesville, April 22 (1945); Savannah, May 2 (1931); Americus, April 25 (1942); Fitzgerald, May 3 (1939); Columbus, April 10 (1945); Macon, May 11 (1935); Milledgeville, April 23 (1938); Atlanta, May 5 (1940); and Athens, May 4 (1922).

Wintering individuals were observed at Augusta, December 2, 1932; Athens, November 19, 1922, February 20 and December 30, 1925; Atlanta, January 1 and February 12, 1916, December 26, 1926, and December 29, 1937; Blakely, December 30, 1933; Bainbridge, January 20, 1937; Valdosta, November 22, 1929; Savannah, December 4 and 6, 1911; McIntosh County, January 7, 1890. Hebard [letter] considers this race a fairly common winter resident in Camden and Charlton Counties.

Odum and Johnston [1951] reported the breeding of the House Wren in Georgia for the first time, three nests, representing two pairs of these wrens, being found at Athens in 1950. One held five nestlings on June 23, the second four fresh eggs on June 29, and the third, a second brood of the first pair, five partially incubated eggs on July 10.

Thirty-five specimens typical of this race have been taken in Georgia between the dates of September 22 (1929) (Athens) and April 30 (1949) (Atlanta), and are from the following localities: Clarke County (Athens), Oconee County (Bogart), DeKalb County (Decatur), Fulton County (Atlanta), Decatur County (Bainbridge), Seminole County (Donalsonville), Grady County (Beachton), Ware County (Waycross), Tift County (Tifton), Ben Hill County (Fitzgerald), Berrien County (Nashville), Chatham County (Savannah), and Glynn County (St. Simons Island). A breeding male taken by Odum and Johnston at Athens on July 18, 1950, was also found referable to *baldwini*.

HABITS AND RECOGNITION: As its name implies, the House Wren over much of its breeding range has accepted the advantages connected with the presence of man, and is commonly found about farmyards, and even in towns and cities where birdhouses have been put up for its use. In the breeding season it is a friendly, inquisitive little bird, tame and easily approached, and apparently little affected by any interest shown in its presence. When it reaches Georgia in the fall, however, it suddenly becomes shy and seems distrustful of man's activities. Haunting the densest thickets and stretches of underbrush, it is usually very difficult to see, and were it not for its harsh, scolding notes, it would be easily overlooked. If its curiosity is aroused, it will appear briefly in the top of a bush, but will almost at once return to the shelter of the thicket and will be seen no more. Birds encountered in the spring will frequently be heard singing, but almost invariably the hurried, bubbling song will emerge from a dense thicket, and only brief glimpses will be had of the singer as, in customary wren fashion, it moves energetically about searching for food. When seen, it will be at reasonably close range, and will be revealed as a small brown wren with a tilted tail that seems to emphasize its saucy disposition.

In recent years the House Wren has been extending its breeding range southward, so its appearance during the summer months at Athens, in 1950, was by no means unexpected. Actually its status as a breeding bird in Georgia had been anticipated, and it is not improbable that in time it will be fairly common throughout at least the upper Piedmont. Odum and Johnston have described the situation of one of the nests found near the Veterinary Clinic Building on the Agricultural Campus of the University of Georgia as follows:

The female was carrying nesting material into the end of a pipe which formed part of a series of fenced enclosures for animals undergoing treatment at the clinic. The particular pipe selected by the birds was a brace set at an angle to the corner post. The pipe was just under two inches in inside diameter, and the bolt at the top restricted the entrance to about one inch. The nest was about nine inches down from the opening.

Two other nests found at this spot were in similar situations. They state further:

The pens in which all nests were located cover about one-half acre and are shaded by a grove of large, old, pecan trees. A number of pens were unused and were overgrown with tall weeds and bushes. The grove was surrounded by lawns or open grassy areas. The wrens were able to get their food and to carry on other activities mostly within the pen area, but the male was observed on a number of occasions to cross the lawn and a road to shrubbery around two nearby houses.

Family Troglodytidae: WRENS

In this connection it is interesting to note the conclusions reached by Odum and Johnston in analyzing this first nesting of the House Wren in Georgia:

> Since the House Wren was not known to nest south of Virginia and Kentucky prior to 1920, but has since appeared in many points of North Carolina, upper South Carolina, and eastern Tennessee, it is clear that a well-marked southward invasion of the southeast by birds of midwestern stock (*baldwini*) is occurring. Progress has been most rapid in the Piedmont Region, east of the Appalachians, where Bewick's Wren is rare or absent as a breeding bird. The invasion . . . has occurred by "jumps"—groups of birds colonizing locally, often at some distance from the last known point of their southern range.
>
> Analysis of climatic conditions and known physiological tolerances of the species leads to the conclusion that biotic rather than climatic factors limited the southern boundary of the range as it existed prior to 1920. However, since the amount of reproduction (as judged by the number of eggs laid and hatched) by the Athens colony was definitely decreased by high temperatures during the egg-laying periods, it is thought that climate, particularly maximum daily temperatures during the breeding season, will exert an increasingly important limiting effect as the species moves southward.

Western House Wren
Trogolodytes aedon parkmanii Audubon

GENERAL DISTRIBUTION: Breeds from southern British Columbia, central Alberta, central Saskatchewan, and southern Manitoba south to northern Lower California, southern Arizona, southwestern Texas, southern Missouri, and southern Illinois. Winters from California, Texas, the Gulf Coast, and northwestern Florida south to southern Mexico.

STATUS IN GEORGIA: Apparently of casual occurrence in the state in the spring.

Three specimens have been taken in Georgia: a female at Athens, April 29, 1928 (Burleigh), and females in Grady County April 9, 1938, and May 5, 1940 (Stoddard).

HABITS AND RECOGNITION: The Western House Wren is similar in appearance to the other house wrens, but is paler and grayer above and duller white beneath. Its actions do not differ.

425

Eastern Winter Wren
Troglodytes troglodytes hiemalis Vieillot

GENERAL DISTRIBUTION: Breeds from southern Alberta, southern Manitoba, northern Ontario, and central Quebec south to central Minnesota, northern Wisconsin, central Michigan, and Rhode Island. Winters from about its southern breeding limit to Texas and central Florida.

STATUS IN GEORGIA: A fairly common winter resident throughout the state.

South of the mountains the Winter Wren appears in October, and is frequently seen until the middle of the following April. Earliest arrivals in the fall were noted as follows: Athens, October 7 (1922); Atlanta, October 9 (1948); Macon, October 8 (1932); Americus, October 25 (1941); Fitzgerald, October 14 (1940); and Savannah, October 9 (1926). In the spring, the last individual was observed at Savannah, April 22 (1910); Hinesville, April 2 (1944); Americus, April 20 (1942); Macon, April 10 (1944); Atlanta, April 28 (1953); and Athens, April 24 (1928). It has also been reported during the winter months at Augusta, Columbus, in the Okefenokee Swamp (Minne's Lake Island and Floyd's Island), and at Newton (Baker County).

Specimens representing this northern race were taken at Comer, Madison County (January 11, 1946); Athens (November 14, 15, 16, 1938; October 11, November 22, December 1, 8, 17, 1945); Stone Mountain (October 31, 1946); Atlanta (November 7, 1946); Blakely (November 26, 1935; February 1, 1936); Newton (January 11, 1932); and Grady County (January 27, 1940).

HABITS AND RECOGNITION: The Winter Wren, as its name implies, appears in Georgia from its summer haunts in the north when the first frosts announce the approach of winter, and then takes up its sojourn in the state until early spring. It is the smallest of the wrens, and its diminutive size causes one to marvel at its ability to make the long journeys from its breeding range without mishap. It must possess the ability to fly for long distances, but once established in a stretch of woods where it will remain for the winter, it depends for safety on the protection of the thickets where it spends its days. If sufficiently alarmed, it will fly a short distance, but it seems to do so reluctantly, and once safely out of sight will be difficult to find again. With its dark coloration and small size, it suggests a mouse as it creeps about in tangled thickets, brush piles, or fallen timber. Wren-like, however, its curiosity is easily aroused, and if not frightened, it will appear briefly in view, bobbing up and down and uttering a short, harsh note that to my ear is very suggestive of that of the Song Sparrow. On its breeding

426

grounds, it displays outstanding ability as a songster, a hurried tinkling song that is a remarkable performance for so tiny a bird. Unfortunately, it rarely if ever sings in migration, even in the early spring, so in Georgia one must accept it as a rather inconspicuous and quiet winter resident.

Appalachian Winter Wren
Troglodytes troglodytes pullus (Burleigh)

GENERAL DISTRIBUTION: Breeds in the Canadian Zone of the southern Appalachians from Virginia south to northern Georgia. Winters at lower altitudes within its breeding range and south to the Gulf Coast and southern Georgia.

STATUS IN GEORGIA: A scarce and local summer resident in the mountain counties and a fairly common winter resident throughout the rest of the state.

At the present time the Winter Wren is known to breed only on Brasstown Bald, in Towns County, but it is possible that it occurs during summer on other high ridges in the extreme northeastern corner of the state. A nest found on Brasstown Bald June 15, 1922, was empty, but judging from its appearance, it had recently held young [Burleigh, 1925]. Another nest found the following year, on May 22, 1923, held five slightly incubated eggs [Burleigh, 1927].

Specimens representing this southern Appalachian race were taken at Athens (December 8, 1928; October 15 and 19, 1947), Stone Mountain (November 9, 1943; December 10, 1944), Decatur (November 25, 1946), Atlanta (December 9, 1941), and in Grady County (October 24, 1940).

HABITS AND RECOGNITION: One of the pleasant surprises the summer of 1922 held in store for me was finding a pair of Winter Wrens breeding on the cool, damp, north slope of Brasstown Bald. The birds were restricted to a narrow area at an altitude of approximately 4,100 feet, but here the male could be heard singing at all hours of the day. Restless and elusive, he could be glimpsed only occasionally as he fed in the tangled thickets and about old logs and uprooted trees. The nest was found June 15 after a long search, but it was empty, and judging from its appearance, the young had but recently left it. Well concealed in the top of the upturned roots of a large hemlock close to a small stream, it was a ball of fine hemlock twigs and green moss, with the entrance at one side and the top.

The following year a more intensive study of this rugged mountain resulted in finding three singing males in coves above an altitude of 4,000 feet. It was again only after a long, hard search that a nest was found on May 22 which held five slightly incubated eggs. It was two and one-half feet from the ground, cleverly concealed in the top of the upturned roots of a large yellow birch that had recently fallen, and was a loose ball of green moss, lacking the twigs that are usually used, the cavity inside being well lined with feathers of a Ruffed Grouse. The female was incubating and flushed when the nest was touched, returning, however, almost at once, and showing great concern over my intrusion. This was at an elevation of approximately 4,000 feet, on a steep slope covered with tangled rhododendron thickets, moss-covered boulders, and fairly large timber that was rather scattered, some of it uprooted.

As far as its appearance and actions are concerned, the Winter Wren of the southern Appalachians closely resembles its more northern relative. It differs in that the upper parts are distinctly darker, a characteristic common to other species limited in their distribution to these mountain ridges.

Newfoundland Winter Wren
Troglodytes troglodytes aquilonaris   (Burleigh and Peters)

GENERAL DISTRIBUTION: Breeds in Newfoundland, and winters south to southern Georgia.

STATUS IN GEORGIA: A scarce winter resident throughout the state.

This recently described race [Burleigh and Peters, 1948] has been taken at Athens (November 25 and December 8, 1945), Atlanta (November 27, 1946), and in Grady County (January 27, 1940). Further collecting will doubtless reveal its presence elsewhere in Georgia during the winter months.

HABITS AND RECOGNITION: The Winter Wren of Newfoundland closely resembles the southern Appalachian race, *pullus*, but differs in having the upperparts tinged with gray. It is noticeably darker, both above and below, than the Eastern Winter Wren, *hiemalis*. Its general appearance and actions are typically those of a Winter Wren, and specimens are necessary to identify it satisfactorily.

Eastern Bewick's Wren
Thryomanes bewickii bewickii   (Audubon)

GENERAL DISTRIBUTION: Breeds from southeastern Nebraska, northern Illinois, and southern Michigan south to northeastern Texas and northwestern Tennessee. Winters south to the Gulf Coast and northwestern Florida.

STATUS IN GEORGIA: A rare winter resident in the northern part of the state.

428

There are at present only four records for the occurrence of *bewickii* in Georgia. Specimens were taken at Athens, December 31, 1930, and December 2, 1933 (Burleigh); at Stone Mountain, October 2, 1948 (Griffin); and at Atlanta, November 27, 1949 (Griffin).

HABITS AND RECOGNITION: This midwestern subspecies of the Bewick's Wren winters largely to the west of Georgia, and consequently will never be of more than casual occurrence in the state. Its appearance and actions are so similar to the Appalachian race that specimens are necessary to identify it.

Appalachian Bewick's Wren
Thryomanes bewickii altus Aldrich

GENERAL DISTRIBUTION: Breeds from northern Ohio and northeastern Pennsylvania south to central Alabama and central South Carolina. Winters south to northeastern Texas and northern Florida.

STATUS IN GEORGIA: A fairly common summer resident in the mountain counties, and locally a fairly common winter resident throughout the rest of the state.

It has been noted during the summer months at Blue Ridge, Margret, Young Harris, Dahlonega, and Rich Mountain (Gilmer County); and there are definite breeding records for Blairville (six well-incubated eggs June 18, 1922) [Burleigh, 1925]; Varnell (eggs taken by Gerhardt April 21, 1854); Roswell (two nests reported found in 1924); and Augusta (two nests reported by Dr. Murphey) [Murphey, 1937].

South of its breeding range, the earliest transients in the fall appeared at Atlanta (Kirkwood), September 20 (1903); Athens, September 15 (1923); Milledgeville, August 30 (1939); Macon, September 5 (1929), and in Ben Hill County, October 7 (1939). The last in the spring were seen at Savannah, March 19 (1909); Ben Hill County, May 1 (1940); Cochran (Bleckley County), March 21 (1934); Macon, April 23 (1925); Milledgeville, March 16 (1938); Athens, April 10 (1926); and Atlanta, April 6 (1930). It has been noted once at Tifton, March 8, 1945 (Gaulding), and in Grady County, November 22, 1924, November 18, 1925, and January 31, 1926 (Stoddard).

A breeding male representing this race was taken at Blue Ridge, May 29, 1945; and transients identified as *altus* have been collected at Athens (October 21, 1928; September 29, 1929; April 8, 1935; and March 24, 1946); Stone Mountain (November 19, 1943, and November 16, 1947); Decatur (December 12, 1946, and January 9, 1949); Atlanta (February 1, 1946, and December 29, 1947); Trenton, Dade County, (December 16,

1946); Fitzgerald (March 4, 1945); Grady County (December 31, 1950); and Thomas County (March 3, 1952).

HABITS AND RECOGNITION: Within its breeding range in Georgia, the Bewick's Wren takes the place the House Wren occupies in the northeastern United States. Whenever I have seen one in the mountain counties—and it is fairly common there during the summer months—it has always been about farmhouses or at the edges of the towns. Here it nests in the barns or sheds and spends its days searching for its insect food in near-by thickets and hedgerows. Unlike the other wrens found in the state, it is a bird of the more open country; it consistently avoids the thick woods, and while attracted by cut-over areas, it prefers thickets and underbrush bordering open fields and country roads. In appearance it is a slender, brown wren, with a long white-tipped tail that is carried erect and that will at once distinguish it from either the larger Carolina Wren or the House Wren, which have rather short, inconspicuous tails. As a songster the Bewick's Wren is outstanding. Birds seen in Georgia in the early spring can frequently be found singing in a tree in a cotton field, or not infrequently on the top of a fence post, the loud, clear song being more suggestive of a sparrow than of a wren. This likeness is further emphasized by the deliberate manner in which the song is uttered, there being none of the nervous haste so evident in the songs of the other eastern wrens.

In Georgia, the nest is usually built in some crevice or cavity about a shed or barn and is frequently a rather bulky structure. The one that I found at Blairsville was on the sill above the door of an unoccupied house, and was substantially built of coarse twigs, dead leaves, grasses, weed stems and green moss, the hollow in the top well lined with chicken feathers, a little horse hair, and fragments of an old snakeskin. The two found by Dr. Murphey at Augusta were quite differently situated, one being "tucked away among exposed roots beneath the overhanging rim of a gulley, the other in the hollow trunk of a dead tree in an abandoned orchard."

Southern Carolina Wren
Thryothorus ludovicianus ludovicianus (Latham)

GENERAL DISTRIBUTION: Resident in the Upper and Lower Austral Zones from southeastern Nebraska, southern Iowa, Ohio, southern Pennsylvania, and the lower Hudson and Connecticut valleys south to central Texas, the Gulf states, and northwestern Florida.

STATUS IN GEORGIA: A common resident over the entire state except the extreme southeastern corner.

Specimens representing this race have been examined from a number of localities throughout Georgia, including Dalton, Blue Ridge, Dahlonega, Lula (Banks County), Athens, Stone Mountain, Atlanta, Washington, Milledgeville, Blakely, Dublin, Tifton, Newton, Cairo, Savannah, Blackbeard Island, and Hinesville.

Wherever it occurs it undoubtedly breeds, but actual breeding records are not numerous, and are as follows:

Rome: Three eggs, July 15, 1944 [Jones, 1947]; nest with well-grown young, April 19, 1953 [Dorsey, letter].

Margret, Fannin County: Four slightly incubated eggs, July 13, 1922 (Burleigh).

Young Harris, Towns County: Five fresh eggs, May 23, 1923; four fresh eggs, June 30, 1923; four slightly incubated eggs, May 2, 1924 (Burleigh).

Clayton, Rabun County: Well-grown young, April 13, 1922; five well-incubated eggs, June 12, 1922 (Burleigh).

Woodville, Greene County: Five well-incubated eggs, April 23, 1922 (D. Barrett); four slightly incubated eggs, June 8, 1922 (Burleigh).

Athens: Ten nests found from 1922 through 1928 between the extreme dates of March 31 (1927) (five partially incubated eggs) and July 30 (1926) (four fresh eggs) [Burleigh, 1938].

Atlanta: Nesting extremes March 3 (1939), one fresh egg, and July 30 (1939), six eggs [Griffin, 1940].

Lincoln County: Five well-fledged young, June 13, 1941 (Denton).

Columbia County: Newly hatched young, May 23, 1950 (Denton).

Fitzgerald: Five eggs, May 10, 1941 (Hopkins).

Baker County: One fresh egg, July 29, 1947 (Norris).

Grady County: Five fresh eggs, May 9 (Stoddard).

Savannah: Nesting extremes, April 8 (1916), five fresh eggs, and June 14 (1915), five slightly incubated eggs (Rossignol); April 9 (1949), five well-incubated eggs; and June 13 (1914), three fresh eggs (Erichsen).

Liberty County: Walthourville, five fresh eggs, April 15, 1913 (Erichsen).

Hinesville: Five eggs, June 6, 1944 [Grimm, 1940].

HABITS AND RECOGNITION: The Carolina Wren is *the* wren of Georgia. And of all the small birds occurring in the state, it is unquestionably the best known. This is due both to its abundance and general distribution and to the fact that it apparently enjoys the proximity of man and can be found about farms, in the smaller towns, and even, where encouraged by feeding tables and birdhouses, in the larger cities. Few birds are less exacting in their requirements. Given a stretch of woods, even of rather limited area, provided it has thickets, underbrush, and a suitable spot in which to nest, and there one will almost certainly find the Carolina Wren. A rugged mountain slope, a river bottom, a cypress swamp, or an island lying off the coast—all seem to meet with equal favor. As a result it is one of the few species that can be found throughout the year in every county in the state, and one that can be seen with little effort on the part of the most casual observer. This last is all the more true because of the irrepressible energy of this wren, its inherent curiosity in all that goes on about it, and its pleasing habit of singing regardless of time or season. The song most frequently uttered is loud and ringing, and on a cold winter day is a welcome sound when heard coming from an otherwise drab and uninviting land-scape. Little difficulty is usually experienced in seeing the Carolina Wren at close range, and it can be readily recognized by its relatively large size, stout build, and the rich reddish-brown color of the upperparts.

In nesting, this wren frequently selects such odd sites that one would suspect it of deliberately doing so in order to make life more interesting. Of the many nests that I have seen in Georgia, no two were situated exact-ly alike, and in a few instances the site chosen was unexpected, to say the least. The following breeding records from my field notes are given in more or less detail to illustrate the originality shown by different pairs in choosing what they considered a suitable spot in which to rear their young:

June 8, 1922, Woodville, Greene County: Nest "built in a small box lying on a shelf in an old barn."

June 12, 1922, Clayton, Rabun County: Nest "sunken flush with the ground in the top of a bank at the side of a road."

May 23, 1923, Young Harris, Towns County: Nest "six feet from the ground in the hollow end of an old log lying propped at an angle of 45 degrees facing up a mountainside."

June 30, 1923, Young Harris: Nest "in a corner of a shelf in a tent put up ten days ago and occupied by the camp cooks; the birds began building the same day the tent was put up, and while a little timid at first, are remark-ably tame now; the female shows lit-tle concern even at night when the lantern is lit and the two men read and smoke within a few feet of her; even when stroked on the back she continues to incubate her four eggs apparently undisturbed by this atten-tion!"

April 23, 1925, Athens: Nest "in an old rusty tin can nailed to the side of a shed."

July 30, 1926, Athens: Nest "well con-cealed in the top of a partly open sack of burr clover seed lying on the floor of a barn."

March 31, 1927, Athens: Nest "well con-cealed at the base of a thick clump of ferns growing in a pot that stood on the front porch of a house facing one of the main streets of the city."

June 23, 1928, Athens: "A rather unusual situation for a nest of this species seen today; for the past week a Ford touring car has been left parked dur-ing the day near a sawmill in a stretch of pine woods, and two days ago a pair of these birds started a nest under the hood of this car, between the steering rod and the engine itself; that night the car was driven away as usual, but was brought back the next morning, and the birds actually finished the nest, with the exception of lining the cavity, by evening!"

Regardless of where it is built, the nest is always bulky and substan-tial, the materials commonly used being weed stems, dead leaves, dry pine needles, and grasses. The entrance is at the side, never at the top, with the cavity inside well lined with fine grasses, feathers, horsehair, and, seem-ingly whenever available, fragments of old snakeskin.

[*Note:* The author concurs with the opinion of other investigators [Lowery, 1940, and Godfrey, 1946] that the Carolina Wren from the ex-treme northern range of the species, described as *Thryothorus ludovicianus carolinianus* (Wilson), is a valid race. Consequently the common names given by the A. O. U. committee to the two races occurring in Georgia are not suitable, and are here changed to conform to the ranges of three, rather than two, eastern subspecies.]

Florida Carolina Wren
Thryothorus ludovicianus miamensis Ridgway

GENERAL DISTRIBUTION: Resident in extreme southeastern Georgia and Florida.

STATUS IN GEORGIA: A common resident in the southeastern corner of the state.

Specimens of this Florida race have been taken in the Okefenokee Swamp (Billy's Island, October 15 and 16, 1931; Minne's Lake, October 16, 1931; Camp Cornelia, December 29, 1945; and Floyd's Island, December 30, 1945) and at Valdosta (November 22, 1929). Those from Valdosta are intermediate in their characters, but are closer to *miamensis* than to *ludovicianus.*

HABITS AND RECOGNITION: The Florida form of the Carolina Wren is characterized by being larger than the nominate race and noticeably darker both above and below. It is a common bird within its rather limited range, with essentially the same habits as *ludovicianus*. Like its more northern relative, it frequently nests in rather odd places, its originality in this respect being equally pronounced. Hebard [letter] states that a pair "raised a brood of five in a Camden County mail box in daily use," and that another pair built a nest "on the floor board next the clutch of a truck converted into a log loader in daily use in Charlton County."

Long-billed Marsh Wren
Telmatodytes palustris palustris (Wilson)

GENERAL DISTRIBUTION: Breeds on the Atlantic Coast from Rhode Island to Virginia. Winters on the Atlantic Coast to southern Florida, and on the Gulf Coast to Louisiana.

STATUS IN GEORGIA: A scarce transient in the northern part of the state and an equally scarce winter resident in the extreme southern counties.

Specimens representing this nominate race have been taken as follows: Sapelo Island (Brewster, 1888), Savannah (October 21, 1908, February 8, 1929), Hutchinsons Island (April 18, 1931), Charlton County (November 26, 1940, and January 16, 1941), Grady County (November 5, 1943, and January 30, 1949), and Athens (September 24 and 29, 1929, and September 24, 1930).

WOOD THRUSH

Hylocichla mustelina

This bird inhabited damp, shady, deciduous woods throughout which most of the trees were mature. Here, where sunlight reached the ground in little patches and where, with care, I could walk noiselessly, I watched the thrushes as they sang their lovely songs, built their nests, and fed their young. An interesting tree in which they sometimes perched was the fever-tree, or Georgia bark. The flowers (which show in my painting) were inconspicuous, but the clusters of pinkish white, tissue-paper-like leaves at the ends of some of the twigs were very showy.

Family Troglodytidae: WRENS

HABITS AND RECOGNITION: As specimens are necessary to identify satisfactorily the various races of the Marsh Wren, it is possible that further
collecting will show *palustris* to be a commoner transient in the state than
is now indicated. On its breeding grounds, it inhabits marshes overgrown
with cattails, reeds, and other aquatic vegetation, and it is in such spots
as this that it should be looked for in Georgia. The few noted at Athens
have been, without exception, in cattails in the open Sandy Creek bottoms.

Worthington's Marsh Wren
Telmatodytes palustris griseus   (Brewster)

GENERAL DISTRIBUTION: Resident on the Atlantic Coast from South
Carolina to northern Florida.

STATUS IN GEORGIA: An abundant permanent resident on the coast.

This race was described by Brewster in 1893 from specimens taken on
Sapelo Island in November. It has been reported from Myrtle Island, Tybee Island, Oysterbed Island, Wilmington Island, Blackbeard Island, St.
Catherine's Island, Brunswick, and St. Marys, and doubtless occurs wherever there is suitable marsh.

Breeding activities begin in April and are said to extend through July.
On Myrtle Island, in 1922, I found nests newly started or partially built
on April 30; and on Tybee Island, in 1923, one nest with five fresh eggs,
and four others with one to three fresh eggs on May 20. Denton reports a
rather early nest on Oysterbed Island that held one fresh egg on April 23,
1950.

In addition to those from Sapelo Island, specimens have been collected in McIntosh County in January and February (Brewster, 1888);
on Tybee Island, February 28, 1929 (Burleigh); and near Brunswick,
May 30, 1929 (Burleigh).

HABITS AND RECOGNITION: Worthington's Marsh Wren is the only race of
the Long-billed Marsh Wren that nests in the state. It is a common bird
within its rather limited habitat, occurring wherever salt marsh affords it
suitable protection and nesting sites. My experience with it as a breeding
bird has been limited to Tybee Island, and here I found it well distributed
and much in evidence. Quoting from field notes taken at the time:

> May 20, 1923, Tybee Island—Scattered pairs of these marsh wrens
> found breeding in the salt marsh bordering the island, the nests being
> in the narrow stretches of tall reeds bordering the open sloughs and
> tidal creeks; none were in the middle of these open marshes where
> the reeds were too low and the growth not as thick; individual pairs

were never within a hundred yards of each other, often farther apart; males singing throughout the day, often hovering singing over the marsh; each pair had four or five nests, including the one which held the eggs, all well built of fragments of reeds and marsh grass, globular, with the entrance at one side near the top; they were unlined unless they held eggs, when they were thickly lined with soft shreds of reeds and soft grasses, and in one case feathers; they were from one and a half to two and a half feet above the water, depending to some extent on the tide, often rather well concealed, but just as often somewhat conspicuous, firmly held in place in clumps of reeds, the green blades being interlaced through the outer part of the nest making it very secure; of some 30 nests examined five held eggs, all fresh, and a few of the others would probably eventually hold eggs; the majority, however, were dummy nests.

Griseus is an unusually well-marked race, the brown coloration of the other long-billed marsh wrens, both on the back and on the flanks, being replaced by pale gray, a character so distinct that it is possible to recognize this subspecies without actually collecting it.

Prairie Marsh Wren
Telmatodytes palustris dissaeptus　(Bangs)

GENERAL DISTRIBUTION:　Breeds from northern North Dakota, southern Manitoba, northern Minnesota, northern Wisconsin, northern Michigan, southern Ontario, southern Quebec, northern New York, Vermont, New Hampshire, and southern Maine south to eastern Kansas, Missouri, southern Illinois, southern Indiana, Ohio, western Pennsylvania, western Virginia, central New York, and Massachusetts. Winters almost to northern edge of the breeding range south to the Gulf Coast from Texas to southern Florida.

STATUS IN GEORGIA:　A scarce transient in the northern part of the state, and a rare winter resident in the Okefenokee Swamp.

Specimens of this interior race have been taken at Augusta, May 7, 1933 (Burleigh); Athens, October 11, 1928, October 6, 13, and 17, 1929, and May 10, 1930 (Burleigh); and in the Okefenokee Swamp (Floyd's Island Prairie), January 17 (Harper).

Murphey [1937] reports the Long-billed Marsh Wren as a fairly common winter resident at Augusta, and Griffin [1941] gives as extreme dates of occurrence for this species at Atlanta, April 11 (1931) and May 16 (1931); and August 16 (1936) and September 28 (1930). At Macon, where it is found during the winter months, extreme dates of occurrence are October 5 (1955) and May 14 (1932) (Johnston). Although no specimens are available, it is probable that many of the birds seen were Prairie Marsh Wrens.

HABITS AND RECOGNITION: On the basis of actual specimens taken, the Prairie Marsh Wren occurs more often as a transient in Georgia than do the other races of the species. Its summer home is in the fresh-water marshes of the prairie states, and it is in spots similar to them that it can be found in Georgia. The open Sandy Creek bottoms north of Athens are apparently well suited to its needs, and here an occasional bird can be seen each fall, and at infrequent intervals in the spring. Feeding as it does in the densest stretches of marsh grass and cattails, it could be easily overlooked were it not for its harsh, scolding notes protesting the invasion of its haunts. Although it is adept at keeping out of sight, its curiosity is nevertheless easily aroused, and if not alarmed, it will appear momentarily in the top of a cattail or tall reed to see what has disturbed it. In the fall it has appeared at Athens as early as September 23 (1923), but has not been seen later than October 21 (1926).

Wayne's Marsh Wren
Telmatodytes palustris waynei   Dingle and Sprunt

GENERAL DISTRIBUTION: Breeds in the coastal marshes from Virginia to southern North Carolina. Winters south to Georgia, and possibly northern Florida.

STATUS IN GEORGIA: Apparently of casual occurrence on the coast during the winter.

Tomkins [1936] has taken one specimen of this race near Savannah (Oysterbed Island, October 1, 1932), and further collecting should reveal its presence elsewhere on the coast.

HABITS AND RECOGNITION: Wayne's Marsh Wren is described as being similar to the Long-billed Marsh Wren, *Telmatodytes palustris palustris,* but smaller and much darker [Dingle and Sprunt, *Auk,* 49:1932, 454]. Within its rather limited range it is confined to the coastal marshes, and its actions are said to differ in no way from the other races of its species.

Short-billed Sedge Wren
Cistothorus platensis stellaris   (Naumann)

GENERAL DISTRIBUTION: Breeds from southeastern Saskatchewan, central Manitoba, southern Ontario, and southern Maine south to eastern

Kansas, central Missouri, central Indiana, and eastern Maryland. Winters from southern Illinois and southern New Jersey to southern Texas, the Gulf Coast, and southern Florida.

STATUS IN GEORGIA: A fairly common but rather local transient and winter resident throughout the state, being most numerous on the coast. There is evidence, inconclusive at present, that it breeds sparingly at Athens.

Earliest transients in the fall were recorded at Savannah, September 27 (1924); Camden County, September 30 (1948); Grady County, October 18 (1924); Fitzgerald, October 11 (1940); and Atlanta, November 6 (1932). Worthington found this species abundant near Darien in the winter of 1890, taking sixteen specimens on Sapelo Island between January 1 and February 22. It is also reported common in winter at St. Marys. Hebard [1941] states that this little wren arrives in the Okefenokee Swamp in November and remains in small numbers through February, and that it is common then in the fields at Coleraine. Murphey [1937] considers it fairly common during the winter months at Augusta, where it frequently is seen as late as the middle of May. The last in the spring were noted at Cumberland Island on April 4 (1902); Savannah, May 8 (1926); Camden County, May 24 (1947); Fitzgerald, May 5 (1940); Macon, May 12 (1928); and Atlanta, May 11 (1917).

At Athens [Burleigh, 1938], the exact status of the Sedge Wren is still rather indefinite, for while it has been found throughout the year in the Sandy Creek bottoms, and possibly breeds there, a nest has never been found. For several years, its appearance there the latter part of July aroused the suspicion that it nested close by, although there was also the possibility that it was a much earlier fall transient than was suspected. Much of these open bottoms are cut over at frequent intervals for hay, making it difficult to study such a species as this for any length of time. On June 13, 1928, a singing male was found in a wide stretch of reeds and marsh grass, but a careful search revealed nothing but a partially built nest. At this late date the young could be well fledged and, for the time being at least, could be almost anywhere in these bottoms, and finding the empty nest, with the marsh grass as thick as it was, would be almost a hopeless task.

Four days later, on June 17, the male was singing at the same spot, and a second bird, probably the female, was seen. It skulked about, scolding, for a few minutes, but soon disappeared and did not reappear. Unfortunately, two days later this stretch of the Sandy Creek bottoms was cut for hay, and the wrens, of course, were not seen again. Considering these circumstances, there is reason to assume that a pair of these birds nested there that year, but as this is so far south of the accepted breeding range of this species, more conclusive evidence will be necessary. The fact remains, however, that the Short-billed Sedge Wren is a characteristic bird of these bottom lands in the late summer, males singing vigorously until the latter part of August. During an occasional winter, these birds are fairly common near Athens, but usually relatively few are seen from the latter part of November until the first of April.

HABITS AND RECOGNITION: Within its breeding range, the Short-billed Sedge Wren is a bird of damp meadows and open marshes, but during the winter months it appears to be far less partial to the vicinity of water. At this season it can be commonly found in dry, broom-sedge fields, and in other open spots where the grass is thick enough to afford it satisfactory cover. Shy and retiring by nature, it can easily be overlooked, and unless actually searched for, it will long go undetected. If its haunts are invaded, however, it will, when alarmed, fly for a short distance over the top of the grass, its flight appearing slow and weak, drop suddenly, and not be seen again. It is one of the smallest of the wrens, and as it is rarely, if ever, found in the cattail growths frequented by its larger relative, the Long-billed Marsh Wren, the brief glimpses one has of it in its preferred habitat should serve to identify it.

Mockingbirds and Thrashers: *Family Mimidae*

Eastern Mockingbird
Mimus polyglottos polyglottos (Linnaeus)

GENERAL DISTRIBUTION: Resident from eastern Nebraska, southern Iowa, Illinois, Indiana, Ohio, and Maryland south to eastern Texas, the Gulf Coast, and southern Florida, north casually to New York and Massachusetts.

STATUS IN GEORGIA: Resident and common throughout all of the state except the mountain counties, where it apparently occurs in rather small numbers.

The Mockingbird is common and generally distributed over all of Georgia north to Atlanta, Athens, and Augusta. It is reported as breeding to a limited extent at Toccoa, Canton, Rising Fawn, and Ellijay; but in the extreme northeastern corner of the state it is a rare summer resident. A single bird was seen at Young Harris, Towns County, March 11, 1922, but it is not definitely known to breed there.

Despite its general abundance, actual breeding records are limited at present to the following:

Rome: Nest with well-grown young, April 25, 1941 [Jones, 1947]; nest with four eggs, June 7, 1953 [Dorsey, letter].

Atlanta: Nesting extremes, three eggs, March 2, 1932, (Dobbs and Greene); three eggs, July 25, 1937 (Griffin) [Griffin, 1940].

Athens: Nesting extremes, nest with well-grown young, April 13 (1927); three incubated eggs, July 23 (1926) [Burleigh, 1938].

Richmond County: Nesting extremes, three eggs, March 20, 1945; three eggs, July 20, 1947 (Denton).

Waynesboro: Three fresh eggs, March 9, 1932 [Stevenson, 1932].

Macon: Four newly hatched young, May 10, 1930; four eggs, May 7, 1931 (Denton).

Columbus: Nest with small young, April 14, 1946 [Straw, 1947].

Fitzgerald: Nesting extremes (sixty-five nests), three eggs, April 6 (1941); one egg, August 15 (1940) [Norris and Hopkins, letter].

Okefenokee Swamp: Four fresh eggs, July 13, 1942 [Hebard, letter].

Savannah: Nesting extremes, four fresh eggs, April 24 (1913); four fresh eggs, June 4 (1910) (Rossignol); three eggs, March 27 (1938); three fresh eggs, July 12 (1914) (Erichsen).

Allenhurst: Four eggs, April 9, 1913; three almost fully fledged young, August 6, 1913 (Erichsen).

Hinesville: Five eggs, April 14, 1942 [Grimm, 1946].

HABITS AND RECOGNITION: The Mockingbird is unquestionably the best-known and certainly the most appreciated bird in Georgia. Found everywhere except in the business districts of the larger cities, it is the one bird that is seen and heard almost daily by the average person. Given thickets or underbrush for shelter and nesting sites, there one will find this popular songster, whether it be in the residential section of a town, about a farm, or in the more open country far removed from man's activities. Thick woods are not to its liking, but clearings and slashings that follow logging operations soon attract one or more pairs.

In appearance, it must be considered one of Georgia's more plainly attired birds, but what it lacks in that respect is more than compensated for by its ability as a songster and mimic. Its own song is vigorous and attractive, but its fame is justifiably based on its apparent delight in imitating perfectly the songs of other birds. An occasional individual appears far more skilled in this pastime than do others—probably an older bird that has developed its technique over a period of years. One spring morning at Savannah, a Mockingbird was heard giving an exceptionally fine performance as it sang from the top of a large water oak, uttering in quick sequence the loud rattle of a Belted Kingfisher, the "phoebe," six times repeated, of a Phoebe, the call of a Flicker, the soft warble of a Bluebird, and finally the broken song of a Red-eyed Vireo. Almost as gifted was another bird heard at Athens on an afternoon late in September, which imitated first a Bluebird, then the loud, clear whistle of a Cardinal, and followed this with the harsh, rolling call of a Red-headed Woodpecker. Except for an interval in late summer when none are heard, the Mockingbird sings with vigor and abandon from early February until the latter part of October. During the winter months, it is quiet and inconspicuous, so much so that, were it not for the occasional harsh notes that it utters, it would go largely unnoticed then.

For nesting, a bush or sapling in a thicket or stretch of underbrush is selected, and a bulky nest is built of rootlets, weed stems, grasses, and dead leaves, lined with fine rootlets and horse hair. The height from the ground varies from three to ten feet, the average nest being within four feet of the ground. In Georgia, two, and possibly three, broods are reared each year, for fresh eggs can be found as early as the latter part of March and as late as the middle of July. Four eggs are normally laid, at times but three, and, rarely, five.

Catbird
Dumetella carolinensis (Linnaeus)

GENERAL DISTRIBUTION: Breeds from central British Columbia, southern Alberta, central Saskatchewan, southern Manitoba, southern Ontario, southern Quebec, and Nova Scotia south to western Washington, Oregon, northern Utah, New Mexico, eastern Texas, central Alabama, southern Georgia, and central Florida. Winters from South Carolina and the Gulf Coast to the Bahamas and Cuba, and through Mexico to Panama.

STATUS IN GEORGIA: A common summer resident and a scarce winter resident in the northern part of the state, and a common winter resident and uncommon summer resident south of the fall line.

Although an occasional bird lingers throughout the winter, the Catbird is usually not seen at Athens or Atlanta before early April or after the latter part of October. Extreme dates of occurrence for Atlanta are April 3 (1893) and October 23 (1945). At Athens, it was noted on three occasions during the winter in the course of field work carried on from 1920 to 1930, single birds being seen January 22, 1921, December 4, 1927, and January 29, 1929. Otherwise, extreme dates of occurrence there were April 9 (1922) and November 4 (1920) [Burleigh, 1938]. Murphey [1937] considers it a common resident species at Augusta. At Macon, it winters in small numbers, but is usually not seen before April 2 (1922) or later than October 19 (1923). Fleetwood [1946] reports a single winter record for Jones County (East Juliette), one bird being seen there December 23, 1945. In Grady County it usually appears in September, the earliest date of arrival being September 16 (1949), and lingers in the spring until early May (May 5, 1940). A rather unexpected record is that of two birds seen, July 29, 1948, indicating the possibility that this species breeds sparingly in the county (Stoddard, MS). It is reported as common during the winter at Savannah, Hinesville, Darien, in the Okefenokee Swamp, and in Grady County.

During the summer, it occurs rarely, if at all, in the southwestern corner of the state, but, elsewhere, it nests from the mountains to the coast. Definite breeding localities are as follows:

Rome: Bird incubating, May 22 to June 2, 1946 [Jones, 1947].

Margret, Fannin County: Three fresh eggs, June 9, 1921 (Burleigh).

Young Harris, Towns County: Two incubated eggs, July 4, 1923 (Burleigh).

Athens: Nesting extremes (fourteen nests), four fresh eggs, May 6 (1921); two slightly incubated eggs, August 1 (1929) [Burleigh, 1938].

Atlanta: Nesting extremes, four fresh eggs, May 2, 1914 (Mills); four eggs, July 29, 1937 (Griffin) [Griffin, 1940].

Fitzgerald: Nesting extremes (ten nests), three eggs May 13 (1941); three eggs August 2 (1940) (Norris and Hopkins).

Hutchinsons Island, Chatham County: Nest with eggs, June, 1927 (Tomkins).

HABITS AND RECOGNITION: The Catbird is a familiar bird throughout its extensive breeding range, for it does not hesitate to nest in shrubbery about houses, and is therefore in evidence every summer day on the farms, in the smaller towns, and not infrequently in the residential sections of the larger cities. Its plumage, dark gray with the exception of the glossy black crown and reddish under tail coverts, would tend to make it an inconspicuous inhabitant of the tangled thickets and dense underbrush it prefers were it not for other outstanding characteristics. Its close relationship to the wrens is shown by its restless energy and by its curiosity toward all that goes on about it. Arouse its interest and it will at once appear in the top of a near-by bush, nervously raising and lowering its tail and uttering the mewing note so suggestive of a cat. If alarmed, it will temporarily disappear from sight, but will soon reappear, and will remain on the scene until the intruder has gone. Like the Mockingbird, it makes up for its sober colors by its ability as a songster. The song is frequently given from the upper branches of a bush or sapling, but as often as not will be heard emerging from a dense thicket. It is a rather hurried, musical outburst that will continue for minutes at a time, and consists of varied trills, warbles, and mellow whistles that cannot fail to attract attention. To some extent the Catbird is an able mimic, the usual song including at least a few notes of other birds found in the neighborhood.

In Georgia, breeding activities begin in late April, and apparently two, and possibly three, broods are reared each year, for fresh eggs can be found from early May until late July. The first nests hold four, rarely three, or occasionally only two, dark-blue eggs. The nest is built in a bush or sapling, varying in height from three to six feet from the ground, and is a compact structure of twigs, weed stems, rootlets, dead leaves, and shreds of bark, well cupped and lined with fine rootlets. It is extremely rare for any bird to use the same nest twice; therefore, one seen at Athens on July 21, 1924, with two slightly incubated eggs, was of unusual interest. This nest had been built early in May, three eggs laid, and then, for some unknown reason, deserted. The eggs remained untouched, and when the female selected this nest for another brood, she merely laid a few grasses and weed stems over these eggs, only partially concealing them, and then laid the two eggs that constituted her last brood for that year. One can only surmise that the hot summer days of late July were responsible for this seeming lack of ambition on the part of this Catbird.

Eastern Brown Thrasher
Toxostoma rufum rufum (Linnaeus)

GENERAL DISTRIBUTION: Breeds from southern Manitoba, northern Michigan, southern Ontario, southern Quebec, and northern Maine south to eastern Louisiana, the Gulf Coast, and Florida. Winters from southeastern Missouri and North Carolina south to central Texas and southern Florida.

STATUS IN GEORGIA: A common resident throughout the state, although less numerous during the winter months north of the fall line.

The Brown Thrasher is one of the most common birds in Georgia and is uniformly distributed throughout the state, being found during the breeding season in such widely diversified spots as the top of Brasstown Bald (the highest point in Georgia), in thickets and underbrush at the edge of cotton fields throughout the Piedmont, in the Okefenokee Swamp, and on the islands off the coast.

It has been noted in every county, and doubtless breeds in all of them. Definite breeding records, however, are limited to the following localities:

Grady County: Fresh eggs as early as April 6 (1940) (Stoddard).

Liberty County: Four eggs, April 20, 1913; four eggs, June 20, 1913 (Erichsen).

Savannah: Nesting extremes, three fresh eggs, April 8 (1916); four slightly incubated eggs, June 4 (1911) (Rossignol); three eggs, July 8 (1931) (Erichsen).

Fitzgerald: Nesting extremes (forty-six nests), one egg, April 5 (1941); four young, July 25 (1940) (Norris and Hopkins).

Richmond County: Three eggs, March 28, 1948; four fresh eggs, May 7, 1952 (Denton).

Athens: Nesting extremes (thirty-four nests), three fresh eggs, March 27 (1925); three incubated eggs, July 23 (1926) [Burleigh, 1938].

Atlanta: Nesting extremes, three eggs, April 5 (1932) (Greene); two eggs, July 24 (1938) (Griffin) [Griffin, 1940].

Young Harris: Three slightly incubated eggs, June 24, 1922 (Burleigh).

Rome: Five eggs, April 17, 1936; young, June 9, 1946 [Jones, 1947]; four eggs, April 2, 1953 [Dorsey, letter].

443

Bent [1948] cites as egg dates for Georgia "25 records, April 16 to June 20; 18 records, April 22 to May 5."

HABITS AND RECOGNITION: The Brown Thrasher is the state bird of Georgia, and this distinction is well deserved. Few species have a wider or more uniform distribution in the state, and, as it seems to prefer the proximity of man, it is well known and familiar to the average person. With its rich brown plumage and heavily streaked underparts it presents an attractive appearance, but its popularity among bird enthusiasts is due to its outstanding ability as a singer. With the first warm days of spring, the thrasher ceases to be a quiet, inconspicuous inhabitant of the thickets and briar patches, and, perched in the top of the tallest tree in the vicinity, proceeds to give its clear, rich song that cannot fail to impress even the casual listener. It is considered by many to be equal to that of the Mockingbird, and some ornithologists even go so far as to call it superior. Dr. Eugene E. Murphey, writing of the birds of the Augusta region, has this to say of the thrasher's song [1937]: "Much of the reclame which has fallen to the Mockingbird is really due to the unperceived efforts of the Brown Thrasher. It is the opinion of many ornithologists that the song of the Thrasher is richer, fuller, and definitely more melodious than that of *polyglottos,* in which opinion the writer wholeheartedly concurs. The native passing beneath some tall tree from the top of which a thrasher is pouring forth his exquisite song, exclaims, 'How beautifully the Mockingbird is singing today!' and goes blissfully on his way oblivious to the fact that he has been listening to quite a different bird."

As two, and possibly three, broods are reared in Georgia each year, the Brown Thrasher is inspired to sing freely from February until July. Early August finds it silent, and other than its explosive note of alarm, it is quiet then and relatively inconspicuous. Because of its size, however, and its habit of scratching vigorously as it searches for food on the ground, it is a bird that is not easily overlooked. The nest is built in a bush or sapling, usually from three to six feet from the ground, and is normally well concealed in a thicket or stretch of underbrush. It is a rather bulky structure, composed of twigs, weed stems, rootlets, dead leaves, and shreds of bark, the well-defined hollow in the top being lined with fine rootlets. Normally three or four eggs are laid, although not infrequently late nests in July hold but two. Few birds show more concern over their eggs or young than does the Brown Thrasher. Any intruder, whether it be a snake, a cat, or a man, is savagely attacked if the nest is threatened, and more often than not the boldness of the birds saves their brood from destruction.

Thrushes and Bluebirds: *Family Turdidae*

Eastern Robin
Turdus migratorius migratorius   Linnaeus

GENERAL DISTRIBUTION: Breeds from northwestern Alaska, northern Mackenzie, northern Manitoba, and northern Quebec south to central Alberta, Kansas, Illinois, Indiana, Ohio, Pennsylvania, and New Jersey. Winters from central Kansas, the Ohio Valley, and eastern Massachusetts to the Gulf Coast and southern Florida, and casually to Nuevo León, Mexico.

STATUS IN GEORGIA: A common transient and winter resident throughout the state.

From the latter part of October until late March, flocks of robins are common throughout Georgia wherever suitable habitat affords food and shelter for these birds. The subspecies are so similar in appearance, however, that only on the basis of actual specimens can their distribution and relative abundance be determined. Consequently, although the nominate race *migratorius* is very probably of general occurrence in the state during the winter months, it has, up to the present time, been definitely recorded from only a few localities. Specimens representing *migratorius* have been taken as follows, and indicate its wide range as a winter resident:

Athens: Seventeen specimens between the dates of October 25 (1929) and April 7 (1929).

Atlanta: Seven specimens between the dates of November 20 (1949) and April 23 (1947).

Decatur: Six specimens between the dates of November 22 (1946) and March 18 (1947).

Lexington: Two specimens, November 8, 1945.

Lithonia: One male, February 24, 1946.

Vienna: One female, March 20, 1947.

Hinesville: One female, February 26, 1946.

HABITS AND RECOGNITION: Although flocks of robins can be seen almost anywhere in Georgia during the winter, they are far more numerous then south of the fall line. Stoddard, in his manuscript on the birds of Grady County, states that this species is an abundant winter resident in that part of the state. His earliest record in the fall is October 16 (1949), his latest in the spring, March 31 (1940). Erichsen [MS] gives almost the same migration extremes for Chatham County, October 20 (1922) and March 30 (1915), while in Camden County Hebard [letter] states that flocks are always present in the spring through early April and have been noted as late as April 23 (1949). At Athens, I noted only an occasional flock from the latter part of November until the middle of February. During mild winters, flocks of varying size appeared in January, but as a usual thing it was only in late February and March, and again the latter part of October and early November that these birds were present in any numbers.

In migration, they can be found both in the scattered stretches of woods and in the open fields, and being restless and noisy, are not easily overlooked. Having a decided preference for the fleshy berries of such trees as the dogwood and black gum, they are more apt to frequent wooded areas in the fall, and to resort to the fields and pastures in the spring. Possibly because of its large size the fruit of the chinaberry is usually ignored in the fall, but in the early spring when other such food is no longer available, chinaberry trees can frequently be found filled with hungry robins.

Southern Robin
Turdus migratorius achrusterus   (Batchelder)

GENERAL DISTRIBUTION: Breeds from southern Oklahoma, southern Missouri, southern Illinois, Indiana, southeastern Kentucky, central West Virginia, eastern Tennessee, northern Georgia, western North Carolina, and central Maryland south to central Texas, northern Louisiana, northern Mississippi, southern Georgia, and central South Carolina, casually to northern Florida and the coast of the Carolinas. Winters in the southern half of its breeding range south to southern Texas and the Florida Keys.

STATUS IN GEORGIA: To some extent a permanent resident throughout the state, breeding commonly to the fall line at Augusta, Macon, and Columbus, and locally as far south as Waycross.

On the basis of actual specimens it would appear that the robins nesting in the northern part of the state largely desert their breeding grounds in the fall and do not reappear until early February. There are a few late November and December records for Decatur, in DeKalb County, but otherwise *achrusterus* has not been recorded north of the fall line before February 4 (1946) or later than early October. Even in the southern part of the state, it is uncommon during the winter months, few specimens taken then representing this southern race. From the large series of robins examined, that were collected in Georgia, the following specimens of *achrusterus* are listed to show its distribution in the state:

Brasstown Bald, Towns County: An immature male, July 16, 1908.

Athens: Eight specimens between the dates of February 4 (1946) and June 8 (1945).

Atlanta: Eight specimens between the dates of February 17 (1947) and July 13 (1947).

Decatur: Thirteen specimens between the dates of February 22 (1947) and December 23 (1946).

Stone Mountain: One male, July 13, 1946.

Dacula: One male, February 12, 1946.

Lavonia: One male, March 6, 1946.

Irwinton: One male, January 29, 1946.

Statenville: One male, March 23, 1947.

Grady County: One male, November 11, 1948.

Hinesville: One female, January 25, 1946.

446

Family Turdidae: THRUSHES & BLUEBIRDS

Originally limited as a breeding bird to the mountain counties, the robin has extended its range southward until at the present time it is known to nest almost to the Florida line. According to Dr. W. H. LaPrade, it nested for the first time at Canton (south of the mountains) in 1905 and in Atlanta in 1914. Since then it has gradually increased its numbers throughout the city until at present it is one of Atlanta's most abundant breeding birds.

Griffin [1940] gives as nesting extremes for the Atlanta region, April 2 (1938), two eggs; and August 8 (1939); four fresh eggs. At Athens, the first evidence of its nesting in the city was the presence of two well-grown young of the year feeding on a lawn on Milledge Avenue on June 7, 1925. The first actual nest to be recorded, however, was one found May 7, 1927, with four fresh eggs [Burleigh, 1938]. As in Atlanta, it gradually became more plentiful as the years went by, and at present it is a common bird throughout the summer months. Murphey [1937] states that the Robin has nested at Augusta since 1929, while at Macon, young just out of the nest were seen by J. Fred Denton in August, 1932 [Greene, 1937]. Denton [1950] reports this species "just beginning to invade the smaller towns" south of Augusta. He observed four young just out of the nest at Thomson on June 22, 1949.

The southernmost breeding record is that of a nest found at Waycross in 1937 [Flagg, 1937]. It was twenty feet from the ground, at the outer end of a limb of a longleaf pine, and because of its inaccessibility its contents could not be ascertained. However, from June 1 through June 19, the female was seen incubating and later carrying food to the nest, so there is little question but that the young were successfully reared. Although not definitely recorded as actually breeding, it is probable that the robin now nests, at least sparingly, at Fitzgerald, birds being observed there by Norris on May 25, 1939, and by Hopkins on May 30, 1941.

In the extreme northern part of the state it has been reported as nesting at Rome (nests with eggs, March 25 through May 30, 1953); Chatsworth; Dahlonega, Young Harris (two fresh eggs June 19, 1929); Clayton (two small young July 24, 1921; three slightly incubated eggs April 13, 1922); and Dillard (four fresh eggs April 14, 1922).

HABITS AND RECOGNITION: Few birds have accepted the proximity of man to the degree that the robin has, but this is not surprising, since the settlement of this country has produced an environment well suited to the requirements of this familiar bird. Shunning the thicker stretches of woods, it has in past years been found in the more open spots where fire or other natural causes have thinned out or eliminated not only the larger trees but much of the undergrowth as well. The appearance of cultivated fields and pastures resulted in a marked increase in the breeding population of robins throughout the once forested areas of the country, and it was not long before these birds were a familiar sight in the towns and even the larger cities. In Georgia, it has been interesting to note in recent years the preference the robin has shown for the towns and cities as it gradually extended its breeding range southward over the state. At Athens, where it now nests commonly, it is rarely observed during the summer months beyond the city limits, and the same observation is to a large extent valid for Atlanta and for Macon. The lawns and shrubbery in the residential sections furnish both food and shelter and the larger shade trees nesting sites, natural hazards have been reduced to a minimum, and the robin has wholeheartedly accepted these favorable conditions. Under such circumstances it is not to be wondered that this bird is so well known to even the average person, at least by name, even if it is not at once recognized when seen.

In Georgia, the robin rears two and possibly three broods a year, for fresh eggs can be found as early as the first week in April and as late as the first week in August. The nest is usually built in a crotch at the outer end of a limb of the largest tree available, varying in height from ten to twenty feet from the ground, and is a compact structure of weed stems, grasses, and mud, deeply cupped and well lined with fine grasses. Three or four light-blue eggs are normally laid.

The Southern Robin has long been recognized by taxonomists as a well-marked race, being smaller and paler than the birds occurring farther north.

Newfoundland Robin
Turdus migratorius nigrideus   Aldrich and Nutt

GENERAL DISTRIBUTION: Breeds in Newfoundland and eastern Labrador. Winters south to the Gulf Coast and southern Georgia.

STATUS IN GEORGIA: A fairly common transient in the northern part of the state and a winter resident south of the fall line.

Since this far northern race is an abundant bird throughout its breeding range it was felt that, although as yet unrecorded in Georgia, it should occur at least casually as a transient. Accordingly a careful study was made of the flocks of robins that were found about Athens throughout February and March in 1946, and this assumption was soon verified. It was of interest to note that these blackish-backed robins were never found in flocks, but as single birds, rarely two or three, associated with flocks of *migratorius*. When feeding in an open field or pasture, *nigrideus* could, within reasonable range, be distinguished from both *migratorius* and *achrusterus* by its perceptibly darker back, this being especially noticeable in occasional individuals where wear had eliminated completely the brown tips that cover the feathers of the back during the fall and winter months. In all, twelve specimens of this race were taken at Athens, males on February 2, 9, 11, 16, and 22, and March 3, 10, 12, 19, 24, and 28, and a female on March 24. [Burleigh, 1947.]

The following year, in March, 1947, robins about Atlanta were given the same careful scrutiny, and four specimens of *nigrideus* were collected from flocks found in the open fields and pastures. All were males, two being taken at Atlanta on March 11 and two at Decatur (DeKalb County) on March 12 and April 12. [Burleigh, 1948].

Fleetwood [1948] collected a partially albino male in Charlton County on December 18, 1947, and Stoddard has taken specimens of this race in Grady County on November 2 and 19, 1949, and January 28, 1951. Thus it appears that *nigrideus* winters to some extent in the southern part of the state. Norris [letter] reports a specimen of *nigrideus* taken at Tifton on March 10, 1952.

HABITS AND RECOGNITION: As is the case with most subspecies, the casual observer will notice little about the Black-backed Robin that will distinguish it in the field. In general appearance and actions it is merely a robin and, as such, given but a passing glance. In the spring it is possible to recognize the male by its black back, but in the fall and early winter this character is absent, and specimens are necessary to identify this race satisfactorily.

Wood Thrush
Hylocichla mustelina (Gmelin)

GENERAL DISTRIBUTION: Breeds from southern South Dakota, central Minnesota, central Wisconsin, southeastern Ontario, and southern Maine south to eastern Texas, the Gulf Coast, and northern Florida. Winters from southern Mexico to Costa Rica, casually north to southern Florida.

STATUS IN GEORGIA: A common summer resident over the entire state.

The Wood Thrush is a bird of the wooded ravines and thicker woods, and in such situations can be found from the mountain counties to the Florida line. It is reported common during the summer months at numerous localities throughout the state, including Chatsworth, Young Harris, Dahlonega, Athens, Atlanta, Columbus, Americus, Blakely, Newton, Thomasville, Savannah, Darien, and Seminole County.

Earliest arrivals in the spring were noted at Savannah, March 28

(1917); Grady County, March 23 (1937); Fitzgerald, April 10 (1942); Americus, April 12 (1942); Columbus, March 31 (1946); Macon, March 25 (1954); Milledgeville, March 25 (1938); Atlanta, March 27 (1944); Dalton, April 3 (1944); Athens, April 1 (1929); and Augusta, April 3 (1945). The last in the fall were seen at Atlanta, October 29 (1953); Athens, October 18 (1925); Milledgeville, October 7 (1942); Macon, October 16 (1920); Augusta, October 8 (1944); Fitzgerald, October 7 (1939); Grady County, October 22 (1940); and Savannah, October 13 (1923).

It doubtless nests wherever found during the summer, but definite breeding records are at present limited to the following localities:

Rome: Four young left nests July 7, 1940, and April 30, 1945 [Jones, 1947].

Young Harris: May 11, 1922, four incubated eggs; June 15, 1922, four incubated eggs (Burleigh).

Athens: Nesting extremes (sixteen nests); three slightly incubated eggs, April 26 (1922); two incubated eggs, July 22 (1924) [Burleigh, 1938].

Atlanta: Nesting extremes, two young, May 6 (1939) (Wolfe); three eggs, July 22 (1939) (Griffin) [Griffin, 1940].

Augusta: Two fresh eggs, May 18, 1945 (Denton).

Columbus: Four eggs, April 30, 1946 [Straw, 1947].

Fitzgerald: Two eggs, May 19, 1941; three eggs, June 27, 1941 (Norris and Hopkins).

Grady County: Two eggs, July 28, 1924; small young, August 13, 1924 (Stoddard).

Thomas County: Female incubating, April 25, 1949 (Stoddard).

Camden County: Three eggs, May 11, 1943 (Hebard).

Savannah: Three incubated eggs, May 13, 1907; three slightly incubated eggs, May 7, 1909 (Rossignol); three slightly incubated eggs, June 29, 1924 (Erichsen).

HABITS AND RECOGNITION: The Wood Thrush is not an especially shy bird, but as its days are spent in thick underbrush, it must be looked for to be seen. In common with the other thrushes of this genus it seems to dislike direct sunlight, rarely leaving the dense shade of the thickets it inhabits. This attitude is reflected in its activities, for during much of the day it is quiet and inconspicuous, and only in the early morning hours and again in the late afternoon can its song usually be heard. It is generally agreed that the liquid, unhurried song of the Wood Thrush is equalled by few other birds, and when heard at twilight on a summer evening, it leaves an impression not soon forgotten.

Much of the food of this thrush is obtained on the ground, and if the bird is approached while feeding, it will fly to the limb of a near-by tree and protest with an emphatic, distinctive note that has been aptly described as "pit, pit, pit." It does not display the mannerisms that distinguish the other members of its genus, for it sits quietly, without any movement of the tail or wings. It can be easily recognized, however, by its relatively large size, bright cinnamon-brown upperparts, and heavily marked breast.

Herbert L. Stoddard, Sr.

Typical southern Georgia river scene.

The nest is built in the top of a sapling or on the horizontal limb of a larger tree, and varies in height from five to eighteen feet from the ground. It is compactly constructed of weed stems, grasses, dead leaves, and mud, the well-defined hollow in which the eggs are laid being invariably lined with fine rootlets. Pieces of paper and bits of cloth seem to have an irresistible appeal, and are often used. In Georgia, two, and possibly three, broods are reared each year, as fresh eggs can be found from the last of April until almost the end of July. Usually four, rarely three, greenish-blue eggs are laid, although late nests may hold but two.

Where conditions are favorable, the Wood Thrush nests to some extent in the cities and larger towns, and here it leads much the same life as does the Robin. It is probable that this radical departure from its usual habits is of recent origin, and if so, this fine songster may eventually be much commoner than it now is in Georgia's cities. Dr. Murphey [1937], in writing of the Wood Thrush at Augusta, says: "In the city the bird loses much of its timidity and may be seen, particularly in the afternoon, busily engaged upon the lawns, and coming out from the bushes to bathe under automatic sprinklers and in bird baths with every evidence of enjoyment, even though the family may be seated a short distance away."

Eastern Hermit Thrush
Hylocichla guttata faxoni   Bangs and Penard

GENERAL DISTRIBUTION: Breeds from Yukon, Mackenzie, northern Manitoba, and Quebec south to central Alberta, southern Saskatchewan, central Minnesota, northern Michigan, Ontario, Connecticut, and Long Island, and in the mountains of Pennsylvania and Maryland. Winters from the lower Delaware and Ohio valleys to Texas, the Gulf Coast, and Florida, and casually north on the Atlantic Coast to Massachusetts.

STATUS IN GEORGIA: A fairly common winter resident throughout the state.

Earliest arrivals in the fall were noted at Athens, October 14 (1929); Atlanta, October 10 (1953); Macon, October 10 (1931); Americus, October 25 (1941); Fitzgerald, October 25 (1941); Grady County, October 18 (1942); Savannah, October 17 (1925); Hinesville, November 5 (1944); and St. Marys, October 28 (1905).

At Athens, it was found to be a fairly common winter resident, being frequently seen in the larger wooded areas from the latter part of October until the middle of April [Burleigh, 1938]. At Augusta, Murphey [1937] reports it common in winter, appearing in late October and being noted in greatest numbers from the first week in December until the end of March.

Hebard [1941] considers it common in the Okefenokee Swamp throughout the winter, and Stoddard gives it the same status in Grady County.

The last Hermit Thrushes in the spring were seen at Hinesville, April 18 (1942); Savannah, April 29 (1910); Grady County, April 21 (1946); Fitzgerald, April 2 (1939); Americus, April 12 (1942); Columbus, April 14 (1946); Macon, May 4 (1944); Milledgeville, April 26 (1938); Augusta, April 14 (1945); Athens, April 26 (1929); Atlanta, April 30 (1944); and Dalton, April 9 (1944).

Specimens representing this race have been examined from many localities throughout the state, and show its widespread distribution in Georgia during the winter. No attempt is here made to list them all, the following being sufficient to outline its range:

Toccoa, Stevens County: March 13, 1946.

Athens, Clarke County: Ten specimens, between the dates of October 24 (1945) and March 22 (1946).

Washington, Wilkes County: December 21, 1945.

Center, Jackson County: January 14, 1946.

Decatur, DeKalb County: Six specimens, between the dates of October 27 (1946) and March 8 (1947).

Forsyth, Monroe County: November 2, 1946.

Yellow Bluff, Liberty County: April 3, 1946.

Statenville, Echols County: March 22, 1947.

HABITS AND RECOGNITION: The Hermit Thrush is well named, for except during the breeding season it is a recluse that leads a solitary existence in the most heavily wooded areas that it can find. To find more than one bird at a time, even in migration, is exceptional. When more than one are seen together, it is usually because a dogwood or a black gum full of ripe fruit has offered a food supply not to be ignored.

It is generally agreed that on its breeding grounds the Hermit Thrush possesses a superb song which is surpassed by that of few other birds, but unfortunately this thrush seldom sings during the winter months, and in Georgia such an occurrence has rarely been recorded. Approached as it feeds on the ground, it will fly to a near-by tree and, nervously raising and lowering its tail, will utter a low-toned "chuck" that is quite distinctive, and the only note that is usually heard from a Hermit Thrush in Georgia.

The thrushes of the genus *Hylocichla* are so similar in appearance that they prove rather perplexing to the average bird student. The Hermit Thrush, however, has a reddish-brown tail that stands out in contrast to the olive-brown back, a characteristic that should identify it within reasonable range of sight. This ordinarily presents few difficulties, for, unlike the other thrushes that are shy and elusive, the Hermit Thrush is rather tame and will permit a fairly close approach unless unduly alarmed. The fact that it is the only thrush that normally will be seen in Georgia from November until April is a further aid in recognizing it.

Newfoundland Hermit Thrush
Hylocichla guttata crymophila   Burleigh and Peters

GENERAL DISTRIBUTION: Breeds in Newfoundland. Known to winter south at least to South Carolina and Georgia, but at present its winter range has yet to be determined.

STATUS IN GEORGIA: Apparently of regular occurrence in the state as a transient and possible winter resident.

There are to date nine records for the occurrence of this far northern race in Georgia: males taken at Bogart, Oconee County, November 16, 1945 (Burleigh); in Fulton County, December 19, 1946, and January 18, 1947 (Griffin); in Grady County, March 14 and November 11, 1948, and November 22 and 24, 1944 (Stoddard); and females in DeKalb County, February 2, 1947 (Griffin), and in Grady County, December 10, 1949 (Stoddard).

HABITS AND RECOGNITION: This recently described race, distinguished by its perceptibly darker upperparts as compared with the Eastern Hermit Thrush, cannot be recognized except in the hand. So far as general appearance and actions go, it is a typical Hermit Thrush.

Alaska Hermit Thrush
Hylocichla guttata guttata   (Pallas)

GENERAL DISTRIBUTION: Breeds from south central Alaska south to Kodiak Island, Cross Sound, and northern British Columbia. Winters south to Lower California, Sonora, Chihuahua, Nuevo León, and Tamaulipas, and casually farther east.

STATUS IN GEORGIA: Of casual occurrence in the state during the winter.

To determine the presence of any of the now recognized western races of the Hermit Thrush in Georgia during the winter months, twenty-seven of these thrushes were taken in various parts of the state between October 24, 1945, and April 11, 1946. Of this number, ten were found to represent the Alaskan race, *guttata*. They were collected at Athens, Clarke County, November 25, 1945, and January 30, 1946; Auburn, Barrow County, November 28, 1945; Atlanta, Fulton County, December 6, 1945; Madison, Morgan County, December 18, 1945; Comer, Madison County, January 1, 1946; Stone Mountain, DeKalb County, January 20, 1946; Lawrenceville, Gwinnett County, February 28, 1946; Jeffersonville, Twiggs County, March 31, 1946; and Hinesville, Liberty County, April 11, 1946. [Burleigh, 1947]. The following year, on February 20, 1947, another specimen of this race was taken at Tucker, DeKalb County. [Burleigh, 1948].

HABITS AND RECOGNITION: At first glance it might appear surprising that the Alaska Hermit Thrush, heretofore unrecorded in the state, should be present in such relatively large numbers, but when the migration route followed in the fall by such species as the Gray-cheeked Thrush and the Black-polled Warbler is taken into consideration, a logical explanation suggests itself. As is well known, these two species nest in Alaska, but are unknown on the Pacific Coast as transients south of their breeding range, migrating east to the Atlantic side of the continent before going south to their winter quarters in South America. This indicates a well-established migration route diagonally across the North American continent. Since it is so consistently followed year after year by the species mentioned above, it is likely that certain populations of other species from the same breeding area follow the same route. Admittedly, definite proof is lacking, but the increasing number of records of western birds occurring in the eastern United States is a strong argument in its favor [Burleigh, 1947].

The characters that separate this race are its small size, and gray, rather than brown, flanks. These cannot be distinguished in the field; therefore, specimens are necessary to identify it satisfactorily. In general appearance and actions it resembles the Eastern Hermit Thrush.

Cascade Hermit Thrush
Hylocichla guttata oromela   Oberholser

GENERAL DISTRIBUTION: Breeds from southern British Columbia and northern Idaho south to central California and northern Nevada. Winters south into Mexico.

STATUS IN GEORGIA: Of accidental occurrence in the northern part of the state.

A male taken at Decatur April 6, 1947 provides the only record for this western race in Georgia [Burleigh, 1948].

HABITS AND RECOGNITION: As in the case of other subspecies, the general appearance and actions of *oromela* are characteristically those of a Hermit Thrush, and specimens are necessary to identify it. While not as yet recognized by the A. O. U. Check-List Committee, it appears to be a valid race.

Eastern Olive-backed Thrush
Hylocichla ustulata swainsoni   (Tschudi)

GENERAL DISTRIBUTION: Breeds from northern Michigan east to central Quebec, south to West Virginia, Pennsylvania, and Massachusetts. Winters from southeastern Mexico south to Bolivia and Argentina.

454

STATUS IN GEORGIA: A fairly common spring transient, and a common fall transient throughout the state.

In the spring, small flocks are most frequently observed in late April and early May, while in the fall, it is the latter part of September and the first half of October when the Olive-backed Thrush can be seen almost daily in the thicker stretches of woods.

Earliest arrivals in the spring were noted at Savannah, April 9 (1922); Columbus, April 29 (1946); Macon, April 19 (1925); Athens, April 10 (1921); Atlanta, April 16 (1937); and Dalton, April 16 (1944). The last in the spring were reported at Savannah on May 21 (1920); Macon, May 17 (1924); Milledgeville, May 13 (1945); Atlanta, May 23 (1954); Canton, May 18 (1916); Athens, May 24 (1928); and Rome, May 16 (1953). Stoddard considers this species a rare spring transient in Grady County, his only records being May 4 and 5, 1940, and Hebard [letter] states he has never recorded it at any time in Camden County.

In the fall, the earliest individuals appeared at Augusta, September 23 (1944); Athens, September 9 (1925); Atlanta, August 24 (1948); Macon, September 4 (1953); Americus, October 5 (1941); Grady County, September 17 (1948); and Savannah, September 11 (1931). The last in the fall were seen at Athens, October 30 (1926); Atlanta, November 9 (1930); Macon, November 10 (1928); Grady County, October 12 (1940); and Savannah, October 29 (1927).

Specimens representing this eastern race have been examined from the following localities:

Young Harris, Towns County: May 4, 1934.

Danielsville, Madison County: October 5, 1945.

Athens, Clarke County: May 11, 1928; October 24, 1929; October 12 and 14, 1945; October 10, 1947.

Stone Mountain, DeKalb County: October 12, 1946.

Decatur, DeKalb County: October 13 and 16, 1946; September 27 and 28, and October 12, 1947.

Atlanta, Fulton County: October 8, 1946; October 9, 1948.

Grady County: May 4 and 5, 1940.

HABITS AND RECOGNITION: Although the Olive-backed Thrush resembles closely in appearance the other thrushes of the genus *Hylocichla,* in actions it is quite a different bird. Being the most numerous of the five species occurring in Georgia (a possible exception being the Wood Thrush), it is usually seen in small flocks rather than singly. It is also noticeably the shyest of the thrushes. Approached as they feed on the ground or on the fleshy fruit of a dogwood, the individuals composing the flock will at once fly into the upper branches of the larger trees in the vicinity. Concealed by the thick foliage, they are then extremely difficult to see, for they sit motionless until convinced that danger no longer threatens. At all times this thrush is quiet, and with its characteristic wariness, it is inconspicuous

455

and easily overlooked. If alarmed, it utters a liquid note aptly interpreted as "whit," so distinctive and readily recognized when once heard that birds flying by overhead at night on their long journeys to the tropics can thus be identified. On its breeding grounds, it is an accomplished singer, but it rarely if ever sings in migration, and there is no record that its song has ever been heard in Georgia. With due caution, it is usually possible to see the characters that will identify the Olive-backed Thrush. In common with the Gray-cheeked Thrush it has uniformly olive-brown upperparts, but can be distinguished by its buffy cheeks and even more noticeable buffy eye ring.

Northwestern Olive-backed Thrush
Hylocichla ustulata incana   Godfrey

GENERAL DISTRIBUTION: Eastern Alaska, southern Yukon Territory, northern British Columbia, and north central Alberta east to Grimshaw and Joussard. Probably breeds also in interior Alaska and western Mackenzie. Winter range unknown.

STATUS IN GEORGIA: But a single record to date for the fall migration.

Four Olive-backed Thrushes killed at the Warner Robins Air Force Base near Macon during the mass bird mortality October 6–8, 1954, have been identified by John W. Aldrich, of the Fish and Wildlife Service, as representing this far western race [Johnston, letter].

HABITS AND RECOGNITION: Godfrey (1951) states that "the nuptial plumage superficially resembles most closely that of *Hylocichla ustulata swainsoni,* but the upperparts are uniformly decidedly greyer (less olivaceous); the buffy areas of the head and breast average paler; the spotting of the breast averages darker; and the edges of the remiges and their coverts are less buffy." As in the case of most subspecies, specimens must be taken for positive identification, the general appearance and actions of *incana* differing in no way from the other Olive-backed Thrushes.

Northern Gray-cheeked Thrush
Hylocichla minima minima   (Lafresnaye)

GENERAL DISTRIBUTION: Breeds from northeastern Siberia through northwestern Alaska, northwestern Mackenzie, and northern Manitoba to central Quebec, and in Newfoundland. Winters in northern South America.

STATUS IN GEORGIA: A scarce spring transient and a fairly common fall transient throughout the state.

456

In the spring, only an occasional bird has been noted, usually in May, while in the fall, single birds, rarely small flocks, have been frequently seen from the latter part of September until the end of October.

Definite records for the spring migration, relatively few in number, are as follows: Atlanta (extreme dates of occurrence), April 13 (1940) and May 24 (1950); Athens, May 20, 1922, and May 22 and 23, 1928; Milledgeville, May 12, 1945; Macon, May 10, 1923, May 18, 1924, May 15, 1926, May 1, 1928, and April 12, 1936; Fitzgerald, May 8 and 13, 1941.

In the fall, extreme dates of occurrence for this thrush are at Athens, September 17 (1932) and October 18 (1925); Atlanta, September 6 (1933) and November 7 (1946); Macon, September 15 (1955) and October 9 (1955); Americus, September 20 (1941) and October 16 (1941). There is also one fall record for Savannah, September 25, 1931.

Specimens representing this far northern race have been taken as follows:

Young Harris, Towns County: September 29, 1945.

Tray Mountain, White County, September 29, 1947.

Cherokee County: October 6, 1905.

Athens, Clarke County: October 7 and 11, 1927, May 22 and October 12, 1928, October 3, 1929, September 17 and 18, 1932, October 4, 17, and 21, 1945.

Decatur, DeKalb County: October 18, 1947, September 25 and October 2, 1948.

Atlanta, Fulton County: November 7, 1946, May 5, 1948, October 3, 1949.

Riverdale, Clayton County: October 2 and 16, 1949.

Grady County: October 10, 1947, and October 5, 1948.

HABITS AND RECOGNITION: The Gray-cheeked Thrush is so similar in appearance to the Olive-back that only at close range can it be satisfactorily identified. In migration it is found in the thicker stretches of woods, and it is such a quiet, inconspicuous bird that more are probably overlooked than are seen. Much of its food is gathered from the ground, and if the bird is approached as it feeds, it will fly into a near-by bush or sapling and, if not unduly alarmed, sit quietly watching the intruder. It does not seem to have the habit common with the Olive-backed Thrush of disappearing in the upper branches of the larger trees, but otherwise its actions are very similar. Observed under favorable circumstances, its gray rather than buffy, cheeks and the absence of the buffy eye ring will readily distinguish it from the Olive-backed Thrush. It also has a distinctive, harsh note, seldom uttered, that is quite unlike the soft "whit" of the Olive-back. There is no instance known of its singing in Georgia. At Athens, there were years when it was relatively common in early October, in small flocks containing three or four individuals. Ordinarily, however, it was single birds that were found, either alone or with flocks of Olive-backed Thrushes. In the fall, it was frequently found feeding on dogwood or black gum berries, and in the spring, it seemed to find mulberries equally to its liking.

Bicknell's Gray-cheeked Thrush
Hylocichla minima bicknelli Ridgway

GENERAL DISTRIBUTION: Breeds in Nova Scotia, the mountains of northern New England, and the Catskills and Adirondacks of New York. Winters in Haiti and Venezuela.

STATUS IN GEORGIA: Of casual occurrence both in the spring and in the fall.

A specimen taken by T. D. Perry at Savannah, May 16, 1910, is apparently the first record for the state [Wayne, 1918]. In recent years, five additional specimens have been taken, as follows: Athens, September 17, 1932 [Burleigh, 1938]; Fulton County, September 6, 1933, by D. V. Hembree [Greene, 1934]; Richmond County, October 17, 1933 [Murphey, 1937]; Riverdale, Clayton County, October 15, 1949 (Griffin); and Chatham County, May 8, 1949 (Tomkins). Greene [1934] reports an injured bird found on Brasstown Bald, Towns County, October 3, 1931, that was carefully measured and identified as *bicknelli*.

HABITS AND RECOGNITION: Bicknell's Thrush is merely a small edition of the Gray-cheeked Thrush, and accurate measurements are necessary to identify it satisfactorily. Because of its limited breeding range and therefore limited numbers as compared to its more northern relative, it will probably never be a very common transient in Georgia, but it doubtless occurs in the state each year.

Eastern Veery
Hylocichla fuscescens fuscescens (Stephens)

GENERAL DISTRIBUTION: Breeds from southern Ontario east to southeastern Quebec, south to northern Ohio and northern New Jersey, and in the Alleghenies to northern Georgia. Winters in southern Brazil.

STATUS IN GEORGIA: A fairly common summer resident in the extreme northeastern corner of the state and an uncommon transient south of the mountains.

As a transient, the Veery has been reported from the following localities:

Augusta: Seen in the fall between September 3 (1944) and October 1 (1944).

Athens: Extreme dates of occurrence in the spring, April 19 (1928) and May 10 (1925); and in the fall, August 30 (1928) and September 22 (1930).

Canton: April 26, 1905.

Atlanta: Extreme dates of occurrence, April 24 (1932) and May 15 (1932),

August 27 (1952) and October 7 (1954).

Milledgeville: May 7, 1939; May 3, 1945.

Macon: Extreme dates of occurrence, April 19 (1944) and May 16 (1923), September 10 (1955) and October 8 (1954).

Columbus: May 1, 1945; April 29 and 30, 1946.

Americus: May 9, 1941.

Fitzgerald: May 12 and 14, 1941.

Grady County: Extreme dates of occurrence in the fall, September 10 (1948) and October 2 (1947).

Savannah: Extreme dates of occurrence in the spring, April 5 (1916) and May 6 (1916), and noted in the fall on September 14, 1905.

St. Marys: September 13, 1905.

It is known to occur during the summer on Brasstown Bald (Towns County), Tray Mountain (White County), and Blood Mountain (Union County), and doubtless can be found then on other mountain ridges where conditions are suitable. Actual breeding records, however, are limited to Brasstown Bald. Here a nest was found on June 24, 1923, with two slightly incubated eggs, and another a week later, on July 2, with three half-grown young [Burleigh, 1927]. Specimens representing this race have been taken at Atlanta (September 11, 1907, September 11, 1948), Newton County (May 4, 1908), Athens (May 2, 1928, April 26, 1929), Grady County (nineteen specimens, all in September), and Chatham County (September 9, 1906).

HABITS AND RECOGNITION: In migration, the Veery seeks the thicker stretches of woods, preferably stream bottoms and shaded ravines, and as it is quiet and unobtrusive, must be looked for to be seen. Solitary by nature, it shuns even its own kind, and while under unusually favorable circumstances two may sometimes be observed at one spot, it never occurs in flocks. In the fall, dogwood and black gum berries tempt it to appear momentarily in the open, but ordinarily its food, largely insects, is obtained on or near the ground in the densest undergrowth. If disturbed, as it searches the dead leaves that cover the ground, it will usually disappear silently in a near-by thicket and not be seen again. Occasionally one will pause for a few moments in the lower branches of a bush or sapling, when its tawny-brown back and faintly spotted breast will aid in identifying it. Its note of alarm is quite unlike that of any of the other thrushes of this genus, being an emphatic "whee-ou," and once heard will in the future reveal its presence beyond any doubt, even though unseen.

On its breeding grounds it is equally elusive. In northern Georgia it haunts the dense rhododendron thickets that cover the upper slopes of the higher ridges, and here its whistled "whee-ou" is usually the only indication that it is close by. As a singer the Veery is considered by many to be unexcelled. Ringing and flutelike, the song possesses a quality difficult to describe, but once heard will never be forgotten. Rarely if ever does this thrush sing in migration, but a morning in early June spent on Brasstown

459

Bald, or on Tray Mountain, will enable one to hear, enjoy, and marvel at the strange beauty of the Veery's song.

As it is early May before many of the birds reach their breeding grounds and it is the latter part of that month before nesting activities are well under way, it is probable that not even as far south as Georgia is more than one brood reared each year. The few nests that have been found on Brasstown Bald were a foot and a half to two feet from the ground in small bushy rhododendrons and were alike in construction, being bulky and loosely built of large dead leaves, intermixed with a few twigs and weed stems, well cupped and lined with fine black rootlets. Usually three or four pale-blue eggs are laid.

Willow Veery
Hylocichla fuscescens salicicola Ridgway

GENERAL DISTRIBUTION: Breeds from southern British Columbia, central Alberta, central Saskatchewan, southern Manitoba, and Michigan south to central Oregon, Nevada, Utah, northern New Mexico, central Iowa, and northern Indiana. Winters in southern Brazil.

STATUS IN GEORGIA: Of casual occurrence as a fall transient.

This western race of the Veery has been reported from Decatur, De-Kalb County, where in 1947 a male was collected on September 7, and two females on September 12 and 28 [Griffin, 1947]; and from Tybee Island, Chatham County, where a female was taken September 21, 1952 (Tomkins).

HABITS AND RECOGNITION: The characters that distinguish this race are its darker upperparts and more heavily spotted breast. Specimens are necessary to identify it satisfactorily, as in general appearance and actions it is typically a Veery. It is possibly commoner than the few records indicate, but further collecting will be required to determine this.

Newfoundland Veery
Hylocichla fuscescens fuliginosa Howe

GENERAL DISTRIBUTION: Breeds in Newfoundland. Winter range unknown, but probably in southern Brazil.

STATUS IN GEORGIA: Probably of casual occurrence both in the spring and in the fall, but at present definitely recorded but three times in the state.

A male was collected at Athens on September 22, 1930 (Burleigh),

460

and another male at Decatur, DeKalb County on September 25, 1948 (Griffin). Johnston (letter) reports a single bird of this race killed at the Warner Robins Air Force Base near Macon during the mass bird mortality October 6–8, 1954.

HABITS AND RECOGNITION: The Newfoundland Veery resembles closely the Willow Veery, being dark above, but its upperparts have a ruddy tinge that is diagnostic. So far as its actions are concerned, it is quiet and shy, and can be easily overlooked unless searched for in suitable habitat.

Eastern Common Bluebird
Sialia sialis sialis (Linnaeus)

GENERAL DISTRIBUTION: Breeds from southern Manitoba, northern Ontario, and southern Quebec south to southeastern Texas, the Gulf Coast, and northern Florida. Winters south of the Ohio valley and the middle states, casually farther north.

STATUS IN GEORGIA: A common permanent resident throughout the state.

The Bluebird is one of the commonest and most widely distributed species in the state, occurring throughout the year in the mountains, in the Piedmont, and on the coastal plain to the Florida line. Essentially a bird of the more open country, it avoids the thicker timber, but otherwise can be found, regardless of season, in every county in Georgia. There is a perceptible increase in the numbers seen in the late fall and winter months when flocks that have been forced south by the rigors of a northern winter appear along the roadsides and in the more open stretches of woods.

It doubtless nests throughout the state, but definite breeding records are not numerous and are limited to the following localities:

Rome, Floyd County: Nest with young, April 12, 1945 [Jones, 1947].

Margret, Fannin County: Five nests found in 1921 between the dates of June 14 (five slightly incubated eggs) and July 13 (three incubated) (Burleigh).

Athens, Clarke County: Nesting extremes (thirteen nests), three slightly incubated eggs, March 17 (1927), and three well-incubated eggs, July 18 (1927) [Burleigh, 1938].

Emanuel County: Three eggs, May 6, 1950 (Denton).

Waynesboro, Burke County: Three fresh eggs, February 29, 1922 [Stevenson, 1932].

Atlanta, Fulton County: Nesting extremes, four fresh eggs, March 13 (1938), and three eggs, July 23 (1939) [Griffin, 1940].

Juliette, Jones County: Female incubating, May 16, 1940 [Fleetwood, 1941].

Macon: Two eggs, March 25, 1932; four eggs, March 24, 1945 (Denton).

Fitzgerald: Nesting extremes (twenty-five nests), three eggs, March 10 (1940), and four eggs, June 29 (1940) (Norris and Hopkins).

Grady County: Four newly hatched young, July 1, 1926; four young just out of the nest, March 29, 1941 (Stoddard).

Savannah, Chatham County: Nesting extremes (twelve nests), five fresh eggs, March 26 (1907); and five slightly incubated eggs, May 27 (1922) (Rossignol).

Hinesville, Liberty County: Well-fledged young, July 14, 1944; four eggs, March 27 1945 [Grimm, 1946].

HABITS AND RECOGNITION: Although in Georgia the Bluebird is not, as it is in the Northern states, the eagerly awaited harbinger of spring, nevertheless, its appearance during the first warm days in late February about the farmhouses and in the towns, where it will later nest, is a welcome sight. During the winter restless flocks rove through the open country, feeding at the edges of the woods or the roadsides. With the first hint of spring, these flocks gradually break up, and mated pairs can be seen investigating the cavities that will eventually hold their broods of young. That the Bluebird is a favorite with everybody is not surprising. The male is a handsome bird with a vivid blue back and rich brown breast, and its popularity is further enhanced by its gentle demeanor and pleasing song. When occasion demands, it can be quite aggressive in defending its nest, but ordinarily its daily life is peaceful and quiet. Where available, fleshy fruits such as those of the mulberry and dogwood are regularly eaten, but the bulk of its food consists of insects. Although these are largely picked up from the ground, the Bluebird seems reluctant to remain there for any length of time and feeds in a manner suggestive of a shrike. Detecting an insect from the limb of a tree or the top of a fence post, it will drop momentarily to the ground, seize its prey, and fly back to the spot it had left with the insect in its bill.

In Georgia, two, and possibly three, broods are reared each year, as fresh eggs can be found from the middle of March until the middle of July. The nest is always built in a cavity, and as an open situation is preferred, a fence post is a favored site. These birds do not excavate a cavity of their own, but find woodpecker holes and other cavities for their homes. A pair will occasionally show a little individuality in this respect, a nest found in Athens on July 8, 1927, with small young, being in a hole in the side of a railroad embankment. Fleetwood [1941] reports a nest in a similar situation in Jones County, the female being seen, on April 26, 1940, carrying nesting materials to a hole in a low bank at the side of a road. Birdhouses are accepted with little hesitation, and one can usually be assured of a pair of these attractive birds about the premises if a suitable house is put up for their use. The nest itself is a simple structure, built of weed stems, dry pine needles, and fine grasses, with not infrequently a few feathers or horsehairs in the lining.

As Bluebirds are noticeably more plentiful in Georgia during the winter than in summer, it has been assumed that their numbers were augmented then by birds that had nested in the Northern states. Recent banding returns show this to be the case. Bent [1949] cites three records of interest in this connection: a young bird banded on Cape Cod on May 17 was caught on December 1 at Soperton; an adult banded at Ravenscliff, Ontario, on May 24, 1938, was found in March, 1939, at Blairsville; and a nestling banded at Lisle, Illinois, on May 20, 1938, was caught on January 23, 1940, at Stockton.

Gnatcatchers and Kinglets: *Family Sylviidae*

Eastern Blue-gray Gnatcatcher
Polioptila caerulea caerulea (Linnaeus)

GENERAL DISTRIBUTION: Breeds from eastern Nebraska, Iowa, and the southern parts of Wisconsin, Michigan, Ontario, southwestern Pennsylvania, Maryland, and southern New Jersey south to southern Texas, the Gulf Coast, and central Florida. Winters from southern Texas, the Gulf Coast, and the coast of South Carolina to the Bahamas, and Cuba, and through eastern Mexico to Yucatán and Guatemala.

STATUS IN GEORGIA: A common summer resident throughout the state, and of casual occurrence during the winter as far north as Atlanta.

The Gnatcatcher normally reaches Georgia in March and departs for its winter home in September. A few individuals noted in early February possibly wintered in the state, and it is probable that those seen in late October and November could likewise be considered as winter visitants.

Earliest spring transients were reported from Sea Island, March 9 (1946); Savannah (Tybee Island), February 28 (1929); Americus, March 20 (1942); Columbus, March 21 (1945); Macon, March 4 (1945); Milledgeville, March 8 (1942); Augusta, March 16 (1945); Athens, March 16 (1923); Atlanta, March 9, (1954); Rome, March 24 (1953); and Dalton, March 26 (1944).

The latest fall transients were seen at Atlanta, October 15 (1949); Athens, October 7 (1929); and Macon, October 10 (1949).

In the southern part of the state, the Gnatcatcher apparently winters regularly and is not uncommon at that season of the year. It has been reported from:

Savannah: December 2, 1911; February 18, 1912; February 7, 1925.

Okefenokee Swamp: Floyd's Island, November 1 and 2, 1932; Jackson's Bay, December 3, 1934 [Hebard, 1941].

Eastern Charlton County: November 25, 1940; January 16 and 27 and February 11 and 15, 1941 [Hebard, 1941].

Grady County: Rare in winter (Stoddard).

Valdosta: November 22, 1929 (Burleigh).

Fitzgerald: Common in December and January, 1938–39, 1939–40 [Norris, 1940].

Macon: January 8, 1950; December 27 and 30, 1951 (Johnston).

North of the fall line single birds have been seen at Milledgeville, October 26 and December 31, 1942 [Burns, 1943]; and at Atlanta (College Park), November 20, 1935 [Griffin, 1939].

There is little question that it breeds throughout the state where conditions are suitable, but actual breeding records are at present limited to the following localities:

Rome, Floyd County: Young in nest, May 21, 1939; four eggs, April 25, 1942 [Jones, 1947].

Margret, Fannin County: Small young in nest, June 22, 1921; five slightly incubated eggs, May 18, 1926 (Burleigh).

Atlanta, Fulton County: Nesting extremes, five fresh eggs, April 26 (1908) (Harris); four young, June 19, 1938 (Griffin and Sciple) [Griffin, 1940].

Athens, Clarke County: Nesting extremes (eight nests), five fresh eggs, May 5 (1923); two well-fledged young, July 27 (1925) [Burleigh, 1938].

Richmond County: Adults feeding young in nest, May 4, 1952 (Denton).

Fitzgerald: Nesting extremes (six nests), four young, May 14 (1941); four eggs, June 6 (1941) (Norris and Hopkins).

Grady County: Nearly completed nests, March 27 and April 24, 1949 (Stoddard).

Savannah: Nesting extremes (sixteen nests), five fresh eggs, April 16 (1912); four fresh eggs, May 30 (1914) (Rossignol).

HABITS AND RECOGNITION: If all small birds were as distinctive in appearance and actions as is the Blue-gray Gnatcatcher, the bird student in Georgia would experience little, if any, difficulty in readily recognizing the various species in the field. Its small size and long, slender tail at once proclaim its identity, and if any uncertainty still exists, a glimpse of its plumage, blue-gray above and white beneath, will eliminate any doubt. It is an active little bird, moving about with a quick, jerky flight, its long tail constantly in motion. During the nesting season especially, its presence is revealed by its characteristic notes, the commonest being a nasal "twee," that is uttered at frequent intervals as the bird forages for food. Its diet is almost entirely small insects, their eggs, and larvae, and these are obtained as the bird moves restlessly about, carefully inspecting the twigs and smaller branches, or momentarily darting into the air for a fly or gnat it had disturbed. Wooded river bottoms are favored spots during the summer, but open pine woods with an understory of oaks and other deciduous hardwoods are almost equally favored.

The nest of the gnatcatcher suggests a large hummingbird's nest, and is a handsome structure. Compact and deeply cupped, it is constructed of shreds of bark, fine grasses, plant down, and, where available, feathers, the outside invariably well covered with green lichens. Saddled on a horizontal limb of a tree, it is far from conspicuous and could easily be overlooked if the birds, with entire lack of timidity, did not usually reveal its presence. Although the average nest is within fifteen feet of the ground, an occasional pair will select an upper branch of the largest tree in their territory, one nest found at Athens being fully sixty feet up in a tall, slender red oak. Apparently only one brood is reared each year, for it is exceptional to find a nest with eggs later than the middle of May. One nest at Athens, which held well-fledged young on July 27, 1925, was surprisingly late, and possibly indicated an unsuccessful effort earlier in the spring.

Eastern Golden-crowned Kinglet
Regulus satrapa satrapa   Lichtenstein

GENERAL DISTRIBUTION: Breeds from central Alberta, central Manitoba, southern Quebec, and Newfoundland south to Minnesota, Michigan, New York, Massachusetts, and in the Alleghenies to North Carolina. Winters from Iowa, Ontario, and New Brunswick to northern Florida and Tamaulipas, Mexico.

STATUS IN GEORGIA: A fairly common winter resident throughout the state.

The Golden-crowned Kinglet usually appears in Georgia about the middle of October and small flocks are in daily evidence until the following April. Earliest fall transients were noted at Dalton, October 15 (1944); Rome, October 9 (1943); Athens, October 6 (1921); Atlanta, October 8 (1932); Milledgeville, October 29 (1942); Macon, October 13 (1945); Americus, November 22 (1941); Fitzgerald, October 15 (1939); Grady County, October 28 (1937); and Hinesville, November 15 (1944). The latest in the spring were seen at Savanah, April 17 (1902); Irwin County, March 11 (1952); Americus, March 18 (1942); Macon, April 6 (1924); Atlanta, April 26 (1947); Dalton, April 9 (1944); Athens, April 15 (1924); and Augusta, March 11 (1945).

Although occurring in winter only as far south as northern Florida, this kinglet is fairly common at that season in southern Georgia. Harper reported it frequently seen in the Okefenokee Swamp during the winter of 1916–17; I noted scattered small flocks at Newton, in Baker County, in December, 1924, and again in January, 1932; and on January 22, 1932, I saw three birds on Blackbeard Island. Stoddard [MS] considers this species "a fairly regular but by no means common winter resident" in Grady County.

HABITS AND RECOGNITION: Because of their small size and their apparent preference for the upper branches of the trees in which they feed, these kinglets can be easily overlooked. However, little difficulty should be experienced in making their acquaintance, for they are active little birds with a thin, wiry note that readily attracts attention. In common with a number of other small birds, during the winter, they are rather socially inclined, and small flocks can usually be found with such kindred spirits as the chickadees, titmice, and nuthatches.

As they move restlessly through a stretch of woods, here one minute and gone the next, it requires constant activity on the part of the watcher to keep these diminutive birds in sight. Closely searching the twigs and terminal buds for the plant lice and other small insects that form the bulk of their food, frequently hovering in the air to get an especially tempting morsel, or clinging momentarily to the under surface of a branch, kinglets are the epitome of nervous energy. Arouse their curiosity, and first one bird and then another will approach until almost within arm's length, uttering their high-pitched "tee-tee" as they scan the intruder. Under such circumstances there can be no question as to what they are. Their small size, olive-gray plumage, and short tails distinguish them at once as king-lets, and the yellow crown, noticeable in both sexes, further confirms their identity. The males have a vivid orange spot in the middle of their crown, but only under exceptional circumstances is it noticeable.

Eastern Ruby-crowned Kinglet
Regulus calendula calendula (Linnaeus)

GENERAL DISTRIBUTION: Breeds from northwestern Alaska, Mackenzie, northern Manitoba, northern Quebec, and Newfoundland south to south-ern Arizona, central New Mexico, northern Ontario, New Brunswick, Nova Scotia, and, casually, Maine. Winters from southern British Columbia, Iowa, and Virginia south over the United States and the Mexican Table-land to Guatemala.

STATUS IN GEORGIA: A common winter resident throughout the state.

The Ruby-crowned Kinglet appears in Georgia the latter part of Sep-tember, and can be seen daily over much of the state until early May. The earliest fall transients were reported from Athens, September 26 (1927); Atlanta, September 28 (1940); Macon, September 13 (1954); Americus, October 4 (1941); Fitzgerald, September 30 (1940); Grady County, Oc-tober 5 (1939); Savannah, October 16 (1910); and Hinesville, October 15 (1944). The latest in the spring were noted at Hinesville, April 17 (1943); Grady County, April 29 (1940 and 1952); Fitzgerald, May 13 (1941); Americus, April 25 (1942); Macon, May 12 (1921); Milledge-ville, May 3 (1945); Augusta, May 1 (1945); Athens, May 10 (1929); At-lanta, May 18 (1938); Rome, May 1 (1953); and Dalton, May 1 (1944).

During the winter, this kinglet apparently occurs commonly from the mountain counties to the Florida line, being reported at this season of the year as far north as Dalton and Augusta, and in the Okefenokee Swamp and at St. Marys in the extreme southern part of the state.

466

Photograph by Brooke Meanley

A coastal plain river swamp, the habitat of many swamp-loving species.

Photograph by Brooke Meanley

*A bald cypress, typical nesting site
of the Parula and Yellow-throated warblers.*

Family Motacillidae: WAGTAILS & PIPITS

HABITS AND RECOGNITION: Although resembling to some extent the Gold-en-crowned Kinglet, the Ruby-crown differs markedly in temperament. In migration, small flocks occur, but throughout the winter, single birds are usually seen, more often than not, feeding alone in underbrush. Stream bottoms are favored spots then, with their stretches of alders and willows, but any stretch of woods where there is an understory of deciduous hard-woods generally attracts one or two of these little birds. On occasion, es-pecially if temporarily feeding with a roving flock of chickadees and titmice, one can be seen in open pine woods, but before long it returns to the deciduous underbrush it prefers. Always tame and confiding, it fre-quently approaches within a few feet of one if its curiosity is aroused, and it utters then a harsh, scolding note, suggestive of that of a wren, which is quite unlike the thin, wiry note of the Golden-crowned Kinglet.

Its plumage is equally distinctive, both sexes lacking the yellow crown patch and white stripe over the eye, and having instead a con-spicuous white eye-ring. Like the Golden-crown, it is also very small and very active, and has the characteristic trait of nervously fluttering its wings as it searches the twigs and smaller branches for the small insects on which it feeds. Before the last birds have left Georgia in May, many are singing, and the song, when heard for the first time, is very impressive. It is a prolonged warble, so surprisingly loud for the size of the diminutive singer that one unconsciously looks for a much larger bird before finally accepting the fact that the male kinglet is actually responsible for this musical outburst.

Wagtails and Pipits: *Family Motacillidae*

American Water Pipit
Anthus spinoletta rubescens (Tunstall)

GENERAL DISTRIBUTION: Breeds in the Arctic Zone from northwestern Siberia, northern Alaska, northern Mackenzie, and the west coast of Greenland south to Great Slave Lake, northern Manitoba, Quebec, and Newfoundland. Winters from the Ohio and lower Delaware valleys to the Gulf Coast and Guatemala.

STATUS IN GEORGIA: A common winter resident in all parts of the state except the mountains.

The Pipit usually reaches Georgia in late October, and is not often seen in the spring after the middle of April, although a few scattered flocks occasionally remain until almost the middle of May.

The earliest fall transients were noted at Athens, October 14 (1928); Atlanta, October 24 (1953); Macon, October 3 (1945); Irwin County, October 25 (1952); Thomas County, November 2 (1937); Savannah, November 12 (1912); and St. Marys, November 9 (1905).

The latest in the spring were seen at Savannah, April 8 (1910); Irwin County, March 6 (1941); Thomas County, March 7 (1941); Macon, May 3 (1944); Atlanta, April 9 (1933); Athens, May 13 (1926) and May 9 (1928); and Augusta, March 20 (1945).

In the winter, small flocks have been reported from such widely separated localities in the state as Atlanta, Reidville, Newton, Okefenokee Swamp, Cumberland Island, and Darien.

HABITS AND RECOGNITION: The Pipit is a bird of open fields and pastures, the small flocks seen in Georgia being normally found feeding in plowed fields or, if on the coast, on the open beaches or mud flats. Their grayish-brown plumage blends so well with their surroundings that such flocks would be rather inconspicuous if it were not for their extreme restlessness. After feeding for a short time, a flock will, for no obvious reason, suddenly take flight, circle overhead in a rather straggling formation, and then with equal suddenness drop down into the same field, even at times to the same spot. On the ground, the individuals comprising the flock scatter widely as they feed, and never remain in a compact group, but if too close an approach causes one bird to fly, the others immediately take alarm and join it in the air. While momentarily quiet, a Pipit can easily be mistaken for a sparrow, but once it begins to feed, it displays traits no sparrow possesses. Instead of hopping, it walks, and as it walks, it constantly wags its tail up and down. If it is forced to fly, the white in the outer tail feathers is at once noticeable.

At Athens, small flocks of Pipits were found throughout the winter in open fields, and it was interesting to note that these flocks invariably gathered together at night at the upper end of the Sandy Creek bottoms. Only infrequently were they observed there during the day, but on many occasions in December and January, they were watched as they came in late in the afternoon from all directions to roost at this spot. The first small flock would appear almost an hour before dark, to be followed by others at frequent intervals until, at dusk, fully a thousand Pipits would be scattered over this marshy field. When they first arrived, they were restless and noisy, continually flying up in a loose straggling group and circling overhead for several minutes before dropping to the ground again, and it was usually too dark to see them any longer before they were finally settled for the night.

468

Family Motacillidae: WAGTAILS & PIPITS

Sprague's Pipit
Anthus spragueii (Audubon)

GENERAL DISTRIBUTION: Breeds from central Alberta, Saskatchewan, and southern Manitoba south to western Montana, North Dakota, and Minnesota. Winters from the Gulf Coast of Mississippi, Louisiana, and Texas south through eastern Mexico to Vera Cruz, Puebla, and Michoacan.

STATUS IN GEORGIA: Apparently largely of accidental occurrence.

Now known from Cumberland Island, Camden County, where nine specimens were taken by Arthur H. Helme from January 19 through April 3, 1903; from Augusta, where six individuals were noted by J. Fred Denton from December 28, 1952, through April 24, 1953, and specimens taken there December 28 and March 13; and from Atlanta, where it was reported February 28, 1953 [C. Gordon, fide Griffin, MS].

HABITS AND RECOGNITION: Denton [MS] has discussed in considerable detail the preferred habitat and actions of the Sprague's Pipits seen at Augusta, and his comments are here quoted:

> The birds showed a decided preference for a particular triangular area of the airfield bounded on two sides by paved runways and on the third by the enclosing fence. In construction of this part of the field the topsoil had been removed entirely, leaving the bright red clay subsoil exposed. Stunted grasses, mostly Bermuda, and weeds sparsely covered the area. Interspersed with the vegetation were areas of bare ground approximately a square yard in area. Apparently the area was mowed late in the fall so that the ground cover, further killed back by the frost, averaged about four inches high. An almost constant and sometimes severe wind blew across the airport all winter and spring. It is conceivable that the wind, also characteristic of the habitat on Cumberland as well as the Gulf Islands, might enhance the attractiveness of the area. Apparently the essential requirement, though, is the short sparse grass with intermingling bare areas covering a dry or well-drained area.
>
> In such a unique habitat the Sprague's Pipit is likely to have few bird associates. At Augusta the most common species, and incidentally the most distracting to the observer, was the Savannah Sparrow (*Passerculus sandwichensis*), about a dozen of which wintered on the area. A flock of about eight Meadowlarks (*Sturnella magna*) and two pairs of Killdeers (*Charadrius vociferus*) frequented the area, eventually nesting. On March 13 a pair of Horned Larks (*Eremophila alpestris*) appeared for the first time and remained to nest. Domestic Pigeons, Mourning Doves (*Zenaidura macroura*), and Starlings

(*Sturnus vulgaris*) occasionally visited the area to feed. From April 7 to 14 four Upland Sandpipers (*Bartramia longicauda*) lingered about the airport. Not once during the winter was the Water Pipit (*Anthus spinoletta*) recorded in the vicinity.

In general Sprague's Pipit in winter is an inconspicuous, obscurely marked, retiring species that is not likely to be observed unless searched for in suitable habitat. Once its specialized habitat is located and its characteristics and habits learned it is not a difficult species to study. Although generally thought of as occurring in small flocks, birds are usually seen or flushed individually, so that much searching is necessary to determine the number in any one area. This bird shows a decided preference for remaining on the ground. When approached slowly, it runs mouse-like through the sparse grass in the manner of a Savannah Sparrow, with tail drooping like a Meadowlark. Frequently it will stop to raise its head high and look around, at which time one is struck by the proportionately small size of the head as compared to the body. In this attitude the bird is quite suggestive of a miniature Upland Sandpiper. While on the ground the most distinctive field mark is the buffy nape interposed between the distinctly streaked back and crown. Not once during many hours of watching was a bird seen to wag its tail as does the Water Pipit.

When forced to flush, the birds never flew very far nor high above the ground. They, seeming reluctant to cross the paved runways, would either fly over my head or circle around me to drop again to the ground. The white outer rectrices usually cited as a field mark were not conspicuous when the birds were on the ground but were easily seen in flight. In flight the white was about as distinct as that in the tail of a Vesper Sparrow (*Pooecetes gramineus*), thus greatly aiding in distinguishing pipits from Savannah Sparrows flushed in the same area. The course of flight was distinctive, being an undulating one markedly like that of the Goldfinch (*Spinus tristis*). Usually, when flushed, birds while on the wing uttered singly or in a series a two-syllable note suggestive of but quite distinct from that of the Water Pipit. This note was also helpful in distinguishing flushed pipits from Savannah Sparrows which in flight gave their characteristic *tseep*.

Waxwings: *Family Bombycillidae*

Cedar Waxwing
Bombycilla cedrorum   Vieillot

GENERAL DISTRIBUTION: Breeds from central British Columbia, central

Family *Bombycillidae:* WAXWINGS

Alberta, central Manitoba, northern Ontario, southern Quebec, and New-foundland south to northern California, northern New Mexico, Kansas, northern Arkansas, northern Georgia, and North Carolina. Winters throughout nearly all of the United States and south to Cuba, Mexico, and Panama.

STATUS IN GEORGIA: A common but erratic winter resident over most of the state, and a fairly common summer resident in the mountains.

Few birds are more irregular in their occurrence during the winter in Georgia than is the Cedar Waxwing. The small flocks that are normally seen may be numerous in some years and few and far between in others. They may appear in the fall as early as the latter part of August, or in September, or, for no obvious reason, not until November or early December. It is only in May that scattered flocks are in evidence almost daily, and they linger until late in the month.

Fall arrival dates at Athens illustrate well the erratic migration movements of this waxwing. In 1921 the first flock appeared October 1; in 1922, November 9; in 1923, October 7; in 1924, October 1; in 1925, August 28; in 1926, December 2; in 1927, September 22; in 1928, September 23; in 1929, October 30; and in 1932, September 17. The earliest fall transients were noted at Dalton, September 30 (1944); Atlanta, October 12 (1938); Milledgeville, November 23 (1942); Macon, August 22 (1954); Fitzgerald, October 16 (1940); Grady County, November 7 (1939); and Savannah, September 18 (1910).

The latest in the spring were seen at Savannah, May 19 (1921); Grady County, May 17 (1952); Fitzgerald, May 23 (1941); Americus, May 16 (1942); Macon, May 24 (1932); Milledgeville, May 13 (1945); Atlanta, June 11 (1946); Rome, May 19 (1953); Dalton, May 18 (1944); Athens, June 2 (1934); and Augusta, June 13 (1935).

The Cedar Waxwing was first recorded as breeding in Georgia in 1922, when two nests were found at Young Harris, Towns County. The first held five well incubated eggs on July 20; the second, one fresh egg on July 21 [Burleigh, 1925]. In 1923, further field work at Young Harris showed this species to be a fairly plentiful summer resident, four occupied nests being found. Two held half-grown young on July 1: one, five half-incubated eggs on July 5, and one, three slightly incubated eggs on July 19 [Burleigh, 1927]. Griffin and Sciple report this species at Cornelia, in Habersham County, during the summer of 1939, and Odum [1945] "four juveniles being fed by one, perhaps two, parents one mile north of Tate," on July 29, 1945.

HABITS AND RECOGNITION: Despite its subdued colors, the Cedar Waxwing is an unusually attractive bird. Its olive-brown plumage has a sleek appearance that gives it the look of always being well groomed, and this look persists even in the late fall when other birds may seem worn and disheveled. As its name implies, the wings are often adorned with small appendages that resemble drops of red sealing wax, adding a touch of color that emphasizes the soft brown of its body.

It is extremely sociable by nature, and only during the nesting season will single birds or pairs be seen. During the remainder of the year Cedar Waxwings occur in flocks of varying size, and in Georgia they will be found where berries of such trees as the dogwood, wild cherry, and black gum furnish an adequate food supply. Insects are eaten to a limited extent, but the waxwing, regardless of season, seems to prefer fruits. This dietary preference is probably one reason for its erratic movements, for once a tree is stripped of its berries, a new supply must be found, and consequently the waxwing leads a nomadic existence apparently governed largely by its needs for food. If hungry, as usually seems the case, a flock will fill a tree until it seems alive with eagerly feeding birds, and more often than not, when the flock departs, few berries remain. As it feeds and when passing overhead in compact flocks, the waxwing utters a high-pitched, lisping call that is the only note heard from this oddly silent bird. If it has a song, it is rarely uttered, for even during the summer months only this distinctive lisping note can be heard.

The waxwing is one of the last birds to nest, for even as far south as northern Georgia, it is late June or early July before many pairs are engaged in rearing their young. This is possibly due to their dependence on fleshy berries as food for the young, although it is known that insects are fed to the nestlings during their early days. As so few nests have actually been found in Georgia, it may be of interest to give in some detail the circumstances surrounding the discovery of the Cedar Waxwing as a breeding bird in the state in 1922 [Burleigh, 1925].

My first nest was found July 20, within two miles of Young Harris, and held on that date five well-incubated eggs. It was forty-five feet from the ground at the outer end of a limb of a large white oak at the side of a road bordering an open field, and was built of weed stems, grasses, rootlets, and light green mosslike lichens, lined somewhat with dry pine needles. The following day, while passing an open grove of scrub pines (*Pinus virginiana*) that bordered the road five miles northeast of Young Harris, the actions of a pair of these birds aroused my suspicions and a short search revealed two apparently new nests. The first was fifty feet from the ground in the top of one of the larger trees, and an investigation revealed that it was without doubt the first attempt of this pair to breed here, broken egg shells in the bottom showing that it had come to a disastrous end. The second nest was thirty feet from the ground at the extreme outer end of a limb of one of the pines, and reaching it necessitated the use of a rope. It held one fresh egg and later was found to be deserted, due I suppose to the treatment it received in my effort to examine it. It was rather shabbily built of dry pine needles and the same light green moss-like lichens, with a few rootlets and grasses.

A year later four nests were located in somewhat similar situations [Burleigh, 1927]:

Two nests were found July 1, in the open grove of scrub pines where, in 1922, one pair had attempted to nest, in each half-grown young. They were within fifty yards of each other, one forty feet from the ground and the other fully sixty, in the upper branches of the larger trees. Another nest found July 5, with five half-incubated eggs, was fifty-five feet from the ground at the extreme outer end of a limb of a large black walnut tree in a farmyard. It was compactly built of hemlock twigs, weed stems, grasses, fine rootlets, and wool, lined with the hemlock twigs, grasses, a little cow hair, and light green lichens. A fourth nest, that on July 19 held three slightly incubated eggs, was in a situation very similar to this, being fully sixty feet from the ground at the extreme outer end of an upper limb of a large black walnut tree close to a house in a farmyard. It was likewise compact and well built of hemlock twigs, rootlets, weed stems, and grasses, lined more or less with dry pine needles and green lichens.

Shrikes: *Family Laniidae*

Southern Loggerhead Shrike
Lanius ludovicianus ludovicianus Linnaeus

GENERAL DISTRIBUTION: Resident in the Lower Austral Zone of the Atlantic and Gulf states from southern North Carolina to Florida and west through southern Georgia and Alabama to Louisiana.

STATUS IN GEORGIA: A common resident throughout all of the state except the mountains.

In eastern Georgia, the shrike has been reported as occurring during the summer as far north as Toccoa, and in the western part of the state, north to Rome. However, it is apparently scarce north of Athens and Atlanta, and rare or entirely absent in the mountain counties. It is common and widely distributed over much of the Piedmont and in the coastal plain, and is one of the characteristic birds of the more open country.

473

Although it doubtless breeds wherever found, actual breeding records are limited to the following localities:

Augusta: "Earliest nesting record, February 24th" [Murphey, 1937]; March 22, 1945, five fresh eggs; March 27, 1946, five eggs (Denton).

Athens: Extreme nesting dates (fourteen nests), March 27 (1927), five fresh eggs; June 7 (1925), six partially incubated eggs [Burleigh, 1938].

Atlanta: Nesting extremes, April 3 (1932), five eggs (Greene); June 29 (1939), three fresh eggs (Griffin) [Griffin, 1940].

Fitzgerald: March 28, 1940, six eggs [Norris, 1940].

Savannah: Extreme nesting dates (twelve nests), February 15 (1919), five fresh eggs; May 30 (1911), five incubated eggs (Rossignol).

Hinesville: Young just out of nest, May 29, 1944; nearly fledged young, August 13, 1945 [Grimm, 1946].

St. Marys: Six eggs, March 17, 1878 (Brewster).

Specimens representing this southern race have been examined from Toccoa, Augusta, Athens, Stone Mountain, Decatur, Auburn (Barrow County), Jackson (Butts County), Roberta (Crawford County), Preston (Webster County), Blakely, Newton (Baker County), Reidsville, Riceboro, Thomasville, and Allenhurst (Liberty County).

HABITS AND RECOGNITION: The Loggerhead Shrike is a bird that is not easily overlooked. Consistently avoiding wooded areas, it spends its days, regardless of season or weather, at the edges of fields or pastures or at the sides of roads. Here it perches on a telephone wire, the top of a telephone pole, or a fence post, scanning the ground beneath it for some tempting morsel. The slightest movement on the part of an insect, a mouse, or even a small bird, and down it drops, to return almost at once carrying its prey in its large hooked bill. Keen, indeed, must be its vision, for rarely does it fail. Unlike the hawks and owls that have similar food habits, a shrike has no talons with which to grasp an object while it is torn into pieces small enough to swallow. As a result, it has developed the habit of impaling its prey on a sharp thorn, or even more often these days, on a barb of a wire fence, where it can be torn to pieces with a minimum of difficulty. So well known is this practice that over much of its range, the shrike is commonly called the butcherbird.

It is questionable whether in Georgia small birds form a very large part of its fare, although on occasion I have known it to kill and eat House Sparrows. On February 2, 1925, I was walking along a road a mile or so south of Athens when a shrike flew by carrying a rather large object in its bill. I at once followed it, and handicapped as it was, it soon dropped this object at the foot of a large honey locust tree. Investigation showed it to be a male House Sparrow, freshly killed. Merely glancing at it, I went on, but on returning an hour later, I found the sparrow impaled on a large thorn a few feet from the ground, with the head completely eaten and a little of the breast gone.

Hopkins (1953d) gives an interesting account of the feeding habits of the shrike as observed in the southern part of the state:

> During October, 1951, Shrikes (*Lanius ludovicianus*) in the Osierfield, Irwin County, area tended to shift their lookout perches from utility lines and fence row trees to peanut stacks in fields where peanuts were being threshed. A single Shrike was noted to kill and impale four house mice during one hour of my observation when stacks were being moved by tractors for threshing, thus exposing the mice. These mice were usually seized with the bird's claws and killed with several swift strikes of the beak. On two occasions the observer was close enough to the bird to see it transfer its prey from talons to beak while in flight. All four of these mice were impaled on plum tree (*Prunus* sp.) thorns.

It is exceptional for a shrike to utter a note of any kind during most of the year, so it comes as somewhat of a surprise to hear one singing in the early spring. Perched in the top of a bush or sapling, it indulges in a long-drawn-out series of gurgles, trills, and warbles, which, while rather harsh in character, serve the purpose of a song.

In Georgia, the shrike apparently raises two broods each year, for fresh eggs can be found in late March or early April, and again in late May and June. Decidedly exceptional, and surprisingly early, was the nest found by Rossignol at Savannah on February 15, 1919, with five fresh eggs. The nest is usually built in a thick bush within five or six feet of the ground, and is a bulky, compact structure of twigs, rootlets, grasses, and, where available, bits of string, cotton, and feathers, well cupped and lined with horsehair, cotton, and feathers. Five eggs are usually laid, although not infrequently six will be found.

Migrant Loggerhead Shrike
Lanius ludovicianus migrans Palmer

GENERAL DISTRIBUTION: Breeds from southeastern Manitoba, southern Ontario, southern Quebec, and New Brunswick south to northeastern Texas, eastern Oklahoma, Arkansas, Missouri, southern Illinois, northwestern Pennsylvania, Kentucky, western North Carolina, Mississippi, Louisiana, and the interior of Virginia (but only locally in the Eastern states). Winters chiefly in the Mississippi Valley and Texas, irregularly north to southern New England.

475

STATUS IN GEORGIA: At present known as an uncommon winter resident.

At Athens, two specimens were taken in the open Sandy Creek bottoms: a female on November 26, 1932, and a male on December 3, 1933 [Burleigh, 1938]. There are also two records for Augusta, December 1, 1932 (Burleigh), and October 12, 1935 [Murphey, 1937]; and two for Grady County, January 16, 1949, and November 22, 1951 [Stoddard, MS].

HABITS AND RECOGNITION: This northern race of the Loggerhead Shrike differs from the southern in being slightly larger and noticeably paler gray above. Since specimens are necessary to identify it satisfactorily, it may prove to be commoner and more widely distributed in the state during the winter than the existing records indicate. So far as its general appearance and actions go, there is nothing to distinguish it from its more southern relative.

Starlings: *Family Sturnidae*

Common Starling
Sturnus vulgaris vulgaris   Linnaeus

GENERAL DISTRIBUTION: Western and central Europe. Introduced in 1890 in New York City, it has since spread as far north as Ontario, Quebec, and Newfoundland, west to the Pacific Coast and south to Texas, the Gulf Coast, and Florida.

STATUS IN GEORGIA: A common permanent resident over the entire state.

The Starling was first recorded in Georgia on November 10, 1917, when a specimen was taken at Savannah by Gilbert R. Rossignol [Wayne, 1918].

At Athens, it was noted for the first time on March 7, 1924, when five birds were seen feeding at the edge of an open field. No more were observed until January 20, 1925, when a flock of approximately sixty of these birds was found in the Sandy Creek bottoms. The Starling nested at Athens for the first time that spring, a nest being found on April 28 that held four fresh eggs. By 1938, the Starling had become abundant the larger part of the year, being relatively scarce only from the latter part of November until the middle of February [Burleigh, 1938]. Greene [1933] records its arrival for the first time at Atlanta on September 26, 1927, when two birds were seen. A single bird was noted there on April 9, 1928, and a flock of possibly twenty-five on January 18, 1929. It later became abundant, a flock that was estimated to contain fully 1,000 individuals being seen in the South River section November 12, 1932.

Family *Sturnidae:* STARLINGS

Griffin [1940] cites as nesting extremes for the Atlanta region, four eggs, April 1 (1937); and two eggs, August 3 (1939). It was reported nesting at Macon in 1929, and there are breeding records for Rome (young in the nest May 5, 1936) [Jones, 1947], and for Folkston (young in the nest May 15, 1942) [Hebard, 1946].

HABITS AND RECOGNITION: The appearance of a Starling is so distinctive that when first seen it becomes the subject of much interest and conjecture. Well versed in the advantages to be gained in proximity to man, its invasion of new territory occurs usually on farms, in and about towns, and, eventually, in even the larger cities. Here it can be seen feeding on the lawns or, if in the country, in the vicinity of the barns or in the open fields. At first sight, it suggests a rather stout blackbird with a very short tail, but a closer look will reveal its plumage to be iridescent purple and green, flecked with buffy white, that gives it a truly alien look. Its long, pointed bill is dull brown during the winter months, but in spring changes to yellow, a character that emphasizes still further its difference from the birds the average person is familiar with.

Because of its phenomenal increase since its introduction into this country, it has become the cause of much concern on the part of many, for unfortunately it has traits that do not endear it to either the agriculturist or the bird lover. Its fondness for fruit often results in considerable destruction to cherries, and there are frequent reports of serious damage to half-ripened corn through this bird's opening the ears and eating the kernels. For nesting, a pair of Starlings will select a suitable cavity, driving away such desirable species as the Bluebird, the Flicker, and even the Crested Flycatcher from many localities where otherwise they would be found during the summer months. Obviously such actions as these have aroused much adverse sentiment, and the impossibility of eliminating the Starling from a spot where it has become established has increased the apprehension felt by many. Detailed studies of its food habits throughout the year have, however, shown that the good it does in destroying injurious insects largely compensates for its harmful actions, and for this reason its presence in Georgia need not be viewed with too much alarm.

Highly gregarious, the Starling occurs throughout the larger part of the year in flocks that are constantly in motion as they feed in the open fields. Usually timid and difficult to approach, a flock will leave the ground at the slightest alarm, their swift, direct flight soon taking them out of sight.

Breeding activities begin rather early in the spring. A nest found at Athens on March 30, 1927, already held five slightly incubated eggs. The nest is never built in the open but in a cavity of some sort, and is a substantial bed of weed stems, coarse grasses, shreds of bark, and dry pine needles.

Vireos: *Family Vireonidae*

Northern White-eyed Vireo
Vireo griseus noveboracensis (Gmelin)

GENERAL DISTRIBUTION: Breeds from southeastern Nebraska, southern Wisconsin, Ohio, New York, and Massachusetts south to central Texas, the northern part of the Gulf states, Georgia, and western North Carolina. Winters from Texas, southern Alabama, southern Georgia, and the coast of South Carolina through eastern Mexico to Yucatán and Honduras.

STATUS IN GEORGIA: A common summer resident throughout all the state, except the southern edge, and locally a fairly common winter resident south of the fall line.

In recent years breeding specimens representing *noveboracensis* have been taken as far south as Macon, but field work carried on in June, 1947, south of the fall line proved conclusively that this northern race extends much farther south than was originally suspected. In the northern half of the state breeding specimens typical of *noveboracensis* have been taken in Chattooga County (Summerville), Polk County (Cedartown), Hall County (Gainesville), Banks County (Homer), Fannin County (Blue Ridge), Cobb County (Smyrna), Fulton County (Atlanta), DeKalb County (Decatur), Clarke County (Athens, Princeton, Winterville), Henry County (McDonough), Carroll County (Carrollton), Fayette County (Fayetteville), Green County (Greensborough), and Meriwether County (Greenville), while farther south specimens referable to this northern race were taken in Houston County (Perry), Twiggs County (Jeffersonville), Schley County (Ellaville), Pulaski County (Hawkinsville), Montgomery County (Tarrytown), Calhoun County (Leary), and Tift County (Ty Ty). [Burleigh, 1948.]

Earliest spring transients were recorded at Tifton, March 8 (1942); Americus, March 30 (1942); Columbus, March 31 (1946); Macon, March 12 (1944); Milledgeville, March 15 (1938); Athens, March 23 (1923); Atlanta, March 21 (1948); Dalton, April 1 (1944); Rising Fawn, April 1 (1885). The latest in the fall were reported from Augusta, October 22 (1944); Athens, October 18 (1925); Atlanta, October 18 (1947); Macon, October 22 (1954); Americus, October 11 (1941); and Fitzgerald, October 24 (1941).

At present there is but a single winter record north of the fall line, that of a male collected in the Sandy Creek bottoms, at Athens, December

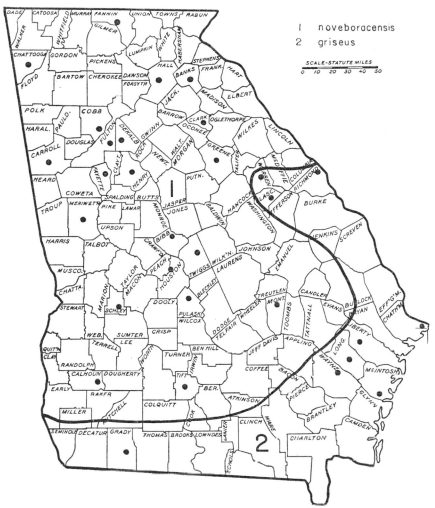

BREEDING DISTRIBUTION OF THE WHITE-EYED VIREO

22, 1946 (Burleigh). At Augusta, the White-eyed Vireo was noted for the first time in the winter in 1945, single birds being seen November 4 and 18 and December 9. Specimens taken then were found to represent this northern race [Denton, 1946]. At Macon, it probably winters sparingly, being noted there December 1, 1922, and November 12, 1928. Farther south in the state it has been reported from Tifton and Fitzgerald on eight occasions between the dates of January 2 to 24, 1942 through 1951 [Norris and Hopkins, 1953]; in the Okefenokee Swamp and Coleraine ("moderately common" October 31 to March 13, from 1931 to 1937) [Hebard, 1941]; in Grady County, December 26, 1937, and December 25, 1938 (Stoddard); Valdosta, November 22, 1929 (Burleigh); Savannah, January 29, 1911 (Rossignol) and February 27, 1933 (Burleigh); Blackbeard Island (fairly common), January 25, 1931 (Burleigh); Sea Island (common January 15 to April 15, 1946–48) [Woodward, 1949]; and St. Marys, January 31, 1902 (Helme).

Although it nests commonly throughout the larger part of the state, actual breeding records are not numerous, and are at present limited to the following localities: Athens, extreme nesting dates, four fresh eggs, April 23 (1922); and three slightly incubated eggs, May 27 (1922) [Burleigh, 1938]; Atlanta, nesting extremes, one egg, April 14 (1929) (Greene); and four eggs, May 27 (1920) (Arpal) [Griffin, 1940]; and Irwin County, four eggs, May 4, 1941 (Hopkins).

HABITS AND RECOGNITION: Being rather small and an inconspicuous olive-green, the White-eyed Vireo could be easily overlooked in the tangled thickets it inhabits were it not for its inquisitive disposition and loquaciousness. Approach its haunts, and one is greeted with a harsh, scolding note that will at once betray its presence. Arouse its curiosity, and it will, with little hesitation, come within a few feet of the intruder, and if not unduly alarmed, will linger until convinced there is nothing to be concerned about. Few birds sing more persistently, and except for a brief interval in the late summer, its loud, emphatic song can be heard from the time it arrives in the spring until its departure in the fall. Once heard, this song will always serve as a ready means of identification, for no other bird song even remotely resembles it. The vigor with which it is uttered is characteristic of this vireo, for it is an active, energetic little bird, with none of the deliberate actions typical of other members of its family. On occasion it may, as it feeds, venture into the lower branches of the larger trees, but on the whole its days are spent in dense underbrush where it is seldom seen.

Although nests with fresh eggs have at times been found in late May, it is doubtful if in Georgia more than one brood is reared each year, for it is in late April and early May that most of the birds appear to be engaged in domestic responsibilities. In common with the other vireos, the nest is invariably pensile, being suspended from a fork of a branch from two to six feet from the ground. It is compactly built of shreds of bark, bits of dead leaves, fragments of crushed weed stems, green moss, and grasses, well cupped, and lined with fine grasses. Four eggs are usually laid, rarely three.

Southern White-eyed Vireo
Vireo griseus griseus (Boddaert)

GENERAL DISTRIBUTION: Breeds from northeastern North Carolina south to southern Florida, and west along the Gulf Coast to eastern Texas. Winters south to Yucatán and Guatemala, north casually to South Carolina and Texas.

STATUS IN GEORGIA: A common summer resident in the southern edge of the state and along the Savannah River as far north as Augusta. Of casual occurrence during the winter months within its breeding range.

The range of typical *griseus* appears to be quite limited for it apparently occurs only in the southern edge of the state in the vicinity of the coast, and along the Savannah River as far north as Augusta. On the coast breeding specimens have been taken in McIntosh County (Darien), Wayne County (Jesup), Long County (Ludovici), Liberty County (Hinesville and Yellow Bluff), and Chatham County (Savannah), while farther north in the vicinity of the Savannah River it has been recorded in Warren County (Warrenton), Glascock County (Gibson), and Richmond County (Augusta). A breeding male taken in Johnson County (Kite) is intermediate in its characters and difficult to assign to either race, although on the basis of size it is closer to *griseus.* [Burleigh, 1948.]

Since the above was written, breeding specimens of this southern race have been taken in Grady County, extending its range during the summer months along the southern edge of the state. Definite winter records are from Blackbeard Island (January 25, 1931), Okefenokee Swamp (December 29, 1945), and Grady County (December 25 and 31, 1950).

HABITS AND RECOGNITION: This southern race of the White-eyed Vireo is distinguished by its paler yellow flanks and the gray wash covering the bright olive-green of the back. Within its rather restricted range in Georgia it is a common bird during the summer months, occurring in thickets and underbrush bordering streams, or in similar situations in swampy woods. A nest that was found at Savannah, on April 29, 1921, held four incubated eggs, and was six and one-half feet from the ground at the outer end of a limb of a red gum sapling in a stretch of thick, swampy woods. It was constructed largely of green moss, and a few crushed fragments of weed stems and spider's down, lined with fine grasses and shreds of bark, and ornamented slightly on the outside with green lichens. Rossignol (personal correspondence) gives as extreme nesting dates for Savannah (seventeen nests), four incubated eggs, April 24 (1907); and three slightly incubated eggs, June 30 (1908).

Walter J. Erichsen made an intensive study of the breeding habits of this vireo at Savannah, his notes discussing in detail seventy-four occupied nests found from 1911 through 1949. Summarizing briefly, he states:

481

SOUTHERN WHITE-EYED VIREO

Vireo griseus noveboracensis

The "pit, pit-i-ta-wheer, chip!" of this vireo's song was a familiar sound
in thick, tangled woods, but not in the open pinelands. A nest found
a few feet from the ground in a dogwood bush was so very beautiful
that I decided to paint it in full detail—tufts of moss, spider egg-cases,
dried petals, bits of cast-off snakeskin, and all. The white bracts had long
since dropped from the branch to which the nest was attached.

Although but one brood is reared in a season, my observations show that among the birds occupying this region, considerable variation occurs in the time of laying of the eggs. Some pairs have full sets of eggs as early as April 16–22, but my observations here lead me to think that the time of maximum abundance of fresh eggs in the nest extends from April 26 to May 11. However, I have frequently recorded sets of fresh eggs between May 15 and May 31. I have only one late nesting record, June 10, 1916, three fresh eggs, but I consider this a second attempt at nesting following the destruction of an earlier nest.

The nests that he found varied in height from two to nine feet above the ground, the majority being under five feet, and were built of fine strips of inner bark, cane leaves, coarse grasses, and weed stems, lined with fine rootlets and, rarely, vine tendrils. In most instances the outside of the nest was ornamented with insect egg-cases and bits of rotten wood, held in place by cobwebs.

He also reports four nests found at Allenhurst, Liberty County, in 1913: two on April 22, one on April 29, and one on May 7, each holding four eggs.

Denton [letter] reports three nests found at Augusta: one on April 5, 1945, with one fresh egg; the second on April 29, 1945, with four small young; and the third on May 16, 1950, with two eggs.

Yellow-throated Vireo
Vireo flavifrons   Vieillot

GENERAL DISTRIBUTION: Breeds from Saskatchewan, southern Manitoba, southeastern Ontario, southwestern Quebec, and Maine south to central Texas, central Louisiana, southern Mississippi, central Alabama, and northern Florida. Winters from Yucatán and southern Mexico through Central America to Colombia and Venezuela, casually in Cuba and the Bahamas.

STATUS IN GEORGIA: A fairly common summer resident throughout the state.

In the spring, the Yellow-throated Vireo appears in Georgia in March, and in the fall lingers until early October. The earliest spring transients were noted at St. Marys, March 16 (1903); Hinesville, March 25 (1945); Savannah, March 15 (1921); Grady County, March 4 (1944); Fitzgerald, March 23 (1941); Columbus, April 3 (1945); Macon, March 25 (1937); Milledgeville, March 18 (1940); Augusta, April 2 (1945); Athens, March 30 (1929); Atlanta, March 25 (1893); Rising Fawn, March 30 (1885); and Dalton, April 7 (1944). The latest in the fall were seen at Athens,

October 14 (1927); Atlanta, October 25 (1948); Macon, October 27 (1934); Americus, October 4 (1941); Fitzgerald, October 19 (1940); Grady County, October 25 (1947); and Savannah, October 13 (1931).

During the summer, this handsome vireo has a wide distribution in Georgia. In the mountains it has been seen to an altitude of 3,100 feet (in Neel's Gap), while elsewhere in the state it has been reported as nesting in many localities south to the Florida line. Definite breeding records are at present limited to the following localities:

Athens: Four well-incubated eggs, May 7, 1924; four well-incubated eggs, May 6, 1925; and three slightly incubated eggs, June 1, 1926 (Burleigh).

Atlanta: Young, May 1, 1938 (Oliver); four young, June 19, 1938 (Griffin) [Griffin, 1940].

Fitzgerald: Four young, May 17, 1941 (Hopkins).

Grady County: Female working on half-completed nest, April 24, 1949 (Stoddard).

Savannah: Four fresh eggs, April 30, 1915; two fresh eggs, May 27, 1922 (Rossignol); four fresh eggs, April 26, 1912; and two slightly incubated eggs, June 18, 1916 (Erichsen).

HABITS AND RECOGNITION: This vireo is a bird of the more extensively wooded areas of the state, frequenting the upper branches of the larger trees, where it leads a leisurely existence far above the ground. On occasion it may be seen at closer range, but its forays in the lower branches are infrequent and brief. A characteristic of most of the vireos is their deliberate movements, and this is certainly true of the Yellow-throated Vireo. It has none of the restless activity of the warblers or the kinglets. It moves slowly about as it feeds, peering under the leaves for an elusive caterpillar, or hesitating as it carefully scrutinizes the twig on which it is perching. Having satisfied its appetite, it may remain quiet for minutes at a time, and, so well does its yellow throat and olive-green back blend with the foliage about it that it is then extremely difficult to see.

Its song is a rich contralto warble that further emphasizes its leisurely disposition, for there is a pause of varying length between the phrases. Delivered in this manner, the song may continue for minutes at a time if the bird is not disturbed.

In nesting, this vireo shows the typical disinclination to approach the ground, the pensile nest being suspended from a fork at the extreme outer end of an upper limb of a large deciduous tree, preferably an oak. Rarely a conifer may be used, the only instance known to me being a nest found by Hebard in Camden County, on which the bird was incubating April 23 through May 1, 1948, that was forty-five feet from the ground in a large loblolly pine (*Pinus taeda*). The nest is a handsome structure, for the outside is always well ornamented with gray lichens in much the same manner as that of a Hummingbird or Wood Pewee. Rather large for the size of the bird, it is compactly built of shreds of bark, vine tendrils, weed stems, and grasses, lined with fine grass. Being generally from thirty-five to fifty feet from the ground, the nest is hard to find, and even harder to reach if one desires to ascertain its contents.

Both male and female take turns in incubating the four eggs that are normally laid, and while so engaged are remarkably fearless. This characteristic was well illustrated in the case of a nest found at Athens on May 28, 1926, that held one fresh egg. Returning four days later for more complete data, I found it impossible to make the incubating bird leave. The nest was fifty feet from the ground at the end of a branch of a large mockernut hickory, but by climbing above it, I was able to get within ten feet of the nest. I then proceeded to shake the limb, clap my hands, and even throw twigs at the nest, but the only effect on the incubating bird was to make it crouch deeper in the nest. Ultimately I gave up, and left the vireo to a well deserved victory.

Blue-headed Solitary Vireo
Vireo solitarius solitarius (Wilson)

GENERAL DISTRIBUTION: Breeds from central Alberta, southern Mackenzie, central Manitoba, central Ontario, and southern Quebec south to northern North Dakota, central Minnesota, Michigan, southern Pennsylvania, and Rhode Island. Winters from the coast of South Carolina, Georgia, and the Gulf Coast south through eastern Mexico to Guatemala.

STATUS IN GEORGIA: A fairly common spring and fall transient throughout the state and an uncommon winter resident as far north as Atlanta and Athens.

On the basis of specimens that have been taken it would appear that typical *solitarius* reaches Georgia in the fall about the middle of October, lingers in small numbers during the winter, and is present in the spring until late April or early May.

Specimens representing this race have been examined from:

Athens: April 30, October 22 and 29, and November 1, 1928; November 4, 1929; October 11, November 11, and December 1, 1945.
Watkinsville: March 1, 1946.
Stone Mountain: December 10, 1944; February 21, 1947.
Decatur: October 15, 22, and 29, November 5 and 28, and December 7, 1946; April 13, 1947.
Blue Ridge: April 18, 1945.
Augusta: March 7, 1891.
Blakely: February 1, 1936.
Newton: January 5, 1932.
Chatham County: January 27, 1908.
St. Marys: February 2, 1904.

Some of the sight records for late September and early October at Athens and at Macon may possibly be referable to *solitarius,* and there is little question that a bird seen at Athens on May 12, 1928 represented this northern race. Further collecting will be necessary to determine such points as this.

HABITS AND RECOGNITION: As a transient in Georgia the Blue-headed Solitary Vireo may be found in the more open woods, feeding alone or with flocks of warblers, chickadees, and kinglets. It never occurs in flocks of its own kind, one or two birds usually being seen feeding silently in the lower branches of the larger trees. In association with other species, its deliberate movements will serve to distinguish it, and a closer glimpse will reveal its conspicuous white eye-ring, a character lacking in the other vireos. In the spring, an occasional bird may be heard singing, the song suggesting that of the Yellow-throated Vireo, but higher in pitch and with a shorter pause between the phrases. Ordinarily, however, this vireo is a quiet, inconspicuous bird, and is easily overlooked.

Mountain Solitary Vireo
Vireo solitarius alticola   Brewster

GENERAL DISTRIBUTION: Breeds from western Maryland south to eastern Tennessee and central Georgia. Winters in the lowlands from South Carolina to Florida and on the Gulf Coast west to eastern Louisiana.

STATUS IN GEORGIA: A common summer resident in the mountains and of local occurrence during the summer months as far south as Jones and Upson counties. A common transient over the entire state, and an uncommon winter resident north at least to Atlanta and Athens.

Specimens critically examined to determine the occurrence and relative abundance of the two subspecies of *Vireo solitarius* occurring in Georgia showed that the Appalachian race is apparently more common as a transient, and present in equal numbers during the winter. Those taken south of the mountains in migration include the following: Athens, fifteen specimens between the dates of March 22 (1928) and April 11 (1928), and October 9 (1928) and November 16 (1938); Stone Mountain, a male, October 28, 1946; Decatur, a male, March 30, 1947; and Atlanta, a male, November 14, 1946.

The winter months are represented by specimens taken at Athens, January 15, 1922, and December 16 and 17, 1945; Center (Jackson County), December 3, 1945; Princeton (Clarke County), February 5, 1946; and St. Marys, January 30, 1904.

Breeding birds have been examined from the following localities: Brasstown Bald, July 14 and 17, 1908, and June 20, 1929; Rich Mountain, July 8, 1908; Cowpen Mountain, June 21, 1927; Dahlonega, June 4, 1927; Round Oak (Jones County), June 6, 1947; and Thomaston (Upson County), June 14, 1947.

Family *Vireonidae:* VIREOS

In the absence of actual specimens, a problem presents itself as to what race should be favored in enumerating available migration data. However, as the Mountain Solitary Vireo is apparently the more common of the two forms, all such records are included in the present discussion, with the qualification that some of them refer to the race *solitarius:*

Atlanta: Extreme dates of occurrence, September 28 (1946) and May 1 (1938).

Augusta: Earliest fall arrival date, October 16 (1933).

Milledgeville: One winter record, January 26, 1938.

Macon: Extreme dates of occurrence, September 7 (1952) and May 6 (1934).

Fitzgerald: September 18 (1941) and April 21 (1941).

Grady County: October 26 (1947) and May 5 (1940).

Savannah: October 17 (1925) and May 1 (1933).

Sea Island: Recorded January 25, 1948.

St. Marys: Latest spring date, April 17 (1905).

Definite breeding records for Georgia are not numerous. On the slopes of Brasstown Bald, in Towns County, thirteen occupied nests were found, the earliest on May 22, 1923, with half-grown young, the latest on June 19, 1922, with four well-incubated eggs [Burleigh, 1925, 1927]. A nest found at Margret, Fannin County, on July 15, 1922 held newly hatched young [Burleigh, 1925]. South of the mountains, Fleetwood [1947] reported a nest with three fresh eggs at Round Oak, Jones County, on June 16, 1946; Odum [1948], a nest with three fresh eggs at Athens, Clarke County, on June 1, 1948; and Johnston [letter], adults feeding young at Athens on May 12 and 26, 1949.

HABITS AND RECOGNITION: The Mountain Solitary Vireo is an unusually well-marked subspecies, being distinguished by its larger size, and especially its larger bill, and by its gray, rather than olive-green, back. When first described by William Brewster in 1886, it was considered a bird of the southern Appalachians, with its breeding range in Georgia limited to the extreme northeastern corner of the state. In recent years, however, it has extended its breeding range southward in the Piedmont almost to the fall line, and while locally distributed at the present time, there are indications that it may eventually be a common summer resident throughout the northern half of Georgia. Odum [1948] has discussed at some length this southward invasion:

In 1945 Burleigh and I suggested that the Mountain Blue-headed Vireo, usually called the Mountain Solitary Vireo (*Vireo solitarius alticola*), might be about ready to extend its breeding range from the Mountains to the Piedmont of Georgia (see *Auk*, 63:389–401, 1946). This suggestion was based on the fact that the species was very abundant in the Mountains (creating potential population pressure), had

487

been observed at very low elevations at the foot of the Blue Ridge (in Habersham and Pickens counties), and was already known to nest on the Piedmont of North Carolina (indicating that it could tolerate Piedmont conditions). In our paper we also stated that "very rapid changes probably are not to be expected." In other words, we assumed that if the bird did extend its range it would do so gradually, a few miles a year.

There can be no doubt that a southward invasion, or at least an attempted invasion, is now occurring as predicted, but the manner of invasion is not as suggested. Instead of a gradual extension, the bird has suddenly appeared at points some distance from its former range and has colonized locally. . . . On June 16, 1946, Raymond J. Fleetwood found a nest of this species on the Piedmont Wildlife Refuge near Macon, at least 120 miles from the previously known limit of the breeding range. In addition to this nesting pair Fleetwood found the Mountain Vireo at eleven other widely separated places on the refuge and adjoining areas in Jones and Jasper counties that summer. During the summer of 1947, Burleigh found singing males in Upson County, also a long way from the mountains. In these cases, of course, one could not be absolutely certain that the bird was new to the areas (as a breeder), and not merely overlooked in the past. This year, 1948, any doubt about a real range extension by this species has been dispelled by its dramatic appearance and nesting at Athens under circumstances which indicate *positively that the bird is new to the area,* and furthermore, that probably we have been fortunate in finding the bird the very first year that it has nested in the region.

Just southwest of the city limits of Athens I own a tract of 28 acres bordering the Middle Oconee River. The predominant vegetation of the tract is a loblolly-short-leaf pine forest ranging from young to fairly mature stand. For three seasons, 1946–48, I have conducted a breeding bird census on the area which was, therefore, visited frequently. I am quite certain that the Mountain Vireo did not occur on the area or anywhere in the vicinity in 1946 or 1947. During March and April of 1948 a Mountain Vireo was noted singing on the hillside below my house, but, since migrants of this species are known to occur here as late as early May, I did not follow the bird too closely or observe a mate. The next thing I knew, on May 16, the bird was feeding bob-tailed young not long out of the nest; it had paired and built a nest (which I never did find) almost under my nose. Fortunately the species is double brooded so I was fully alerted the next time and had no trouble locating the nest next built by the pair, which, when found on May 31, contained 2 eggs. The set of 3 eggs was complete the next day and incubation begun by both sexes as is characteristic of the species.

Since the above was written, Denton [1951] reports two singing males in southern Wilkes County, fifteen miles north of Thomson, on June 22, 1949, and again on May 30, 1950. He was unsuccessful in finding a nest, but in view of the date there is little question that these birds were breeding there.

For both feeding and nesting this vireo seems to prefer the saplings and lower branches of the larger trees, although on occasion it will be found well up from the ground. The nest is built in both conifers and hardwoods, although in the mountains of Georgia hardwoods seem to be preferred. Of seven nests found on the slopes of Brasstown Bald, May 22–24, 1923, two were in laurels, two in red maples, and one each in white oak, yellow birch, and mountain magnolia (*Magnolia fraseri*). They varied from six feet to, in one case, as high as forty feet from the ground, although the average was between fifteen and twenty feet. In construction they were much alike, being characteristically pensile and compactly built of grasses, fragments of weed stems, and shreds of bark, lined with fine grasses, vine tendrils, and fine hemlock twigs, and well covered on the outside with green lichens and, in several instances, fragments of an old hornet's nest. Three or four eggs are normally laid, and two broods are apparently reared in Georgia each year, the first in early May and the second in late June.

Red-eyed Vireo
Vireo olivaceus (Linnaeus)

GENERAL DISTRIBUTION: Breeds from southern British Columbia, western Mackenzie, central Manitoba, central Ontario, and Cape Breton Island south to northern Oregon, Washington, Idaho, southern Montana, eastern Wyoming, eastern Colorado, central Nebraska, central Texas, the Gulf Coast, and central Florida. Winters in South America from eastern Ecuador to western Brazil.

STATUS IN GEORGIA: A common summer resident throughout the state.

The Red-eyed Vireo reaches Georgia in the spring in March, and lingers in the fall until the latter part of October. The earliest spring transients were seen at St. Marys, March 19 (1905); Cumberland Island, March 25 (1902); Savannah, March 17 (1911); Grady County, March 21 (1944); Fitzgerald, March 21 (1942); Macon, March 23 (1952); Augusta, March 24 (1945); Athens, April 8 (1928); Atlanta, March 31 (1893); Rome, April 4 (1953); and Dalton, April 8 (1928).

The latest in the fall were noted at Athens, October 26 (1925); Atlanta, October 29 (1948); Macon, October 24 (1922); Fitzgerald, October 18 (1940); Grady County, October 31 (1937); and Savannah, November 5 (1931).

As a breeding bird, this vireo has a wide distribution in the state. Open pine woods are not to its liking, but it is doubtful that there are many stretches of deciduous hardwoods of any size, from the mountains to the coast, where one or more pairs cannot be found during the summer months. It occurs on the slopes of Brasstown Bald, Georgia's loftiest mountain, to an altitude of 4,000 feet, in the wooded stream bottoms of the Piedmont, and in the tupelo swamps of the coastal plain. There is little question that it nests wherever observed in the late spring and summer, but definite breeding records are at present restricted to the following localities:

Margret, Fannin County: Three fresh eggs, June 22, 1921 (Burleigh).

Young Harris, Towns County: Four fresh eggs, May 19, 1927 (Burleigh).

Athens, Clarke County: Nesting extremes (eight nests), three fresh eggs, May 13 (1921); three partially incubated eggs, July 5 (1925) [Burleigh, 1938].

Atlanta: Nesting extremes, two eggs, May 12 (1913) (Hembree); three fresh eggs, July 1 (1936) (Griffin) [Griffin, 1940].

Irwin County: Three eggs, May 18, 1941 (Hopkins).

Savannah, Chatham County: Nesting extremes (nineteen nests), three fresh eggs, May 1 (1912); three incubated eggs, June 17 (1906) (Rossignol); June 26 (1927), three slightly incubated eggs (Erichsen).

Allenhurst, Liberty County: Three eggs, May 21 (1913); three eggs, June 2 (1913) (Erichsen).

HABITS AND RECOGNITION: Because of its wide distribution and relative abundance, the Red-eyed Vireo is undoubtedly the best-known member of its family. That it is so well known, however, is due to a large extent to its persistence as a singer. In common with most of the vireos, its movements are deliberate and unhurried as it feeds overhead, and its plumage, olive-green above and white beneath, blends so well with the foliage that, were it consistently quiet, it would be inconspicuous and difficult to see. As it happens, quite the opposite is the case. From the time it arrives in the spring and until late summer, it sings throughout the entire day. There are undoubtedly intervals when it is quiet, but the impression it gives is that of a bird that never tires as it repeats the short phrases that comprise its song. Although it usually feeds well above the ground, its persistent singing makes it an easy bird to locate, and sooner or later it will approach close enough to enable one to see the gray crown, black-bordered white line over the eye, and lack of wing-bars that distinguish it.

For nesting, an upper branch of a tall sapling is usually selected although not infrequently a larger tree is used. The average height of the nest from the ground varies from ten to twenty feet, and as is true of all vireo nests, it is pensile and suspended from a fork at the outer end of a limb. It is compactly built of shreds of bark, grasses, and crushed fragments of weed stems, well cupped, and lined with fine strips of bark. An interesting characteristic of the vireos is their habit of ornamenting the outside of their nests, and the Red-eye is no exception. Almost invariably white spider's down is used, and not infrequently pieces of paper, birch bark, fragments of an old hornet's nest, and bits of rotten wood.

In Georgia, three eggs are normally laid, rarely four, and two broods apparently are reared each year, the first in May, the second in late June and early July.

Philadelphia Vireo
Vireo philadelphicus (Cassin)

GENERAL DISTRIBUTION: Breeds from northern Alberta, southern Manitoba, northern Ontario, New Brunswick, and Maine south to northern North Dakota, northern Michigan, and New Hampshire. Winters from Yucatán and Guatemala south to Panama.

STATUS IN GEORGIA: A rare fall transient.

Specimens of this inconspicuous little vireo have been taken in Georgia as follows:

Richmond County: September 17, 1890, by George P. Butler [Murphey, 1937].
Athens: October 7, 1933 [Burleigh, 1938].
Tifton: October 8, 1941 [Norris, 1941]
Atlanta: October 9, 1946 [Burleigh, 1947]; October 6, 1951 [Parks, 1952b]; October 3, 1953 [Parks, 1954]; September 11, 1954 [Parks, 1954]; and October 7, 1954 [Griffin, 1955].
Macon: October 8, 1954 [Johnston, 1955].

There are also four sight records: single birds seen at Macon, October 12, 1922, and October 24, 1925 (Meanley); Americus, October 4, 1941 [Denton, 1943]; Atlanta, October 9, 1948 [Parks, 1949].

It has yet to be noted during the spring migration, but it is possible that it occurs in small numbers then.

HABITS AND RECOGNITION: The Philadelphia Vireo is a bird that can be easily overlooked, for in both appearance and actions there is nothing about it to attract the observer. Small and inconspicuously colored, it is almost a part of the foliage in which, in characteristic vireo fashion, it leisurely feeds. Seen at close range, its olive-green back and yellow underparts suggest those of a Tennessee Warbler, but its stockier build and heavier bill should distinguish it from that species. Its song resembles very closely that of the Red-eyed Vireo but is softer; in migration it is consistently silent, and so far as the few individuals seen in Georgia are concerned, it has not been known to utter a note of any kind.

491

Wood Warblers: *Family Parulidae*

Black and White Warbler
Mniotilta varia (Linnaeus)

GENERAL DISTRIBUTION: Breeds from western Mackenzie, central Manitoba, northern Ontario, and Newfoundland south to eastern Texas, Louisiana, central Alabama, northern Georgia, and northern South Carolina, west to South Dakota and casually to Wyoming, Montana, and Colorado. Winters from northern Mexico south to northern South America (Colombia, Ecuador, and Venezuela), and in coastal South Carolina, Georgia, Florida, the Bahamas, and the West Indies.

STATUS IN GEORGIA: A fairly common summer resident in the northern part of the state, and a common transient and uncommon winter resident south of the mountains.

The earliest spring transients were noted at Savannah, February 23 (1908); Columbus, March 31 (1946); Macon, March 14 (1952); Milledgeville, March 29 (1940); Augusta, March 20 (1891); Athens, March 13 (1921); Atlanta, March 10 (1902); and Dalton, March 26 (1944). The latest in the fall were seen at Atlanta, October 26 (1947); Athens, November 19 (1923); Augusta, November 30 (1944); Milledgeville, November 30 (1944); Macon, October 10 (1925); and Savannah (Tybee Light), October 29 (1925).

South of its breeding range in the northern part of the state, the Black and White Warbler was first observed in the fall at Savannah on July 17 (1908) and July 28 (1909), and in the spring as late as May 21 (1910). At Darien, it has been seen as late in the spring as May 18 (1945); at Fitzgerald, May 6 (1941), and at Augusta, May 15, 1945. At Augusta, the earliest record for the fall migration is July 30 (1944); at Tifton, July 11 (1951); and in Grady County, July 11 (1945).

In the winter it has been seen at Augusta (January 31, 1925), Athens (January 14, 1923); Atlanta (December 31, 1930, December 22, 1932, December, 1941, February 2, 1946, December 27, 1953); Milledgeville (December 31, 1942, January 16, 1947); Macon (December 17, 1943, December 31, 1950, December 10, 1952); Newton (January 5, 1932); Fitzgerald (January 28, 1939, December 25, 1940); Wilcox County (January 27, 1946); in the Okefenokee Swamp (December 20, 1933, December 4, 1934); and Sea Island (January, 1946–48). In Camden County and in Grady County it has been found wintering regularly, but in rather small numbers.

Although it occurs during the summer in the northern part of the state and undoubtedly nests more or less commonly, there are at present few definite breeding records. At Emory University there is a set of five eggs taken by Hembree near Atlanta on April 23, 1921 [Griffin, 1940]; and Griffin (1941) reports a nest found at North Fulton Park, which, on May 9, 1941, held five eggs. At Athens, young just out of the nest were seen on May 28, 1922 [Burleigh, 1938], and another brood barely able to fly was noted at Woodville, in Greene County, May 18, 1923 (Burleigh). At Milledgeville, two birds were reported July 5, 1939 [Burns and Anderson, 1939], but as the southward movement of this species begins in July, it is probable that these were early transients.

HABITS AND RECOGNITION: Few birds are better named than the Black and White Warbler, for these are the only two colors in its plumage. This alone would give it a unique distinction in a family famed for its bright colors, which, in varying shades of orange, yellow, or green, are displayed by the numerous species occurring in Georgia. In actions, also, it is equally distinctive, for in much the manner of a nuthatch it creeps about the branches and trunks of trees. To the other warblers is left, to a large extent, the task of searching the leaves and smaller twigs for insects and their larvae, for the Black and White Warbler is primarily interested in what it can find in the crevices of the bark, and while it lacks the agility of a nuthatch, it is adept in working up the trunk of a tree or in clinging to the under surface of a branch. In migration it is commonly found associated with other warblers, but its distinctive method of feeding makes it readily recognized. It can be found, to some extent at least, in open pine woods, but as a breeding bird it shows a marked partiality for deciduous hardwoods. Consequently, south of the mountains it is rather local in its distribution, and in the Piedmont of Georgia is confined to ravines and to wooded hillsides along the larger streams.

The nest is built on the ground, and being well concealed at the base of a stump or large rock, it is extremely hard to find. Once the female begins to incubate, she will leave the nest only when almost stepped on. Although breeding activities begin in mid-April and the young are well fledged by the latter part of May, only a single brood is reared in Georgia each year. This is possibly due to the fact this species is one of the earliest fall migrants, appearing well south of its breeding range in early July.

Prothonotary Warbler
Protonotaria citrea   (Boddaert)

GENERAL DISTRIBUTION: Breeds from northeastern Nebraska, southeastern Minnesota, southern Wisconsin, southern Michigan, Ohio, central Delaware, and eastern Maryland south to eastern Texas, the Gulf Coast, and northern Florida. Winters from Nicaragua to Colombia, and casually in Venezuela and southern Mexico.

STATUS IN GEORGIA: A common summer resident south of the fall line and locally distributed during the summer months on the Chattahoochee River and its tributaries, north at least to Atlanta.

In the northern part of the state, the Prothonotary Warbler is irregular and local in its occurrence, and has been reported from but a few localities. Alexander Gerhardt found it breeding at Varnell Station in 1859, as recorded in the egg catalog of the United States National Museum. Dorsey [letter] reports six birds seen "at small swampy ponds" near Rome on May 31, 1953, but no nests were found despite a careful search. At Atlanta [Griffin, 1941], it breeds in small numbers, and has been noted between the dates of April 14 (1921) and October 8 (1939). An occupied nest, contents undetermined, was found in the South River section, May 4, 1930 [Greene, 1933]; and another with young on Peachtree Creek, June 1, 1946 [Griffin and Major, 1947]. At Athens [Burleigh, 1938], it was found to be a scarce and rather irregular transient in both spring and fall and was seen only at infrequent intervals in stretches of woods bordering the Oconee River. Extreme dates for the spring migration there are April 14 (1926) and May 17 (1929), while in the fall it was recorded only in 1929, single birds being seen August 9, 13, and 21. Denton [1951] saw a pair in a small swamp seven miles north of Lincolnton on May 23, 1950, that were apparently breeding birds, but failed to find the nest. Tait [1946] reports it at Milledgeville, April 12, 1942, and in fall migration, July 5, 1939. At Dalton, there are two records, May 4, 1940, and May 7, 1941.

South of the fall line, the earliest spring transients were observed at Cumberland Island, April 10 (1902); Sea Island, April 7 (1946); Savannah, April 1 (1912); Okefenokee Swamp, April 1 (1945); Grady County, April 5 (1940); Fitzgerald, March 21 (1942); Americus, April 10 (1942); Columbus, April 3 (1945); Macon, March 26 (1945); and Augusta, March 29 (1947). The latest in the fall were noted at Augusta, September 8 (1944); Macon, September 24 (1955); Tifton, August 29 (1942); Grady County, September 24 (1948); Savannah, September 29 (1928); and Camden County, September 27 (1946).

It has been reported as breeding at St. Marys, Darien, Savannah, in the Okefenokee Swamp, Newton, in Seminole County (near Chattahoochee, Florida), Americus, Marshallville, and Macon; and there are definite nesting records for the following localities:

Camden County: Four young in nest, June 18, 1944; and fully fledged young, May 15, 1952 (Hebard).

Chatham County: May 14, 1927, five eggs [Bassett, 1927].

Grady County: Nest with three large young, July 6, 1946 (Stoddard).

Fitzgerald: May 27, 1940, five eggs; June 3, 1940, three young (Hopkins) [Norris, 1940].

Macon: May 13, 1943, five eggs (Denton).

Augusta: June 1, 1924, three almost fully fledged young (Burleigh); June 5, 1950, three small young (Denton).

HABITS AND RECOGNITION: With its bright orange-yellow head and under-parts, the male Prothonotary Warbler is one of the handsomest of its family, but unfortunately its haunts are such that it is seldom seen by the average person. Water is a primary requisite for its existence, and in the summer months it is largely confined to wooded swamps and river bottoms. To one sufficiently interested, however, to penetrate a cypress swamp or a flooded river bottom, the first glimpse of a Prothonotary Warbler will leave a lasting impression, its glowing colors standing out in vivid contrast to its surroundings. Dr. Eugene E. Murphey, writing of the bird life of the Augusta region [1937], has given us this charming description of the bird and its haunts, which is here quoted in full:

> Primarily a bird of the deep cypress swamps and river bottoms, although it does to some extent follow the smaller water courses up into the hills. But the cypress is its home and there it is most abundant. It is particularly fearless going about its small businesses with little attention to the fisherman whose haunts are identical with its own. So much is the golden flash of the Prothonotary and its persistent song a part of the swamp picture of black water, tall cypress, tupelo, and sombre grey moss that its absence could be likened only to the omission of some important instrument from an orchestra or a primary color from a painter's palette.

In contrast to the other warblers that breed in Georgia, this species invariably selects a cavity in an old, rotten stub in which to build its nest, if possible over water, and usually within arm's reach. The bottom of the cavity is lined with grasses, shreds of bark, and dry cypress leaves, and on this more or less substantial bed, four or five eggs are laid. Apparently in Georgia but one brood is reared each year.

Lowland Swainson's Warbler
Limnothlypis swainsonii swainsonii (Audubon)

GENERAL DISTRIBUTION: Breeds from southeastern Missouri, southern Illinois, southern Indiana, and the Eastern Shore of Maryland and Virginia south to eastern Texas, Louisiana, southern Alabama, and northern Florida. Winters in Jamaica.

STATUS IN GEORGIA: A fairly common summer resident south of the fall line.

Earliest spring transients were noted at: Cumberland Island, April 15 (1902); McIntosh County, April 12 (1889); Savannah, March 25 (1910) and March 30 (1916); Macon, March 31 (1944); and Augusta, April 1 (1950). In the fall there are records of birds striking the Tybee Light,

495

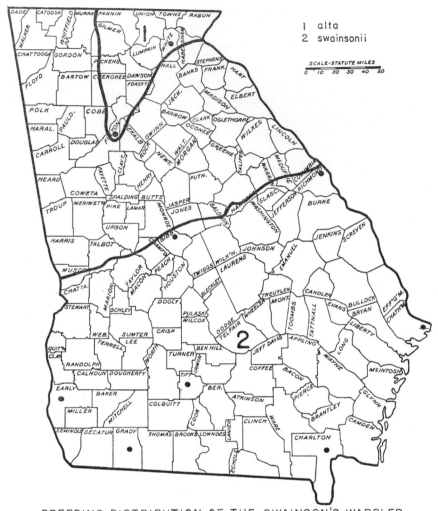

1 alta
2 swainsonii

SCALE-STATUTE MILES
0 10 20 30 40 50

BREEDING DISTRIBUTION OF THE SWAINSON'S WARBLER

near Savannah, on October 2, 1908, September 23 and 24, 1924, and October 18, 1929. The latest fall date for Augusta is September 22 (1944); for Macon, September 16 (1944); for Tifton, September 20, 1941; and for the Okefenokee Swamp, October 8, 1954.

It has been found during the summer months in the Okefenokee Swamp and at Beachton and Blakely, and there are definite breeding records for the following localities:

Savannah: April 29, 1921, nest nearly completed (Burleigh).

Augusta: May 6, 1922, three fresh eggs; May 14, 1922, three incubated eggs [Burleigh, 1923]; June 24, 1945, three fresh eggs; May 12, 1950, four eggs (Denton).

Macon: May 18, 1944, three fresh eggs; June 19, 1944, two young (Meanley, 1945).

Tifton: June 13, 1946, three eggs [Norris and Hopkins, 1947].

Family Parulidae: WOOD WARBLERS

HABITS AND RECOGNITION: Swainson's Warbler is a singularly difficult bird to become acquainted with in its summer haunts. During its sojourn in Georgia, it frequents, to a large extent, heavily wooded swamps, and it is so shy and retiring that even when its song betrays its presence, it is extremely hard to see. Its food is gathered on the ground, and here its rather drab plumage, olive-brown above and dull, yellowish-white beneath, blends so well with its surroundings that in thick brush it is inconspicuous almost to the point of invisibility. Unlike those of most of the other warblers, its movements are deliberate and unhurried, and, as it searches the dead leaves and other debris that litter the drier portions of the swamp, it walks rather than hops. Its appetite satisfied, it will fly into a bush and remain motionless for long intervals, a trait not suspected in a warbler. As long as it is quiet, it usually escapes notice, but its loud, ringing song at once attracts attention. This song, suggestive of the songs of the Hooded Warbler and the Northern Water-thrush, is an unexpected performance on the part of an otherwise undemonstrative bird, and when first heard arouses immediate curiosity about its source. One's curiosity will seldom be easily satisfied, however, for there is a ventriloquial quality to a Swainson's Warbler's song that makes the bird disconcertingly hard to locate.

In Georgia, this warbler nests in late April and May, and it is doubtful that more than one brood is reared each year. The nest is built in a low bush or clump of canes, usually within one or two feet of the ground, and although rather a bulky structure, it is fairly well concealed. Dead leaves form the bulk of the material used, the well-defined hollow in the top being lined with fine weed stems, Spanish moss, dry cypress sprays, rootlets, and pine needles. Three—at times four or but two—plain white eggs are laid. Unique in many ways, Swainson's Warbler possesses the added distinction of colonizing in small groups during the nesting season, three or more pairs sometimes being found within a rather limited area.

Appalachian Swainson's Warbler
Limnothlypis swainsonii alta Meanley and Bond

GENERAL DISTRIBUTION: Breeds in the Appalachian Mountains from West Virginia south to Georgia. Winter range unknown, but probably in Jamaica.

STATUS IN GEORGIA: A scarce and local summer resident in the northern part of the state.

In northern Georgia, Swainson's Warbler has been reported from but three localities. It formerly nested at Atlanta, but apparently no longer does so. Greene [1933] states that some years ago two nests were found by

497

PROTHONOTARY WARBLERS
Protonotaria citrea

The plumage of this warbler has a wonderful light-catching quality.
As the bird flits about above the dark swamp water, it calls to mind a little
flame wandering from place to place. I watched several pairs but did not
find a nest until, using an old flat-bottomed boat, I visited every stub in a
woodland pond. The nest was only a few inches above the water in a small,
hollow sweet-gum stub which almost collapsed when I touched it.
My painting shows the adult male and the first chick of the brood
to leave the nest.

Family Parulidae: WOOD WARBLERS

La Prade in Collier's Woods, one on May 27, 1920, with three eggs, the other (deserted) on May 30, 1922, with one egg. The only recent records are of single birds noted, April 19, 1936, and April 18, 1948 (Griffin), and April 12, 1947, and April 17, 1954 (Parks). At Athens, it has been observed on only two occasions in the spring, singing males being seen in woods bordering the Oconee River on May 20, 1921, and April 26, 1928 [Burleigh, 1938]. On June 3, 1948, a singing male was observed at close range in a wooded ravine near Robertstown, White County [Denton, 1948], and subsequent field work in this area proved conclusively that this elusive warbler was breeding there.

"When the area was first visited in the spring on May 8, 1949, and May 9, 1950, the birds were already there, three singing males on the first occasion, four on the latter. These birds seemed to have established territories which centered around small alder-lined streams which dropped down the side of the ravine to empty at right angles into White Branch. Repeated searches for active nests by us and others have failed although an old nest apparently of this species was found on May 31, 1950. The same day, while quietly watching a singing male, a female emerged from the thick undergrowth and flew to his perch on a low bare limb. Copulation followed and the female disappeared in the undergrowth." [Denton and Neal, 1951.] Specimens representing this recently described race were taken at Robertstown, White County, by Denton, June 3, 1948; and at Atlanta by Parks, April 12, 1947, and by Griffin, April 18, 1948. Their characters confirm the validity of the race, *alta*, although its subspecific status has yet to be recognized by the A.O.U. Checklist Committee.

HABITS AND RECOGNITION: It has been only since 1939 that the Swainson's Warbler has been found nesting in the southern Appalachians, but the presence of a valid race in this region would indicate that, because of its retiring nature, this species has been merely overlooked until recent years. Despite this warbler's spirited, ringing song, few birds, when quiet, are more inconspicuous. The habitat of the mountain race is quite unlike that of the representative of this species farther south in the state, as it frequents wooded ravines with a dense undergrowth of bushes and small saplings. The vicinity of water is given preference, but it would appear that swift-running streams are as suitable for this race as the stagnant pools of the cypress swamps of the coastal plain are for *swainsonii*.

As in the case of most other subspecies, specimens are necessary to identify satisfactorily this southern Appalachian race. It differs in having the underparts but faintly tinged with yellow and the upperparts noticeably browner.

Worm-eating Warbler
Helmitheros vermivorus (Gmelin)

GENERAL DISTRIBUTION: Breeds from southern Iowa, northern Illinois, southern Pennsylvania, and New York south to southern Missouri, northern Alabama, northern Georgia, and the mountains of South Carolina. Winters from Chiapas, Mexico, to Panama, and in Cuba, the Bahamas, and, rarely, Florida.

STATUS IN GEORGIA: A fairly common summer resident in the northern part of the state and a fairly common transient south of the mountains, although less frequently seen in the coastal plain both in the spring and in the fall.

The earliest spring transients were noted at Sea Island, April 12 (1947); Savannah, April 4 (1912); Fitzgerald, April 11 (1941); Macon, April 12 (1944); Milledgeville, April 19 (1942); Augusta, April 13 (1949); Athens, April 15 (1926); Atlanta, April 11 (1946); Canton, April 20 (1905); Roswell, April 21 (1933); and Rome, April 23 (1953). On April 16, 1902, eight birds were reported striking the light on Cumberland Island. The last in the spring were seen at Augusta, May 2 (1948); Macon, May 10 (1921); Athens, May 5 (1924); Chatham County, May 9 (1909); and Cumberland Island, May 7 (1902).

The earliest fall transients appeared at Athens, June 29 (1927) and July 1 (1939); Augusta, August 5 (1945); Macon, August 2 (1955); and Irwin County, August 8 (1951). The latest were noted at Atlanta, October 10 (1946); Athens, October 15 (1926); Augusta, October 9 (1943); Macon, September 30 (1932); and Fitzgerald, September 28 (1940). There are two records for Americus, September 12 and 14, 1941; and two for Grady County, September 20 and October 5, 1948; while on Tybee Island, birds were reported striking the light on October 6, 1923, and September 24 and 25, 1924.

This species has been observed throughout May and June on the lower slopes of Brasstown Bald, at Margret, Fannin County, and at Atlanta. The only definite breeding record is that of a nest with young found on Tray Mountain, June 25, 1947 [Denton and Neal, 1951].

HABITS AND RECOGNITION: The Worm-eating Warbler is another quiet, unobstrusive bird that must be sought to be seen. In migration, it feeds on or near the ground in thickets and dense underbrush, and being inconspicuously colored, olive-green above and buffy beneath, can be easily overlooked. It is not particularly shy, and if not alarmed can be approached without much difficulty. Seen at reasonably close range, its conspicuously striped crown, olive-buff and black, will readily identify it. Its actions are

500

deliberate and suggest those of a vireo as it peers beneath the under surface of a leaf or twig, and on occasion it creeps much in the manner of a Black and White Warbler. It apparently prefers the vicinity of water, as at Athens it was commonly encountered in thick woods bordering the Oconee River, or in underbrush at the edge of the Sandy Creek bottoms.

The nest is built on the ground, usually on a rather steep slope, and so well concealed at the base of a bush or sapling that it is extremely difficult to find. Although singing males heard on the slopes of Brasstown Bald in late May and early June have on more than one occasion encouraged careful search for a nest, none with eggs was found.

Golden-winged Warbler
Vermivora chrysoptera (Linnaeus)

GENERAL DISTRIBUTION: Breeds from central Minnesota, southeastern Ontario, and Massachusetts south to southern Iowa, northern Illinois, northern Indiana, and northern New Jersey, and in the mountains to northern Georgia and South Carolina. Winters from Guatemala to Colombia and Venezuela, casually north to southern Mexico.

STATUS IN GEORGIA: A fairly common summer resident in the extreme northern part of the state, and a not uncommon transient south of the mountains, although as yet only infrequently observed on the coastal plain in the fall.

The earliest spring transients were noted at Macon, April 19 (1924); Milledgeville, April 12 (1941); Augusta, April 28; Athens, April 26 (1923); Atlanta, April 10 (1948); and Roswell, April 24 (1933). The last in the spring were seen at Macon, May 6 (1926); Atlanta, May 8 (1938); and Athens, May 13 (1925).

In the fall, extreme dates of occurrence for Atlanta are August 6 (1948) and October 9 (1943); for Athens, August 13 (1939) and October 4 (1929); for Augusta, August 22 (1948) and September 16 (1944); and for Macon, August 31 (1933) and October 8 (1954). The Golden-winged Warbler has also been seen at Montezuma, September 15, 1914, Irwin County, September 21, 1941, and September 6, 1942; Fitzgerald, September 2, 1946; and Grady County, October 3, 1937, September 24, 1942, September 24, 1948, and September 17, 1951.

It was first reported as breeding in the state by Gerhardt, who found it nesting in Whitfield County between the dates of May 6 and 15, 1859 [Baird, Brewer, and Ridgway, 1874]. Some doubt exists, however, as to the reliability of this record. On June 24, 1885, J. T. Park saw a pair feeding young at Rising Fawn, in Dade County. In recent years it has been noted during the breeding season at Young Harris, Towns County; Blood

Mountain, Union County; and Oglethorpe Mountain, Dawson County; while at Margret, Fannin County, where it proved to be a fairly common summer resident, a nest was found June 13, 1929, with five slightly incubated eggs (Burleigh).

HABITS AND RECOGNITION: The Golden-winged Warbler, except locally in the mountains, is not a common bird in Georgia. South of its breeding range in the mountains, it can be seen in migration in both spring and fall, but usually as single individuals feeding with other warblers. More often than not, it will be in the upper branches of one of the larger trees, and with characteristic restlessness will be difficult to locate and watch as it flits about overhead. The male is a handsome bird, its soft gray plumage being offset by a vivid black throat, bright yellow crown, and broad yellow wing-patch. Females and young of the year lack the black throat, but can be distinguished by the yellow of the crown and wings.

Once it reaches its breeding grounds in the spring, the Golden-winged Warbler deserts the larger trees, and is found then in old clearings and fields overgrown with scrubby underbrush. In northern Georgia, it is chiefly a bird of the mountain valleys, although if suitable clearings are available, it will nest almost to the tops of the higher ridges. On May 30, 1933, I found a pair about an abandoned clearing on Blood Mountain, at an altitude of 3,300 feet, and Odum [1945] reports a male feeding two young on May 30, 1945, in underbrush at the top of Oglethorpe Mountain (3,000 feet). The nest found in Fannin County, June 13, 1929, was entirely characteristic of this species, being two inches from the ground in a briar thicket, and bulkily built of dead leaves and weed stems, with a lining of fine grasses.

Blue-winged Warbler
Vermivora pinus (Linnaeus)

GENERAL DISTRIBUTION: Breeds from southeastern Minnesota, southern Michigan, western New York, and Connecticut south to Kansas, Missouri, Kentucky, Maryland, and Delaware, and in the mountains to northern Georgia. Winters from southern Mexico to Guatemala and casually to Colombia.

STATUS IN GEORGIA: A rather uncommon and local summer resident in the northern part of the state, and a scarce transient south of its breeding range.

At Atlanta, where it breeds, the earliest spring transient was noted March 26 (1936). Elsewhere, spring transients have been seen at St. Marys, April 27, 1952; Cumberland Island, April 16, 1932; Savannah, May

3, 4, and 6, 1925; Fitzgerald, April 24, 1940; Macon, April 11, 1926 and April 29, 1951; Milledgeville, April 12, 1942; Augusta, April 24 and 28; Athens, April 16, 1922; Canton, April 20, 1905; and Dalton, April 30, 1941.

In the fall, it was last seen at Atlanta on September 24 (1943). In other parts of the state fall transients have been reported from Augusta, September 3 and 26, 1944, and August 15, 1946; Athens, September 9, 1925, September 12, 1926, and September 20, 1929; Macon, September 24, 1923, and September 18, 1926; Columbus, July 28, 1946; Americus, September 24, 1941; Tifton, September 13 and 17, 1941, and September 13, 1942; and Savannah, September 6, 1909.

In the mountains, it has been observed in late May and June at Young Harris, Towns County; at Margret, Fannin County, where a male was seen feeding a young bird already out of the nest on June 8, 1921; and at Ellijay, Gilmer County.

At Atlanta, it was first reported as nesting by W. H. LaPrade [1922], who stated that young just out of the nest were last seen by D. C. Peacock on May 26, 1916. Griffin [1939] saw similar-age young in 1936, 1937, and 1938, and on June 14, 1939, found a nest in Collier Woods that held three well-fledged young.

HABITS AND RECOGNITION: The Blue-winged Warbler possesses few characteristics that give it any prominence in a family noted for diversity of plumage and actions. Apparently satisfied with its own company, it is usually seen in Georgia feeding alone in thickets and underbrush, and being unhurried in its movements and inconspicuously colored, can be easily overlooked in the thick foliage it frequents. As its name implies, its wings are bluish-gray, marked with two prominent white bars, and when the bird is seen at reasonably close range, this character will identify it. Otherwise, it is only a small yellow bird, with little about it to attract attention. This doubtless accounts for its seeming scarcity in Georgia, for as it is a fairly common bird throughout the northern part of its range, it should be more abundant as a transient both in spring and fall than the relatively few records indicate. It rarely feeds in the larger trees, and only once at Athens did I see a single bird in late September associated with other warblers in a stretch of open woods.

In nesting, it shows the same preference the Golden-winged Warbler does for old clearings and abandoned fields overgrown with scrubby underbrush, and it is in such situations that it will usually be found in northern Georgia during the spring and late summer. The nest is on, or within, a few inches of the ground, and is usually well concealed in a thick clump of weeds. It is rather bulky for the size of the bird, and constructed of dead leaves, rootlets, and grasses, and lined with shreds of bark and finer grasses.

Bachman's Warbler
Vermivora bachmanii   (Audubon)

GENERAL DISTRIBUTION: Breeds in southeastern Missouri, northeastern Arkansas, western Kentucky, northern Mississippi, Alabama, and near Charleston, South Carolina. Winters in Cuba.

STATUS IN GEORGIA: Formerly bred in small numbers near Savannah, and, until recent years, a rare transient north of the coastal region. Now largely of accidental occurrence anywhere in the state.

Rossignol [letter] reports a nest with three fresh eggs taken at Savannah, June 24, 1908, the only definite breeding record for Georgia. However, according to Fargo [1934], Walter Hoxie noted this elusive warbler at Pritchard's Crossing (Chatham County, June 27, 1908, watched the adult birds feeding young near Savannah, June 3, 1910, and again observed it near Savannah, July 31, 1913. Three specimens, now at Emory University in Atlanta, were taken by Arnow at St. Marys, August 14 and 15, 1908. The most recent record is that of a bird which struck the Tybee Light on the night of September 24, 1924. Away from the coast, there are two sight records: one for Atlanta (James Sanford) on April 18, 1914, and one for Macon (Mrs. B. T. Mounts) on April 30, 1921.

HABITS AND RECOGNITION: Bachman's Warbler is one of the rarest warblers in North America today. It was at one time a fairly common bird within its rather limited range, but was apparently unable to cope with the changes that have taken place in its environment and has gradually disappeared. During the breeding season it was found in heavily timbered swamps, and as these were logged, burned over, and not infrequently drained for one purpose or another, conditions became unsuitable for an exacting species such as this one. It has in recent years been seen in widely separated areas in northern Mississippi, northern Alabama, and the coast of South Carolina under conditions that suggested breeding birds, but it is doubtful if it will ever regain its former numbers, or will ever be other than of accidental occurrence in Georgia.

Those fortunate enough to have seen Bachman's Warbler in the wooded swamps it frequents during the spring and summer months have found it very elusive and difficult to study. The male consistently feeds in the upper branches of the larger trees, where its small size and somewhat deliberate movements make it rather inconspicuous. While singing, it usually remains motionless on an outer branch, but the song is hard to place accurately, the usual result being that the bird is not detected until it suddenly flies to another part of the swamp, where it may or may not be seen again. The song is quite distinct, and once heard will be readily recognized. The beginning is much like that of a Parula Warbler, but it ends with a trill suggestive of that of a Worm-eating Warbler.

The nest, of dead leaves, weed stems, grasses, and rootlets, is built in a thick bush or tangle of briers, from one to three feet from the ground, and, being in the densest part of the swamp, is far from easy to find. Three or four plain white eggs are laid, and apparently only a single brood is reared each year.

Tennessee Warbler
Vermivora peregrina (Wilson)

GENERAL DISTRIBUTION: Breeds from the upper Yukon valley, southern Mackenzie, northern Manitoba, central Quebec, and Anticosti Island south to southern British Columbia, southern Alberta, southern Manitoba, northern Minnesota, northern Michigan, Ontario, New York (Adirondacks), northern Maine, and New Hampshire. Winters from southern Mexico (Oaxaca) to Colombia and Venezuela.

STATUS IN GEORGIA: An extremely scarce spring transient, and a fairly common fall transient, although less frequently noted in the coastal plain than in other parts of the state.

In the spring, the few records of occurrence are as follows: Grady County, April 14 and 21, 1940; Athens, May 18, 1924, May 1 and 2, 1928, and May 7, 1947; Atlanta, May 9, 1948, April 24, 1916, May 6, 1951, and May 16, 1954; and Rising Fawn, April 26, 1885.

In the fall, it has been seen at Athens between the dates of September 23 (1928) and November 2 (1926); in the Atlanta region between the dates of September 6 (1952) and November 5 (1954); at Macon between the dates of September 24 (1955) and October 21 (1954); and in Grady County, September 17 (1944) and October 20 (1940). It has also been noted at Dalton, October 30, 1942, and September 30, 1944; in Cherokee County, October 4, 1905, and September 18, 1915; at Fitzgerald, October 21, 1940; and at Tifton, October 8, 1941. A single bird struck the Tybee Light, October 29, 1925.

HABITS AND RECOGNITION: In the spring, the Tennessee Warbler migrates largely through the Mississippi Valley, and is a scarce bird at that time anywhere on the Atlantic Coast. For this reason the appearance of one of these little warblers in Georgia in the spring is worthy of special comment. The few records for Georgia at this season of the year involve, without exception, singing males, but this is not surprising, for as this species feeds in the upper branches of the larger trees, the presence of a female would attract no attention, and it could be easily overlooked. Males in breeding plumage appear bright yellowish-green above, dull white beneath, while a closer glimpse will reveal the inconspicuous gray crown and nape and the narrow white line over the eye.

In the fall, this species changes its habits somewhat, for, while again found with other warblers in the larger trees, it is just as apt to be seen in thickets and underbrush bordering the fields and streams. At Athens, it was not uncommon in October to observe small flocks under such circumstances. Birds in fall plumage are uniformly olive-green above, dull yellow beneath, and so similar in appearance then to the Orange-crowned Warbler that care must be taken in identifying them. One of the outstanding characteristics of the Tennessee Warbler, regardless of season, is its restlessness. There is never anything deliberate in its actions as it feeds overhead, and, because of its nervous activity, keeping one in sight for any length of time is difficult.

Eastern Orange-crowned Warbler
Vermivora celata celata (Say)

GENERAL DISTRIBUTION: Breeds from Kowak River, Alaska, southeast to northern Manitoba. Winters in the Gulf and South Atlantic states north to South Carolina, casually to Ohio and Massachusetts, and in Mexico.

STATUS IN GEORGIA: A scarce transient and winter resident in the northern part of the state, and a fairly common winter resident south of the fall line.

Extreme dates of occurrence at Atlanta are October 21 (1945) and May 2 (1953); Athens, October 12 (1937) and April 21 (1926); Augusta, October 8 (1944) and April 27; Macon, December 15 (1944) and April 10 (1954); Fitzgerald, December 17 (1938) and February 9 (1941); and Grady County, November 1 (1951) and April 22 (1940). At Savannah, the latest spring record is May 5 (1925). There is one fall record for Rome, October 19, 1952.

It is found regularly during the winter months at both Atlanta and Athens, but in rather small numbers. It has also been noted at this season of the year at Augusta (December 30, 1891; January 13 and February 11, 1945); Newton (January 5, 1932); Blakely (December 30, 1933); Grady County (almost daily from late November until March); Okefenokee Swamp (between the dates of December 1 [1932] and February 13 [1941]); and Sea Island (January 18, 1946).

HABITS AND RECOGNITION: The Orange-crowned Warbler is a rather drab-colored little bird with so little to distinguish it that it hardly attracts attention during its sojourn in the state. It will usually be seen feeding alone in thickets and stretches of underbrush where the thick foliage so effectively conceals it that it must ordinarily be looked for to be seen. It has a sharp "chip" that is quite distinctive and will readily identify it, but, unless alarmed, it is normally quiet and inconspicuous. It seems to prefer the vicinity of water, and both in migration and during the winter months can commonly be found in alders and willows fringing streams. In actions, it is one of the more active of the warblers, its restlessness usually rewarding one with a brief glimpse as it appears momentarily and then vanishes in the thicket in which it is feeding. Seen under such circumstances, it is merely a small yellowish-green warbler, which, lacking any noticeable characteristic such as wing-bars or an eye ring, can be recognized because it is so nondescript.

In Grady County, Stoddard reports it frequenting feeding stations throughout the winter months, feeding on pecan fragments at intervals each day. One individual, because of its apparent familiarity with the feeding trap it visited, was suspected of appearing at Sherwood Plantation for five successive years.

Rocky Mountain Orange-crowned Warbler
Vermivora celata orestera   Oberholser

GENERAL DISTRIBUTION: Breeds from British Columbia and Alberta south to southeastern California and central New Mexico. Winters from southern California south into Mexico.

STATUS IN GEORGIA: Of accidental occurrence.

There are two records for the occurrence of this western race in Georgia, specimens having been taken at Athens, April 21, 1926 (Burleigh), and at Atlanta, November 9, 1947 (Griffin).

HABITS AND RECOGNITION: The Rocky Mountain Orange crowned Warbler differs from typical *celata* in being yellower, and less green, both above and below.

Eastern Nashville Warbler
Vermivora ruficapilla ruficapilla   (Wilson)

GENERAL DISTRIBUTION: Breeds from southern Saskatchewan, Ontario, and southern Quebec south to Nebraska, northern Illinois, northern Pennsylvania, northern New Jersey, and Connecticut. Winters from Vera Cruz and Chiapas to Guatemala, and casually in southern Texas and Florida.

STATUS IN GEORGIA: Apparently a regular but scarce fall transient in at least the northern part of the state, and of accidental occurrence in the spring.

So much doubt has existed concerning the occurrence of this warbler in Georgia that only in recent years has it finally been removed from the hypothetical list. In the *Birds of Georgia* [Greene et al, 1945], several sight records are given, but the species is not included in the accredited list, the statement being made that "Specimens in the Emory University Museum collected by D. V. Hembree in 1918 and by Robert W. Smith in DeKalb County [Green, 1933], proved on examination by Griffin and Norris to be an Orange-crowned Warbler and a Tennessee Warbler, respectively, and now there appear to be no preserved specimens known for the State." In view of these circumstances a special effort was made during the fall migration of 1945 to determine whether the Nashville Warbler actually occurs as a transient in Georgia, and while further field work will be necessary before any definite conclusions can be reached, it now appears that it is a scarce but regular transient north of the fall line.

"I noted my first bird, an adult male, at Commerce, in Jackson County, on October 9, feeding with other warblers in willows bordering a stream. Another bird, a female, was seen near Atlanta on October 15, feeding with Tennessee Warblers in underbrush at the edge of the Chattahoochee River. Still a third bird, another adult male, was seen at Athens on November 3, feeding with kinglets in alders in the Sandy Creek bottoms." [Burleigh, 1946.]

The female seen near Atlanta was collected, and would appear to be the first specimen taken in the state. Its status remained unchanged in this respect until the fall of 1954. On the night of October 7 (Johnston, 1955), thousands of small birds were killed at the Warner Robins Air Force Base near Macon, through an unfortunate combination of adverse weather conditions and bright lights. These were to a large extent carefully identified, and of unusual interest was the discovery that four Nashville Warblers were among the birds killed that night.

The only record for the spring migration is that of a single bird seen at Demorest on May 2, 1948 [Neal, 1949b].

HABITS AND RECOGNITION: The Nashville Warbler is a small, inconspicuously colored warbler, which, in migration, seems to prefer underbrush in the vicinity of water. On its northern breeding grounds, it commonly frequents clearings and old pastures partially overgrown with aspens and birches, and seemingly at all times shuns the larger, heavier timber. Those fortunate enough to encounter one in Georgia will find it an exceedingly active little bird. For a brief moment it can be watched as it restlessly feeds in the outer branches of an alder or willow. Then it is gone and, despite a diligent search, will probably not be seen again. Birds in fall plumage suggest in appearance both the Orange-crowned Warbler and the Tennessee Warbler, but can be recognized within reasonable range by the gray head and noticeably white eye ring.

Parula Warbler
Parula americana   (Linnaeus)

GENERAL DISTRIBUTION: Breeds from eastern Nebraska, northern Minnesota, central Ontario, Anticosti Island, and Cape Breton Island south to Texas, Louisiana, and Florida. Winters in Florida, in the Bahamas and the West Indies, and from southern Mexico to Nicaragua.

STATUS IN GEORGIA: A fairly common summer resident in the mountains and a locally common summer resident south of the fall line. It apparently does not breed in the Piedmont, where it occurs as a common spring and fall transient. Of accidental occurrence during the winter.

In the spring the first Parula Warblers appear in the southern part of the state in early March, but it is usually a month later before they are seen north of the fall line. The earliest spring transients have been reported from Camden County, February 12 (1950); Hinesville, March 5 (1944); Sea Island, March 2 (1947); Savannah, March 1 (1908); Okefenokee Swamp, February 28 (1936); Fitzgerald, March 8 (1952); Macon, March 22 (1953); Augusta, March 11 (1945); Athens, April 5 (1929); Atlanta, April 4 (1946); and Canton, April 11 (1905). Birds seen at Savannah on February 1, 1891, and February 8, 1923, were possibly individuals that had wintered, for these dates would be early for spring transients and the Parula Warbler is known to occur in small numbers in Florida during the winter. The only definite winter record for Georgia is that of a single bird seen by Stoddard in Grady County on December 25, 1947.

The fall migration begins very early, as in the upper Piedmont, where this species is not known to breed, the first transients appear in the scattered stretches of woods in June, and they are invariably numerous by early July. The southward movement extends over a longer interval than is the case with other warblers, for it is September before there is any noticeable decrease in the number of Parula Warblers that are seen, and it is the middle of October, rarely November, before the last bird has finally departed. The latest fall transients have been noted at Augusta, October 23 (1942); Athens, November 4 (1929); Atlanta, October 17 (1931); Macon, October 10 (1949); Americus, October 5 (1941); Fitzgerald, October 13 (1940); Grady County, October 31 (1937); Savannah, October 18 (1908); and St. Marys, October 10 (1905). Individuals have

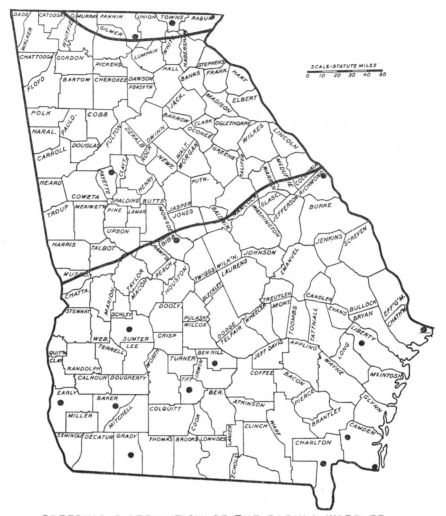

BREEDING DISTRIBUTION OF THE PARULA WARBLER

been reported striking the Tybee Light on October 6, 1923, September 25, 1924, and September 29, 1928.

In the mountains, the Parula Warbler has been found nesting at Margret, Fannin County (four well-incubated eggs May 23, 1926) (Burleigh); and at Young Harris, Towns County (completed nest, apparently deserted, May 24, 1929) (Burleigh). It doubtless breeds elsewhere in high, wooded ravines where conditions are suitable.

Away from the mountains, there is a wide gap in its breeding range. With one exception, there is no evidence that it nests anywhere in the Piedmont. Near Jonesboro, but in Fayette County (twenty miles south of Atlanta), three "bob-tailed" young were seen June 4, 1950, being fed by the parent birds [Sciple and Griffin, 1951].

510

Family *Parulidae:* WOOD WARBLERS

South of the fall line, it has been reported during the breeding season at St. Marys, Allenhurst, Hinesville, Newton, Blakely, Tifton, Fitzgerald, Americus, and Augusta, and there are definite breeding records for Fitzgerald (nest with four young, May 15, 1941) (Hopkins); Grady County (female working on nest March 27, 1949; one newly hatched young and two eggs May 20, 1952) (Stoddard); the Okefenokee Swamp (nest with young April 19, 1945) (Hebard); Coleraine, western Camden County (three eggs, April 19, 1945) (Hebard); and Savannah (nesting extremes, thirteen nests, four slightly incubated eggs, April 3 [1921]; 3 slightly incubated eggs, May 5 [1907] [Rossignol]).

HABITS AND RECOGNITION: In Georgia the Parula Warbler has a dual personality. In the southern part of the state, it behaves as one would expect it to, being found in the river bottoms and timbered swamps where the Spanish moss (*Tillandsia*), hanging from the trees, affords characteristic nesting sites. So dependent is it known to be upon this moss that one would never look for it in drier woodlands where this characteristic southern epiphyte is wanting. Thus it would not be expected to occur as a breeding bird throughout the Piedmont, which lacks the Spanish moss. However, in the mountains, where also there is no Spanish moss, it is found breeding in the wooded ravines. To one familiar only with its nesting habits in the coastal lowlands, its presence there comes as a surprise, but what has been learned of its nesting habits has revealed its adaptability to this radically different environment. Without exception, breeding pairs have been seen in moist, well-wooded ravines where the hemlock (*Tsuga canadensis*) grows along the streams. It is at the ends of the upper branches of this tree that the nest is built. A light-green, mosslike lichen is here available as a substitute for the moss in the construction of the nest. This plant is used almost exclusively, the result being that the nest is soft but compact, and so well concealed in a thick, drooping spray that only by seeing the bird go to it can it be located.

Farther south in the state, nest construction is less complicated, a well-defined hollow being made in the Spanish moss, and lined with fine grasses. Height from the ground is apparently a secondary consideration, some nests being almost within reach from the ground while others are in the very tops of trees. Apparently only one brood is reared each year, the majority of the birds having nests with fresh eggs the latter part of April. Of the thirteen nests found at Savannah by Gilbert Rossignol, eight held fresh eggs between the dates of April 23 and April 28. However, two were much later than this, and probably represented second attempts to raise young after the first nest was destroyed.

Eastern Yellow Warbler
Dendroica petechia aestiva (Gmelin)

GENERAL DISTRIBUTION: Breeds from Minnesota east to Maine, south to southern Missouri, northern Alabama, central Georgia, and northern South Carolina. Winters from Yucatán to Guiana, Peru, and northern Brazil.

STATUS IN GEORGIA: A fairly common but local summer resident in the northern half of the state and a rare transient south of the fall line except on the coast, where it is common.

In the spring, the Yellow Warbler reaches Georgia in early April, the earliest transients being seen at Savannah, April 4 (1912); in the Oke-fenokee Swamp, April 3 (1945); at Macon, April 9 (1945); Athens, April 7 (1929); Atlanta, April 2 (1917); Rome, April 7 (1949); Dalton, April 13 (1944); Canton, April 12 (1905); and Augusta, April 8 (1943). At Americus, where it does not breed, it has been noted as late as May 15 (1942), while at Fitzgerald the latest spring date is May 2 (1940). In Grady County, there are but two records for the spring migration, May 4, 1926, and April 30, 1952.

The fall migration begins very early, there being a noticeable decrease in the number of birds seen after the middle of July, and by the first of August the Yellow Warbler is usually gone from the stream bottoms where it has nested. An occasional individual noted after that date is probably a transient from farther north. Latest dates of occurrence in the fall are Athens, August 23 (1928); Atlanta, September 5 (1930); Augusta, August 27 (1946); Macon, October 8 (1954); Fitzgerald, August 30 (1940); and Savannah, September 22 (1908) and October 3 (1909).

In the northern part of the state the Yellow Warbler nests commonly as far south as Athens and Atlanta; localities where it has been reported during the breeding season include Young Harris, Margret, Blue Ridge, Chatsworth, Rome, Tate, Canton, Gainesville, and Toccoa. In the lower Piedmont, it is rather local in its distribution, but nests to the fall line. Denton [1945] reports a breeding pair at Augusta, June 11, 1945, and [1951] at least two breeding pairs in the Ocmulgee River bottom at Macon, June 7, 1947. Definite breeding records are limited at present to Athens (four slightly incubated eggs May 26, 1924; three incubated eggs June 4, 1925) (Burleigh); and Atlanta (five eggs May 17, 1931) (Giles).

HABITS AND RECOGNITION: The Yellow Warbler is beyond any question a successful species. Found from coast to coast and from the Arctic tundra to northern South America, it apparently merely requires a stretch of willows and alders in a stream bottom, or mangrove thickets along the tropical coasts, to be thoroughly satisfied with its environment. As climatic conditions vary considerably over its vast range, a number of geographic races have gradually evolved, but to the casual eye this species is the same familiar bird wherever it is seen. It is undoubtedly the best known of all the warblers, since, avoiding the thicker stretches of woods, the deep swamps, and the higher slopes of the mountains, it spends its days in the proximity of man. With its bright yellow plumage and clear, spirited song, it is not easily overlooked and, as the "Wild Canary" or "Summer Yellowbird," is widely familiar. In migration, an occasional bird may be found with other warblers in open woods, but to become acquainted with the Yellow Warbler, one must seek the willows that fringe the creeks and larger streams. In feeding, it does not hesitate to search the alders and birches in its vicinity for such insect life as is available, but it is in the willows that much of each day is spent.

Less discrimination is shown by the female in selecting a nesting site, for with foliage sufficiently dense to afford concealment, practically any tree or shrub, conifers excepted, is used. Nests found in Georgia have been in alders, and on two occasions in a small water oak, and in an elm. The height varies from six to, rarely, fifteen feet above the ground. In construction, the nest is neat and compact, the materials used being gray plant fibers, grasses, shreds of bark, and, almost invariably, more or less cotton. Only a single brood is reared each year.

Newfoundland Yellow Warbler
Dendroica petechia amnicola Batchelder

GENERAL DISTRIBUTION. Breeds from northern Mackenzie, southern Ungava, and Newfoundland south at least to Nova Scotia. Winter range unknown but probably in South America.

STATUS IN GEORGIA: Probably of casual occurrence in migration, but known at present from but three records.

A male taken by Arnow at St. Marys on September 12, 1908, has been found to represent this northern race; and it was taken again in the fall, at Atlanta, on October 7, 1954 [Griffin, letter]. The only spring record is that of a female collected at Decatur on May 10, 1946 [Burleigh, 1948].

HABITS AND RECOGNITION: When first described in 1918, the Newfoundland Yellow Warbler was thought to be limited in its distribution to one Canadian province, and accordingly it was given the common name it now bears. However, field work carried on since that time has shown that it actually has an extensive breeding range in northern Canada, west to northern Mackenzie. It should, therefore, be numerous and probably of regular occurrence in Georgia in both spring and fall, but further collect-

Parula Warblers
Parula americana

These pretty warblers spent most of their time high in deciduous trees.
Their songs, which were wiry, not very musical, ascending trills, ended
with a sharp "tsip" not unlike their usual alarm note. One pair had a
nest in the very middle of a great scarf of Spanish moss. The pair in my
painting are perched in the top of a scarlet or swamp maple.
The male bird is above.

ing will be necessary to determine this point. Specimens can be readily distinguished by the fact that the yellowish-green of the upperparts is darker than in *aestiva*.

Magnolia Warbler
Dendroica magnolia (Wilson)

GENERAL DISTRIBUTION: Breeds from southwestern Mackenzie, central British Columbia, central Manitoba, central Quebec, and Newfoundland south to central Alberta, southern Saskatchewan, Minnesota, northern Michigan, and northern Massachusetts, and in the mountains of New York, Pennsylvania, Maryland, West Virginia, and Virginia. Winters from southern Mexico to Panama, and also rarely in Haiti and Porto Rico.

STATUS IN GEORGIA: An uncommon spring transient and a common fall transient, although less often observed in the southern part of the state.

In spring, the Magnolia Warbler usually appears in Georgia in small numbers in April and early May, although there are occasional years, as in 1924 and again in 1928, when it was fairly plentiful at Athens. In fall, however, it is invariably common in the northern part of the state and is present almost daily from the middle of September until the latter part of October. Farther south it is apparently scarce at all times.

Earliest spring transients were noted at Savannah, April 9 (1931); Baker County, April 19 (1951); Macon, April 16 (1921); Milledgeville, April 14 (1935); Athens, April 15 (1921); and Atlanta, April 17 (1902). The last in the spring were seen at Macon, May 24 (1945); Milledgeville, May 14 (1945); Augusta, May 14 (1945); Athens, May 18 (1924); Atlanta, May 23 (1954); Margret, Fannin County, May 25 (1928); Tray Mountain, White County, May 31 (1950); and Rome, May 18 (1953).

In the fall, extreme dates of occurrence are Dalton, September 30 (1944) and October 23 (1944); Atlanta, August 27 (1937) and November 7 (1954); Athens, September 5 (1926) and October 28 (1927); Augusta, September 23 (1944) and October 22 (1944); Macon, September 6 (1955) and October 19 (1934); and Grady County, September 28 (1948) and October 26 (1947). It has also been reported at Americus, October 21, 1942; and Fitzgerald, October 16 and 23, 1940.

HABITS AND RECOGNITION: Words are inadequate to describe the beauty of some of our birds. Such is certainly the case with the Magnolia Warbler. It is generally conceded to be the handsomest of the warblers, and the first sight of a male in full spring plumage will leave no room for argument on that point. Fortunately it is possible to watch the bird at reasonably close range, for it prefers to feed in the lower branches of the larger trees rather than high overhead. When it is seen thus, its vivid colors—varying shades of yellow, black, and gray that form an intricate pattern on its head, back and breast—cannot fail to arouse the admiration of the onlooker. As it moves about, it displays a nervous temperament in its quick actions and the frequent spreading of its tail, which appears largely white, bordered by a black band. The female is duller in color, but resembles the male closely, and is also an attractive bird.

The occurrence of this species at Augusta [Murphey, 1937] is more or less typical of its status over much of the northern part of the state. Murphey says of it: "Rare in spring, very abundant during the autumnal migration at which time it is not only to be found in the dense thickets around the swamp, but invades the roadside hedgerows and tall weeds on the edges of roads and fields."

Cape May Warbler
Dendroica tigrina (Gmelin)

GENERAL DISTRIBUTION: Breeds from southern Mackenzie, northern Ontario, New Brunswick, and Nova Scotia south to southern Manitoba, northern Maine, and New Hampshire. Winters in the Bahamas and the West Indies.

STATUS IN GEORGIA: In the northern part of the state a common spring transient and a rare fall transient. South of the fall line at times common, but irregular in occurrence in the spring except on the coast, where it is apparently equally common both in the spring and in the fall.

In spring, extreme dates of occurrence are Savannah, March 11 (1923) and May 6 (1915); Grady County, April 6 (1948) and April 21 (1940); Macon, April 7 (1928) and May 9 (1955); Milledgeville, April 17 (1940) and May 2 (1942); Augusta, April 10 (1943) and May 2 (1943); Athens, April 14 (1928) and May 21 (1949); and Atlanta, April 10 (1948) and May 12 (1951). The Cape May Warbler has also been seen in the following localities:

Western Camden County: April 26 and May 13, 1943, April 12, 1945, and April 23 to 26, 1947.
Okefenokee Swamp: April 20, 1941.
Baker County: April 14 and 28, 1950, and April 20, 1951.
Tifton: April 28 to May 3, 1944.
Fitzgerald: April 11 to May 12, 1941.

Americus: April 10 to April 25, 1942.
Cochran: April 11, 1933.
Roswell: May 6, 1932.
Canton: April 21 and May 1, 1905.
Dalton: April 14, 1944.
Rising Fawn: April 26, 1885.
Rome: April 20 to May 10, 1953.

The fall migration would appear to be confined largely to the Atlantic Coast since this warbler is then rarely observed in the interior of the state.

It has been noted at Dalton, October 5 and 14, 1942; Commerce, October 10, 1945; Athens, October 12, 1937, and October 18, 1942; Atlanta, October 5, 1929, October 1, 1949, October 3–11, 1953 and November 14, 1954; Augusta, October 6, 1944; Macon, October 10, 1949 and October 8, 1954; and Fitzgerald, September 28 and October 3, 1940. On the coast, birds were reported striking the Tybee Light on October 2, 1908; September 24 and 25, 1924; and October 27 and 29, 1925. The latest fall record is that of two birds seen at St. Marys, October 31 (1905). However, one was reported at St. Marys by Richard G. Kuerzi on January 1, 1951, a rather unexpected record for this season of the year [Hebard, letter].

HABITS AND RECOGNITION: At one time the Cape May Warbler was considered rare, but it has apparently increased perceptibly in numbers and is now commonly observed in Georgia in migration. At Athens, it proved to be one of the more common transient warblers in spring, being especially numerous in late April and early May, when it could be found almost daily in many of the scattered stretches of woods. On its breeding grounds in the north, it is said to remain consistently in the upper branches of the tallest trees, but in Georgia it shows no inclination to feed far above the ground, and being relatively unsuspicious, can be watched with little difficulty. It is one of the handsomer warblers, with chestnut cheek patches that contrast strongly with the deep yellow underparts, which are heavily streaked with black. This gives it an exotic appearance that cannot fail to attract attention. In common with the other *Dendroica*, it moves actively about as it feeds overhead, but it lacks the nervous temperament so evident in the Magnolia Warbler.

Northern Black-throated Blue Warbler
Dendroica caerulescens caerulescens   (Gmelin)

GENERAL DISTRIBUTION: Breeds from northern Minnesota, central Ontario, and southern Quebec south to central Minnesota, southern Ontario, Pennsylvania, and northern Connecticut. Winters from the Florida Keys to the Bahamas, Greater Antilles, and Cozumel Island, and casually to Guatemala and Colombia.

STATUS IN GEORGIA: A common transient in the northern part of the state. Uncommon south of the fall line, and rarely observed in the southwestern counties.

In the spring, extreme dates of occurrence are these:

Savannah: April 3 (1926) and May 26   Fitzgerald: April 11 (1941) and May 6
  (1909).   (1939).

Macon: April 8 (1923) and May 16 (1932).

Milledgeville: April 12 (1942) and May 11 (1945).

Augusta: April 3 (1942) and May 14 (1945).

Athens: April 7 (1926) and May 27 (1950).

Atlanta: April 12 (1947) and May 23 (1954).

It has also been reported at Cumberland Island, April 8, 1902; Sea Island, April 16, 1947; Woodbine, April 24, 1947; Darien, May 20, 1945; and Hinesville, April 23, 1943, and April 25 and 30, 1944.

For the fall migration, extreme dates of occurrence are Augusta, August 16 (1944) and October 21 (1944); Athens, September 18 (1926) and November 2 (1925); Atlanta, September 7 (1930) and October 27 (1929); and Macon, September 6 (1904) and October 24 (1943). There are also records for Roswell (October 28, 1925), Cochran (October 3, 1932), Fitzgerald (November 2, 1940), Tifton (September 23, 1941), Grady County (September 24, 1947), and Thomasville (October 26, 1943). On Tybee Island, birds were reported striking the light on October 6, 1923, September 24, 1924, October 29, 1925, and September 23, 1928.

At Athens, specimens representing this northern race have been taken on April 19 and October 4, 1928; April 22, 26, and 30, and October 5, 1929, and October 8, 1933 [Burleigh, 1938]; at Atlanta, on October 10, 1948 (Griffin); and at Darien, April 25, 1946 (Burleigh).

In view of the impracticability of identifying subspecies in the field, it is probable that a certain proportion of the records cited above refer to *cairnsi,* but as there is no way of determining this fact, all migration data are included under the nominate race.

HABITS AND RECOGNITION: On its northern breeding grounds, the Black-throated Blue Warbler occurs in thick, moist woodlands, where it feeds in the underbrush and among lower branches of the larger trees. Such conditions seem to be sought even in migration, and in Georgia one is more apt to see this distinctively marked warbler in wooded bottom lands in the vicinity of water. Rarely, if ever, will it be found in the tops of the trees, and since it is rather unsuspicious and easily approached, no hardship will be experienced in making its acquaintance. At Athens, it was most frequently observed in woods bordering the Oconee River, where, in late April and early May and again in October, it was present almost daily. Few birds are easier to recognize. The male is uniformly dark, grayish-blue above, with a black throat that is emphasized by the clear white of the breast. Each wing is marked with a conspicuous white spot, a character likewise noticeable in the more obscurely plumaged female and a ready means of identification at all times.

Cairn's Black-throated Blue Warbler
Dendroica caerulescens cairnsi   Coues

GENERAL DISTRIBUTION: Breeds in the southern Alleghenies from Maryland to northern Georgia. Winters in the West Indies.

STATUS IN GEORGIA: A common summer resident in the northeastern corner of the state.

This southern race of the Black-throated Blue Warbler has been noted during the breeding season on Rabun Bald (Rabun County), Brasstown Bald (Towns County), Tray Mountain (Towns and White counties), Rich Mountain (Gilmer County), and Flattop Mountain (Fannin County); and it possibly nests elsewhere in the mountains where conditions are suitable. Definite breeding records are available only for Brasstown Bald, where six nests have been found, as follows: May 12, 1922, two nests, in each, three slightly incubated eggs [Burleigh, 1925]; May 22, 1923, four fresh eggs; June 23, 1923, three slightly incubated eggs; May 26, 1925, two nests, in one, three slightly incubated eggs, in the other, four fresh eggs [Burleigh, 1927]. On Tray Mountain [Denton and Neal, 1951], adults were seen feeding young out of the nest on June 18, 1948 and June 20, 1949.

South of its breeding range in Georgia, specimens have been taken in Cherokee County (April 28, 1905), near Atlanta (April 18, 1948 and October 2, 1948), Athens (April 27, 1929, April 19, 1933, April 18, October 9 and 11, 1947), Bibb County (September 6, 1904), Fitzgerald (September 28, 1940), Chatham County (April 29, 1908), Tybee Light (October, 1923), and on Cumberland Island (April 9, 1897).

HABITS AND RECOGNITION: In northern Georgia, breeding Black-throated Blue Warblers occur on the steep mountain slopes, but are commonly observed only above an altitude of 3,000 feet. In the ravines at the foot of the ridges, an occasional pair can be found, but one must usually climb well up from the valleys before hearing the first singing male. The song has a husky quality that is quite distinctive, and consists of three notes that suggest the syllables "zwee zwee zwee." Once heard it will readily identify this species. Its distribution in Georgia seems influenced to some extent by the presence of mountain laurel (*Kalmia latifolia*), for while the birds normally feed in the deciduous undergrowth that covers these rugged mountain sides, it is in the laurel thickets that the female usually conceals her nest. The few that have been found have been well hidden within a foot or two of the ground, and were compactly built of shreds and strips of bark, grasses, and, in several instances, bits of rotten wood, well cupped and lined with black vine tendrils, fine rootlets, moss stems, and a little horsehair. Although a nest with almost fresh eggs was found in late June, it is doubtful if more than one brood ordinarily is reared each year.

As a subspecies, *cairnsi* is exceptionally well marked. In the male the dark, grayish-blue of the back is distinctly spotted with black, which, in some individuals, forms a solid patch. The female is noticeably darker, both above and below, than in typical *caerulescens*.

Eastern Myrtle Warbler
Dendroica coronata coronata   (Linnaeus)

GENERAL DISTRIBUTION: Breeds from northern Manitoba, northern Quebec, and Newfoundland south to northern Minnesota, northern Michigan, central Ontario, New Hampshire, and Maine, and in the mountains of New York, Vermont, and Massachusetts. Winters from Kansas, the Ohio Valley, and New Jersey (casually southern New England) south to the Greater Antilles, Mexico, and Panama.

STATUS IN GEORGIA: A common transient and a locally common winter resident throughout the state.

Although the Myrtle Warbler appears in Georgia in the fall as early as the latter part of September, and lingers in the spring until after the middle of May, it is during the latter part of April, and again the latter part of October, that it occurs in greatest numbers. It is then that numerous small flocks can be found in scattered stretches of woods over much of the state.

Extreme dates of occurrence are as follows:

Rome: October 19 (1952) and May 11 (1953).

Dalton: October 12 (1944) and May 8 (1944).

Atlanta: September 22 (1930) and May 20 (1928).

Athens: October 8 (1925) and May 11 (1928).

Augusta: October 7 (1942) and May 14 (1950).

Milledgeville: October 22 (1942) and May 5 (1942).

Macon: October 14 (1950) and May 18 (1955).

Americus: October 21 (1941) and April 26 (1942).

Grady County: October 14 (1945) and May 1 (1949).

Savannah: October 23 (1910) and May 10 (1910).

Hinesville: October 24 (1943) and April 28 (1943).

At Fitzgerald, the latest spring date is May 4 (1940); at Columbus, April 30 (1946); and at Hephzibah (Burke County), May 8 (1933). At Tifton the earliest record for the fall migration is October 11 (1941).

During the winter, it is found over all the state, but is far more numerous south of the fall line. At Athens, it proved to be a rather irregular winter resident, being common some winters and scarce others. It was reported abundant in winter at Augusta, in Grady County, in the Okefenokee Swamp, in western Camden County, and on the coast.

HABITS AND RECOGNITION: In some respects, the Myrtle Warbler is quite different from other members of its family occurring in Georgia. It is a hardy bird, and the last of the warblers to appear in the fall, the small flocks seen then seldom being present before late October. By this date, other warblers that have been passing through the state since early August are largely gone, and when one sees a flock of Myrtle Warblers, it is unusual to find other species at the same time. Insect life is at its minimum from late fall until early spring, but this species seems little inconvenienced, its diet during the colder months of the year being supplemented to a large extent by certain berries available at that season. In the interior of the state, it shows a marked fondness for the fruit of the poison ivy, this vine being apparently one of its main sources of food when freezing temperatures prevail. On the coast, it shows an equal liking for the berries of the wax myrtle, and its constant presence in the vicinity of myrtle thickets is so noticeable that one soon realizes the aptness of its common name.

It is the most abundant and widely distributed of its family in Georgia, and probably the best known. Unsuspicious of man, it shows no hesitation in feeding about houses and in the shade trees in the towns, where it is a familiar sight. Its winter plumage is rather drab, but in flight it displays a conspicuous yellow rump that will readily identify it. It likewise possesses a distinctive, sharp "tchip" that is constantly uttered as it moves actively about and, once learned, will always be recognized. The breeding plumage is acquired before departure in the spring, and the Myrtle Warbler is then a handsome bird.

Alaska Myrtle Warbler
Dendroica coronata hooveri   McGregor

GENERAL DISTRIBUTION: Breeds from northwestern Alaska and northern Mackenzie south to northern British Columbia and southern Alberta. Winters from central Oregon to southern California and northern Lower California, casually east to the Gulf Coast, Georgia, and South Carolina.

STATUS IN GEORGIA: A scarce winter resident in the northern part of the state.

Specimens representing this western race have been examined from the following localities: Comer (Madison County), January 11, 1946; Athens, January 3, 1941, February 3 and March 3, 1946; Atlanta, April 10, 1947; and Trenton (Dade County), December 16, 1946.

521

HABITS AND RECOGNITION: The Alaska Myrtle Warbler is distinguished from its more eastern relative by its larger size and the more extensive black of the underparts. Since specimens are necessary to identify it, further collecting will be required before its exact status in Georgia can be stated definitely. There are at the present time no records for *hooveri* in the southern part of the state, but it is probable that it occurs there in at least limited numbers during the winter months. The few occasions when it has been noted in Georgia, single birds have been found feeding with flocks of Eastern Myrtle Warblers. In general appearance and actions there is nothing about this subspecies to distinguish it in the field.

Northern Black-throated Green Warbler
Dendroica virens virens (Gmelin)

GENERAL DISTRIBUTION: Breeds from central Alberta, southern Manitoba, central Ontario, central Quebec, and Newfoundland south to southern Minnesota, southern Wisconsin, northern Ohio, and northern New Jersey. Winters from southern Texas south through Mexico to Guatemala, Costa Rica, and Panama.

STATUS IN GEORGIA: A fairly common transient in the northern part of the state, but usually scarce south of the fall line.

In spring, the Black-throated Green Warbler appears in Georgia in late March, and is present then over much of the state until the middle of May. In fall, it reappears shortly after the middle of September, and can be found almost daily in scattered stretches of woods until late October.

For the spring migration, extreme dates of occurrence are Augusta, March 31 (1946) and May 14 (1945); Athens, March 24 (1921) and May 14 (1926); Atlanta, March 25 (1945) and May 11 (1940); and Rome, March 27 (1953) and May 29 (1953). At Macon, the earliest spring date is April 5 (1951); at Rising Fawn, April 1 (1885); and at Dalton, April 1 (1944). It has been noted on Cumberland Island, April 15, 1932, and at Fitzgerald, March 28, 1942.

In fall, the earliest transients were seen at Atlanta, September 6 (1937); Athens, September 18 (1932); Augusta, September 28 (1944); and Macon, September 15 (1929). The latest were reported at Dalton, October 15 (1944); Atlanta, October 30 (1949); Athens, November 1 (1925); Augusta, October 30 (1948); and Milledgeville, October 26 (1941). At Tifton, it was noted October 22 and 24, 1941; and in Grady County, Stoddard reports it frequently common in the fall between the dates of September 10 (1925) and October 26 (1947).

As two races are involved, it is probable that these migration dates refer to both *virens* and *waynei,* but as specimens are largely lacking, all records are included in the discussion of the present race.

Specimens representing this race have been taken at Athens (males September 22, 1928 and April 30, 1929, and females March 30 and October 26, 1928), and at Danielsville (a female October 5, 1945).

HABITS AND RECOGNITION: The Black-throated Green Warbler is exactly what its name implies, being black throated, with a bright, olive-green back. It is one of the many species of small warblers which, in mixed flocks, move leisurely through Georgia in both spring and fall, being found wherever there are sufficient trees to afford food and shelter. It has no marked mannerisms, and while active and restless, is easily approached and readily identified. On occasion it will be found feeding in underbrush, but normally it remains in the larger trees, where its activities cover almost any part of the tree. In late April and early May, the males can be heard uttering their distinctive song that possesses a drowsy quality suiting perfectly the first warm days of early spring.

Wayne's Black-throated Green Warbler
Dendroica virens waynei Bangs

GENERAL DISTRIBUTION: Breeds from southeastern Kentucky and southeastern Virginia south to central Alabama, northern Georgia, and southeastern South Carolina. Winter range unknown.

STATUS IN GEORGIA: A fairly common but local summer resident in the northern part of the state.

This southern race of the Black-throated Green Warbler was found breeding on Lookout Mountain, in Dade County, by J. T. Park in 1885. In July, 1908, it was noted on Rich Mountain and on Brasstown Bald [Howell, 1909], but subsequent field work there in late May and June failed to substantiate the conclusion tentatively advanced that the individuals seen represented a breeding population. In recent years, however, this species has become established as a breeding bird in the mountains of the extreme northern part of the state, and while at present rather local in its distribution, it may in time become common and more widely distributed. Definite localities where it has been reported as now breeding are as follows:

Ellijay, Gilmer County: Breeding in 1945 [Odum, 1945a].

Burnt Mountain, Pickens County: Three singing males seen at an altitude of 2,000 feet on May 30, 1945 [Odum, 1945a]; male feeding two young, June 23, 1945; four other singing males seen the same day [Odum, 1945b].

Pinelog Mountain, Cherokee County: Female feeding two young, July 29,

1945 [Denton and Odum, 1945]; adult birds feeding fledglings, May 25, 1946 [Griffin and Odum, 1946].

Woody's Gap, Union and Lumpkin counties: Female feeding two young, July 4, 1950 [Johnston, 1950].

Tray Mountain, White County: Young recently out of the nest seen June 18, 1948 [Denton and Neal, 1951].

Cloudland Canyon State Park (Sitton's Gulch): Parent birds feeding young out of the nest, May 31, 1953 [Dorsey, letter].

Three males representing the breeding population and typical of *waynei* were taken on Lookout Mountain, May 26, 1933. Also characteristic of this southern race were specimens taken by A. H. Howell on Rich Mountain, July 8, 1908, and on Brasstown Bald, July 15, 1908.

HABITS AND RECOGNITION: In the northern part of its range, this species shows a definite partiality for conifers, being found where white pine and hemlock predominate. In Georgia, however, it apparently is not so exacting in its requirements. Odum [1945] states that "the species shows preference for ravines or ridges where there is a scattering of Virginia pine, although pairs may be found in pure deciduous woods," and this same impartiality has been noted by other observers. During the breeding season, the males consistently remain in the upper branches of the larger trees, where, were it not for their distinctive and readily recognized song, they could be easily overlooked.

In appearance, Wayne's Black-throated Green Warbler differs little from its more northern relative, the one character distinguishing it in any plumage being its smaller, more slender bill.

Cerulean Warbler
Dendroica cerulea (Wilson)

GENERAL DISTRIBUTION: Breeds from southeastern Nebraska, southeastern Minnesota, southern Michigan, southern Ontario, and western New York south to northeastern Texas, Louisiana, and central Alabama. Winters in Venezuela, Ecuador, and Peru.

STATUS IN GEORGIA: A regular but uncommon transient in the northern part of the state and a rare fall transient south of the fall line.

In the Piedmont of Georgia, the Cerulean Warbler has been noted in small numbers in April and early May, and again from late July through the middle of September. There are at present few records south of the fall line, all in autumn.

Extreme dates of occurrence in the spring are Athens, April 19 (1933) and May 5 (1924); and Atlanta, April 13 (1916) and May 14 (1915). It has also been seen at Rising Fawn, April 22, 1885; Canton, April 27, 1905; and Roswell, April 20, 1933.

For the fall migration, extreme dates of occurrence are Augusta, August 16 (1947) and September 16 (1944); Athens, July 28 (1939) and September 14 (1928); and Atlanta, July 29 (1946) and September 11 (1948). There is also an early fall record for Cherokee County, a specimen taken there, July 24, 1905, and one record for Macon, September 30, 1932. In the southern part of the state, this species has been reported by Stoddard in Grady County in 1948 on September 18 [letter]; and in 1951 by Norris [1952] in Irwin County, August 8, 20, and 29, and September 3; Wilcox County, August 13; Macon County, August 16; and Decatur County, September 1.

LaPrade [1922] reports several singing males in Collier Woods in Atlanta throughout May and June, but no nests were found, and in recent years no further evidence has been secured indicating definitely that the Cerulean Warbler breeds in the state.

HABITS AND RECOGNITION: In its summer home, the Cerulean Warbler is a bird of the wooded stream bottoms and hillsides, where its days are spent in the upper branches of the largest trees. In migration, it shows the same preference for feeding well above the ground, and unless looked for, can easily escape notice. In spring, the males sing freely as they feed high overhead, but as the song is somewhat suggestive of that of the Parula Warbler, it is doubtful if it normally would attract much attention. In adult plumage, this species resembles no other warbler, and can be readily recognized if seen at reasonable range. In the male, the upperparts are light blue, the underparts clear white with a distinct bluish-black band across the breast. The female differs in being greenish above and lacking the breast band, but is nevertheless noticeably unlike other female warblers of this genus. Being an uncommon transient in the Atlantic Coast states, the Cerulean Warbler will probably never be observed in Georgia, either in the spring or in the fall, other than in small numbers and at infrequent intervals.

Blackburnian Warbler
Dendroica fusca (Müller)

GENERAL DISTRIBUTION: Breeds from central Manitoba, central Ontario, Quebec, and Cape Breton Island south to central Minnesota, Wisconsin, northern Michigan, Massachusetts, and Connecticut, and in the Alleghenies from Pennsylvania to northern Georgia. Winters from Venezuela and Colombia to central Peru, casually north to Yucatán.

STATUS IN GEORGIA: An uncommon spring transient and a fairly common fall transient over most of the state. In the mountain counties, a fairly common but local summer resident.

Apparently the Blackburnian Warbler follows a different migration route in the spring than in the fall, as south of its breeding range in Georgia only an occasional bird is noted each year from late March until early May, while in the fall it appears regularly in August and is frequently observed until late October.

The earliest spring transients were seen at Savannah, March 21 (1925); in the Okefenokee Swamp, April 5 (1945); at Milledgeville, April 6 (1940); Athens, March 29 (1926); Atlanta, April 2 (1895); and Dalton, April 13 (1941). The last in the spring were noted at Atlanta, May 22 (1954); and Athens, May 13 (1925). For Fitzgerald, there is a single spring record, April 21, 1941.

In fall, the earliest transients appeared at Athens, August 4 (1939); Atlanta, August 20 (1898); Macon, September 7 (1952); Grady County, September 13 (1942); and Savannah, August 10 (1912). The latest were seen at Athens, October 29 (1920); Atlanta, October 30 (1948); Macon, October 10 (1949); and Grady County, October 25 (1940). There are also fall records for Augusta (September 23, 1943 and October 7, 1945); Americus (October 4, 1941); Fitzgerald (October 22 and 23, 1940); and Tifton (September 27 and November 2, 1941).

In the extreme northern part of the state, it has been reported during the breeding season on Brasstown Bald, Towns County; Blood Mountain, Union County; and Ellijay, Gilmer County; and there are definite breeding records for Margret, Fannin County, male feeding a young bird just out of the nest June 8, 1921 (Burleigh); Burnt Mountain, Pickens County, nest with four young June 23, 1945 [Odum, 1945c]; and for Tray Mountain, White County, nest with young June 3, 1948 [Denton and Neal, 1951]. Further field work will doubtless show that it nests elsewhere in the mountain counties.

HABITS AND RECOGNITION: With its vivid orange throat and breast, the male Blackburnian Warbler is a handsome bird, and the first sight of one in spring leaves a lasting impression. It is essentially a bird of the heavier timber, and prefers to feed well above the ground, but if watched long enough will sooner or later come within reasonable range, where its beauty can be more clearly seen and appreciated. It has no mannerisms that distinguish it from other species of the genus *Dendroica,* and when seen in migration in Georgia, is usually one of a mixed flock of small warblers.

It was not until 1945 that a nest of the Blackburnian Warbler was found for the first time in Georgia. Odum [1945c] has given us an interesting account of this discovery as follows:

On June 23, 1945, I was fortunate enough to locate a nest of the Blackburnian Warbler on Burnt Mountain in the northeast corner of

Pickens County very near the extreme southernmost limit of the species' breeding range in eastern United States. After spending all morning near the summit of Burnt Mountain and the ridge which connects this mountain with Oglethorpe Mountain four miles to the south, I decided to descend from the ridge to the head of a cove in order to get water to go with my lunch. After walking about a mile through thick scrub, I came to a fine spring located in a mature stand of oak-chestnut forest at an estimated elevation of 2,600 to 2,800 feet. The chestnuts, of course, were all dead, some of them fallen, but large chestnut oaks, red and white oaks, tulips, and hickories were present; there were no conifers whatsoever. While eating my lunch by the spring I noticed a pair of Blackburnians hanging around and after some watching discovered their nest almost directly over my head in an enormous white oak. The nest was nearly out to the end of a long limb at least 30 feet from the trunk and about 55 feet above the stream over which it swung. The nest appeared compact but was easily visible from below as were four young birds. Both parents fed the young, but the female much more frequently. The female did all her food getting in the vicinity of the nest, favoring especially a large hickory tree. The male seemed to range much further in quest of food.

Over most of its range the Blackburnian Warbler is very partial to tall mature stands of conifers, rarely nesting in any other habitat. In Georgia, the species may be found summering in hemlock and white pine stands where such are available, but the majority of individuals have become adapted to mature stands of deciduous trees, thus retaining their partiality to tall timber even though choosing broad-leaved trees instead of conifers.

The nest found on Tray Mountain by Fern Doris and Lucille Rotchford on May 16, 1948 [Denton and Neal, 1951], was in a situation very similar to the one described above, being forty feet from the ground at the extreme end of an upper limb of a large white oak.

Eastern Yellow-throated Warbler
Dendroica dominica dominica (Linnaeus)

GENERAL DISTRIBUTION: Breeds from southern Maryland, Delaware, and southern New Jersey south to middle Florida. Winters in southern Florida, the Bahamas, and Greater Antilles, and casually north to Georgia and South Carolina.

STATUS IN GEORGIA: A common summer resident in the mountains and foothills of the northern part of the state and in the coastal plain. There is

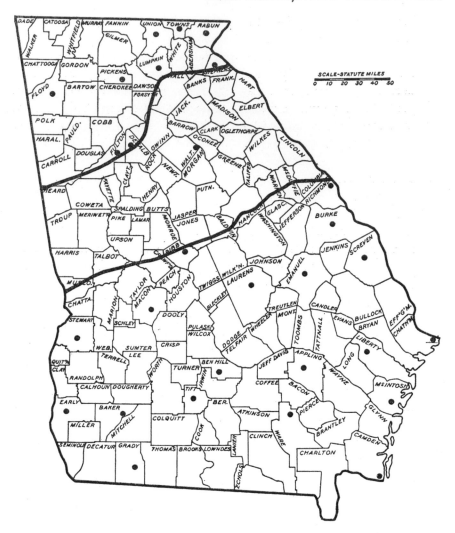

SCALE-STATUTE MILES
0   10   20   30   40   50

BREEDING DISTRIBUTION OF THE YELLOW-THROATED WARBLER

only one breeding record in the Piedmont, where it occurs as a regular, but somewhat scarce, transient. Present in small numbers during the winter south of the fall line.

At Athens, where it is not known to nest, it has been noted in small numbers in both spring and fall, extreme dates of occurrence being March 25 (1929) and April 23 (1925), and July 8 (1928) and October 11 (1945) (Burleigh). At Atlanta, where it is a fairly common summer resident, it has been observed between the dates of March 12 (1907) and October 6 (1947). There are two winter records, November 17, 1903, and December 29, 1936 [Griffin, MS]. Murphey [1937] considers it an abundant breeding bird at Augusta, "present during every month except December, January, and February." Extreme dates of occurrence there are February 20 (1948) and November 28 (1943) (Denton). Elsewhere, the earliest spring transients have been recorded at Columbus, March 22 (1945); Macon, March 12 (1944); Milledgeville, March 15 (1938); Canton, March 27 (1905); Dalton, April 1 (1944); and Rome, March 16 (1944).

There are winter records for Augusta, January 1 and February 18, 1950 (Denton); and numerous winter records for the southern part of the state, including the following:

Wilcox County: January 27, 1946.

Fitzgerald: December 22, 1939, February 2, 1940, January 21 and February 11, 1945.

Newton: January 5, 1932.

Grady County: Winters regularly in small numbers.

Bryan County: January 27, 1931.

Liberty County: January 1, 1930.

Darien: February 4, 1888.

Brunswick: December 22, 1940.

Camden County: Winters regularly in small numbers.

Okefenokee Swamp: December 4, 1934, December 29, 1935, January 16, 1938.

The breeding range of the Yellow-throated Warbler in Georgia is rather perplexing, for while it is common during the summer months in suitable habitat in the mountains, a wide area exists between the foothills and the edge of the coastal plain where this species is not known to nest. In the extreme eastern edge of the state, it is found on the Savannah River as far north as Augusta, but otherwise apparently does not occur as a breeding bird south of Toccoa and Dahlonega.

Farther west, it nests more or less commonly as far south as Stone Mountain, in DeKalb County, and at Atlanta, but between Fulton County and the fall line it has yet to be reported as breeding. Hence, the fact that a breeding pair was noted by Johnston at High Shoals, in Walton County, in 1950 [Johnston, 1950] is of considerable interest, as it indicates a possible recent extension of range of this species into this part of the Piedmont. The birds were seen at the same spot on April 17 and on May 6, 10, 19, and 26; on the last date the female was carrying food for young that were unquestionably close by.

Definite breeding records for the Yellow-throated Warbler in Georgia are for the following localities:

Young Harris: Two fresh eggs, May 20, 1927 (Burleigh).

Margret, Fannin County: Four almost fledged young, May 28, 1927 (Burleigh).

Atlanta: Four eggs, April 18, 1939; two young, June 15, 1939 [Griffin, 1940].

Augusta: Adults feeding young in nest, April 15, 1945 (Denton).

Grady County: Three well-grown young, April 30, 1952 (Stoddard and Sutton).

Savannah: Extreme nesting dates (twenty-one nests), April 11 (1914), four fresh eggs; May 21 (1922), three slightly incubated eggs (Rossignol).

Camden County: Fully fledged young, April 24 and June 12, 1948 (Hebard).

Eastern Yellow-throated Warblers
Dendroica dominica dominica

These beautiful birds, which spent most of their time high in moss-festooned trees, were of special interest to me, for I had recently named a geographical race of the species for my friend Herbert Stoddard. Southwestern Georgia specimens proved to be not quite long-billed enough for *Dendroica dominica stoddardi,* a form which breeds only, so far as is known at present, in northwestern Florida. The Yellow-throated Warbler nests I found all were high. Obtaining a stub-tailed young bird, in the plumage-stage shown here, necessitated some climbing as well as use of the longest fish-pole we could find. Above the young bird are its parents, the male to the right.

HABITS AND RECOGNITION: The Yellow-throated Warbler is remarkably like the Parula Warbler in its distribution in Georgia. It shows the same partiality for moist woods where Spanish moss covers the branches of the trees, and in the southern part of the state occurs commonly in the cypress and tupelo swamps. Here its nest is likewise built among thick strands of hanging moss, usually at some distance from the ground, where it is so well concealed that only by seeing the female go to it can a searcher find it. In the mountains, however, where this moss does not grow, it is almost equally common, and here it is a bird of the open pine woods, spending its days in the upper branches of the larger trees. Its partiality for conifers is so marked that one will look for it in vain on ridges where deciduous hardwoods predominate. The few nests that have been found in northern Georgia have been, almost without exception, in pines, well up from the ground and some distance out from the trunk. The one that I located at Young Harris on May 20, 1927, with two fresh eggs, was up fully ninety feet in the top of a large white pine; it was compact and deeply cupped, and built largely of fine shreds of bark, with a few grasses and dry pine needles, well lined with white chicken feathers and a few horsehairs. Johnston [MS] reports a nest found in Cobb County in 1942 that was but ten feet from the ground in a post oak.

In appearance and actions this warbler is one of the more attractive of its family. It is a handsome bird, with its slate-gray back and bright yellow throat and breast, both sexes being so nearly alike that it is difficult to distinguish between them. The male possesses a loud, ringing song that will at once attract attention to its presence, but as it is rather deliberate in its movements and frequently sings for minutes at a time from one spot, it is often far from easy actually to see it.

Sycamore Yellow-throated Warbler
Dendroica dominica albilora Ridgway

GENERAL DISTRIBUTION: Breeds from southeastern Nebraska, southern Wisconsin, southern Michigan, Ohio, West Virginia, and western North Carolina south to central Texas, Louisiana, and southern Mississippi. Winters from Mexico to Nicaragua and Costa Rica, and casually in the lower Río Grande Valley.

STATUS IN GEORGIA: A scarce transient.

At the present time there are four records of this western race of the Yellow-throated Warbler in Georgia. It was added to the state list for the first time by George P. Butler, who collected a specimen in Richmond County, April 21, 1893. Another was taken in Cherokee County, April 20,

1905; a third at St. Marys, by Arnow, on October 28, 1910; and the fourth at Roswell, by D. V. Hembree, July 2, 1913.

HABITS AND RECOGNITION: The main characters separating this race are the line in front of the eye (which in *dominica* is yellow and in *albilora*, white), and the smaller, more slender bill. In general appearance and actions it differs in no way from the Eastern Yellow-throated Warbler.

Chestnut-sided Warbler
Dendroica pensylvanica (Linnaeus)

GENERAL DISTRIBUTION: Breeds from central Saskatchewan, central Manitoba, central Ontario, and southern Quebec south to eastern Nebraska, Illinois, Indiana, Ohio, northern New Jersey, and Long Island, and in the Alleghenies to Tennessee, northern Georgia, and South Carolina. Winters from Guatemala to Panama.

STATUS IN GEORGIA: A common summer resident in the mountains and a common spring and fall transient over all of the state except in the extreme southern counties, where it is rarely observed in the spring.

Extreme dates of occurrence in the spring, south of the breeding range, are Fitzgerald, March 22 (1941) and May 2 (1940); Macon, April 15 (1944) and May 11 (1932); Atlanta, April 17 (1896) and May 23 (1931); Athens, April 20 (1927) and May 21 (1946); and Augusta, May 1 (1945) and May 14 (1945). It has also been reported at St. Marys, April 12, 1905; Grady County, May 5, 1940 and April 20, 1944; Columbus, April 28, 1946; Milledgeville, May 2, 1940; Rising Fawn, April 29, 1885; and Rome, April 17, 1944.

In the fall, extreme dates of occurrence are Atlanta, August 8 (1901) and November 19 (1946); Athens, August 15 (1929) and October 20 (1926); Augusta, August 20 (1944) and October 11 (1944); Macon, September 10 (1955) and October 16 (1945); Fitzgerald, August 29 (1951) and October 1 (1941); and Grady County, September 11 (1949) and October 25 (1947). At Dalton the earliest fall transient was noted August 15 (1944).

It was not until 1925 that the Chestnut-sided Warbler was first definitely recorded as breeding in the state, but it is now known to nest commonly on Rabun Bald (Rabun County), Brasstown Bald (Towns County), Tray Mountain (White and Towns counties), Blood Mountain (Union County), Black Mountain (Lumpkin County), Flattop Mountain (Fannin County), Burnt Mountain (Pickens County), and Mt. Oglethorpe (Dawson County). Further field work will doubtless show it nesting elsewhere in the mountains wherever there is suitable habitat. Actual breeding records are at present limited to Brasstown Bald (three nests May 28, 1925, one with two half-grown young and two infertile eggs, another with four fresh eggs, and the third with two fresh eggs) [Burleigh, 1927]; Blood Mountain (nest in Neel's Gap that on June 7, 1945, held three young) [Major, 1945]; Burnt Mountain (female feeding "bob-tailed young" June 23, 1945) [Odum, 1945b]; and Tray Mountain (nest with three eggs June 17, 1949) [Denton and Neal, 1951].

HABITS AND RECOGNITION: The Chestnut-sided Warbler originally did not occur as a breeding bird in Georgia, for as recently as 1908, Arthur H. Howell failed to find it during field work carried on in June on the upper slopes of Brasstown Bald. The actual year it first nested there will, unfortunately, never be known, but in 1925 I found it already fairly common at the top of the mountain, and since then it has been reported during the summer months at a number of other spots in the northern part of the state. One can only theorize as to the reason for the appearance and rapid increase of the Chestnut-sided Warbler in Georgia, but it is logical to assume that it is the result of the changes that have taken place during the past fifty years in the southern Appalachians. The heavy timber covering the mountainsides has gradually disappeared as the result of logging operations and the chestnut blight, and the overgrown slashings and brush-covered ridges that have resulted offer ideal conditions for a species, which, throughout its breeding range, is largely restricted to such a habitat. It is at present found in Georgia during the summer on the higher ridges above an altitude of 3,000 feet, but it is not improbable that as it increases in numbers it will gradually appear in the valleys.

As so few nests of the Chestnut-sided Warbler have been found in the state, it is of interest to give in some detail the circumstances under which it was first found nesting on Brasstown Bald [Burleigh, 1927]:

> Within a few hundred yards of the top of Brasstown Bald the south slope is covered with small stunted oaks that are few enough in number to encourage a thick undergrowth of laurel and huckleberry bushes. In this limited area the Chestnut-sided Warblers are actually plentiful, and are among the few birds that can be found breeding there. On May 28, 1925, we spent the entire morning searching this spot for nests, and by noon had succeeded in finding three. All were within two feet of the ground, two being in laurels and one in a huckleberry bush, and while they were not so very well concealed, the brush was so thick that it was necessary to be almost over them to see them. One held two half-grown young and two infertile eggs, another two fresh eggs, and the third four fresh eggs, so seemingly

individual pairs breed at widely separated intervals. The nests were alike in construction, and distinct enough not to be confused with those of any other species found here, being loosely and somewhat shabbily built of grasses, and a few rootlets and shreds of bark, lined with fine grass stems and, in one case, a little horse hair, and held in place on the twigs by felted insect down and wool.

The nest found on Tray Mountain in 1949 (Denton and Neal) was in a similar situation to those described above, being two feet from the ground in the top of a laurel bush.

Bay-breasted Warbler
Dendroica castanea (Wilson)

GENERAL DISTRIBUTION: Breeds from northeastern Alberta, central Manitoba, and central Quebec south to southern Manitoba, northern Maine, the mountains of Vermont and New Hampshire, and the Adirondacks of New York. Winters in Panama and Colombia.

STATUS IN GEORGIA: In the northern part of the state a fairly common spring transient and a common fall transient. South of the fall line an uncommon fall transient only, there being to date no spring records for the coastal plain. Accidental in winter.

At Athens, the Bay-breasted Warbler was found to be a fairly common transient in the spring and invariably quite plentiful in the fall, when throughout October small flocks were seen in scattered stretches of woods. Extreme dates of occurrence in the spring are April 26 (1928) and May 18 (1924); and in the fall, October 3 (1929) and November 5 (1925) [Burleigh, 1938]. At Atlanta, Griffin [MS] gives as migration extremes April 22 (1929) and May 22 (1954), and August 29 (1920) and November 3 (1948). It has also been noted in the spring at Macon, May 8, 1921, April 29, 1923, and May 10, 1937 (Johnston); Dalton, May 9, 1941 (Hamilton); and at Rome between the dates of April 28 and May 11, 1953 (Dorsey); and in the fall at Young Harris, September 29, 1945 (Burleigh); Augusta, between the dates of October 8 (1944) (Denton) and October 24 (1908) (Murphey); Macon, between the dates of October 8 (1954) and October 16 (1920) (Johnston); in Grady County, between the dates of October 12 (1940) and October 26 (1947) (Stoddard); and at Fitzgerald, October 19, 1940 (Norris).

A rather unexpected record was that of a female taken in the South River area five miles south of Atlanta on January 21, 1950 [Griffin, 1950]. So far as known, this was the first record of this species in the United

States in winter. The following year, however, on December 17, 1951, one bird was reported at St. Marys by Richard G. Kuerzi [Hebard, letter].

HABITS AND RECOGNITION: At one time the Bay-breasted Warbler was considered one of the rarer warblers observed in migration, but it apparently has increased in numbers in recent years, for through the Piedmont of Georgia it occurs regularly now in both spring and fall. There is a possibility also that because of its remarkable similarity to the Black-polled Warbler in the fall, it was largely overlooked in the past at that season of the year. It is generally believed that these two species are very difficult to identify in fall unless actually collected, but from long experience in the field I have found that this is not always the case. The average Bay-breasted Warbler reveals its identity by the trace of chestnut on its flanks and by its buff, rather than yellow, underparts. The buff under tail coverts, in contrast to the white ones of the Black-polled Warbler, likewise aid in separating these two species, but unfortunately there is more or less variation in this respect. The best field mark to bear in mind is the color of the legs. In the Bay-breasted Warbler, they are dark brown, in some individuals almost black, while in the Black-poll they are light colored, almost yellowish. Since both species are rather unsuspicious and, for warblers, deliberate in their movements, it is often possible to observe them at reasonably close range and note these characters.

In spring plumage, the male Bay-breasted Warbler is a handsome bird, the buffy crescent on the side of the neck standing out in strong contrast to the chestnut crown and throat and black face and giving it a rather exotic look. The female is not as highly colored, though equally distinctive.

Black-polled Warbler
Dendroica striata (Forster)

GENERAL DISTRIBUTION: Breeds from northwestern Alaska, northern Mackenzie, northern Manitoba, northern Quebec, and Newfoundland south to northern British Columbia, Manitoba, Michigan, northern Maine, and the mountains of New York, Vermont, and New Hampshire. Winters from Guiana and Venezuela to Brazil.

STATUS IN GEORGIA: A common spring transient over most of the state, infrequent, however, in the extreme southwestern counties. A rare fall transient everywhere but on the coast, where it occurs commonly throughout October.

Extreme dates of occurrence in the spring are as follows:

Camden County: April 23 (1946) and June 6 (1952).

Savannah: April 12 (1924) and June 3 1907.

Fitzgerald: April 7 (1942) and May 23 (1941).

Augusta: April 26 (1945) and May 25 (1943).

Macon: April 20 (1933) and May 24 (1934).

Athens: April 19 (1928) and May 30 (1926).

Milledgeville: April 11 (1936) and May 16 (1926).

Atlanta: April 12 (1954) and May 29 (1907).

It has also been reported in Grady County, April 27 through April 30, 1952; at Blackshear, May 3, 1946; Baker County, April 28, 1950; Americus, April 25 to May 6, 1942; Rising Fawn, April 17, 1885; and Dalton, April 18, 1944.

In the interior of the state there are very few records of the fall migration. It has been noted at Augusta, October 10, 1942, September 23 and 28, 1944, and September 8, 1945; at Athens, October 14 and 15, 1929; at Atlanta, October 15, 1945; and at Macon, September 14, 1953 and October 8, 1954. On the coast, the earliest fall record is October 6 (1923), when a bird struck the Tybee Light; the latest, October 30 (1905), at St. Marys.

HABITS AND RECOGNITION: To one familiar with the bird life of Georgia the Black-polled Warbler stands out as the last transient to disappear in the spring. In late May, when other birds are busily engaged in nesting, this species is still leisurely moving northward, and there are years when it is early June before the last individual has departed. The deliberate, sibilant song of the male is frequently heard during the warm days that are characteristic of the latter part of May, and has come to be associated with that season. Spring comes late in the far north, and it is the middle of June before the snows of the long winter have melted and mild temperatures have brought out the insect life on which this warbler feeds. Seeming to realize this, the Black-poll lingers until conditions in its summer home become suitable for nesting, and one cannot but respect its judgment in prolonging its stay in Georgia.

In migration, the Black-poll is apt to appear almost anywhere, but it prefers the larger trees and is seldom seen in underbrush near the ground. For a warbler, it is rather deliberate in its movements, and being tame and unsuspicious, is easily observed. In the spring, there will never be any question about its identity, but in the fall the situation is quite different. Its plumage then so closely resembles that of the Bay-breasted Warbler that only under the most favorable circumstances can it be satisfactorily identified. This has resulted in considerable confusion in the past concerning the status of these two species in Georgia, but it is now generally accepted that the Black-poll, in its long journey south in the fall, is common only on the coast, and to a large extent is then merely a straggler in the interior of the state.

536

Northern Pine Warbler
Dendroica pinus pinus (Wilson)

GENERAL DISTRIBUTION: Breeds from northern Manitoba, northern Michigan, southern Ontario, southern Quebec, and New Brunswick south to eastern Texas, the Gulf Coast, and northern Florida. Winters from southern Illinois and the coast of Virginia to Florida, eastern Texas, and eastern Mexico (Tamaulipas), casually farther north on the Atlantic Coast to Massachusetts.

STATUS IN GEORGIA: A common permanent resident throughout the state.

The Pine Warbler is rather local in its occurrence in the mountain counties, but otherwise is generally distributed from the foothills of the mountains to the Florida line. It is doubtful that there is a stretch of open pine woods anywhere in the state where one or more pairs will not be found nesting. During the winter, its numbers are increased by birds from the northern part of its breeding range, and small flocks are numerous then.

There is little question that it nests in every county in the state, but definite breeding records are limited to the following localities:

Woodville, Greene County: Four fresh eggs June 8, 1922 (Burleigh).

Athens: Extreme nesting dates (sixteen nests), four fresh eggs, March 15 (1927); four fresh eggs, April 25 (1924) (Burleigh).

Atlanta: Nesting extremes, three fresh eggs, March 28 (1913) (Hembree); four young May 15 (1939) (Griffin) [Griffin, 1940].

Fitzgerald: Four eggs, April 27, 1940 [Norris, 1940].

Augusta: Adults feeding young in nest, April 8, 1945 (Denton).

Grady County: Nest with well-grown young, April 8, 1937 (Stoddard).

Savannah: Extreme nesting dates (thirteen nests), four fresh eggs, March 27 (1907); three fresh eggs, June 7 (1914) (Rossignol).

HABITS AND RECOGNITION: No bird is more characteristic of the southeastern United States than the Pine Warbler. Over wide areas, one or more of the pines indigenous to this part of the country are found in either pure or mixed stands, and where there are pine woods, one will find the Pine Warbler. During the greater part of the year it rarely if ever leaves these conifers, its days being spent in the branches of the larger trees, where it feeds, mates, rears its young, and otherwise carries on the activities that satisfy its normal requirements. Deciduous hardwoods may be close by, but they have no appeal and are consistently ignored. During the winter months, however, its habits change somewhat, for then small flocks can be seen feeding on the ground in open fields and pastures, often accompanying restless flocks of Bluebirds. It has also been observed at this season of the year feeding in cypress swamps, and in the evergreen magnolias and live oaks growing on higher ground at the edge of such swamps.

The Pine Warbler is one of the larger and more plainly colored members of the genus *Dendroica*. Both sexes are yellowish-green above, brighter yellow beneath, the female, as is usually the case, being noticeably duller in appearance. In actions, this species lacks the restless activity characteristic of many of the warblers, its movements being unhurried and rather deliberate. The males sing throughout much of the year, their slow, clear trill being one of the most familiar sounds in the pine woods of Georgia.

Breeding activities normally begin rather early in the spring, although the date is governed to some extent by the weather. At Athens, it was not unusual to find fresh eggs by the latter part of March, my earliest breeding record, the result of mild weather during much of February, being that of a nest that held four fresh eggs on March 15, 1927. The female was first observed working on this nest on February 17, and it was then already so well started that, although fully eighty feet from the ground at the outer end of a limb of a large loblolly pine, it was plainly visible. Later that month, and again in early March, there were intervals when the weather was cold and rainy, but although delayed for days at a time, the female persisted in her efforts, and finally, after a full month had passed, had finished the nest and laid the usual complement of four eggs. The nest is always in a pine, and is usually well up from the ground and at the outer end of a limb. The average height varies from twenty-five to forty feet, rarely lower, but not infrequently much higher. It is compact and deeply cupped, and well built of rootlets, weed stems, grasses, dry pine needles, and shreds of bark, lined with plant down, feathers, and horsehair. A female seen near Athens on March 18, 1925, was gathering nesting material from the side of a crow's nest that held eggs but from which the owner was temporarily absent; and another observed a few days later was busily engaged in lining her nest with bunches of fur plucked from a dead cat lying in an open field. As nests with fresh eggs can be found in early June, it is probable that two broods are sometimes reared each year.

Kirtland's Warbler
Dendroica kirtlandii (Baird)

GENERAL DISTRIBUTION: Breeding range limited to north central Michigan. Winters in the Bahamas.

STATUS IN GEORGIA: A rare transient on the coast.

Kirtland's Warbler was first recorded in Georgia by Arthur H. Helme, who collected a female on Cumberland Island, April 12, 1902. He also took another female there on April 14, 1903, and a male on April 27, 1904 [Helme, 1904]. Isaac Arnow took a specimen at St. Marys, April 16, 1902;

and T. D. Perry reported one seen at Savannah on August 27, 1909. There are no recent records.

HABITS AND RECOGNITION: Because of its extremely restricted breeding range, Kirtland's Warbler will always be one of the rarest of the warblers. It possibly occurs oftener in Georgia than the few available records would indicate, but in such small numbers that one must be fortunate indeed to find one. If seen, it can be recognized by its large size as compared with other warblers, gray crown, brown back heavily streaked with black, and yellow underparts and sides streaked with black. It commonly feeds on the ground, where it walks rather than hops and, when nervous, wags its tail up and down much in the manner of a Palm Warbler.

Northern Prairie Warbler
Dendroica discolor discolor (Vieillot)

GENERAL DISTRIBUTION: Breeds from eastern Nebraska, eastern Kansas, central Michigan, southern Ontario, and southern New Hampshire south to southwestern Missouri, northern Mississippi, southern Alabama, and southeastern Georgia. Winters in the Bahamas and West Indies and casually on islands off the coast of Central America.

STATUS IN GEORGIA: A local but fairly common summer resident over all the state except the southwestern and south central portions.

In the mountains, the Prairie Warbler is rather local in its distribution; it has been noted during the breeding season at Young Harris, Towns County, and Margret, Fannin County, and doubtless occurs in many of the open valleys where conditions are suitable.

In the eastern part of the state, it nests to the coast, but farther west it is not found as a breeding bird south of a line running from Sumter and Stewart counties southwestward through the western edge of Randolph, Clay, and Early counties. Norris [1951] has shown that this limited range in southwestern Georgia approximates the lower boundary of the geologic formation known as the Red Hills Belt, characterized by topography and vegetation similar in many respects to that of the Piedmont of Georgia.

In spring, the earliest transients have been noted at:

St. Marys: March 23 (1905).	Macon: March 30 (1945).
Cumberland Island: March 16 (1902).	Milledgeville: March 31 (1936).
Sea Island: March 26 (1948).	Augusta: April 3 (1945).
Savannah: March 8 (1908).	Athens: April 5 (1927).
Grady County: March 24 (1952).	Atlanta: March 26 (1938).
Fitzgerald: April 3 (1941).	Canton: March 31 (1905).
Americus: April 10 (1942).	Dalton: April 7 (1944).
Columbus: April 14 (1946).	

The last in the fall were seen at Augusta, October 12 (1945); Athens, October 14 (1928); Atlanta, October 30 (1946); Macon, October 18 (1924); Americus, October 4 (1941); Tifton, October 22 (1941); and Savannah, October 10 (1909).

As is the case with so many of the common summer residents of the state, actual breeding records are not numerous, and are limited to the following localities:

Woodville, Greene County: Four small young, May 23, 1922; three fresh eggs May 18, 1923; four fresh eggs May 20, 1924 (Burleigh).

Atlanta: Nesting extremes, four eggs May 6, 1919 (Arpal); five fresh eggs, August 5, 1903 (Mills) [Griffin, 1940].

Jones County: Three young June 30, 1942 [Fleetwood, 1945].

Grady County: Four fresh eggs, May 7, 1952 (Sutton).

Savannah: One fresh egg May 29, 1909; four fresh eggs April 22, 1916 (Rossignol).

HABITS AND RECOGNITION: The Prairie Warbler is not well named, for actually it is a bird of old slashings, abandoned fields and pastures overgrown with scrubby underbrush, and deciduous undergrowth in the stretches of open pine woods. Approaching such a spot during the spring months, one will at once be attracted by the peculiar and distinctive song of the male as it sings from the upper branches of the largest tree in its vicinity. The song is a series of six to eight syllables, "zee-zee-zee-zee-zee-zee," uttered in a drawling manner and with a gradually rising inflection. It is only when singing that the male leaves the thickets and underbrush in which its days are spent, for this little warbler prefers to feed near the ground and even in migration is rarely seen in the larger trees. It is one of the more active of its family, but is normally easily approached and just as easily recognized because of its distinctive plumage. Both sexes are alike in appearance, having bright yellow underparts, the sides streaked with black, and an olive-green back, marked in the middle with reddish-chestnut spots that form a distinct patch. Observed within reasonable distance, the pattern of the back will always identify the Prairie Warbler.

The nest is placed in a bush or small sapling, usually within two or three feet of the ground, and is always well concealed. It is compactly built of grasses, shreds of bark, and plant down, well cupped, and lined with finer grasses, horsehair, and feathers. A nest that I found in Greene County was unlike any other I have ever seen—the female, taking advantage of a cotton field adjoining the open slashing in which it was nesting, had built the nest almost entirely of cotton, giving it a unique appearance. Normally four eggs are laid, and only one brood is reared each year; it is exceptional to find an occupied nest in Georgia after the latter part of June.

Western Palm Warbler
Dendroica palmarum palmarum (Gmelin)

GENERAL DISTRIBUTION: Breeds from southern Mackenzie and northern Manitoba south and southeast to northern Minnesota. Winters from the Gulf Coast, Georgia, and the coast of South Carolina south through the Bahamas and Greater Antilles to Yucatán, casually north on the Atlantic Coast to Massachusetts.

STATUS IN GEORGIA: A common transient and winter resident over most of the state, being less frequently observed, however, in winter north of the fall line.

Throughout the Piedmont of Georgia, the Western Palm Warbler is rather local in its distribution during the winter and irregular in its occurrence then, there being years when it is scarce and only infrequently observed. It is a common transient, however, in both spring and fall, being most often seen during the latter part of April and the latter part of October. In the southern half of the state, it is of common occurrence from September until May.

In the fall, the earliest transients have been noted at:

Augusta: September 11 (1943).
Hartwell: September 15 (1949).
Athens: September 16 (1945).
Atlanta: September 12 (1931).
Macon: September 17 (1932).
Cochran: September 22 (1932).

Americus: October 4 (1941).
Irwin County: September 21 (1940).
Grady County: September 24 (1948).
Savannah: September 4 (1910).
St. Marys: September 20 (1905).

The last in the spring were seen at:

Darien: May 18 (1945).
Cumberland Island: May 6 (1902).
Savannah: May 6 (1921).
Grady County: May 8 (1945).
Fitzgerald: May 11 (1939).
Americus: May 9 (1942).

Cochran: May 7 (1934).
Macon: May 9 (1933).
Atlanta: May 28 (1949).
Athens: May 12 (1928).
Augusta: May 9 (1942).

Specimens representing this western race have been taken at Athens (December 4, 1928; January 9, February 4, and April 25, 1929; December 7, 1944; September 16 and December 10, 1945; February 3 and 11, and March 3, 1946); Montreal, DeKalb County (November 15, 1946); Decatur (October 7, 1946; April 12 and 22, and September 26, 1947); Atlanta (October 30, November 4 and 8, and December 21 and 28, 1946; January 6, 1947); Soperton (April 14, 1946); Blakely (February 11, 1936); and Thomasville (February 14, 1924).

HABITS AND RECOGNITION: Few birds are easier to identify and become acquainted with than the Palm Warbler. It is a small, inconspicuously plumaged warbler that will usually be seen feeding on the ground at the edge of an open field or pasture. Not infrequently it will be found in thin woods, or in slashings during winter, but on the whole its preference is for the more open country. Small flocks can be approached with little difficulty, and the observer will at once become aware of the incessant up and down wagging of the tail that distinguishes this species. If alarmed, the birds fly into the nearest bushes, and for a moment or two they may be quiet. Soon, however, the tails begin the characteristic pump-handle motion, and first one bird and then another will fly to the ground and resume feeding. During the fall and winter, the appearance of both sexes is rather drab, the one touch of color being the yellow of the under tail coverts that is noticeable only when the birds are off the ground. With the approach of spring, both male and female acquire a reddish-chestnut crown and a yellow throat and upper breast, and then look more like what one would expect in this genus of usually brightly colored wood warblers.

Yellow Palm Warbler
Dendroica palmarum hypochrysea   Ridgway

GENERAL DISTRIBUTION: Breeds from Hudson Bay, northern Quebec, and Newfoundland south to Nova Scotia, New Brunswick, and eastern Maine. Winters from Louisiana to Florida, and casually north to North Carolina.

STATUS IN GEORGIA: An uncommon transient and winter resident over most of the state.

Although this race can frequently be satisfactorily identified in the field, there is always the possibility of error with sight records. Hence it seems advisable, for present purposes, to accept only those records based on actual specimens. It is generally agreed, however, that this eastern race is only infrequently seen either as a transient or as a winter resident, and compared to *palmarum*, it is a rather scarce bird in Georgia.

Specimens representing *hypochrysea* have been examined from the following localities:

Washington: December 21, 1945.

Athens: February 29, 1928; February 8, 1929; April 10, 1935; November 29 and December 12, 1945.

Decatur: April 6, 1947.

Atlanta: April 11, 1947.

Roswell: April 6, 1933.

Reidsville: December 16, 1916.

Fitzgerald: April 5, 1941.

Bainbridge: January 20, 1937.

Glennville: April 5, 1946.

Grady County: December 3, 1949.

Okefenokee Swamp: January 3, 1917; April 8, 1932; April 13, 1933; November 25, 1935; and January 9, 1936.

Chatham County: January 1 and April 14, 1900.

Family Parulidae: WOOD WARBLERS

It is probable that the Yellow Palm Warbler occurs more often than these records indicate, but on the basis of available data it appears that this race is seen in the state rather late in the fall (earliest date, November 29 [1945]), and rarely lingers in the spring later than the first week in April (latest date April 14 [1900]).

HABITS AND RECOGNITION: The two races of the Palm Warbler are unique in one respect. The Yellow Palm Warbler occupies the eastern part of the breeding range of the species, but in migration it follows a route that takes it west to the Gulf Coast, where it winters commonly from Louisiana to northern Florida. The Western Palm Warbler, on the other hand, migrates east to the Atlantic Coast, where it is common throughout the winter months from South Carolina to the Florida Keys. It seems odd that one race should spend the winter where the other would be expected, and one can only guess the reason for this crossing of migration routes between breeding and wintering ranges.

The Yellow Palm Warbler is a well-marked subspecies that can usually be easily recognized in the field if seen within reasonable range. Unlike the western race, the underparts, regardless of season, are entirely deep yellow and the brown of the back is tinged with olive. In actions there is little to distinguish it from *palmarum,* with which it can often be found feeding in open fields.

Eastern Oven-bird
Seiurus aurocapillus aurocapillus   (Linnacus)

GENERAL DISTRIBUTION: Breeds from southwestern Mackenzie, central Ontario, and central Quebec south to Kansas, southern Missouri, Kentucky, Pennsylvania, and Maryland. Winters from northern Florida, casually South Carolina, through the Bahamas and West Indies to St. Thomas, and from Mexico (Nuevo León) to Colombia.

STATUS IN GEORGIA: A common spring and fall transient throughout the state and a rare winter resident in the southern part of the coastal plain.

South of its breeding range in Georgia, the Oven-bird can normally be seen in spring from early April until after the middle of May; and in fall from the middle of August until the latter part of October.

Earliest transients in the spring were noted at:

Savannah: April 1 (1917).   Atlanta: April 2 (1954).
Grady County: March 17 (1937).   Dalton: April 16 (1944).
Fitzgerald: April 11 (1941).   Athens: April 3 (1924).
Macon: April 10 (1954).   Augusta: April 10 (1943).

The latest were seen at Darien, May 20 (1945); Savannah, May 18 (1907); Fitzgerald, May 8 (1941); Macon, May 9 (1926); Milledgeville, May 13 (1945); Augusta, May 12 (1945).

Earliest transients in the fall appeared at Augusta, August 11 (1946); Macon, September 1 (1936); Irwin County, August 29 (1951); Savannah, August 18 (1909); and St. Marys, September 6 (1905). The last were recorded at:

Augusta: October 22 (1944).
Athens: October 25 (1925).
Atlanta: October 21 (1946).
Macon: October 16 (1932).

Fitzgerald: October 15 (1939).
Grady County: November 3 (1939).
Savannah (Tybee Light): November 11 (1925).

There are seven records for the winter months: two birds seen in eastern Charlton County, January 5, 1943 [Hebard, 1945]; single birds in Grady County, December 23, 1937, and February 15, 1944 [Stoddard, MS]; another seen in Thomas County, February 15, 1949 [Stoddard, MS]; and West Point, December 10, 1950, through March 3, 1951 [Whiteman, 1952]; and one taken at Fitzgerald, February 11, 1945 [Meanley, 1945].

Since the races of the Oven-bird cannot be recognized in the field, it is probable that all of them are included in the above migration data, and it seems advisable, in view of the wide distribution and relative abundance of *aurocapillus,* to refer all sight records to the nominate race. Specimens representing *aurocapillus* have been taken at Harlem (April 16, 1947); Danielsville (October 5, 1945); Athens (May 17, 1928); Decatur (April 24, 1947); Atlanta (October 21, 1946, October 3, 1947); Grady County (October 12, 1947, August 22, 1948, September 18, 1948); and Darien (May 5, 1946).

HABITS AND RECOGNITION: The oven-bird prefers dry, deciduous woodlands. Swampy areas and pine woods may be visited briefly in migration, but are not favored as regular habitats. The heaviest timber is most preferred, and here, as the bird passes through the state in spring and again in fall, it can be found feeding on the ground where there is not much underbrush. Only when alarmed or singing will it be seen in the lower branches of one of the larger trees, and rarely, if ever, does it venture far overhead. As it feeds, it walks casually through the dead leaves covering the ground, and observed under such conditions, it suggests a small thrush. This impression is further emphasized by its olive-green back and black-streaked underparts, the one touch of color, noticeable only under the most favorable conditions, being the orange crown, bordered by a narrow but distinct black line. It is not especially shy, and as it passes through the state in migration is not difficult to find and become acquainted with.

544

Family Parulidae: WOOD WARBLERS

Newfoundland Oven-bird
Seiurus aurocapillus furvior   Batchelder

GENERAL DISTRIBUTION: Breeds in Newfoundland. Winters through the Bahamas and West Indies to Mexico, and rarely north to South Carolina.

STATUS IN GEORGIA: Of casual occurrence in the fall.

Although heretofore unrecorded in the state, this northern race of the Oven-bird was found to be of at least casual occurrence in the fall, and possibly occurs also as a spring transient. Further collecting will be necessary, however, to determine its status during the spring months, for as yet it has not been taken at this season of the year. In the series of Oven-birds available for study five specimens were found referable to *furvior.* These were a male taken at Commerce (Jackson County) on October 9, 1945, and four females taken at Athens on September 3 and October 3, 1929, on October 12, 1937, and on August 15, 1939. [Burleigh, 1948.]

Specimens have also been taken in Grady County by Stoddard on August 15 and October 3, 1948.

HABITS AND RECOGNITION: The oven-bird that breeds in Newfoundland is distinguished by its perceptibly darker upperparts. So far as its actions and general appearance go, it differs in no way from the other oven-birds.

Gray Oven-bird
Seiurus aurocapillus cinereus   Miller

GENERAL DISTRIBUTION: Breeds from southern Alberta and southeastern Montana south to southeastern Colorado and central Nebraska. Winter range unknown.

STATUS IN GEORGIA: Apparently of casual occurrence in the fall.

On the nights of October 6–7 and 7–8, 1954, adverse weather conditions resulted in an appalling destruction of small birds at brightly lighted towers or buildings or at airport ceilometers at seven widely separated spots in Georgia. At the Warner Robins Air Force Base at Macon an estimated 50,000 birds were killed. Of this number a total of 236 were identified as oven-birds. Ten were saved as study skins and sent to John W. Aldrich, of the Fish and Wildlife Service, for racial determination. Seven were found to represent the Rocky Mountain race, *cinereus,* a rather surprising ratio in view of the fact that it had heretofore never been recorded

HOODED WARBLER

Wilsonia citrina

This painting I made well back in the woods. I sat on a little plank bridge, so close to the stream that I dipped my brush in it. A pair of Hooded Warblers lived in the immediate vicinity. Each time one of the birds came into full view it spread its tail quickly, flashing the white of the outer feathers. The flowering plant is a dwarf buckeye.

in the state. This would indicate that not only has it passed through the state in past years undetected, but that it possibly breeds farther east than was originally supposed [Johnston, 1955].

HABITS AND RECOGNITION: The oven-bird that breeds on the eastern slopes of the Rocky Mountains differs from the nominate race, *aurocapillus,* in being grayer and paler, the upperparts being less intense olive-green. There appears to be no size difference. In general appearance and actions there is nothing to distinguish it from its eastern relatives.

Southeastern Oven-bird
Seiurus aurocapillus canivirens   Burleigh and Duvall

GENERAL DISTRIBUTION: Breeds from eastern Virginia and West Virginia south to northern South Carolina, northern Georgia, and northern Alabama. Winters, so far as now known, in the West Indies and Yucatán.

STATUS IN GEORGIA: A common summer resident in the mountains, and of casual occurrence during the breeding season as far south as Athens and Atlanta.

The oven-bird is another species that is apparently extending its breeding range in Georgia. It has long been known to nest commonly in the mountains and locally in the foothills as far south as Toccoa, Dahlonega, and Atlanta, but there is now definite evidence that it is invading the upper Piedmont. Until 1944, its status at Athens was that of a common spring and fall transient, but that year a singing male was seen on June 10, near Whitehall, under conditions that suggested the presence of a nest close by [Odum, 1944].

Two years later, in 1946, I had occasion to carry on a limited amount of field work at Athens, and was interested to find two pairs of oven-birds unquestionably nesting on wooded hillsides at the upper end of the Sandy Creek bottoms. It was on May 14 that my attention was attracted by the uneasiness displayed by a male that had been singing close to an old woods road I was following. A search for a nest proved unsuccessful, but the female appeared and, on being collected, was found to have a well-pronounced brood patch. Ten days later, on May 24, another singing male was seen on the opposite side of the bottoms under similar circumstances, but again I failed to find the nest that I am confident must have been in this stretch of woods. It is possible that the oven-bird will gradually increase in numbers in this eastern edge of the state, and eventually be found as a breeding bird through much of the Piedmont.

Definite breeding records for this southern Appalachian race in Georgia are not numerous. At Margret, in Fannin County, I was fortunate enough to find three nests in 1921: two on June 17 with four fresh eggs each, and one on June 25 with three slightly incubated eggs; while in 1926 I succeeded in finding a fourth nest that on May 23 held five half-incubated eggs. Griffin [1940] gives as nesting extremes for the Atlanta region, four eggs on April 24 (1922) (Hembree), and three young on June 4 (1939) (Griffin).

HABITS AND RECOGNITION: Throughout its breeding range in Georgia, the oven-bird is largely limited in distribution to the heavily timbered mountainsides, nesting from the valleys to the tops of the ridges. Here it would be inconspicuous and easily overlooked were it not for the loud, ringing song that the male utters throughout the day, either from a lower limb of a tree or sapling, or from the ground as it walks about searching the dead leaves for insects. This song is commonly interpreted as "teacher, teacher, teacher, teacher, teacher," each syllable being given with a gradually rising inflection, and once heard will never be confused with that of any other species.

The nest of the oven-bird is equally distinctive, and because of its resemblance to an old Dutch oven this warbler bears the name by which it is commonly known. Other than that the ground be well covered with dead leaves, the female is little concerned about the site chosen. The nest itself is usually in the open, but being arched over and with the entrance at the side instead of at the top, is well concealed and difficult to see. It is always bulkily built of dead leaves and grasses, the cavity inside being lined with finer grasses, rootlets, and, if available, horsehair. It is doubtful that even as far south as Georgia more than one brood is reared each year. Breeding activities in the mountain counties are seemingly of minor consideration until the first warm days in May, and by the last of June only an occasional pair is still nesting.

This recently described race can be distinguished by its paler upperparts, the back in all specimens examined being grayish-green rather than bright green. Breeding birds typical of *canivirens* have been taken in Georgia at Margret, Young Harris, Blood Mountain, Tray Mountain, Smyrna, Atlanta, Decatur, and Athens. South of its breeding range, specimens have been taken by Stoddard in Grady County on September 30, 1950, and on February 10, 1951.

Common Northern Waterthrush
Seiurus noveboracensis noveboracensis (Gmelin)

GENERAL DISTRIBUTION: Breeds from northern Ontario and northern Quebec south to southern Ontario, northwestern New York, and northern New England, and in the mountains to Pennsylvania and West Virginia.

Winters from the Valley of Mexico to Colombia and British Guiana, and in the Bahamas, West Indies, and Florida.

STATUS IN GEORGIA: A rather scarce spring and fall transient.

In view of its eastern breeding range, this race was for many years considered to be the form commonly occurring in migration in the state. A critical examination, however, of a large series of specimens taken in Georgia resulted in a different conclusion. It is possible that in migration *noveboracensis* is largely restricted to the coast, but further collecting will be necessary to determine this point. At the present time, so far as the interior of the state is concerned, it must be considered of infrequent occurrence in either spring or fall. The few specimens representing this race were taken as follows: Athens, a male taken August 21, 1929, and females, August 29, 1928, September 14 and 24, 1929, and May 21, 1946; Atlanta, a male, April 15, 1947 (Burleigh); Tifton, a male, September 15, 1941 (Norris); and Brunswick, Glynn County, a male, August 25, 1951 (Norris).

HABITS AND RECOGNITION: Like the oven-bird, the Northern Waterthrush suggests a small thrush when first glimpsed in the swampy woods it normally frequents, its upperparts being uniformly dark-olive, its throat and breast streaked with black. However, if watched for even a few moments, it displays a mannerism no thrush possesses, that of continually tilting its body as it walks about on the ground. Temporarily alarmed, it may fly to the lower branches of a near-by bush or sapling, but even here the tipping of its body continues. In migration, necessity may at times cause it to spend the day in thickets or underbrush far removed from any water, but it will usually be seen feeding at the edge of stagnant pools in wooded swamps or stream bottoms.

Grinnell's Northern Waterthrush
Seiurus noveboracensis notabilis   Ridgway

GENERAL DISTRIBUTION: Breeds from northwestern Alaska, northern Yukon, northwestern Mackenzie, and northern Manitoba south to central Montana, northwestern Nebraska, northern Minnesota, northwestern Michigan, and western Pennsylvania. Winters in Cuba, Haiti, Puerto Rico, and the Bahamas, and from Lower California and Mexico to northern South America.

STATUS IN GEORGIA: A common spring and fall transient throughout the state, and of accidental occurrence on the coast during the winter.

In spring, the waterthrush appears in Georgia in March, but only during the latter part of April and early May is it commonly seen. A few birds occasionally linger until almost the end of May, but it is unusual to observe one after the middle of the month. In the fall the waterthrush is common from the latter part of August until the first week of October.

Earliest transients in the spring were noted at:

St. Marys: March 22 (1902).
Cumberland Island: March 26 (1902).
Savannah: March 27 (1910).
Macon: March 15 (1945).

Augusta: April 25 (1943).
Athens: April 15 (1923).
Atlanta: April 15 (1947).

The latest were seen at:

Darien: May 20 (1945).
Savannah: May 15 (1908).
Americus: May 6 (1942).
Macon: May 17 (1930).

Atlanta: May 23 (1939).
Athens: May 22 (1925).
Augusta: May 16 (1945).

In Grady County, it has been noted on April 18 and 28, 1952, and at Fitzgerald, on April 28, 1941.

In the fall the earliest transients appeared at:

Augusta: August 28 (1944).
Athens: August 18 (1929).
Atlanta: August 17 (1952).
Macon: August 29 (1936).

Tifton: August 29 (1942).
Grady County: August 13 (1950).
Savannah: July 24 (1909).

The latest were recorded at:

Augusta: October 22 (1944).
Athens: October 17 (1929).
Atlanta: October 20 (1923).
Macon: October 14 (1928).
Americus: October 11 (1941).

Fitzgerald: October 18 (1941).
Grady County: October 21 (1947).
Savannah: October 10 (1908).
St. Marys: October 8 (1905).

The only definite winter record is that of a bird seen at Savannah, December 26, 1931. Denton [1946] collected a female (identified as *notabilis*) at Augusta on the unusually early date of March 2, 1945, but as he has pointed out, this was probably an exceptionally early spring transient:

Since the collection of this specimen Hebard (*Oriole* X:5) has reported seeing a Water-thrush (*Seiurus* sp.) in Camden County, Georgia, on February 26, 1945. Also Brooke Meanley and Lewis H. Mounts, both competent field observers, have reported (personal communications) unusually early records of the Northern Waterthrush (*Seiurus noveboracensis* subsp.) at Macon, Bibb County, Georgia. Meanley observed a single bird about six miles southeast of Macon on March 15, and Mounts observed a single bird near his home north of the city on March 25. In view of these additional 1945 records and the statement of Griscom (*Audubon Magazine,* July–August, 1945, p. 252) that during the 1945 spring season "The birds wintering in tropical America began arriving in North America on *earliest dates ever known,*" it seems more likely that my specimen as well as the others observed in 1945 were early spring transients.

An additional early record that spring was of a bird seen at Milledgeville on March 18 [Tait, 1946].

In view of the impossibility of recognizing the various races of the Northern Waterthrush in the field, it is probable that all of them are included in the migration data cited above, most of which must necessarily refer to sight records. However, as *notabilis* is the common form occurring in Georgia it seems advisable to include all such records under this race. Specimens representing *notabilis* have been taken at Athens on many occasions between the dates of April 18 (1927) and May 13 (1929), and August 19 (1929) and October 12 (1928); at Decatur, between the dates of September 4 (1948) and October 3 (1948); at Atlanta, between the dates of April 19 (1945) and May 13 (1946), and August 22 (1946) and October 9 (1948); at Riverdale, Clayton County, October 2, 1949; at Canton, May 2, 1905; at Macon, September 17, 1904; at Tifton, September 15, 1941; in Grady County, between the dates of September 28 and October 21, 1947, August 13, 1950 and April 18 and 28, 1952; and in Chatham County, September 23, 1908, and August 17, 1952.

HABITS AND RECOGNITION: In general appearance and actions there is nothing to distinguish *notabilis* from the other waterthrushes when seen in the field. From *noveboracensis* it differs, when in hand, in being perceptibly darker above and in having very little yellow on the throat and breast. In May, an occasional bird can be heard singing, its ringing, bubbling song having a hurried quality about it that is quite distinctive of the waterthrushes.

Sooty Northern Waterthrush
Seiurus noveboracensis limnaeus   McCabe and Miller

GENERAL DISTRIBUTION: Breeds in northern and central British Columbia. Winters so far as is known within the range of the other waterthrushes.

STATUS IN GEORGIA: Of casual occurrence in both spring and fall.

Specimens of this race have been taken at Atlanta (April 19, 1945) and at Athens (September 23, 1928 and October 3, 1945 [Burleigh, 1948a]; and at Brunswick, Glynn County (August 25, 1951) [Norris, 1952b].

HABITS AND RECOGNITION: This far western race is distinguished by its very dark upperparts, and by the almost complete absence of yellow on the throat and breast.

Newfoundland Northern Waterthrush
Seiurus noveboracensis uliginosus   Burleigh and Peters

GENERAL DISTRIBUTION: Breeds in Newfoundland and the adjacent French islands of St. Pierre and Miquelon. Winter range unknown.

STATUS IN GEORGIA: Of casual occurrence both in spring and fall.

Specimens of the Newfoundland race have been taken at Athens (May 11 and September 4, 1929, and October 4, 1945) (Burleigh), and in Grady County (September 30, 1950) (Stoddard).

HABITS AND RECOGNITION: Compared with the other races of *Seiurus noveboracensis,* the waterthrushes breeding in Newfoundland are paler and more olivaceous above and more intensely yellow on the throat and breast.

Louisiana Waterthrush
Seiurus motacilla   (Vieillot)

GENERAL DISTRIBUTION: Breeds from eastern Nebraska, southeastern Minnesota, and the southern parts of Michigan, Ontario, New York, and New England south to northeastern Texas, southern Alabama, southwestern Georgia, and central South Carolina. Winters from northern Mexico to Colombia, and in the Greater Antilles, Antigua, and the Bahamas.

STATUS IN GEORGIA: A fairly common summer resident over practically all of the state except the coastal region.

The Louisiana Waterthrush is one of the earliest transients to reach Georgia in the spring, appearing even in the mountains before the end of March. Departure in the fall is equally early, for by early August there is already a noticeable decrease in the number of these birds, and only an occasional individual is noted after the first of September. October records are probably of belated transients from farther north.

Earliest transients in spring were seen at:

Savannah: March 14 (1925).
Grady County: April 2 (1939).
Fitzgerald: March 9 (1941).
Macon: March 13 (1944).
Milledgeville: March 29 (1943).

Augusta: March 11 (1950).
Athens: March 15 (1946).
Atlanta: March 5 (1907).
Young Harris: March 19 (1929).
Dalton: March 25 (1944).

Family Parulidae: WOOD WARBLERS

Reports of birds from Savannah, July 28, 1909, and August 14, 1910, indicate the early dates at which this species begins its fall migration. The latest records for the fall are:

Augusta: August 31 (1946).
Athens: September 6 (1925).
Atlanta: October 11 (1937).
Macon: October 12 (1924).

Fitzgerald: August 30 (1940).
Grady County: October 5 (1940).
Savannah, October 23 (1910).

Definite information relative to the breeding range of the Louisiana Waterthrush in Georgia is rather fragmentary, but there is evidence that, while local in distribution, it nests over much of the state. Birds have been seen, under conditions that suggested breeding, at Hephzibah, Burke County (May 8, 1933); Americus (May 24, 1942); Fitzgerald (May 27, 1940); Blakely (May 20, 1933); Newton (May 9, 1931); and Beachton, Grady County (May 15, 1933); and further study may show that this waterthrush is not uncommon as a breeding bird in the coastal plain. At present, actual breeding records are limited to the Piedmont and the mountains and are as follows:

Margret, Fannin County: Nest half-built, April 23, 1921 (Burleigh).
Young Harris: Four slightly incubated eggs, May 4, 1924 [Burleigh, 1927].
Athens: Four half-grown young, May 7, 1921; five slightly incubated eggs April 19, 1925 [Burleigh, 1938].
Atlanta: Four eggs, April 21, 1903; four eggs, May 3, 1937 [Griffin, 1940].
Macon: Five eggs, May 9, 1937 (Denton).

HABITS AND RECOGNITION: The Louisiana Waterthrush is not easy to get acquainted with, for it is a shy bird which seeks to evade observation. Its haunts are along the clear, swift-running streams in wooded ravines, and here one usually gets but a momentary glimpse of the bird as it feeds at the edge of the water. Attempt to approach it, and it slips away so quietly that it is gone before one realizes it, and only by following the stream can one see it again. On occasion it is possible to watch one at a distance as it walks close to the water's edge, and under such circumstances the nervous teetering of its body will soon identify it. Only when alarmed will it leave the ground, but even when it is perching on a lower limb of a sapling, the constant up and down motion of its body is continued. Few birds have a finer song than has this waterthrush. Wild and ringing in quality, it symbolizes the rugged ravines and rushing streams that are its chosen haunts, and one cannot but admit that it suits perfectly its surroundings. While the bird itself is hard to see, its nest is even more difficult to find. Sunken in the ground in a bank or hillside facing the water, it is always concealed by an upturned root, or clump of vegetation, and more often than not escapes the most careful search. Its construction aids in its concealment, for it is a mass of large dead leaves, the hollow in the top being well lined with dry pine needles, grasses, and usually a little horsehair. Four or five eggs are laid in April or early May, and but one brood is reared each year.

Kentucky Warbler
Oporornis formosus (Wilson)

GENERAL DISTRIBUTION: Breeds from southeastern Nebraska, southern Wisconsin, northern Ohio, southern Pennsylvania, and the Hudson Valley south to eastern Texas, Louisiana, southern Alabama, southwestern Georgia, and South Carolina. Winters in Mexico and through Central America to Colombia.

STATUS IN GEORGIA: A fairly common but local summer resident over all the state except the southeastern corner, where so far as is now known, it occurs only as a common spring and fall transient.

The Kentucky Warbler appears in Georgia in the spring in early April, rarely the latter part of March, and in the fall usually lingers until the latter part of September.

Earliest transients in the spring were seen at:

Savannah: April 8 (1894). Athens: April 19 (1925).
Grady County: April 6 (1941). Atlanta: April 1 (1896).
Tifton: April 26 (1942). Rising Fawn: April 16 (1885).
Macon: March 27 (1944). Dalton: April 13 (1944).
Milledgeville: April 17 (1941).

The last in the fall were noted at:

Atlanta: October 7 (1954). Macon: October 8 (1954).
Stone Mountain: September 29 (1947). Tifton: September 17 (1941).
Athens: September 23 (1923). Grady County: September 30 (1940).
Augusta: September 14 (1946). Savannah: October 1 (1908).

A bird seen at Fitzgerald (where it does not nest), on August 30, 1940, indicates that the southward movement of this species was underway at that time. The same supposition applies to another seen in Camden County on August 10, 1948.

In the eastern part of Georgia the Kentucky Warbler has not been found as a breeding bird south of Athens and Hephzibah, Burke County, but further field work may show that it nests sparingly, where there is suitable habitat, to the edge of the coastal plain. Farther west in the state it occurs during the breeding season practically to the Florida line. In 1933, I found it fairly common at Blakely in late May, and Norris [1951] reports it locally fairly common in mid-June (1947 and 1948) at Colquitt, Fort Gaines, Albany, Newton, Faceville, and near Butlers Landing, in Seminole County.

Actual breeding records for Georgia are not numerous. At Young Harris, I succeeded in finding but one nest which, on July 21, 1922, had been deserted and held a single fresh egg. At Athens, I was equally unsuccessful, my only definite evidence of breeding being a male seen on June 3, 1923, feeding a young bird just out of the nest. Griffin [1940] cites as nesting extremes for the Atlanta region, five eggs, May 7 (1921), and one egg, June 5 (1936); and Werner [1945] reports a nest at Atlanta holding four small young on May 31, 1945. Murphey [1937] reports a nest at Carmichael's Pond, Richmond County, that held young on June 8. Stoddard, in his unpublished manuscript on the birds of Grady County states that on many occasions he has seen adults feeding young, and mentions a nest from which the young birds had just flown, which was found on Sherwood Plantation, June 2, 1933. Denton reports finding one in Columbia County on May 21, 1950, with five eggs.

HABITS AND RECOGNITION: In Georgia the Kentucky Warbler is a bird of damp, heavily wooded stream bottoms and ravines. Here, partially concealed by the rank undergrowth, it walks sedately about on the ground, searching for its insect food in the dead leaves. It is not especially shy, but must be looked for to be seen, and because of the nature of its haunts can be easily overlooked. During the nesting season, the male spends much of its time singing, remaining motionless for long intervals on a lower branch of one of the larger trees as, with brief intervals of silence, it utters a loud, clear song resembling that of the Carolina Wren. It is one of the more vividly colored of the warblers, having an olive-green back and deep yellow underparts that are emphasized by a black crown and black patch on the sides of the head and neck. Seen for the first time, it suggests a large yellowthroat (*Geothlypis trichas*), but the yellow line over the eye will differentiate the two.

The nest is built on the ground, and is always well concealed by the surrounding vegetation. One found at Young Harris was in a laurel thicket, and was rather bulkily constructed of dead leaves and coarse rootlets, the well-defined hollow in the top being lined with fine black rootlets.

Connecticut Warbler
Oporornis agilis (Wilson)

GENERAL DISTRIBUTION: Breeds from Alberta and Manitoba to central Minnesota and northern Michigan. Winters in Colombia, Venezuela, and northern Brazil.

STATUS IN GEORGIA: An uncommon spring and fall transient over most of the state.

The Connecticut Warbler migrates largely through the Mississippi Valley in the spring, and consequently at this season occurs only casually in Georgia. In fall, the migration route it follows is east of the Allegheny Mountains, so, while largely absent from the interior of the state, this species should be found regularly at that season on the coast. Not until 1954, however, was it recorded there for the first time. However, being shy and difficult to observe, it has probably merely been overlooked.

It is early May before this elusive warbler appears in Georgia in the spring, and usually but two or three individuals are noted over a period of several weeks. Actual records are not numerous, and are at present limited to the following localities:

Glynn County: May 12, 1943.

Woodbine: May 14, 1943 [Hebard, letter].

Fitzgerald: May 9 and 18, 1940 [Norris, 1940].

Macon: May 12, 1945 [Meanley, 1945].

Athens: Extreme dates of occurrence, May 7 (1929) and May 24 (1928) [Burleigh, 1938].

Atlanta: Migration extremes, May 5 (1929) and May 24 (1940) [Griffin, 1941].

Roswell: May 10, 1922 and May 20, 1930 (Hembree).

Dalton: May 19 and 23, 1940 [Hamilton et al, 1940], and May 17, 1941 (Hamilton).

Not until the fall of 1954 was this species noted other than as a spring transient in the state. On October 7 (Johnston, letter) an appalling destruction of small birds occurred during the night at widely separated spots in the state, literally thousands being found dead in the morning as a result of an unfortunate combination of adverse weather conditions and bright lights. As far as possible these were carefully identified, and it was interesting to note that the Connecticut Warbler was represented by two specimens from Macon (Warner Robins Air Force Base), two from the Okefenokee Swamp (Camp Cornelia), and three from Savannah.

HABITS AND RECOGNITION: If one goes afield in Georgia in May definitely searching for the Connecticut Warbler, it is possible that his ambition may be realized. If, on the other hand, this is not the primary objective, it is doubtful that he will get even a glimpse of this rare and retiring bird. The few that have been seen at Athens were feeding on the ground in dense underbrush, and were so quiet and inconspicuous that it was more often than not merely by accident that they were noticed. On one occasion, I was standing watching a Canada Warbler in a tree over my head when suddenly the unmistakable song of a Connecticut Warbler attracted my attention. The bird had been perching quietly in a bush within twenty feet of me, but would never have been seen if it had not so unexpectedly uttered its loud, emphatic song. Attempt to approach one as it walks in a rather deliberate manner through the dead leaves covering the ground, and it will fly at once and will probably not be seen again despite a careful search. All the birds I have seen in Georgia have been males, which were readily identified by their gray heads and conspicuous white eye ring.

Mourning Warbler
Oporornis philadelphia (Wilson)

GENERAL DISTRIBUTION: Breeds from east central Alberta, central Saskatchewan, central Manitoba, Nova Scotia, Newfoundland, and the Magdalen Islands south to central Minnesota, Michigan, and central Ontario, and in the mountains of New York, Pennsylvania, Massachusetts, and West Virginia. Winters from Nicaragua and Costa Rica to Venezuela, Colombia, and Ecuador.

STATUS IN GEORGIA: An extremely rare transient in the spring.

J. T. Park reported single individuals seen at Rising Fawn, May 14, 15, and 20, 1885, but it was not until 1931 that it was recorded again in the state and a specimen taken. A male was collected that year on May 23 near Roswell, Fulton County, by L. M. Taylor, and is now deposited in the Emory University Museum [Greene, 1933]. There are no other records.

HABITS AND RECOGNITION: The Mourning Warbler suggests in appearance a small Connecticut Warbler, but can be distinguished by the absence of the conspicuous white eye ring. In migration, its actions are much like those of the yellowthroat (*Geothlypis trichas*), and it is found then in thickets and stretches of underbrush bordering open fields. Its movements are less deliberate than those of the Connecticut Warbler, and when on the ground it hops rather than walks. In its long journeys from its breeding grounds to its winter quarters in the tropics, it follows a route that consistently avoids the southeastern part of the United States, and south of North Carolina it has been rarely observed. In Georgia, therefore, it will probably always be largely accidental in occurrence.

Maryland Yellowthroat
Geothlypis trichas trichas (Linnaeus)

GENERAL DISTRIBUTION: Breeds in eastern Pennsylvania, Maryland, and eastern Virginia. Winters from the Gulf Coast and northern Florida south to the Bahamas and Nicaragua.

STATUS IN GEORGIA: An uncommon transient and rare winter resident.

Specimens representing this race have been taken at Commerce (October 9, 1945); Athens (September 19 and November 2, 1945, and March

14, 1946); Jeffersonville (March 31, 1946); Vidalia (April 13, 1946); the Okefenokee Swamp (December 31, 1945); and Hinesville (April 23, 1946).

HABITS AND RECOGNITION: Because of its restricted breeding range (and consequent limited numbers), this race of the yellowthroat will never be of more than casual occurrence in Georgia. In appearance and actions there is nothing to distinguish it from the other subspecies in the field.

Northern Yellowthroat
Geothlypis trichas brachidactyla   (Swainson)

GENERAL DISTRIBUTION: Breeds from Newfoundland and southern Quebec south to northern Georgia and northwestern South Carolina. Winters from the Gulf Coast and Florida, casually north to Georgia and South Carolina, through eastern Mexico to Costa Rica, and in the Bahamas and West Indies.

STATUS IN GEORGIA: A fairly common summer resident in the northern part of the state and a common transient and uncommon winter resident south of its breeding range.

The exact limits of this race as a breeding bird in the state are still imperfectly known, but it would appear that it occurs during the summer months only in the extreme northern counties. Specimens representing the breeding population have been taken at: Young Harris (June 19, 1929 and June 21, 1934); Blairsville (June 12, 1936 and May 26, 1945); Rome (May 26, 1933); and Marble Hill, Pickens County (May 28, 1945). The last two localities apparently mark the farthest south that it now nests in Georgia.

Transients referable to *brachidactyla* have been examined from the following localities:

Elberton: September 21, 1945.

Athens: October 6, 1928; March 17, April 10, and October 11, 1929; April 12, 1931; October 7, 1945; May 12 and 19, 1946.

Atlanta: April 1 and September 15, 1903; January 18, 1942; January 4, 1947.

Americus: March 20, 1942.

Grady County: October 7, 1948 and February 11, 1950.

Savannah: April 8 and September 18, 1908; May 9, 1909; February 28 and October 15, 1929.

Darien: April 25, 1946.

HABITS AND RECOGNITION: In Georgia, the Northern Yellowthroat is a bird of the mountain valleys, frequenting thickets and stretches of underbrush fringing the streams. It shows a decided preference for the vicinity of water and, shunning the heavy timber, never ventures far up the mountainsides. Its nest has yet to be found in the state, but doubtless is similar,

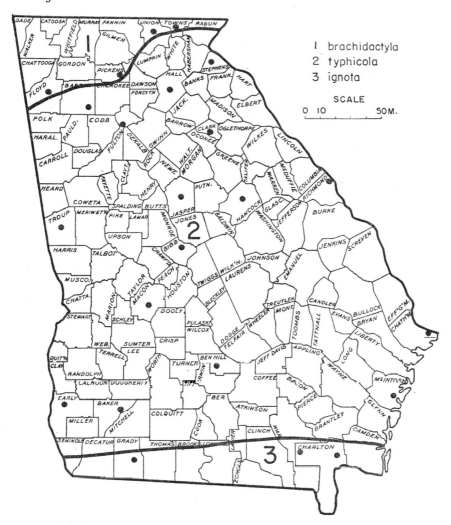

1 brachidactyla
2 typhicola
3 ignota

BREEDING DISTRIBUTION OF THE YELLOWTHROAT

both in construction and site selected, to those of the other races of this abundant and widely distributed species.

As a race *brachidactyla* resembles *trichas* in having the upperparts distinctly olive-green, but it is a larger bird and the underparts are more extensively yellow.

Florida Yellowthroat
Geothlypis trichas ignota Chapman

GENERAL DISTRIBUTION: Resident on the Gulf Coast west to Louisiana, in extreme southern Georgia, and throughout Florida south to the Keys.

STATUS IN GEORGIA: Apparently resident in the extreme southern edge of the state.

The Florida Yellowthroat was first added to the state list by Robert Norris, who took specimens in eastern Charlton County on November 22, 1941, and in the Okefenokee Swamp on March 24, 1942. Additional specimens were taken by me in the Okefenokee Swamp on December 29, 1945, and January 1, 1946; and by Herbert L. Stoddard in Grady County on January 2, 1947, and April 30 and May 9, 1948.

Definite breeding records are limited to Grady County, where Stoddard reports three nests, two found by him (May 26, 1943, two eggs and two newly hatched young, and June 7, 1944, four eggs); and one by George M. Sutton (April 29, 1952, one fresh egg).

HABITS AND RECOGNITION: The Florida Yellowthroat is distinguished by its relatively large size, distinctly brown upperparts that show little trace of olive-green, and extensively yellow underparts. Like the other yellowthroats, it frequents thickets and underbrush near water, but in Florida is said to occur to some extent in the dry palmetto thickets in the open pine woods. Nests found by Stoddard in Grady County were described as being "deeply cupped and constructed of grass stems, bits of shredded leaves, and weeds."

Athens Yellowthroat
Geothlypis trichas typhicola   Burleigh

GENERAL DISTRIBUTION: Breeds from central Alabama and southeastern Virginia south to southern Alabama, southern Georgia, and the coast region of South Carolina. Winters from Georgia and South Carolina, casually north to North Carolina, and south to Nicaragua and Jamaica.

STATUS IN GEORGIA: Common and largely resident throughout all of the state except in the mountains and in the extreme southeastern corner; less numerous during the winter north of the fall line, where its occurrence at this season of the year is governed to some extent by the severity of the weather.

Breeding specimens of this race have been taken at various localities in Georgia, including Cartersville, Gainesville, Toccoa, Athens, Augusta, Atlanta, LaGrange, Monticello, Sparta, Macon, Montezuma, Blakely, Newton, Savannah, and Darien. Actual nesting records, however, are not numerous, and are limited to Athens (four incubated eggs May 4, 1921; four fresh eggs April 22, 1922; four fresh eggs April 26, 1924; four slightly incubated eggs May 5, 1924 [Burleigh]); Atlanta (four eggs May 1, 1938

[Hames]; four eggs May 23, 1937 [Griffin]) [Griffin, 1940]; and Savannah (two fresh eggs May 1, 1921 [Burleigh]).

That the yellowthroat winters commonly in the state was shown by a Christmas Census taken in December, 1940, when two birds were noted at Atlanta, one at Round Oak, eleven at Fitzgerald, seven in Grady County, and three at Brunswick. It is probable that these records refer largely to *typhicola,* but more winter specimens will have to be taken before definite conclusions can be reached. This assumption is borne out, however, by the fact that, although few birds have been collected at this season, seven out of eleven critically examined are referable to *typhicola.* All were males and were taken at Athens (January 22 and November 9, 1928), Atlanta (December 4, 1946, January 25, 1948), Blakely (December 30, 1933), the Okefenokee Swamp (December 29, 1945), and Hinesville (January 26, 1946).

HABITS AND RECOGNITION: The yellowthroat is an inquisitive little bird that does not let its presence remain long in doubt. Approach a thicket in which the male is feeding, and one will be almost at once greeted with its low, harsh call note, and, if not alarmed, it will soon appear in full view in a near-by bush. Its curiosity satisfied, it will disappear in the shrubbery, but its characteristic note of protest will continue as long as one is in the vicinity. Seen under such circumstances, it will be readily recognized by its conspicuous black mask and yellow throat. The female lacks this mask, but is otherwise enough like the male to be easily identified.

During the breeding season, this little warbler frequents underbrush near water, feeding both in the bushes and on the ground and moving restlessly about as, wren-like, it examines the foliage and outer twigs for the insects that form the bulk of its food. It appears partial to the vicinity of cattail growths, and where this vegetation is present at the edge of sloughs and stagnant pools, there the yellowthroat is almost sure to be found. The song of the male is one of the most distinctive of any of the warblers, a rapidly repeated "witchety witchety witchety," which, once heard, will never be confused with that of any other species.

Nest construction in Georgia is well under way by the middle of April, and by the first week in May it is the exceptional pair that is not busily engaged in rearing young. The nest is placed in a thick clump of marshgrass or in a small bush, usually within a few inches of the ground, and is always so well concealed that it is not easily found. It is rather bulky, but compact and well cupped, and is built of weed stems, dead leaves, and coarse grasses, lined with fine grasses and horsehair. So far as is now known, only a single brood is reared each year.

The Athens Yellowthroat is distinguished from the Florida race by its smaller bill and less brownish upperparts and flanks.

FLORIDA PURPLE GRACKLE

Quiscalus quiscula quiscula

Many a person living in Georgia sees this bird flying about, calls it a
"crow blackbird," and never dreams how beautiful it is. Males are
considerably more richly colored than females. The species nests in small
groups or colonies as a rule, often near water. The birds I saw fed
principally along the edges of ponds. The flowering shrub
shown in my painting is a buttonbush.

GEORGE MIKSCH
SUTTON
1952

Family Parulidae: WOOD WARBLERS

Eastern Yellow-breasted Chat
Icteria virens virens (Linnaeus)

GENERAL DISTRIBUTION: Breeds from southern Minnesota, southern Wisconsin, southern Michigan, southern Ontario, central New York, and southern New England south to southeastern Texas, the Gulf Coast, and northern Florida. Winters from southern Mexico to Costa Rica, rarely in southern Louisiana and southern Florida.

STATUS IN GEORGIA: A common summer resident over the entire state except in the extreme southeastern corner, where it is rarely observed. In recent years of casual occurrence during the winter.

Few birds are more widely distributed in the state than the chat. In the mountains it is found both in the valleys and on the ridges to an altitude of approximately 4,000 feet, and throughout the Piedmont and coastal plain it occurs wherever there is suitable habitat. In northern Florida, it is considered a scarce summer resident, but apparently its numbers decrease rather suddenly below the border, since in southern Georgia during the summer it is almost as common as it is farther north in the state. In spring, it usually appears about the middle of April, and in fall is rarely observed after the latter part of September, October records being somewhat exceptional.

Earliest spring transients were noted at:

Sapelo Island: April 18 (1888).   Milledgeville: April 14 (1942).
Savannah: April 12 (1924).   Augusta: April 9 (1944).
Grady County: April 17 (1952).   Athens: April 14 (1929).
Fitzgerald: April 9 (1942).   Atlanta: April 14 (1944).
Americus: April 22 (1942).   Dalton: April 16 (1944).
Macon: April 14 (1929).

The last in the fall were seen at Atlanta, September 23 (1951); Athens, October 3 (1928) and October 18 (1925); Augusta, September 3 (1944); Milledgeville, September 28 (1945); Macon, October 8 (1954); and Fitzgerald, October 12 (1940).

Woodward [1949] reports a single bird seen on Sea Island, February 28, 1947, so early an arrival date as to suggest that the chat occasionally winters on the coast. It would appear now that this one bird did so, for chats have recently been reported as wintering in widely separated parts of the state. Hight [letter] writes that a chat appeared at a feeding station at Rome on December 30, 1953, and after almost daily visits was eventually caught and banded by Mrs. J. L. Henderson on January 19, 1954. In February, 1954, it was still appearing regularly at this feeding station. Birds seen at Macon on March 4, 1950 [Johnston, MS], and at Atlanta on February 4, 1953 (Calder), would also appear to have wintered, since it is the middle of April before the chat normally reaches Georgia.

It has been reported as breeding throughout the state, and there are definite nesting records for the following localities:

Margret, Fannin County: Four slightly incubated eggs, June 7; three slightly incubated eggs, June 9; four incubated eggs, June 27—all in 1921 (Burleigh).

Young Harris, Towns County: Three well-incubated eggs, June 24, 1922 (Burleigh).

Tray Mountain, White County: Four young, May 31, 1950 [Denton and Neal, 1951].

Athens: Four fresh eggs, May 18, 1922; four slightly incubated eggs, June 6, 1926 (Burleigh).

Rome: Three eggs, May 24, 1939 [Jones, 1947].

Atlanta: Nesting extremes, four eggs, May 15, 1927 (Greene); three eggs, May 24, 1921 [Griffin, 1940].

Grady County: Four eggs, May 22, 1940 (Stoddard).

Savannah: Four slightly incubated eggs, May 5, 1907; four slightly incubated eggs, May 26, 1911 (Rossignol).

HABITS AND RECOGNITION: Were it not for its unique behavior, the chat would be a difficult bird to become acquainted with. Frequenting the densest thickets and always suspicious and alert to any threatened danger, it discourages any intimacy on the part of the observer, and, were it not for its odd notes, its presence would long go undetected. Pass a briar thicket in which a chat is lurking, and one's attention will be attracted by an emphatic "chee-uck." Remain quiet, and if it is the male that has aroused this interest in its identity, the silence will suddenly be broken by an astonishing outburst of whistles, gurgles, and other notes, both musical and discordant, that defy description. Usually this strange medley is given as the bird remains well concealed in the depths of the thicket, but on occasion fervor overcomes caution and the resulting spectacle justifies many minutes of watchful waiting. Flying high into the air, the chat drops slowly, wings flapping over its back, tail jerking up and down, and legs dangling loosely, all the while uttering with complete abandon its indescribable song. Considerable patience is needed to acquire even a casual knowledge of this strange warbler, but its large size and characteristic actions will at once identify it if glimpsed even briefly as it skulks in dense underbrush.

As can be readily appreciated, finding its nest usually requires a long and arduous search, for more often than not it is placed in a tangled briar thicket where access is both difficult and painful. The average height is from two to four feet above the ground, and while not especially bulky or compact, the nest is well built of weed stems, dead leaves, and grasses, lined with fine grasses. Four, rarely three, eggs are laid, and but a single brood is reared each year.

Family Parulidae: WOOD WARBLERS

Western Yellow-breasted Chat
Icteria virens auricollis Lichtenstein

GENERAL DISTRIBUTION: Breeds from southern British Columbia, northern Montana, and North Dakota south to Lower California, Jalisco, Guanajuato, and Mexico, and east to central Nebraska. Winters on the tableland and west coast of Mexico from Chihuahua to Oaxaca.

STATUS IN GEORGIA: Of accidental occurrence in the southern part of the state.

Herbert L. Stoddard, Sr. (letter dated April 17, 1954), reports a chat at his feeding station on Sherwood Plantation, Grady County, from January 24 until March 6, 1954, on which latter date it was collected for subspecific identification. Allen J. Duvall, of the Fish and Wildlife Service, has identified this specimen as *auricollis,* stating that while in size and the color of the yellow underparts it approaches *virens* it is closer in its characters to the western race. Apparently this bird represents the breeding population at the extreme eastern range of the Western Yellow-breasted Chat.

HABITS AND RECOGNITION: This western race differs from the birds of the eastern United States in being larger, in having the upperparts gray rather than olive-green, and the throat and breast a deeper yellow. In its actions it is typically a chat, frequenting dense thickets where it is more often heard than seen.

Hooded Warbler
Wilsonia citrina (Boddaert)

GENERAL DISTRIBUTION: Breeds from southeastern Nebraska, northern Iowa, southern Michigan, central New York, and the lower Connecticut Valley south to the Gulf Coast and northern Florida. Winters from Vera Cruz and Yucatán to Panama.

STATUS IN GEORGIA: A common summer resident over the entire state.

The Hooded Warbler is another species widely distributed over the state, being equally common in the ravines in the mountains, in wooded stream bottoms throughout the Piedmont, and in the cypress and tupelo swamps of the coastal plain. Its preference for damp, shady woods limits its occurrence somewhat, but it is doubtful that there are any counties in Georgia where, under suitable conditions, the Hooded Warbler cannot be found during the summer. In spring, it appears even in the northern part of the state shortly after the middle of March, and in fall lingers until almost the end of October.

Earliest spring transients were seen at:

St. Marys: March 25 (1904).
Grady County: March 14 (1944).
Fitzgerald: April 6 (1941).
Cuthbert: March 27 (1923).
Columbus: March 29 (1945).
Americus: March 23 (1942).

Macon: March 18 (1945).
Milledgeville: March 27 (1928).
Augusta: March 27 (1943).
Athens: March 30 (1922).
Atlanta: March 17 (1943).
Dalton: April 8 (1944).

The last in the fall were reported from Atlanta, October 28 (1923); Athens, October 20 (1923); Augusta, October 10 (1948); Macon, October 31 (1920); Fitzgerald, October 5 (1940); Grady County, October 9 (1944); and Savannah, October 28 (1909).

Despite its relative abundance, actual breeding records are not numerous and are limited to the following localities:

Augusta: Three eggs, May 11, 1946; two small young, June 26, 1947; three eggs, May 2, 1950 (Denton).

Athens: Nesting extremes (eleven nests), April 24 (1922), four fresh eggs; and May 29 (1927), three incubated eggs (Burleigh).

Atlanta: Nesting extremes, May 12 (1921), four fresh eggs (Hembree), and June 28 (1936), four eggs (Griffin) [Griffin, 1940].

Savannah: May 15, 1919, three fresh eggs (Rossignol).

HABITS AND RECOGNITION: Because of the nature of its haunts, the Hooded Warbler is an unfamiliar bird to the average person, and that is unfortunate, since it is one of the most attractive of the warblers. In Georgia, one must penetrate the wooded ravines and stream bottoms to see it during the summer, for only in moist, shaded woods near water does it find conditions to its liking. Here in the underbrush beneath the larger trees it flits actively about, frequently darting out into the air for a passing insect and continually opening and shutting its tail in a manner that emphasizes its restless disposition.

The male with his jet-black hood cannot be confused with any other species, and his loud, clear song, distinctive enough to be instantly recognized when once heard, aids in making this species easily identified. The female lacks the black on the head to a large extent, but otherwise so closely resembles the male in appearance and actions that her identity should never remain long in doubt. Both sexes usually become somewhat concerned when their haunts are invaded but show little fear then of the intruder, often approaching within a few feet as they flit nervously about showing their white outer tail feathers.

In one respect this species differs from most other warblers—it sings persistently during the summer months. Once the breeding season is over, indeed, the average bird becomes silent and, for an interval at least, is inconspicuous and infrequently seen. Such is emphatically not the case with the Hooded Warbler in Georgia. After the first of August, when the intense heat has apparently subdued even such irrepressible birds as the Red-eyed Vireo, male Hooded Warblers can often be heard singing throughout the day. One that I collected at Athens, on August 8, 1943, was in moult and rather ragged in appearance, but its song was as unrestrained and vigorous as during the spring months.

In the mountains, the nest is usually built in a laurel or in a rhododendron, while farther south in the state, the situation generally chosen is a clump of canes near water, the average height being from two to four feet above the ground. The nest is compactly constructed of dead leaves, coarse grasses, and shreds of bark, deeply cupped, and lined with fine grasses and horsehair. It is possible that two broods are occasionally reared each year, for, on July 10, 1927, I watched a female at Athens that was feeding young birds but a day or two out of the nest.

Wilson's Pileolated Warbler
Wilsonia pusilla pusilla (Wilson)

GENERAL DISTRIBUTION: Breeds from northwestern Mackenzie, northern Manitoba, central Quebec, and Newfoundland south to southern Saskatchewan, northern Minnesota, central Ontario, New Hampshire, Maine, and Nova Scotia. Winters in Central America from Guatemala to Costa Rica, and casually north to southern Louisiana and northern Florida.

STATUS IN GEORGIA: A rather scarce spring and fall transient.

In its long journeys from its summer home in the far north to its winter quarters in the tropics, Wilson's Pileolated Warbler consistently follows the mountains, and is always a scarce bird anywhere in the southeastern part of the United States. In Georgia, an occasional individual appears both in the spring and in the fall, but this species is uncommon enough to make the sight of one anywhere in the state a noteworthy event.

It has been noted during the spring migration at Waynesboro (April 25, 1931); Athens (May 8, 1921, May 10, 1925, and May 13, 1927); Decatur (May 18 and 22, 1946); Atlanta (April 26, 1940, and May 26, 1943); Dalton (May 16, 1940); and Rising Fawn (May 1 and 4, 1885).

In fall, there are records for Union County (September 8, 1921); Atlanta (September 20, 1930, September 18, 1943, and September 11, 1954); Commerce (October 9, 1945); Athens (October 18, 1925, September 17, 1932, September 2, 1939, and October 6, 1945); and Fitzgerald (October 31, 1940).

HABITS AND RECOGNITION: Wilson's Pileolated Warbler is a jaunty little bird which, in Georgia, one will see at rather infrequent intervals feeding in underbrush fringing the streams. The males would seem to be more venturesome in their yearly migrations, for the few individuals that I have seen in the northern part of the state were invariably of that sex. Even a brief glimpse will readily identify this small, restless warbler, its glossy black crown, bright olive-green back, and clear yellow underparts being quite distinctive. If one watches it for any length of time, he cannot help but be impressed by its inexhaustible energy. Not satisfied with actively searching the foliage and outer twigs for the small insects on which it feeds, it continually darts out into the air much in the manner of a fly-catcher, and if it hesitates even briefly as it devours a choice tidbit, its tail begins to jerk spasmodically. Birds seen in the spring can frequently be heard singing, the song being loud and clear and characteristically hurried in its utterance.

Canada Warbler
Wilsonia canadensis   (Linnaeus)

GENERAL DISTRIBUTION: Breeds from southern Alberta, central Manitoba, central Ontario, and central Quebec south to central Minnesota, central Michigan, southern Ontario, central New York, and Connecticut, and in the Alleghenies to Tennessee and northern Georgia. Winters in Ecuador and Peru, and casually in Guatemala and Costa Rica.

STATUS IN GEORGIA: A common but local summer resident in the northeastern corner of the state and a fairly common transient in the upper Piedmont. It is apparently extremely rare in the coastal plain, where it has been noted on but three occasions.

At Athens, extreme dates of occurrence in the spring are as follows: April 27 (1928 and 1929) and May 24 (1928); at Atlanta, April 23 (1929) and May 22 (1954); and at Rome, May 1 (1953) and May 18 (1953). The earliest spring transients have also been reported at:

Rising Fawn: April 26 (1885).
Dalton: May 9 (1941).
Canton: April 28 (1905).
Roswell: May 1 (1934).
Augusta: May 8, 1925, May 7, 1944, May 6, 1945, and May 19, 1946.

Macon: May 9, 1926, and May 6, 1945.
Newton: May 11, 1931.
Tifton: April 29, 1944.
St. Marys: April 27, 1952.

In fall, extreme dates of occurrence at Athens are August 16 (1943) and September 30 (1928); and at Atlanta, August 6 (1949) and October 4 (1953). Denton [1944] reports a single fall record for Augusta, August 19, 1944, and Johnston [MS] also reports a single fall record for Macon, October 8, 1954.

The nest of the Canada Warbler has yet to be found in the state, but the bird has been noted during the breeding season on Brasstown Bald (male carrying food on June 20, 1922) [Burleigh, 1925]; Blood Mountain (May 30, 1933, Burleigh); Rabun Bald (June 1, 1933, Burleigh); and Tray Mountain (a pair feeding young just out of the nest on June 17, 1950) [Denton and Neal, 1951].

HABITS AND RECOGNITION: To become really acquainted with the Canada Warbler in Georgia, one should see it in its summer home in the mountains. Here on the rugged slopes of the higher ridges, always above an altitude of 4,000 feet, it finds congenial surroundings, similar to those in the northern part of its range. Moss-covered boulders and tangled rhododendron thickets characterize these mountaintops, and it is in such a habitat that the Canada Warbler prefers to spend the summer. It is an active, restless bird, but not especially shy, and if one invades its haunts, the male will soon appear to delight the observer with his sprightly beauty and hurried, rippling song. Since he feeds in the underbrush and lower branches of the larger trees, little difficulty will be had in watching him and seeing to advantage his handsome and distinctive plumage. Viewed at reasonable range, he need be confused with no other species, for across the deep yellow of the breast is a conspicuous necklace of black spots that will identify him at once. Females and young of the year have this same necklace, but it is duller and less noticeable.

The nest is placed on the ground, and is so well concealed at the side of an old moss-covered stump or rock that to find it requires long and arduous search. The incubating female will not flush until almost stepped on, and the male rarely, if ever, reveals by his actions the fact that a nest with eggs or young is anywhere in his vicinity.

Southern American Redstart
Setophaga ruticilla ruticilla (Linnaeus)

GENERAL DISTRIBUTION: Breeds from Illinois and southern Maine south to Louisiana, southwestern Georgia, and the mountains of South Carolina and Georgia. Winters in the West Indies, and from central Mexico (Puebla) to Ecuador and British Guiana.

STATUS IN GEORGIA: A rather local but fairly common summer resident in the mountain counties and in the western part of the state as far south as Blakely. Recently reported as breeding in Richmond County. A common spring and fall transient over all of Georgia.

In spring, the Redstart appears in Georgia in early April, and south of its breeding range lingers until almost the end of May. The fall migration begins early and extends over a rather long period, transients being

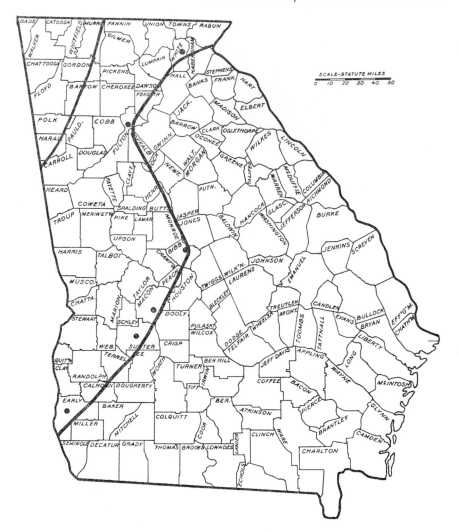

BREEDING DISTRIBUTION OF THE REDSTART

present over much of the state from the latter part of July until almost the end of October, and, in one instance, early November.

The earliest spring transients were noted at:

St. Marys: April 9 (1902).
Savannah: April 9 (1912).
Grady County: April 7 (1936 and 1937).
Baker County: April 11 (1950).
Fitzgerald: April 9 (1942).

Macon: April 7 (1928).
Augusta: April 13 (1948).
Athens: April 7 (1926).
Atlanta: April 6 (1894).
Rising Fawn: April 10 (1885).

The last for the spring migration, south and east of where the species nests in the state, were seen in the Okefenokee Swamp, May 18 (1912); at Darien, May 20 (1945); Grady County, May 5 (1937); Newton, May 11

570

(1931); Fitzgerald, May 20 (1941); Augusta, May 30 (1952); and Athens, May 28 (1928).

The fall migration begins in midsummer, the earliest transients appearing at Athens, July 18 (1926) and July 22 (1927); Augusta, July 9 (1949); Fitzgerald, July 29 (1940); and Savannah, July 28 (1909). The last for the year were observed at:

Atlanta: October 21 (1945).

Athens: October 26 (1920, 1923, and 1925) and October 27 (1927).

Augusta: October 12 (1945).

Milledgeville: October 26 (1942).

Macon: October 27 (1925).

Fitzgerald: October 21 (1940).

Grady County: October 26 (1947).

Savannah: October 26 (1908).

Camden County: November 7 (1945).

Two races of the American Redstart are now recognized, and there is little question that both are represented in the migration data summarized above. However, all such sight records are arbitrarily included under the southern race.

The breeding range of the American Redstart in Georgia is a rather unusual one. The bird nests locally in the mountain counties, but in the eastern part of the state has not been reported as breeding south of Tray Mountain, in White County.[1] Here Denton and Neal [1951] saw an adult feeding young out of the nest on June 17, 1949, and state that "this species for some unexplained reason was uncommon and spottedly distributed." It has never been known to breed at Athens, but at Atlanta it is a fairly common summer resident, especially along the Chattahoochee River, where scattered pairs nest each year. Farther south in the state its distribution is conjectural, but from the available information, the Redstart appears to be limited during the breeding season to heavily wooded bottom lands along the larger streams. It is reported as nesting at Macon (one definite breeding record—Mrs. Mounts), Montezuma (several singing males seen June 17, 1938, and an immature male taken that was not long out of the nest—Burleigh), Americus (female watched working on an almost completed nest May 16, 1942) [Denton, 1942], and Blakely (three singing males seen May 20, 1933, and a female collected that had a well-pronounced brood patch Howell and Burleigh). Apparently not many occupied nests have been found in Georgia. One that I saw at Margret, Fannin County, on June 8, 1921, held half-grown young; and Griffin (1940) cites as nesting extremes for the Atlanta region, four fresh eggs May 5, 1917 (Arpal), and three eggs June 19, 1937 (Griffin).

HABITS AND RECOGNITION: The American Redstart is one bird that will

[1] Since the above was written Denton (letter) reports the Redstart nesting on Spirit Creek 11 miles south of Augusta in Richmond County. On June 30, 1953 a male "accompanied by a young bird just out of the nest" was noted there, while on June 19, 1954 a mated pair was observed in this same general area.

never be overlooked. Not so much because of the striking orange and jet-black of the male, which coloration in itself justifies more than a casual glance, but because of this warbler's extreme activity. In this latter respect it is unique. As it feeds overhead, it indulges in feats of agility that few other birds can approach, darting out suddenly for a passing insect, fluttering in mid-air as it plucks a small caterpillar dangling from its web, searching the foliage well above the ground one minute and abruptly dropping almost to the ground the next as it swiftly pursues its prey. From time to time it may hesitate briefly, and then it half opens its wings and spreads its tail, displaying the contrasting orange and black of its plumage. In females and young, the orange is replaced by yellow and the back is olive-green, but their actions are so much like those of the male that their identity is not long in doubt.

At all times, the Redstart is a bird of deciduous woodlands, and in Georgia the nest is usually built in a tree close by, or at the edge of, a stream. One I found in Fannin County was twenty feet from the ground in a red maple at the edge of the Toccoa River, and Denton reports a nest at Americus as being fifty feet from the ground in a black gum that leaned well out over Muckalee Creek. Nests vary little in construction, being compactly built of shreds of bark, grasses, and gray plant fibers, well cupped, and lined with fine grasses and horsehair.

Northern American Redstart
Setophaga ruticilla tricolora   (Müller)

GENERAL DISTRIBUTION: Breeds from northern British Columbia east to Newfoundland and south to Oregon and northern Maine. Winters in the West Indies, and from Mexico to Ecuador and French Guiana.

STATUS IN GEORGIA: A fairly common spring and fall transient throughout the state.

A number of specimens of this northern race of the Redstart have been taken at Athens between the dates of May 8 (1946) and May 17 (1946), and September 2 (1940) and October 12 (1945) (Burleigh); at Atlanta on May 24, 1950 (Griffin), and between the dates of August 18 (1948) (Griffin) and October 8 (1946) (Burleigh); in DeKalb County on August 15, 1945 and September 7, 1947 (Griffin), and August 26, 1946 and September 29, 1947 (Burleigh); at Lawrenceville, May 18, 1946 (Burleigh); Commerce, October 10, 1945 (Burleigh); Danielsville, October 5, 1945 (Burleigh); Tifton, September 17, 1941 (Norris); and in Grady County on October 25, 1947, and September 24 and October 6, 1948 (Stoddard).

Family Ploceidae: WEAVER FINCHES

HABITS AND RECOGNITION: In general appearance and actions, *tricolora* varies in no way from *ruticilla.* As a race it differs in being smaller and in having the orange or yellow spot in the wing smaller. The females also are more grayish above rather than olive-green.

Weaver Finches: *Family Ploceidae*

European House Sparrow
Passer domesticus domesticus (Linnaeus)

GENERAL DISTRIBUTION: Europe, except Italy, and the British Isles, east to Siberia. Introduced into North America in 1850 at Brooklyn, New York, and now common and generally distributed in Canada, throughout the United States, and in northern Mexico.

STATUS IN GEORGIA: Resident and common over the entire state.

It is doubtful that there is a community of any size anywhere in Georgia where this introduced species cannot be found throughout the year. Under suitable conditions it also frequents the vicinity of farms, but is less numerous there than in the towns and cities.

Little attention has been paid to the breeding habits of the House Sparrow in Georgia, but limited observation has shown that it nests wherever it occurs and raises at least three broods each year. At Savannah, Rossignol reports two nests found on April 2, 1910, in one, five incubated eggs; in the other, five fresh eggs. At Athens, extreme breeding records are a nest that held four fresh eggs on March 24 (1921), and one that held four slightly incubated eggs on July 20 (1927) [Burleigh, 1938]. Griffin [1940a] gives as breeding extremes for the Atlanta region, three fresh eggs March 4 (1939), and four eggs July 28 (1939). At Rome, Jones [1947] reports a nest with eggs on April 2, 1928.

HABITS AND RECOGNITION: It is unfortunate that the House Sparrow is so called, for, although it is not actually a sparrow, its bad reputation has tended to discredit our native sparrows that are beneficial and worthy of protection. To the average person, a sparrow is a sparrow, and there is little about the House Sparrow to arouse any liking. Its plumage is rather drab, its voice harsh and unmusical, and its disposition leaves much to be desired. There is reason to tolerate it in the cities, for here it adds a bit of life that otherwise would be lacking. On farms, however, its pugnacity and aggressiveness soon drive away such desirable species as the Bluebird and the Carolina Wren unless radical measures are adopted to dis-

573

courage it. For a time, its abundance was the cause of real concern, but in recent years there has been a noticeable decrease in its numbers, and it is to be hoped that this trend will continue. In all fairness, however, it must be admitted that recent studies have shown that it is now eating injurious weed seeds and insects in appreciable quantities, and it may ultimately become an economic factor worthy of favorable consideration.

Its breeding habits are conspicuous and easily observed. The nest, of weed stems, grasses, and feathers, is either a bulky mass in the upper branches of a tree, or meagerly constructed and more or less concealed in any cavity large enough to hold the brood. Relative safety from molestation is apparently the one consideration in selecting a suitable site, and many and varied are the situations chosen. Three or more broods are reared each year, nesting activities beginning in early spring and continuing almost without interruption until late summer.

Meadowlarks, Blackbirds, and Troupials: *Family Icteridae*

Bobolink
Dolichonyx oryzivorus (Linnaeus)

GENERAL DISTRIBUTION: Breeds from southeastern British Columbia, central Alberta, central Saskatchewan, southern Manitoba, southern Ontario, southern Quebec, and Cape Breton Island south to northeastern California, northern Nevada, Utah, Colorado, northern Missouri, Illinois, Indiana, central Ohio, West Virginia, Pennsylvania, and New Jersey. Winters in South America to southern Brazil, Bolivia, Peru, northern Argentina, and Paraguay.

STATUS IN GEORGIA: A common spring transient and an uncommon fall transient throughout the state.

In spring, the Bobolink appears in Georgia in large flocks and is a conspicuous part of the bird life of the state during late April and much of May. In the fall, however, only an occasional small flock is seen, usually in September and early October.

Earliest spring transients were noted at:

Savannah: April 9 (1912).
Grady County: April 23 (1940).
Tifton: April 18 (1945).
Macon: March 29 (1929).

Milledgeville: April 3 (1939).
Athens: April 14 (1928).
Atlanta: April 17 (1902).
Rising Fawn: May 2 (1885).

574

Family Icteridae: MEADOWLARKS, BLACKBIRDS, & TROUPIALS

The latest were seen in:

Grady County: May 21 (1940).
Fitzgerald: May 14 (1941).
Macon: May 30 (1955).
Milledgeville: May 10 (1943).

Augusta: May 22 (1945).
Athens: May 27 (1926) and June 10 (1925).
Atlanta: May 20 (1940).

It has also been reported at Hinesville, May 3, 1942, and April 28, May 6, and May 9, 1944; Albany, May 6, 1950; and Americus, May 2 and 9, 1942.

In fall, extreme dates of occurrence are Atlanta, August 30 (1952) and October 19 (1940); Athens, September 6 (1928) and October 18 (1925); Macon, September 13 (1955) and October 8 (1954); Savannah, July 27 (1912) and October 10 (1912). At Augusta the earliest arrival date is August 30 (1944). In Grady County, the Bobolink has been noted but once in the fall, on September 24, 1924. A rather surprising record is that of a single bird seen in the Ocmulgee River bottoms, near Macon, on December 25, 1944, this being one of the very few occasions on which this species has been seen anywhere in the United States during the winter months [Meanley, 1945c].

HABITS AND RECOGNITION: It is an unobservant person indeed who can overlook the arrival of the Bobolink in Georgia in the spring. Approach a field in which a flock is feeding, and one is greeted with an outburst of rollicking music that defies description. Each male in the flock seems unable to restrain for long its ardor, and at any one time more birds may be heard singing in the air, or in the top of a tree, than are engaged in searching for food. The song is delivered with a rapidity that renders the individual notes almost indistinguishable, but the general effect when many birds are singing at the same time makes this springtime chorus both impressive and pleasing. The first flocks to appear consist largely of males, but by early May the females begin to outnumber the males, and by the latter part of the month few males will be seen. Even a single bird will make its presence known, however, for a male Bobolink in the spring seems to have an irrepressible urge to fill the air with its ecstatic music.

In fall, the handsome black, white, and buff plumage of the male has been replaced by a streaked brown coat resembling that of the female, and an equally noticeable change will be observed in its demeanor. Instead of feeding in the open fields and pastures at this season, the small flocks will be found in open marshes. Quiet, except for a characteristic metallic note of alarm, the individuals comprising a flock spend the day feeding in the thick marshgrass, where they are so inconspicuous that, unless searched for, they could easily be overlooked. At Athens, flocks observed in the fall were invariably in the open Sandy Creek bottoms, and here it was usually necessary to approach each bird closely before it revealed its presence by reluctantly leaving the concealment of the reeds and marshgrass.

Eastern Common Meadowlark
Sturnella magna magna (Linnaeus)

GENERAL DISTRIBUTION: Breeds from eastern Minnesota, southern Ontario, southern Quebec, and New Brunswick south to northern Texas, Missouri, Tennessee, northern Georgia, and North Carolina. Winters from the Potomac and Ohio valleys south to the Gulf states, and north casually to the Great Lakes and southern Maine.

STATUS IN GEORGIA: A local summer resident in the extreme northern part of the state and a fairly common winter resident south of its breeding range.

"The present status of this northern race is that of a winter resident over the larger part of the state, but on the basis of a breeding male taken at Young Harris (Towns County) on June 22, 1932, it would appear that *magna* is the breeding form in the extreme northeastern counties. This specimen has a wing measurement of 120 mm., whereas the maximum for *argutula* is 118.9 mm., with 111.8 as the average. In color it also agrees with the northern birds with which it was compared, being paler above and less intensely yellow beneath than in *argutula*." [Burleigh, 1948a.]

Since the above was written, a critical examination of material in the United States National Museum has revealed two additional breeding specimens of *magna* taken in the state by A. H. Howell, both males, one collected at Chatsworth, June 18, 1927, and the other at Chickamauga National Park, May 26, 1933.

That this northern race winters fairly common in Georgia is indicated by specimens taken as follows: Blairsville, November 23, 1945 (Burleigh); Atlanta, November 8 and 9, 1946 (Burleigh), and December 25, 1948 (Griffin); Decatur, December 23, 1946 (Burleigh); Athens, January 10 and 17, 1929, and February 28, 1947 (Burleigh), and Grady County, February 22, 1942 (Stoddard).

HABITS AND RECOGNITION: So far as its appearance and actions are concerned, the Eastern Meadowlark is indistinguishable in the field from its more southern relative. It is a larger bird and paler both above and below, but specimens are necessary to determine these characters. Being a hardy species, it winters largely north of Georgia, and its occurrence in the state in winter is probably governed to some extent by the severity of the weather. Both at Athens and at Atlanta, a few small flocks have been seen, but usually one or two individuals will be found with flocks of the Southern Meadowlark in the open fields and pastures.

Southern Common Meadowlark
Sturnella magna argutula   Bangs

GENERAL DISTRIBUTION: Resident from southern Illinois, southwestern Indiana, and South Carolina south to southeastern Texas, the Gulf Coast, and Florida.

STATUS IN GEORGIA: Resident and common throughout all of the state except the extreme northern counties.

The Southern Meadowlark is another bird with a wide distribution over the state, being found in every county within its breeding range where there is suitable habitat. North of the fall line, it is found in open fields and pastures, while in the coastal plain it is equally common in the wide stretches of open pine woods.

Specimens representing this southern race have been taken at numerous localities in Georgia, including Atlanta, Athens, Toccoa, Claxton, Hinesville, Waycross, Ft. Gaines, and Newton.

It unquestionably nests wherever seen during the summer months, but actual breeding records are not numerous. At Athens, two broods apparently are reared each year, extreme breeding records (five nests), being five fresh eggs, May 7 (1925); and three slightly incubated eggs, July 13 (1926) [Burleigh, 1938]. Griffin [1940a] reports a nest at Atlanta that held five young on June 3, 1938, and Straw [1947], one at Columbus, April 29, 1946, with four eggs. At Waycross, I flushed a female from a nest with four fresh eggs on May 3, 1929. Hopkins gives as nesting extremes for Fitzgerald, four fresh eggs, May 10 (1941); and three young, June 18 (1940).

HABITS AND RECOGNITION: The meadowlark is a familiar bird to practically everybody, even those having but a slight interest in bird life. Frequenting open fields throughout the year, it is in sight or hearing much of the day, and especially during the nesting season is not easily overlooked. Then the males select a prominent perch on the top of a telephone pole, fence post, or tree, and fill the air with their clear, sweet song. Approached while feeding on the ground, the meadowlark displays the white lateral feathers in its tail as it flies away, its flight being an alternate flapping and gliding that is quite distinctive, leaving no question about its identity. If alarmed, it utters a spluttering note of protest, but otherwise it usually departs silently.

To those familiar with this species in the northern part of its range, it comes as rather a surprise to find it a common bird in the open pine

EASTERN SUMMER TANAGERS

Piranga rubra rubra

The brilliant red body-plumage of the male Scarlet Tanager is replaced by
olive-green in winter, but the male Summer Tanager, once it has become
fully mature, stays red all year. In this painting I show a mature male (above)
and a young male about a year old. In the plumage worn by the
stub-tailed young bird at about the time it learns to fly, the underparts
are streaked with dusky brown.

woods characteristic of the southern part of Georgia. Elsewhere through-out the country its distribution is limited to meadows and open fields, wooded areas being avoided. However, conditions are well suited for the meadowlark over much of the southern part of the state, for here in the pine woods the ground is well covered with grass, and there is little under-growth other than thickets of scrub palmetto. Nevertheless, when first en-countered in open pine woods, the meadowlark seems oddly out of place.

The nest is always placed on the ground and, even where the grass is short and sparse, is well concealed. It is invariably sunken flush with the ground and arched over with grasses and weed stems, leaving a small opening on the side, which is so inconspicuous that only by flushing the female while she is incubating will it be noticed. Grasses are used almost exclusively in the construction of the nest, even the lining lacking the horsehair utilized by so many other birds. In Georgia, four or five eggs are usually laid and two broods reared each year, the first in early May, the second in late June and early July.

Western Meadowlark
Sturnella neglecta neglecta   Audubon

GENERAL DISTRIBUTION: Breeds from southern British Columbia, central Alberta, and southern Manitoba south to Lower California, northern Mex-ico, and central Texas. Winters from southern British Columbia and Iowa south to southern Mexico, and casually east to Wisconsin, southern Michi-gan, and northern Illinois.

STATUS IN GEORGIA: Of accidental occurrence on the coast.

There is but a single record for the Western Meadowlark in Georgia, a specimen being taken by A. H. Helme near St. Marys, March 16, 1903 [Helme, 1904a]. The identification of this specimen was confirmed by H. C. Oberholser.

HABITS AND RECOGNITION: In all respects but one the Western Meadow-lark so closely resembles the eastern bird that it could be easily misidenti-fied in the field. Its plumage, both above and below, is paler, and the yel-low of the throat is more extensive, but these differences are seldom notice-able, even at close range. Its notes, however, are so distinct that, once heard, it will always in the future be instantly recognized. This is especial-ly true of the song, which is bubbling, full toned, and mellow. It is so unlike the clear sweet whistle of the Eastern Meadowlark that one is amazed that two birds so similar in appearance should have such remark-ably different voices.

It is possible that this species occurs more often in Georgia than the record given would indicate, for a Western Meadowlark, if silent, would not be recognized, and consequently would probably not be noticed.

Yellow-headed Blackbird
Xanthocephalus xanthocephalus (Bonaparte)

GENERAL DISTRIBUTION: Breeds from southern British Columbia, southern Mackenzie, central Manitoba, and northern Minnesota south to southern California, Arizona, and southern Mexico, and east to southern Wisconsin, central Iowa, northern Illinois, and Indiana. Winters from southern California, southern Arizona, and southwestern Louisiana south to southern Mexico.

STATUS IN GEORGIA: Of accidental occurrence in the fall.

The Yellow-headed Blackbird was first recorded in Georgia by Dr. Eugene E. Murphey, who collected an adult female in Richmond County, September 23, 1893 [Murphey, 1937b]. The only other record is that of a flock of seven birds seen at Half-moon Lake, near Savannah, by Mrs. Victor H. Bassett, November 26, 1927 [Bassett, 1928].

HABITS AND RECOGNITION: In its breeding range, the Yellow-headed Blackbird frequents open marshes and, where conditions are favorable, occurs in large, noisy colonies. The male is a handsome bird, and one whose identity will never be questioned, its deep yellow head and throat standing out in striking contrast to its jet-black body. The female is far less conspicuous, the yellow being confined to the throat and upper breast, but, as in the male, the wings have a conspicuous white patch that will distinguish it wherever seen. In migration and during the winter, this species commonly associates with other blackbirds, and is found then not only in the marshes but in the open fields, especially those under cultivation. Before the grain crops are harvested, serious damage may result, but in Georgia this species occurs too infrequently and in too small numbers to be of any concern in this respect. It has been reported from many localities on the Atlantic Coast, but merely as a straggler during the fall migration.

Eastern Redwing
Agelaius phoeniceus phoeniceus (Linnaeus)

GENERAL DISTRIBUTION: Breeds from Ontario, Nova Scotia, and Quebec south to central Alabama, Georgia, and northern Florida. Winters largely south of the Ohio and Delaware valleys, casually north to Massachusetts.

Family Icteridae: MEADOWLARKS, BLACKBIRDS, & TROUPIALS

STATUS IN GEORGIA: Resident and common throughout all of the state, except the extreme southern edge; locally less numerous during the winter north of the fall line.

The Redwing shows a definite preference for water during the nesting season, and anywhere in Georgia where there are open marshes or streams or ponds bordered by reeds and marshgrass, there one will find it breeding in colonies of varying size from early spring until late summer. It can also be found then, but less commonly, in heavy pastures of clover, lespedesa, vetch, and so on, even at a distance from water. Highly gregarious at all times, it gathers in flocks as soon as the young are fully fledged, and throughout the winter these flocks can be found over much of the state feeding in open fields and pastures. In the coastal plain, it is abundant then, while over most the Piedmont its numbers are usually apparently governed by the severity of the weather. At Athens, during some winters small flocks were numerous, while in other years, only an occasional small flock was seen until late February or early March. About Atlanta, however, Griffin [letter] states that he has seen "flocks in the tens of thousands, and they regularly winter in large, not small, flocks."

It is reported as nesting in many localities from the mountain counties to the coast, but actual breeding records are limited to the following widely separated areas:

Augusta: Nesting extremes, nineteen nests, four eggs, May 6 (1945); and a single small young, July 5 (1945) (Denton).

Athens: Nesting extremes, nineteen nests, three fresh eggs, May 5 (1923); and two slightly incubated eggs, July 11 (1926) (Burleigh).

Atlanta: Nesting extremes, two eggs, April 25 (1938); and three eggs, July 16 (1939) (Griffin).

Young Harris: Two incubated eggs, July 4, 1923 (Burleigh).

Rome: Four eggs, May 2, 1953; three eggs, June 7, 1953 (Dorsey).

Fitzgerald: One fresh egg, April 27, 1941; three eggs, June 24, 1940 (Hopkins).

Newton: Two incubated eggs, July 13, 1929 (Burleigh).

Brunswick: Numerous nests holding from one to three eggs, or young, June 19, 1939 (Norris).

Savannah: Nesting extremes, three fresh eggs, May 9 (1919) (Rossignol); and three fresh eggs, June 16 (1923) (Burleigh).

Breeding specimens representing this race have been taken in various parts of the state, including Chatsworth, Margret (Fannin County), Toccoa, Cartersville, Atlanta, Decatur, Athens, Blakely, Newton (Baker County), Savannah, and Woodbine (Camden County).

HABITS AND RECOGNITION: In the Northern states the Redwing, like the Bluebird and the Robin, is one of the harbingers of spring, its appearance in late February or early March being one of the first indications that winter will soon be only a memory. In Georgia, however, only the more observant will become aware of the approach of spring through the activity of this familiar blackbird. Throughout the winter, restless flocks forage through the more open country, frequenting grain fields, pastures, and even the pine woods, if the trees have borne a good crop of cones. At this season of the year the males will be found in one flock, the females in another, and in the northern part of the state, it is almost without exception the males which comprise the flocks that are encountered. Farther south both sexes occur in equal number, but one will notice a definite tendency for the males to remain apart from the females, each sex, if feeding in the same field, maintaining a more or less compact group, and not intermingling.

As spring approaches, the males separate and appear at the spots where they will later nest, and their presence then in the open swamps and cattail marshes is an infallible sign that winter is over. Selecting the top of a tree or fence post, each male will claim priority over certain territory, driving away other males that appear and challenging such potential rivals with his musical "kon-ka-ree." As the days pass, his ardour finds expression in short flights over the marsh, circling with fluttering wings low overhead, and revealing to full advantage his deep-red epaulets. Eventually the smaller, streaked females appear, and after a period of courtship, breeding activities begin. Unlike most birds, the Redwing is not averse to polygamy, and if the nesting area is large enough, it is not unusual to find each male with two or more females.

As this is essentially a gregarious species, suitable marsh will generally contain a breeding colony of these blackbirds, the size depending upon available nesting sites, but it is not uncommon to find a single pair about a pond or stream where facilities for concealing a nest are limited. In Georgia, at least two broods are reared each year, the first in early May, the second in late June and July. The nest is built in a thick clump of marshgrass, in cattails, or in alders or willows, and is usually within three or four feet of the ground. It is compactly constructed of pieces of reeds, coarse grass, and mud, well cupped, and lined with fine grasses. Normally three or four eggs are laid, although not infrequently late nests are found to hold but two eggs.

Florida Redwing
Agelaius phoeniceus mearnsi   Howell and van Rossem

GENERAL DISTRIBUTION: Resident over the larger part of the Florida peninsula from the Okefenokee Swamp south to the lower Kissimmee and Caloosahatchee valleys, and west on the Gulf Coast to Appalachicola.

STATUS IN GEORGIA: Resident in the extreme southern edge of the state. A small series of Redwings taken by Isaac Arnow at St. Marys, Camden County, in 1902 and 1903, have recently been critically examined by Allen J. Duvall of the Fish and Wildlife Service, and seven specimens found to represent this Florida race. These were collected on May 5 and 19, 1902, January 15 and 22 and February 25, 1903, indicating that *mearnsi* occurs throughout the year in this part of the state. That it is the breeding form in the Okefenokee Swamp is shown by specimens taken there May 4 and 5, 1929 (Burleigh). In Grady County, the farthest west in the state where it is known to occur, Stoddard [MS] reports it a common resident. Specimens representing the winter population were taken February 27, 1938, January 19, 1945, and January 2, 1949; and breeding females, May 1, 1947, and April 10, and May 1 and 7, 1949.

HABITS AND RECOGNITION: The Florida Redwing is a common bird in the Okefenokee Swamp, occurring in and about the open "prairies," where, during the summer, at least, it is a conspicuous part of the bird life. To my ear, the song of the male sounds quite different from that of the birds nesting farther north in the state, being shorter and rather hoarse and wheezy, a difference that was noticeable enough to cause me to suspect the presence of *mearnsi* on my first visit to the Swamp. Nesting activities here begin later than I would have thought, for three nests that I found, May 5, 1929, were but half-built. They were within a few inches of the water in clumps of reeds and constructed of fragments of reeds and coarse grasses.

Like practically all subspecies, *mearnsi* can be satisfactorily identified only on the basis of actual specimens. It differs from *phoeniceus* in being slightly smaller, in having a longer and more slender bill, and, in the females, having the plumage perceptibly browner both on the back and in the dark streaks on the throat and breast.

Gulf Coast Redwing
Agelaius phoeniceus littoralis Howell and van Rossem

GENERAL DISTRIBUTION: Gulf Coast from Choctawhatchee Bay, Florida, west at least to Galveston, Texas.

STATUS IN GEORGIA: Possibly of casual occurrence in the southern part of the state during the winter months, although at present there is but a single record.

Stoddard (letter) reports that three females taken in Thomas County on March 24, 1954, were identified by Allen J. Duvall, of the Fish and Wildlife Service, as this Gulf Coast race.

HABITS AND RECOGNITION: The circumstances under which *littoralis* was added to the Georgia list would suggest that the Gulf Coast Redwing is of more than accidental occurrence in the state. Quoting from Stoddard's letter:

It has been necessary to control some mammals and birds that were proving destructive to sprouting corn in the Greenwood Farms seed corn project in Thomas County. Mr. E. V. Komarek, supt. of Greenwood Farms, kindly presented to me all the birds picked up dead for examination. To date I have examined over 100 Redwings. As a whole they were a mixed lot; six, as yet unidentified, I believe to be also *littoralis;* many seemed typical of *mearnsi,* some seemed nearer *phoeniceus,* while the majority impress me as intermediate between the three races. It is interesting to see that it is the redwings that breed near by that were damaging the corn; not northern migrants.

Littoralis is the darkest of all the eastern races of *Agelaius phoeniceus.* In the females the underparts are less buffy, and the dark streaks are broader and blacker.

Giant Redwing
Agelaius phoeniceus arctolegus   Oberholser

GENERAL DISTRIBUTION: Breeds from Mackenzie and Keewatin (rarely to Cape Prince of Wales, Alaska) south to Montana, North Dakota, Minnesota, Wisconsin, and northern Michigan. Winters south and east to Texas, Louisiana, Kansas, Illinois, Arkansas, and Alabama.

STATUS IN GEORGIA: Of accidental occurrence in the southern part of the state.

There is a single record of this western race in Georgia, that of a female taken by Robert Norris at Tifton, January 17, 1942. The identification of this specimen was confirmed by H. C. Oberholser.

HABITS AND RECOGNITION: In general appearance and actions, this race differs in no way from the other Redwings. According to Norris [1942e], the specimen he collected "is characterized by larger size (wing, 106 mm.). It was in a group of some 300 Red-wings and Cowbirds inhabiting a pecan grove."

Orchard Oriole
Icterus spurius   (Linnaeus)

GENERAL DISTRIBUTION: Breeds from North Dakota, Minnesota, Wisconsin, Michigan, southeastern Ontario, central New York, and Massachusetts south to southern Texas, the Gulf Coast, and southern Florida, and in Mexico to Oaxaca and Jalisco. Winters from southern Mexico to northern Colombia.

STATUS IN GEORGIA: A common summer resident over the entire state.

The Orchard Oriole appears in Georgia in early April, and within a few days of its arrival can be found from the mountain counties to the coast. In fall, it is one of the earliest of the breeding birds to leave the state, becoming scarce in mid-August and being rarely observed after the first of September.

Earliest transients in the spring were noted at:

St. Marys: April 1 (1902).
Hinesville: April 2 (1945).
Savannah: April 6 (1927).
Grady County: March 25 (1938).
Tifton: March 29 (1944).
Americus: April 10 (1942).
Cochran: April 8 (1933).
Columbus: April 14 (1946).

Macon: April 7 (1923).
Milledgeville: April 3 (1940).
Augusta: April 15 (1945).
Athens: April 13 (1929).
Atlanta: April 11 (1929).
Rising Fawn: April 16 (1885).
Dalton: April 14 (1944).

The last in fall were seen at Augusta, September 7 (1944); Athens, September 6 (1925); Atlanta, August 12 (1939); Macon, September 12 (1934); Tifton, August 7 (1951); and Savannah, September 5 (1910).

The Orchard Oriole has been reported as nesting at many localities throughout the state, and there are definite breeding records as follows:

Rome: Partly completed nest, May 4, 1953 (Dorsey).
Augusta: Half-completed nest, May 27, 1945; adults feeding young in nest, June 6, 1946 (Denton).
Athens: Nesting extremes, eight nests, newly hatched young, May 21 (1922); and four fresh eggs June 11 (1924) [Burleigh, 1938].
Atlanta: Nesting extremes, five eggs, May 16 (1938), and four young, July 1 (1939) [Griffin, 1940a].

Fitzgerald: Two eggs, May 6, 1941; small young, June 2, 1941 (Hopkins).
Grady County: Nest about completed, April 23, 1927; young just out of the nest, May 29, 1926 (Stoddard).
Savannah: Nesting extremes, forty-six nests, four fresh eggs, April 27 (1906), and four slightly incubated eggs, June 15 (1907) (Rossignol).

HABITS AND RECOGNITION: The Orchard Oriole is well named, for in Georgia not only is it commonly found about orchards, but it also frequents fruit trees in the vicinity of farmhouses. A pear tree in a farmyard will usually attract a pair of these birds, and a persimmon tree standing at the edge of a cotton field seems equally desirable as a nesting site. Its willingness to accept the proximity of man makes this oriole a familiar bird to the average Georgian, the more so as its behavior is such that it is constantly in sight or hearing throughout the day. During the nesting season, the male sings continuously from early morning until dusk, its clear, spirited song filling the air as it moves restlessly about from tree to tree. The adult male is not as vividly colored as the other orioles, but its black and chestnut plumage makes it one of Georgia's most attractive birds. This plumage is not acquired until the second year, one-year-old males resembling the olive-green and yellow females, but having a black throat that will readily identify their sex.

The nest of the Orchard Oriole is almost always suspended from the outer end of a limb, where it is difficult to reach, and is usually from ten to twenty-five feet from the ground. A pear tree is a favorite site, but such deciduous hardwoods as the persimmon, sweet gum, and yellow poplar are also commonly used. Only once have I seen a nest in a conifer, this one exception being a nest that I found at Athens in 1927 that was eight feet from the ground in the top of a loblolly pine sapling. Nests vary little in construction, being built of green grasses that gradually turn yellow as the days pass, but affording suitable concealment during much of the time they are in use. As in the case of all nests built by orioles, the relatively thin walls form a roomy cavity that is lined at the bottom with bits of cotton and plant down. In Georgia, four eggs are normally laid, and it is probable that two broods may be reared each year. That this actually happened in one instance was noted by Herbert L. Stoddard in Grady County, when a pair started the construction of a new nest within five days after the first brood had left the nest in late May.

Nesting over with, the male becomes quiet, and by late July there is a noticeable decrease in the number of Orchard Orioles. Adults of both sexes apparently begin their long jurney to the tropics in early August, but birds in immature plumage are present in small numbers until September. An occasional individual seen after the first of September is probably a transient from farther north.

Baltimore Oriole
Icterus galbula (Linnaeus)

GENERAL DISTRIBUTION: Breeds from central Alberta, central Saskatchewan, southern Manitoba, Ontario, New Brunswick, and Nova Scotia south to southern Texas, central Louisiana, northern Alabama, and northern Georgia. Winters from southern Mexico through Central America to Colombia.

STATUS IN GEORGIA: A scarce and rather local summer resident in the northern part of the state and an equally scarce transient both in the spring and in the fall south of its breeding range. Of casual occurrence in recent years during the winter.

586

Family Icteridae: MEADOWLARKS, BLACKBIRDS, & TROUPIALS

In the spring, the Baltimore Oriole can be seen south of its breeding range in Georgia at infrequent intervals from early April until late May, but its occurrence then is so irregular that there will be years when none will be noted. In fall, it is rarely observed, records for that time of the year being limited to Atlanta and Athens.

At Atlanta, where it breeds sparingly, the Baltimore Oriole has been noted between the dates of April 15 (1893) and September 16 (1931). At Athens, extreme dates of occurrence in spring are April 25 (1927) and May 22 (1926). For the fall migration there are but two records, September 17, 1926, and September 20, 1949. Elsewhere in the state, it has been reported in the spring as follows:

Savannah: April 6, 1922.
Columbus: April 10 and 11, 1945, and
    April 14, 1946.
Macon: April 18, 1945.
Milledgeville: April 5, 1941.

Augusta: May 20, 1944.
Canton: April 28, 1905.
Rome: May 3 to 11, 1953.
Dalton: April 26, 1940.

At Macon it has been noted in the fall between the dates of August 29 (1936) and October 8 (1954).

It was first recorded in the state during the winter by Mrs. V. H. Bassett, who saw a single bird at Savannah, December 9, 1927. An immature male taken by Denton in Richmond County on November 7, 1948, can be considered a wintering individual, for under ordinary circumstances this species is not present in Georgia much after the middle of September. Stoddard [1951] has three winter records for Grady County: immature males on February 14 and 20, 1948, and an adult male on November 29, 1949. Since these were collected, there can be no question as to their identity. Johnston (MS) reports this species at Macon on November 21, 1953, and February 11 and 12 and March 19, 1954.

As a breeding bird, the Baltimore Oriole is rather local in its distribution in the state. Pindar (1926) reported it during the summer of 1919 at Chickamauga Park, and in 1922, and for several years thereafter, a pair nested at Young Harris, Towns County (Burleigh). It doubtless breeds elsewhere in the mountain counties where conditions are suitable. At Atlanta, a nest with four slightly incubated eggs was collected by Wallace Rogers on May 15, 1920 [Greene, 1933], but a number of years then elapsed before this species was again reported as breeding there. In 1945, two birds were observed at the same spot from April 27 through June 1 [Werner, 1945], and as the female was on one occasion carrying nesting material, the nest was probably close by. An unoccupied nest, identified as that of a Baltimore Oriole, had been found in this same locality the previous year.

LaPrade has reported this species as breeding at Canton, Oxford, and

Washington; and it has also been found during the breeding season at Clarkston, DeKalb County, and Indian Springs, Butts County. In the extreme eastern part of the state, states Murphey [1937], "on July 4th, 1910, between Lincolnton and Little Mountain, Lincoln County, Georgia, I observed a pair in a gigantic Liriodendron tree, which stood in a pasture near the banks of a small creek, very busy about the upper branches and apparently feeding young." He also noted a male in June, 1919, in the extreme northern edge of Warren County.

HABITS AND RECOGNITION: It is unfortunate that the Baltimore Oriole is not more common in Georgia, for the male is unquestionably one of the handsomest birds in the eastern United States. Were it shy and retiring, its beauty might be overlooked, but quite the opposite is true. Avoiding heavily wooded areas, this oriole frequents the large deciduous hardwoods standing well out in the open, and as the shade trees on the streets and in the parks of northern Georgia's larger towns and cities afford ideal conditions, there one is most apt to see it during the nesting season. One might almost suspect that the male takes delight in calling attention to his brilliant orange, black, and white plumage, his loud mellow whistle being heard constantly as he feeds high overhead. Even in flight, his exuberance seems unrestrained, his spirited song being frequently uttered in the air as he flashes from one tree to another. The female is much duller colored, and while noticeably larger than the female of that species, suggests in appearance the Orchard Oriole. Like the male, however, she displays a loquaciousness that finds expression in a harsh, scolding note that is commonly heard throughout the nesting season, and soon reveals its presence.

Bird architecture is always interesting, and where the Baltimore Oriole is concerned, unusually so. The nest is suspended from the drooping end of an upper limb of the largest tree available, is large and purse-shaped, and is skillfully constructed of grasses, plant fibers, pieces of string, and, not infrequently, horsehair. Exposed to weather and wind, it is so securely attached that the most violent storms leave it unharmed, and one cannot but marvel at the ability displayed in weaving so stout a fabric with the available materials. As the nest is inaccessible from both above and below, the young encounter few hazards until fully fledged and ready to face the uncertainties of life.

Common Bullock's Oriole
Icterus bullockii bullockii (Swainson)

GENERAL DISTRIBUTION: Breeds from southern British Columbia, southern Alberta, and southern Saskatchewan to northern Mexico (northern

Lower California, Sonora, and Durango), and from the Pacific Coast to eastern South Dakota, central Nebraska, and western Kansas. Winters in Mexico south to Colima, Michoacán, Guerrero, and Puebla.

STATUS IN GEORGIA: Apparently of accidental occurrence during the winter in the southern part of the state.

The Bullock's Oriole was added to the accredited list of Georgia birds by Herbert L. Stoddard, Sr., who collected two males in immature plumage in Grady County—the first on February 5, 1947; and the second, on November 22, 1948 [Stoddard, 1951]. There are no other records.

HABITS AND RECOGNITION: In view of the increasing number of western birds that have in recent years been recorded in the eastern United States, indicating a definite southeastward movement in the fall, it is not unexpected that the Bullock's Oriole has finally appeared in Georgia. The date of occurrence, however, is at first rather surprising, for actual winter records for this species anywhere in the United States are few and far between. Stoddard [1951] has discussed in some detail the presence of both the Bullock's and the Baltimore Orioles in Georgia and South Carolina during the winter months, and his comments are worth quoting here:

> One fact stands out: many of the orioles are first noted following the passing of "cold fronts" out of the northwest. Such storms in this region are usually accompanied by high winds and penetrating cold. It looks as though the orioles not infrequently ride in on these "cold fronts," possibly from points to the northwestward.
>
> In any case, it would seem that the deep Southeast is now a favorable region for wintering orioles of this genus; the fine condition of the four specimens skinned is evidence of that. The writer, who is as familiar with the "agricultural face lifting" in South Carolina as he is with that in Georgia, has been impressed with the profound ecological changes in the region during the past 20 years, most of it in the last ten. The preference of both the Bullock's and Baltimore Orioles for largely open country with scattered tree growth is now being met in the Southeast by the extensive areas being opened up for improved pasture, an important part of the "agricultural revolution." More than two million acres of such pasture land have been developed in Georgia alone since 1925. A scattering of trees, many of which are important fruit bearing species like the black gum, are customarily left for shade for the livestock. Tractor farming for peanuts, corn, cotton, and other row crops has opened up further large areas. The agricultural changes coming with such rapidity are being reflected by equally rapid changes in the birdlife; the case of the orioles is just one of many.

The Bullock's Oriole resembles somewhat the Baltimore Oriole, but can be recognized by the conspicuous white patch in the wing, and by the fact that the black on the head of the male is limited to the crown and throat. In the male Baltimore Oriole the entire head is black.

Common Rusty Blackbird
Euphagus carolinus carolinus   (Müller)

GENERAL DISTRIBUTION: Breeds from northern Alaska, northern Mackenzie, northern Manitoba, and northern Quebec south to central British Columbia, central Alberta, central Ontario, New York, northern New England, New Brunswick, and Nova Scotia. Winters mainly south of the Ohio and Delaware valleys to the Gulf Coast and southern Florida.

STATUS IN GEORGIA: A fairly common winter resident throughout the state.

The Rusty Blackbird is a hardy bird, and rarely appears in Georgia in the fall before the latter part of October or the first of November. Small flocks can then be found in suitable habitat until the middle of the following March, when the bulk of these birds leave on their long journey to their breeding grounds. A few individuals frequently linger until late April, however, and not infrequently can be seen in early May.

At Athens, extreme dates of occurrence are October 26 (1925) and May 7 (1926); at Atlanta, September 20 (1936) and May 1 (1932); and at Fitzgerald, October 18 (1940) and May 11 (1940). In the fall, it has been reported at Milledgeville as early as November 5 (1942); in the spring, at Savannah as late as April 17 (1913); and at Rome, May 14 (1952). Both at Athens and Atlanta, it is of irregular occurrence during the winter, being most frequently seen in November and again in late February and early March. Murphey [1937] considers it a fairly common winter resident at Augusta. Hebard [1941a] reports large flocks at Coleraine from November 22 through December 15, 1940; and Stoddard [MS] states that in Grady County the first flocks appear the first week in November, his earliest record being November 2, 1939.

Specimens representing this race have been taken at Augusta (January 20, 1935), Athens (February 7 and April 2, 1929, and March 20, 1946), Decatur (January 9, 1949), Atlanta (March 2, 1940 and March 16, 1947), and Grady County (December 25, 1950 and January 28, 1951).

HABITS AND RECOGNITION: On its northern breeding grounds, the Rusty Blackbird commonly frequents spruce woods that border streams and ponds, and this preference for the less open country is clearly shown during the winter months spent in Georgia. Then, unlike the other black-birds, it can be found in stretches of thick, swampy woods or in alder thickets fringing open marshes. Not infrequently one will encounter small flocks feeding in the open fields, but more often than not the field will be marshy, with alder thickets and woods close by. At Athens, I noted this species with some degree of regularity only in the willows of the Sandy Creek bottoms. At times, flocks were found in woods bordering the Oconee River, but elsewhere in Clarke County I rarely saw the Rusty Blackbird.

A characteristic of all the blackbirds is the "spring chorus" indulged in by the males of a flock in the early spring, and the Rusty is no exception. Assembled in the top of a tree, the birds give utterance to a repertoire of shrill whistles, creaky gurgles, and chuckling notes that will never be confused with any other sound.

This species is a medium-sized blackbird, the male a uniform glossy bluish-black, the female gray and lacking the streaked appearance of the female Redwing with which at times it is found feeding. When they first reach Georgia in the fall, both sexes have a distinct rusty-brown edging to the feathers of the back and breast, this characteristic being the reason for the name Rusty Blackbird. This gradually disappears during the winter, and by spring little or none remains, the males then acquiring the distinction of being the only wholly black blackbird.

Newfoundland Rusty Blackbird
Euphagus carolinus nigrans   Burleigh and Peters

GENERAL DISTRIBUTION: Breeds in Newfoundland and in the Magdalen Islands, Gulf of St. Lawrence. Winters on the Atlantic Coast south at least to Georgia.

STATUS IN GEORGIA: Apparently of at least casual occurrence in the state during the winter.

Four specimens of this recently described race have been taken in Grady County by Herbert L. Stoddard: a male and two females on December 25, 1950, and a male on February 4, 1951. There are at present no other records.

HABITS AND RECOGNITION: In general appearance and actions, this race of the Rusty Blackbird has little to distinguish it, and specimens are necessary for satisfactory identification. The males differ in being more intensely black, both above and below, the gloss of the entire body being more bluish and less green. The females are a darker, clearer gray, with the upperparts, as in the males, perceptibly glossier and bluer.

591

Brewer's Blackbird
Euphagus cyanocephalus   (Wagner)

GENERAL DISTRIBUTION: Breeds from central British Columbia, southern Alberta, and central Manitoba to northern Lower California, New Mexico, and western Texas, and from the Pacific Coast to northwestern Minnesota, western Nebraska, Wisconsin, and Kansas. Winters from southern British Columbia and Wisconsin and Kansas south to Guatemala, casually east to North Carolina, South Carolina, Georgia, and Florida.

STATUS IN GEORGIA: An uncommon and irregular transient and winter resident over the entire state.

The first published record of Brewer's Blackbird in Georgia is that of a female collected from a flock of ten birds seen at Augusta November 30, 1932 [Burleigh, 1933]. At the time, it was thought that this was the first record of this species for the state, but a later publication by Earle R. Greene [1933] lists two specimens taken earlier at Roswell: a female by D. V. Hembree on March 1, 1931, and a male by L. M. Taylor on March 27, 1932. In subsequent years this blackbird has been noted at irregular intervals over much of the state, definite records to date being as follows:

1933: Athens, three males seen in the Sandy Creek bottoms, December 3, and one collected (Burleigh).

1935: Athens, four birds, three males and a female, seen on the University campus, April 9, and the female collected (Burleigh); Macon, two birds seen, December 30 (Denton).

1938: Atlanta, noted November 14 (Griffin).

1940: Atlanta, one flock of five birds seen December 22 (Griffin).

1943: Augusta, flocks of twenty to seventy-five birds seen from January 8 to March 24 (Belger, et al.); Grady County, one bird seen December 16 (Stoddard).

1947: Grady County, several birds seen December 7 (Stoddard).

1949: Macon, noted November 25 (Denton).

1951: Cartersville, two males seen at Lake Aubrey, April 1 (Sciple).

1953: Floyd County, one bird seen March 9 (Dorsey).

HABITS AND RECOGNITION: In view of the fact that the Brewer's Blackbird has in recent years been gradually extending its breeding range eastward, it is not surprising that it is now of frequent occurrence in Georgia. Actually, it is probably more common as a winter resident than the relatively few records indicate, as it can be easily overlooked because of its close resemblance to the Rusty Blackbird. At a distance, the male is another all black blackbird, the purplish sheen of the head that distinguishes it (instead of the greenish sheen of the Rusty Blackbird) being noticeable only at close range. The female is also browner than the female Rusty Blackbird, but this is rarely apparent in the field. In habits, however, the Brewer's Blackbird differs radically, and if this fact is borne in mind, its identity should be suspected whenever encountered in the state.

Family Icteridae: MEADOWLARKS, BLACKBIRDS, & TROUPIALS

Throughout its extensive breeding range in the West, this species frequents open country, showing a definite partiality for the vicinity of farms and ranch houses, and feeding about livestock somewhat in the manner of the cowbird. This trait persists during the winter, so a blackbird, too large to be a cowbird, seen feeding in the open fields and following grazing horses or cattle, will almost certainly be the Brewer's. For nesting, willows and alders fringing open water or swampy fields are preferred, and in migration the edges of open marshes offering much the same habitat are used for night roosts. At no time, however, will one find this blackbird in Georgia feeding in the stretches of thick swampy woods frequented by the wintering flocks of Rusty Blackbirds.

Northern Boat-tailed Grackle
Cassidix mexicanus torreyi Harper

GENERAL DISTRIBUTION: The Atlantic Coast, from New Jersey south to Georgia, occurring in winter in Florida.

STATUS IN GEORGIA: Resident and common in the coastal marshes from Savannah to St. Marys.

The Boat-tailed Grackle has been reported from Chatham County, St. Catherine's Island, Cumberland Island, Sea Island, Darien, Brunswick, and St. Marys, and doubtless occurs elsewhere on the coast wherever there are suitable marshes. It rarely ventures far inland, a small breeding colony found by Ivan Tomkins at Nahunta, in Brantley County, being rather exceptional so far as Georgia occurrence is concerned. Hebard |1941a| reports small numbers on Chase Prairie, in the Okefenokee Swamp, November 25, 1932, and February 26, 27, and 28, 1936; and in eastern Charlton County, January 15, 1938.

My own breeding records are limited to Chatham County, and include the following localities: Ossabaw Island (three well-incubated eggs, April 30, 1921); Myrtle Island (three well-incubated eggs, April 30, 1922); Cabbage Island (three fresh eggs, April 25, 1926); and Tybee Island (four fresh eggs, April 26, 1926; three incubated eggs, June 13, 1927). Rossignol's nesting extremes for Savannah are three fresh eggs, May 3 (1907), and three slightly incubated eggs, June 18 (1911).

Specimens taken on Tybee Island January 23, 1931, and January 27, 1946 were found to represent *torreyi*, a race originally described from Virginia [Harper, 1934a] but now known to occur on the coast as far north as New Jersey.

HABITS AND RECOGNITION: Within its limited range in the state, the Jackdaw, as the Boat-tailed Grackle is commonly called, is a well-known

EASTERN CARDINALS

Richmondena cardinalis cardinalis

From the very first of my stay in Georgia the Cardinals were going about
in pairs, and they nested early. Both males and females sang, but the males'
songs were the longer and fuller-toned and the more often given from treetops
or other exposed positions. Here the pair are in a flowering dogwood.
The male, of course, is above.

bird. The male is by far the largest of the blackbirds, with a long tail, keel-shaped in flight, which even at a distance attracts attention. Highly gregarious, both sexes occur in flocks throughout much of the year, and even in the nesting season it is unusual to find a single pair alone.

In Georgia, this species is largely confined to the coastal marshes, and here it is a conspicuous feature of the landscape. Flying by overhead or feeding at the edge of a pool in the salt marsh or on a stretch of open beach, it is in sight throughout the day. Its food is largely such aquatic life as fiddler crabs, shrimp, and small fish, and these are caught with little difficulty as the bird wades in the shallow water. The Jackdaw is a noisy bird, with a variety of harsh, unmusical notes that soon reveal its presence. During the breeding season, the male utters a peculiar rattling sound both in pursuing a female or in merely flying from one spot to another, and this noise is accompanied by a fluttering of the wings that gives the bird a rather grotesque appearance. To the casual onlooker, this sound appears to be made by the wings, but careful observation has shown that it is caused by a rapid movement of the mandibles.

The Boat-tailed Grackle is polygamous, each male having two or more females during the breeding season. Almost without exception, this species nests in colonies, the size seeming to depend on the available nesting sites. The nests may be built in thick clumps of reeds in the salt marsh, in the tops of myrtle bushes on the islands, or, not infrequently, in live oaks. The largest colony I have seen was on Tybee Island in 1926. Here, in a grove of live oaks covering roughly two acres, was a large rookery of Louisiana Herons and Snowy Egrets, and scattered among the herons' nests, I estimated there were approximately forty grackles' nests. They were built both in the live oaks and in the myrtle bushes that formed an almost impenetrable thicket under the oaks, a few of the larger trees holding as many as eight. This was on April 26, and all contained eggs, varying in number from incomplete clutches of one or two, to in most cases, three, and in one, four. Like all the other nests of this species that I have seen, they varied little in construction, being compactly built of coarse marsh-grasses and mud, deeply cupped, and lined with finer grasses. On Ossabaw Island, in 1921, I found a small colony nesting in cattails in a fresh-water swamp, but this is the only instance I have personally known of this species' breeding under such conditions. Apparently only one brood is reared each year, for there are few nests with eggs after the middle of May.

As a race *torreyi* can be distinguished from the birds resident on the Gulf Coast by its more uniform color of back, breast, and abdomen, longer wing, and pale yellow rather than grayish-brown iris. Otherwise, so far as its appearance and actions are concerned, it is like other subspecies of the Boat-tailed Grackle.

Florida Purple Grackle
Quiscalus quiscula quiscula (Linnaeus)

GENERAL DISTRIBUTION: Resident on the Atlantic Coast from North Carolina to southern Florida, and on the Gulf Coast west to southeastern Texas.

STATUS IN GEORGIA: Largely resident over much of the state, north at least to Augusta, Athens, and Covington. Of irregular occurrence during the winter north of the fall line, but abundant at that season throughout the coastal plain.

Breeding specimens of this southern race have been examined from Augusta, Metter, Athens, Covington, Montezuma, Cochran, Americus, Vienna, Early County, Baker County, Albany, Sylvester, Grady County, Waycross, the Okefenokee Swamp, and Hinesville.

It probably nests wherever found during the late spring and summer, but actual breeding records are limited to three localities. On Billy's Island, in the Okefenokee Swamp, I found a small nesting colony on April 28, 1923, three nests examined that day holding partially incubated eggs; in two, five; and in the third, four. Stoddard has found a number of nests in Grady County, one with recently hatched young on May 24, 1938, and another with four young several days old on May 23, 1940. At Fitzgerald, Hopkins gives as nesting extremes, four eggs on April 19 (1941) and two eggs on June 24 (1940).

HABITS AND RECOGNITION: Because of its evident partiality for the proximity of man, the grackle is a familiar bird to even the most casual observer. Sociable by nature, it nests in small colonies that are, more often than not, close to or even within the corporate limits of settlements and towns, and it is common in a residential section to see one or more of these large blackbirds feeding on a lawn or vacant lot. Away from the towns, nesting colonies are often located in wooded areas in the vicinity of farms, the birds feeding in the open fields and pastures and showing little hesitation in venturing into the farmyards in their search for food. Less frequently, an isolated cypress swamp is selected as a nesting site, but once the young are reared, flocks comprising both adults and young soon appear about the farms.

The grackle is a noisy bird, its harsh, unmusical notes making it conspicuous. Its large size and plumage, which at a distance appears black, have given it the name of Crow Blackbird, by which it is commonly known in Georgia. At reasonably close range, however, the male is revealed as a rather handsome bird, the head being a metallic violet-purple and the body a dark, metallic green. The female is smaller and duller colored, but otherwise closely resembles the male. Much of the time the grackle feeds on the ground, walking about in a deliberate, unhurried manner. Accustomed to the presence of people, it shows little concern when approached, but if forced to fly, the long keel-shaped tail of the male will at once attract attention.

The nest is usually well up from the ground at the outer end of a limb of one of the larger trees, and while not well concealed, is protected by its inaccessible position. The birds that I found nesting on Billy's Island in 1923 had selected a group of longleaf pines at the edge of a logging camp, the nests, never more than one to a tree, ranging in height from twenty-five to fully one hundred feet from the ground and being at the outer ends of the upper branches, where, while plainly visible, they were almost impossible to reach. The three that I succeeded in examining were alike in construction, being bulkily built of gray Spanish moss intermixed with dry pine needles and grasses, coated on the inside with mud and then well lined with fine grasses. In contrast to this breeding colony is the situation chosen by the Florida Grackles in Grady County, Herbert L. Stoddard reporting them building their nests in rotted-out hollows in old snags and in bushes growing in shallow water.

A single brood only is reared each year, and by early June, when the young are well grown, the grackles begin to gather in flocks that lead a nomadic existence, foraging in the more open country until the following spring.

Eastern Purple Grackle
Quiscalus quiscula stonei Chapman

GENERAL DISTRIBUTION: Breeds from the north shore of Long Island Sound and the lower Hudson Valley west to the Alleghenies and south to northern Georgia, northern Alabama, and eastern Tennessee. Winters mainly south of the Delaware Valley, reaching the Gulf Coast in the winter season.

STATUS IN GEORGIA: A fairly common resident in the northern part of the state.

On the basis of specimens, the Purple Grackle nests as far south as Atlanta. This is clearly shown by a series of fourteen birds collected near that city by William W. Griffin between the dates of March 29 (1941) and December 24 (1948), representing both sexes and all typical of *stonei*. However, northern Georgia is apparently an area of intergradation between the various races of *Quiscalus*, as, among other specimens examined, there were some that were far from typical. Males taken at Chatsworth, June 20 and 23, 1927, and May 27, 1933, showed definite evidence of intergradation with the Bronzed Grackle, *versicolor;* and the same was found to be true of a male collected at Atlanta, May 24, 1933, and a female from Decatur, July 17, 1947. On the other hand, a male taken at Roswell, March 1, 1926, is almost typical of the Florida Grackle, *quiscula.*

The only definite breeding records are from the Atlanta area, where Griffin [1940a] cites as nesting extremes, 4 young, May 28, 1937, and two young, June 2, 1939; and from Athens, where Hopkins [1953a] found three nests with almost fully fledged young the last week of May, 1951.

HABITS AND RECOGNITION: Unless seen at close range, the Purple Grackle appears similar in every respect to the other grackles. However, it is a quite recognizable bird, especially the male. Approach one as it feeds on the ground, and an apparently black bird will be revealed as having a glossy, greenish-bronze head and an iridescent, purplish-bronze back. Little difficulty will be experienced in becoming acquainted with this large, handsome blackbird, for during much of the year it can be found in the towns and even the larger cities in the northern part of the state. During the winter, large numbers assemble each night at certain spots well within the city limits of Atlanta, one such roost at East Lake [Werner, 1945b] being said to harbor fully 50,000 birds, in this instance the grackles sharing these quarters with equally large numbers of starlings and cowbirds. Werner writes:

> They come in to roost just before dark, at which time many large trees are actually black with perching birds waiting to select favorite canes for their nights' rest. The circling and chattering masses suggest large groups of Chimney Swifts. Often several thousand will fly into view in a compact mass, and frequently a bare poplar seems suddenly to be taking flight as every bird will fly as though by a prearranged signal.

Characteristically gregarious, this grackle nests in small colonies that usually occupy a group of large trees in the residential section of a city. Possibly the birds have learned from experience that under such circumstances they are relatively safe from such predators as hawks and owls, and for this reason are rarely if ever found far from the vicinity of houses during the breeding season.

Bronzed Purple Grackle
Quiscalus quiscula versicolor Vieillot

GENERAL DISTRIBUTION: Breeds from Great Slave Lake, northern Manitoba, Nova Scotia, and Newfoundland south to Montana and Colorado (east of the Rocky Mountains) and southeast to Pennsylvania (west of the Alleghenies), New York, Massachusetts, and northern Connecticut. Winters mainly from the Ohio Valley south to southern Texas.

STATUS IN GEORGIA: An uncommon winter resident throughout the state.

As specimens are necessary to identify satisfactorily the grackles in Georgia, it is possible that further collecting will show the Bronzed Grackle to be more common than present records indicate. There is little to distinguish one grackle from another when seen in flocks at any distance, and during the fall and winter, two or more races are usually found in the same flock. Consequently, further study will be necessary before the status of *versicolor* can be determined with any degree of accuracy. At present it is known from the following localities, specimens having been taken on the dates given: Roswell (February 28, 1925); Atlanta (March 4, 1904; January 14, 1907; December 24, 1948; December 31, 1949), Cherokee County (November 6, 1905), Athens (March 6 and 8, 1929; February 17, 1946), Richmond County (October 17, 1933), and Fitzgerald (November 22, 1940).

HABITS AND RECOGNITION: In Georgia, the Bronzed Grackle can be found in flocks during the late fall and winter feeding in the open fields. Since it is a hardy bird, its abundance is probably governed to some extent by the severity of the winters farther north, but it doubtless occurs in at least small numbers each year. In appearance and actions, it differs in no way from the other grackles. Seen at close range, as is possible at times, the males can be distinguished by the uniform glossy bronze of the back and underparts. The females are similar, but much duller, and therefore less apt to attract attention.

Eastern Brown-headed Cowbird
Molothrus ater ater (Boddaert)

GENERAL DISTRIBUTION: Breeds from southern Ontario, southern Quebec, Nova Scotia, and New Brunswick south to central Texas, Louisiana, Georgia, and northern South Carolina, and west to Minnesota, northeastern Iowa, southeastern Nebraska, southwestern Kansas, and New Mexico. Winters from the Ohio and Potomac valleys, casually north to New York and Michigan, south to Florida and the Gulf Coast.

STATUS IN GEORGIA: Until recent years a common transient and locally common winter resident throughout the state. Now known to breed in the northern part of the state and apparently increasing in numbers each year.

The status of the cowbird in Georgia has long been perplexing and subject to much conjecture on the part of those interested in the bird life of the state. In an article dealing with a collection of birds' eggs from Wayne and McIntosh counties, H. B. Bailey (1883) lists a cowbird's egg taken there, but as in subsequent years there was no further evidence of this species' breeding anywhere in the state, it was generally assumed that this was an error in identification. During the ten years I lived at Athens, from 1920 to 1930, I never failed to find young cowbirds of the year, fully grown, in the open fields and pastures from the latter part of July through August, although at that time adults were conspicuous by their absence. Since it is a hardy species and one that normally lingers in the Northern states until the latter part of October, I found it difficult to reconcile the presence of these immature birds with a very early southward movement in midsummer. Further field work in North Carolina, and a review of published records on the distribution of the cowbird in the southeastern United States showed that this same situation existed throughout the Southern states.

Consequently I proposed the theory [Burleigh, 1936] that this unique species sometimes laid eggs while migrating north in the spring, this radical departure from the normal habits of any known bird accounting for the otherwise unexplained presence of numerous young of the year in midsummer. As might be expected, this suggestion met with more or less skepticism, but until 1945 no further information came to light that either proved or disproved the hypothesis. On July 12, 1945, at Augusta, Denton [1946a] found an unmistakable cowbird's egg in an Indigo Bunting's nest that also held two eggs of the rightful owner, thus definitely giving the cowbird the status of a breeding bird of the state for the first time. No adults were seen that day, but on a later visit, July 21, Denton was more successful in this respect:

> Soon after arriving on the levee just south of Augusta, I noted a flock of 18 Cowbirds perched in a tree growing in the borrow pit. It consisted of one adult male, two adult females, and 15 young of the year. Just a few minutes later a second flock of approximately 250 Cowbirds was noted on the telegraph wires beside a railroad. Within this flock, which also was predominately young of the year, 25 adult males were actually counted and more than this number of females noted.
>
> Reference to notes made the two previous summers that I have been in Augusta revealed that in 1943 the first summer flock of Cowbirds was observed on July 25. Although no specific notes were made on the individuals comprising this flock of approximately 25 birds, it was noted that it contained both adult males and females. My first record of the Cowbird for the summer of 1944 was a flock estimated

to contain 500 birds noted on July 16. This flock also contained some adult birds.

Several years later the cowbird was again found breeding in the state by Parks [1950a], who on May 19, 1949, found a Hooded Warbler's nest at Atlanta that held one young warbler, one young cowbird, and one un-hatched egg. The following year, on May 27, 1950, he watched a young cowbird, three or four days out of the nest, being fed by a pair of White-eyed Vireos within a hundred yards of the spot where he had discovered the Hooded Warbler's nest [Parks, 1950b]. On the first occasion, no adult birds could be found in the vicinity, but in 1950 an adult female and at least one adult male were seen with a flock of starlings in a near-by pasture. Johnston [1950a] reports seeing adult cowbirds, both males and females, on the University dairy farm south of Athens from May 16 through June 30, 1950, and collecting a female there June 13 that contained an egg "probably ready to be laid"; therefore, it appears that this species is now well established as a breeding bird in at least the northern part of the state.

One can only theorize concerning the apparent absence of adult birds in past years and their present relative abundance in proportion to the number of young of the year now seen during the summer months, but a possible explanation suggests itself. That is, the adults now observed in increasing numbers are birds hatched from eggs laid in Georgia in past years. Under such circumstances it is logical to assume that such individuals would not have a tendency to go farther north in the spring. This would bear out, to some extent at least, the hypothesis of egg-laying while migrating. The cowbird is rather conspicuous during the breeding season, and it is difficult to believe that adults, although almost never seen after early May, were as abundant twenty years ago as they are today.

HABITS AND RECOGNITION: The cowbird is an interesting bird, but one whose presence during the summer months must be accepted with mixed emotions. Unique among North American birds, it never builds a nest of its own or makes any effort to rear its own young, its eggs being laid in the nests of other species. Vireos, warblers, and sparrows are commonly imposed upon, and because of the large size and aggressive disposition of the young cowbird, rarely if ever do such foster parents succeed in rearing young of their own. Sooner or later their eggs or young are pushed from the nest and destroyed, and the ultimate outcome is that a young cowbird alone is reared to maturity. One can readily visualize the harmful effect on the bird life of any community in which this parasitic blackbird is at all common. In other ways as well, the cowbird appears to follow the lines of least resistance in its daily existence.

As its name implies, it is commonly seen feeding close to cattle, in open fields or pastures, watching for any insects disturbed by the livestock as they move about. During the breeding season the cowbird is found in pairs. However, at other times, it is a highly gregarious species, and throughout much of the year birds of both sexes are found in flocks of varying size. Preferring, as it does, the more open country and being rarely if ever found in wooded areas, it has unquestionably increased in numbers as farms, with their cultivated fields and pastures, replaced the original wilderness. It is certainly a common bird in Georgia today, and one not easily overlooked. It can be readily recognized wherever seen, for it is the smallest of the blackbirds, its size being immediately apparent when it is observed at reasonably close range. Males are characterized by a brown head that contrasts with the otherwise black body; females, by their uniform gray, with no suggestion of the streaked plumage of the female Red-winged Blackbird.

Tanagers: *Family Thraupidae*

Western Tanager
Piranga ludoviciana (Wilson)

GENERAL DISTRIBUTION: Breeds from northwestern British Columbia, southwestern Mackenzie, and southwestern South Dakota to the mountains of southern California, northern Lower California, southern Arizona, and central western Texas. Winters from central Mexico and Cape San Lucas through the highlands to Costa Rica.

STATUS IN GEORGIA: Of accidental occurrence in the southern part of the state.

The first record of this species in Georgia is that of a female collected by Herbert L. Stoddard, November 11, 1954, on Birdsong Plantation, Grady County. He was advised of its presence there by Mrs. E. V. Komarek, who saw it at her bird bath and recognized it as "different" because of the white wing-bars. David W. Johnston [letter] reports another specimen, also a female, taken at Warner Robins, near Macon, on March 19, 1956. He writes that this bird appeared at the feeding station of Mrs. Gladys Black "on Dec. 24, 1955, and was observed almost daily until Mar. 11, 1956, at which time an unsuccessful trapping attempt apparently frightened it away—we thought it was gone for good. But, it returned on Mar. 18 and was caught the next day."

HABITS AND RECOGNITION: With its crimson head, light yellow underparts, and black wings, back, and tail, the male Western Tanager is a handsome bird, and one that can be recognized at a glance. The olive-green female so closely resembles the other female tanagers, however, that were it not for the two yellowish or white wing-bars, characteristic of this species, it could, except within its breeding range, be easily over-looked. As it occurs during the summer months on the higher mountain ridges of the Western states the appearance of this tanager in Georgia is further evidence of a west-east migration noticeable in recent years. It is doubtful, however, that the Western Tanager will ever be other than accidental in occurrence in the state.

Scarlet Tanager
Piranga olivacea   (Gmelin)

GENERAL DISTRIBUTION: Breeds from southern Saskatchewan, southern Manitoba, southern Ontario, southern Quebec, New Brunswick, and Nova Scotia south to southern Kansas, northern Arkansas, northern Alabama, northern Georgia, and northern South Carolina. Winters from Colombia to Bolivia and Peru.

STATUS IN GEORGIA: A fairly common summer resident in the mountain counties and a regular and fairly common transient, both in the spring and in the fall, over the rest of the state, although less often observed south of the fall line.

Extreme dates of occurrence in the spring, south of the breeding range, are:

Savannah: April 1 (1912) and May 14 (1921).

Grady County: April 30 (1929) and May 8 (1940).

Fitzgerald: April 22 (1939) and May 8 (1941).

Macon: April 9 (1935) and May 16 (1954).

Milledgeville: April 11 (1941) and May 9 (1946).

Augusta: May 5 (1945) and May 16 (1945).

Athens: April 11 (1927) and May 26 (1927).

Atlanta: April 4 (1920) and May 25 (1930).

It has also been seen at Newton, Baker County, May 11, 1931; Cochran, Bleckley County, April 8 and 17, 1933; Columbus, April 13 and May 9, 1945; Rising Fawn, April 18, 1885; Rome, April 28 to May 8, 1953; and Dalton, April 21, 1944.

In the fall, extreme dates of occurrence are Athens, September 20 (1929) and October 19 (1928); Atlanta, September 6 (1947) and October 29 (1946); Grady County, October 3 (1946) and October 23 (1949); Savannah, September 15 (1908) and October 14 (1906). At Augusta, it was last noted, October 11 (1944). There is a single fall record for Cochran, September 24, 1932, and one for Fitzgerald, September 15, 1940.

It has been reported as breeding at Brasstown Bald, Rabun Bald, Cowpen Mountain, Rich Mountain, Grassy Mountain, Lookout Mountain, Margret, Toccoa, Dahlonega, Demorest, and Yonah Mountain; and it doubtless nests elsewhere in the mountains and foothills where conditions are suitable. Griffin [1947] calls attention to an apparently valid breeding record for East Point, Fulton County, the farthest south that this species has ever been known to nest in the state. He quotes from an article by William J. Mills [*Wilson Bulletin,* 14:124–25, 1902], in which the statement is made that a set of four eggs of the Scarlet Tanager was collected at East Point in 1902, under circumstances that would seem to justify this identification. Of significance is the fact that the following year a male was collected by Mills near Fairburn, a few miles south of East Point, on June 17, an exceptionally late date for even a belated spring transient. However, Griffin places in that category a singing male seen by him near Vinings, in Cobb County, on June 4, 1939.

Definite breeding records for the state are otherwise limited to Margret, Fannin County, where I succeeded in finding four nests, as follows: June 7, 1921, two well-incubated eggs; June 8, 1927, three half-incubated eggs; three small young; June 10, 1927, one newly hatched young and two pipped eggs.

HABITS AND RECOGNITION: The first glimpse of a male Scarlet Tanager cannot fail to evoke admiration difficult to express in ordinary adjectives. With its bright scarlet body and vivid black wings and tail, it is certainly one of the handsomest birds one will see in Georgia, and its arrival in the spring is an event always to be looked forward to. In the fall, however, its appearance is so different that only familiarity with its inconspicuous plumage at this season of the year will make it possible to identify it readily. Few birds undergo so complete a change. The scarlet is replaced by a subdued yellowish-green, with the black of the wings and tail less conspicuous. It closely resembles the female then, the only difference being the darker coloration of the wings and tail.

Both in migration and in its summer home the Scarlet Tanager seeks out the deciduous hardwoods and shows an evident partiality for such species as the oaks and hickories. Only through necessity will it accept pines or other conifers in which to feed or find shelter. Its days are spent in the upper branches of the larger hardwoods, and despite the vivid coloration of the male, it is so adept at concealing itself in the thick foliage that only its song and characteristic alarm notes ordinarily reveal its presence. The song is a prolonged carol much like that of the Robin, but it possesses a husky quality that is quite distinctive. Rather deliberate in its movements, the male will frequently sing from one spot for minutes at a time, and unless a sudden movement betrays its whereabouts, it is surprisingly difficult to locate. During the summer months, both sexes, if alarmed, utter a deep toned "chip-churr," which, once heard, will never be confused with the call of any other bird.

The few nests that have been found in Georgia have varied in height from fifteen to thirty feet from the ground, and have been at the outer ends of limbs, where they were difficult of access. The site chosen apparently depends on the whim of the female, no two being alike. One nest was in an apple tree in the front yard of a long-abandoned farmhouse, another in a post oak at the side of a road, and a third in a large black walnut tree at the edge of a clearing well up a mountainside. In construction, however, they were much alike, being far from substantial, though compactly built of weed stems, vine tendrils, and grass, and lined with fine grasses. Three eggs seem to be the usual number laid in Georgia, and only one brood is reared each year.

Eastern Summer Tanager
Piranga rubra rubra (Linnaeus)

GENERAL DISTRIBUTION: Breeds from southeastern Nebraska, southern Iowa, southern Wisconsin, central Indiana, central Ohio, Maryland, and Delaware south to northeastern Mexico, the Gulf Coast, and southern Florida. Winters from central Mexico and Yucatán to Ecuador, Peru, and Guiana.

STATUS IN GEORGIA: A common summer resident throughout the state.

In spring, the Summer Tanager appears in Georgia the latter part of March or early April, and is common until early October. An occasional individual lingers until the last of October, but such records are exceptional. There is one winter record.

Earliest transients in the spring were noted at:

St. Marys: March 26 (1905).
Savannah: March 18 (1912).
Grady County: March 16 (1941).
Tifton: March 28 (1945).
Macon: March 30 (1953).
Milledgeville: March 30 (1929).

Augusta: April 3 (1945).
Athens: April 9 (1921).
Atlanta: April 3 (1894).
Rising Fawn: April 12 (1885).
Dalton: April 10 (1944).

The last in the fall were seen at:

Dalton: October 18 (1942).
Athens: October 26 (1925).
Decatur: October 26 (1946).
Atlanta: October 10 (1929).
Macon: October 12 (1923).

Americus: October 4 (1941).
Fitzgerald: September 28 (1940).
Grady County: October 25 (1947).
Savannah: October 20 (1908).

Apparently the only winter record is that of a single bird seen by Herbert L. Stoddard, Sr., on Sherwood Plantation, Grady County, December 19, 1947.

As a breeding bird, the Summer Tanager has a wide distribution in the state, occurring during the summer months from the mountains to the coast and nesting wherever there is suitable habitat. Definite breeding records, however, are limited to the following localities:

Rome: Nest with young, May, 1938 [Jones, 1947].

Margret, Fannin County: Four incubated eggs, June 26, 1921 (Burleigh).

Young Harris, Towns County: Two incubated eggs, June 22, 1922; four fresh eggs, May 19, 1927 (Burleigh).

Atlanta: Nesting extremes, three eggs, May 15 (1933) [Barkalow, 1940]; and four fresh eggs, June 8 (1938) [Griffin, 1940].

Athens: Nesting extremes, three slightly incubated eggs, May 21 (1921); and four well-incubated eggs, June 5 (1923) (Burleigh).

Woodville, Greene County: Four incubated eggs, May 23, 1922 (Burleigh).

Augusta: Four young, July 3, 1953 (Denton).

Macon: Four eggs, May 30, 1930; and two eggs, May 31, 1944 (Denton).

Fitzgerald: Nest with young, June 1, 1940 [Norris, 1940].

Grady County: Three eggs, May 19, 1924 (Stoddard).

Savannah: Nesting extremes (forty-five nests), three slightly incubated eggs, May 5 (1921); and four fresh eggs, June 1 (1907) (Rossignol).

HABITS AND RECOGNITION: Because of its relative abundance and wide distribution the Summer Tanager is a familiar bird in Georgia. Absent during the winter, it is commonly known as the Summer Redbird to distinguish it from the Cardinal, which, likewise an entirely red bird, is present throughout the year. In contrast to the Scarlet Tanager, the Summer Tanager likes the open pine woods, and while occasional pairs can be found in deciduous hardwoods in the stream bottoms, it is most apt to be seen in the larger stretches of pines. These areas usually have a scattering of such hardwoods as the post oak, dogwood, and sweet gum. Summer Tanagers feed indiscriminately in the lower branches of the pines and in the hardwoods, where they are easily observed. The male is an attractive bird, its entire body being a rose-red when in fully adult plumage. Occasionally an individual will be seen that has failed to acquire this adult plumage after the post-juvenal moult, and presents an odd appearance, the back and underparts being patched with rose-red and olive green.

The song of the male is much like that of the Scarlet Tanager, being a prolonged carol resembling somewhat that of the Robin, but it is clearer and lacks the husky quality of the song of its more handsome relative. The alarm note, however, uttered by both sexes throughout the spring and early summer—an emphatic "chick-tucky-tuck"—is distinctive and will readily identify this tanager.

With its evident fondness for the pines, the Summer Tanager might be expected to nest in them, but with few exceptions, however, all nests that have been found in Georgia have been found in hardwoods. At Athens, the post oak was usually given preference, although an occasional nest was built in a sweet gum; and at Young Harris, a pair selected an apple tree in a farmyard. In Grady County, Stoddard found dogwood the preferred tree, with pecans and tung trees also used. The height of the nest from the ground varied from six to forty feet, the average nest being within twelve or fifteen feet of the ground and at the outer end of a limb, where it was only partially concealed by the foliage. Compact but not very substantial, the nests were much alike in construction, being of weed stems, rootlets, and grasses, lined with finer grasses. Four eggs, only infrequently three, were found in the nests examined, and it is doubtful that more than one brood is reared in Georgia each year.

Although largely beneficial in its habits, this tanager is known to be fond of bees, and thus is heartily disliked by beekeepers. Stoddard, in his unpublished manuscript on the birds of Grady County, says: "Summer Tanagers bear a bad reputation among beekeepers on account of their bee-eating habits. They also extract pupae and 'grubs' from wasp nests, and are said to kill the wasps before partaking of the grubs. This seems probable, as no wasps have been noted flying around the vicinity of nests the Tanagers were raiding."

Grosbeaks, Finches, Sparrows, and Buntings: *Family Fringillidae*

Eastern Cardinal
Richmondena cardinalis cardinalis (Linnaeus)

GENERAL DISTRIBUTION: Resident from southeastern South Dakota, southern Iowa, northern Indiana, northern Ohio, southern Ontario, and southern New York south to southern Georgia and western Florida.

STATUS IN GEORGIA: Resident and common throughout the state except the extreme southeastern corner.

Specimens representing this race have been examined from numerous localities in Georgia, including the following: Dalton, Young Harris, Robertstown (White County), Augusta, Athens, Decatur, Madison, Waynesboro, Dublin, Alamo (Wheeler County), Blakely, Newton, Seminole County, Grady County, Savannah, and Hinesville.

It unquestionably nests wherever it occurs, but actual breeding records are limited to the following localities:

Rome: Nesting, April 8, 1929; fledglings, August 6, 1939 [Jones, 1947].

Margret, Fannin County: Four well-in-

cubated eggs, June 11, 1921; four fresh eggs, July 14, 1922 (Burleigh).

Atlanta: Nesting extremes, two eggs,

April 9 (1933); four eggs, July 22 (1939) [Griffin, 1940].

Athens: Nesting extremes (eighteen nests), small young, April 6 (1927); three fresh eggs, July 22 (1926) [Burleigh, 1938].

Augusta: Nesting extremes (twelve nests), four fresh eggs, March 16 (1945); three eggs, July 20 (1947) (Denton).

Macon: Four young, two days old, March 31, 1945 (Denton).

Fitzgerald: Nesting extremes (twenty-three nests), three eggs, April 13 (1940); one young bird and one egg, August 23 (1940) (Norris and Hopkins).

Savannah: Nesting extremes (nineteen nests), three fresh eggs, May 5 (1911); three slightly incubated eggs, June 17 (1912) (Rossignol).

Grady County: Young in the nest as early as April 17 (1938), and females incubating eggs as late as July 2 (1924) (Stoddard).

HABITS AND RECOGNITION: It is doubtful that any bird in Georgia, other than the Mockingbird, is better known than the Cardinal or held in more esteem. Beauty in both plumage and song is sufficient reason for public approval. Thickets or dense underbrush in which to nest or to take shelter when danger threatens seems to be all this handsome songster demands, and where these requirements are met, the Cardinal will be found. Shrubbery about houses is just as acceptable as a thicket deep in the wilderness; in fact, the proximity of man seems preferred where conditions are suitable, and not only about farmhouses but in the towns and cities as well, the Redbird, as it is commonly called, is a familiar sight.

As the males retain their bright red plumage throughout the year, they add a welcome touch of color to the landscape during the short, bleak days of winter, and many bird lovers encourage their presence by putting out seeds and nut meats for them at that season. These are readily accepted, and in some instances depended upon by the birds. Stoddard mentions the feeding of Cardinals in his unpublished manuscript on the birds of Grady County, stating that for over twenty years fragments of the meats of the pecan have been supplied for these birds on Sherwood Plantation. He adds, "While the writer places the nut meat bits in the feeder soon after daylight each morning, the Cardinals wait impatiently, some less than a yard distant. As soon as he is through, they flock onto the tray. There are forty or more in the waiting line that derive much of their sustenance at the feeders."

During the winter, small flocks are commonly seen, and it is not improbable that these are family groups that have remained together after the young are fully grown and able to care for themselves. Both sexes can be found in the same flock, and the birds are quiet, except for a sharp "chip" that is distinctive. In early February, the males announce the approach of spring with their loud, clear whistle, and shortly thereafter the flocks break up and nesting activities are underway.

The Cardinal is a prolific species, and in Georgia rears three broods each year: the first in March and early April, the second in May, and the third in late June and July. Normally three eggs are laid, at times four, and rarely but two in late clutches. The nest is placed in a bush or sapling and, while usually in underbrush, is seldom well concealed, and more often than not is easily seen. It is generally within three or four feet of the ground, and although not very substantial, is compactly built of coarse weed stems, dead leaves, shreds of bark, and grasses, well cupped and lined with rootlets and fine grasses. The young when they leave the nest resemble the female, immature males retaining this inconspicuous, olive-brown plumage until late summer, when they acquire the bright red dress of the adult male.

Florida Cardinal
Richmondena cardinalis floridana (Ridgway)

GENERAL DISTRIBUTION: Resident in southeastern Georgia and peninsular Florida.

STATUS IN GEORGIA: Resident in the extreme southeastern corner of the state, as far west as the Okefenokee Swamp, and north to Darien.

Specimens of this Florida race have been examined from the Okefenokee Swamp (a male from Billy's Lake, October 16, 1931, and a male and a female from Minne's Lake, October 17, 1931); St. Marys (two females, April 7, 1946); Woodbine (a male, May 11, 1933, and a male and a female, May 12, 1933); and Darien (a male, April 25, 1946).

Definite breeding records are limited to Coleraine, lying in extreme eastern Charlton County and extreme western Camden County, where Hebard [letter] reports the following nests: May 11, 1942, naked young; May 18, 1942, three eggs; June 27, 1942, three large young; and May 13, 1943, three large young.

HABITS AND RECOGNITION: The Florida Cardinal differs from its more northern relative in being smaller and deeper red in color. However, in general appearance and actions, there is little to distinguish the cardinals at St. Marys or in the Okefenokee Swamp from birds seen farther north in the state.

Rose-breasted Grosbeak
Pheucticus ludovicianus (Linnaeus)

GENERAL DISTRIBUTION: Breeds from south central Mackenzie, central Manitoba, central Ontario, southern Quebec, and Cape Breton Island south to central Kansas, southern Missouri, central Ohio, central New Jer-

EASTERN BLUE GROSBEAKS
Guiraca caerulea caerulea

Blue Grosbeaks lived in scattered pairs in thicket-dotted openings in the forest. I found one nest low among the outer branches of a tung tree, another in a five-foot sapling hickory near a pond. At the latter nest, very early one morning, I saw the female lay an egg. Since this was not the last egg of her clutch, she did not settle down to incubation but flew off and joined her bright mate. Here they are in a flowering white (or false) indigo plant. The bright-colored bird is the male.

sey, and in the mountains to northern Georgia. Winters from southern Mexico and Yucatán to Colombia, Venezuela, and Ecuador.

STATUS IN GEORGIA: A local but not uncommon summer resident in the mountains in the northeastern corner of the state, and a scarce and irregular transient, both in the spring and in the fall, south of its breeding range.

The Rose-breasted Grosbeak apparently passes through Georgia in rather small numbers. In spring, it can be seen at infrequent intervals in April and the first half of May, while in fall, an occasional bird will be noted from the middle of September until the latter part of October.

Earliest transients in the spring were reported from Savannah, April 4 (1913); Macon, April 18 (1932); Athens, April 22 (1929); Atlanta, April 9 (1906); and Rising Fawn, April 22 (1885). The latest were noted at Athens, May 14 (1928); Atlanta, May 15 (1932); and Macon, May 12 (1945). There are single spring records for the Okefenokee Swamp (Billy's Island), May 8, 1921; Grady County, May 5, 1940; Americus, April 22, 1942; and Columbus, April 29, 1946.

In fall, extreme dates of occurrence are Athens, September 15 (1930) and October 22 (1920); Atlanta, September 16 (1938) and October 30 (1943); Macon, September 24 (1953) and October 17 (1943); and Grady County, October 7 (1939) and October 25 (1947). It was noted at Dalton, September 22, 1944; and at Americus on October 9, 1941.

This grosbeak has been reported as breeding on Rabun Bald (Rabun County) and Blood Mountain (Union County); and there are definite nesting records for Brasstown Bald (Towns County), three fresh eggs, May 26, 1925 [Burleigh, 1927]; and Tray Mountain (White County), nest with male incubating, June 16, 1949 [Denton and Neal, 1951].

HABITS AND RECOGNITION: If one wishes more than a passing acquaintance with the Rose-breasted Grosbeak in Georgia, it is necessary to venture into its summer haunts in the mountains. Here, on the higher ridges, above an altitude of 3,000 feet, it finds a congenial spot in which to rear its young, and is one of the characteristic birds of these steep, rugged slopes. Follow the trail leading to the top of Brasstown Bald, and as the valley is left far below, there will soon be heard a clear, melodious song which suggests that of a robin but has a hurried quality that is quite distinctive. A search of the trees in the vicinity will ultimately reveal a male Rose-breasted Grosbeak, half-concealed in the foliage, where, despite its striking plumage, it could easily be overlooked. Even a brief glimpse will identify it, the rosy-red breast spot standing out in contrast to its otherwise white underparts and its black head and throat. If the female is close by, the actions of the male will probably reveal her presence, and one will see a brown, partially streaked bird, which, except for its unusually heavy

611

bill, looks like a large sparrow. Tangled rhododendron thickets seem necessary to keep this grosbeak in Georgia during the summer months, for where there are no rhododendrons there are no grosbeaks. In most instances the nest is built in a rhododendron, although an occasional pair of these birds uses other sites. As relatively little is known concerning the breeding habits of this species in Georgia, it is of interest to detail the circumstances under which it was first found nesting in the state [Burleigh, 1927]:

They apparently are limited in their distribution to the proximity of the scattered rhododendron thickets that are so characteristic of the higher slopes, and it is here that almost invariably the nests can be found. As might be expected, the birds breed late, and it is the latter part of May before many are building. In May, 1923, a female was seen carrying nesting material to a nest but half built, and other birds noted that day were seemingly unconcerned as yet over domestic duties. It was the latter part of June before I had the opportunity to spend more time with them, and by then the young had in each case left the nest. A close search of the rhododendron thickets resulted in finding six nests from which the young had flown, all of them from five to ten feet from the ground at the outer end of a limb on one of the larger rhododendrons. From this limited experience I felt that it would be useless to look for a nest except in these rhododendron thickets, but a few days spent on the Bald in May, 1925, showed me that this preference was not always shown. The first nest, found on the 26th, was fully built but as yet empty, and was in the usual situation, fifteen feet from the ground at the outer end of a limb of a large rhododendron. A second nest found the same day, however, was twenty-five feet from the ground at the extreme outer end of a leaning yellow birch sapling, while a third nest found the following day, on the 27th, was fully fifty feet from the ground at the extreme outer end of an upper limb of a tall, slender chestnut. In both these latter nests there were three fresh eggs, the first being compactly built of weed stems, rootlets, twigs, and vine stalks, well lined with fine rootlets, the second rather frail and loosely built of twigs, sparingly lined with black rootlets. In each case the female was incubating and flushed reluctantly, showing great concern over my intrusion.

The nest found on Tray Mountain, June 16, 1949 [Denton and Neal, 1951], was thirty feet from the ground in a chestnut oak, and, as is frequently the case with this species, the male was incubating.

Eastern Blue Grosbeak
Guiraca caerulea caerulea (Linnaeus)

GENERAL DISTRIBUTION: Breeds from western Nebraska, Missouri, southern Illinois, and Maryland south to eastern Texas, southern Alabama, and central Florida. Winters from southern Mexico to Honduras and casually in Guatemala and Costa Rica.

STATUS IN GEORGIA: A fairly common summer resident throughout the state except in the mountains and the extreme southeastern corner. In the northeastern corner of Georgia it has been recorded during the summer months north to Clayton, Rabun County, and farther west it nests to the Tennessee line.

The Blue Grosbeak reaches Georgia in the spring in early April, and within two weeks is fairly common and generally distributed over the larger part of the state. In fall, small flocks are common until late in September, but they disappear rather suddenly, and only an occasional individual is observed in early October.

Earliest transients in the spring were seen at:

Camden County: April 13 (1942).
Savannah: April 12 (1885).
Grady County: April 4 (1939).
Tifton: April 21 (1952).
Americus: April 20 (1942).
Columbus: April 15 (1946).

Macon: April 12 (1953).
Milledgeville: April 11 (1929).
Augusta: April 21 (1945).
Athens: April 11 (1947).
Atlanta: April 20 (1939).

The last in the fall were noted at:

Augusta: September 22 (1944).
Athens: October 7 (1926).
Atlanta: October 5 (1946).
Macon: October 20 (1955).

Fitzgerald: September 28 (1940).
Grady County: October 7 (1939).
Camden County: September 23 (1944).

It has been reported as breeding at many localities throughout the state, as far north as Rome and south to Seminole County and on the coast, but definite nesting records are limited to the following:

Helen, White County: Nest with two well-grown young, June 8, 1949 [Denton, 1950].
Atlanta: Nesting extremes, four young, June 9 (1937); four eggs, July 23 (1939) [Griffin, 1940].
Athens: Nesting extremes (seven nests), three partially incubated eggs, May 23 (1925); three slightly incubated eggs, July 7 (1924) [Burleigh, 1938].
Augusta: Four eggs, June 7, 1945; two fresh eggs, July 6, 1945 (Denton).

Tifton: Two young and one egg, July 31, 1942 (Norris).
Grady County: Three incubated eggs, June 9, 1947; three fresh eggs, May 24, 1952 (Stoddard).
Savannah: Nesting extremes (twenty-seven nests), four fresh eggs, May 6 (1908); four incubated eggs, June 18 (1908) (Rossignol).
Camden County: Nest with four young, June 5, 1942 (Hebard).

613

HABITS AND RECOGNITION: The Blue Grosbeak, although it has a wide distribution in the state, is not a common bird anywhere and is not well known. It is a bird of the more open country, inhabiting thickets and stretches of underbrush in and at the edge of fields and pastures. Fields abandoned and partially overgrown with scrubby underbrush are favored spots, as are open slashings left after a logging operation. Here the males sing their somewhat weak, melodious warble from the top of a bush or sapling, disappearing in the nearest thicket if approached, for they are shy and retiring. In appearance, adult males suggest overgrown Indigo Buntings, but differ in having dull black wings that are marked with two broad chestnut-brown bars. Females are uniformly brown, with buffy wing-bars, and are sufficiently like the males in size and actions to be recognized without much difficulty.

The nest is built in a bush or sapling within two or three feet of the ground and is usually fairly well concealed by the surrounding vegetation. It is compact and substantial, and constructed of weed stems, rootlets, dead leaves, grasses, and not infrequently bits of paper and cotton, well cupped and lined with fine grasses and horsehair. At times fragments of old snakeskin are used, but this odd material either is not easy to find or is not especially sought, for only an occasional nest includes it. Stoddard, in his unpublished manuscript on the birds of Grady County, comments on a recent radical departure in the nesting habits of this grosbeak on Sherwood Plantation:

> Like the Indigo Buntings, the Blue Grosbeaks have almost deserted the brushy spots in the open pine woods on Sherwood and now concentrate in the tung-oil groves for breeding. A striking and abrupt change from something good to something better! Here the lightly constructed, rather deep nests are built and lined with grasses and rootlets, usually being placed from five to fifteen feet up in the tung trees. A pair to about three acres of grove approximates the breeding density at this time; the birds have increased many fold since the tung groves have grown to the size where they are attractive for nesting.

It is probable that two broods are frequently reared in Georgia each year, as fresh eggs can be found in late May and again in July. Three are laid as often as four, and on one occasion, on June 1, 1909, Rossignol found five eggs in a nest at Savannah, a most unusual occurrence.

Although beneficial in its habits, the Blue Grosbeak is very fond of ripening grain, and in the spring, fields of oats offer a source of food rarely ignored. Little damage is done, however, for the birds are not numerous enough to make their depredations of economic importance. In the fall, sorghum patches are equally attractive, and it is in such spots that these birds are usually seen prior to their departure in late September.

Indigo Bunting
Passerina cyanea (Linnaeus)

GENERAL DISTRIBUTION: Breeds from eastern North Dakota, central Minnesota, northern Michigan, southern Ontario, southern Quebec, and southern New Brunswick south to central Texas, southern Louisiana, central Alabama, southern Georgia, and northern Florida. Winters from Morelos and Yucatán through Central America to Panama, and in Cuba.

STATUS IN GEORGIA: A common summer resident over all the state except the coast region, where it breeds sparingly.

This handsome little bunting normally appears in Georgia in the spring in early April, soon becomes plentiful, and remains so until the middle of October. A few individuals may linger until shortly after the end of the month, but the small flocks seen earlier are missing.

Extreme dates of occurrence are as follows:

Grady County: March 27 (1949) and October 31 (1948).

Fitzgerald: April 25 (1952) and October 30 (1940).

Macon: April 12 (1955) and October 24 (1937).

Augusta: April 14 (1945) and October 6 (1944).

Athens: April 5 (1923) and October 30 (1927).

Atlanta: April 5 (1941) and November 3 (1946).

It was also reported at Hinesville, April 4 (1944); Milledgeville, as early as March 16 (1945); Dillard, Rabun County, April 14 (1922); and Dalton, April 16 (1944). At Savannah the latest date of the fall migration is October 11 (1908), and in Camden County, November 7 (1945).

With its wide distribution over the state, it undoubtedly breeds in every county where there is suitable habitat, but definite nesting records are not numerous and are limited to the following localities:

Augusta: Two nestlings and one egg, June 9, 1945; three incubated eggs, June 24, 1945; three fresh eggs, July 7, 1945 (Denton).

Woodville, Greene County: Three incubated eggs, June 8, 1922 (Burleigh).

Athens: Nesting extremes, three slightly incubated eggs, May 23 (1924); three partially incubated eggs, July 15 (1926) [Burleigh, 1938].

Atlanta: Nesting extremes, three fresh eggs, May 17 (1916) (Arpal); four eggs, July 23 (1939) (Griffin) [Griffin, 1940].

Baker County: Four young "still naked and blind," July 5, 1951 (Norris).

Seminole County: Three half-incubated eggs, May 19, 1933 (Burleigh).

Grady County: Three eggs, July 20, 1940 (Stoddard).

Savannah: Nest with incubated eggs found by T. D. Perry in 1887.

HABITS AND RECOGNITION: In most respects the Indigo Bunting is a miniature of the Blue Grosbeak. Although considerably smaller, the males appear at a distance the same uniformly bright blue, while the females are the same inconspicuous brown. Like the grosbeak, the bunting is found in the more open country, partially overgrown fields and slashings, hedgerows, and underbrush bordering roads seeming to be preferred as nesting sites. Stream bottoms are also acceptable, and while the vicinity of water is apparently not essential, there is nevertheless a noticeable tendency for this species to be more numerous along the creeks and rivers where the woods are open and there are suitable thickets in which to nest.

Few birds are more conspicuous during the summer months than the Indigo Bunting, largely on account of the persistent singing of the male. In late spring, when other birds gradually become silent and less and less noticeable, the spirited song of this little bunting, uttered from the upper branches of a tall tree, increases in vigor and volume. The bright, hot days of late June and July have little apparent effect on its ardor, and it is not until mid-August, when the fall moult begins, that it finally becomes quiet. It is then that the male loses its bright blue coat and appears in the garb of the female, the only noticeable difference being a trace of blue here and there.

Two broods are reared in Georgia each year, the first in late May and early June, the second in July. The nest is usually built in a bush or sapling within two or three feet of the ground, and in a thicket or underbrush where it is fairly well concealed. At Athens, an occasional pair was found nesting in canes along a stream, both the situation and construction of the nest being so much like those of the Hooded Warbler that until I glanced at the bluish-white unmarked eggs, I was uncertain at what nest I was looking. Murphey [1937] states that at Augusta the Indigo Bunting showed the same liking for cane thickets near water. The average nest is small and compactly built of weed stems, coarse grasses, and dead leaves, well lined with fine grasses; if it is in canes, the bulk of the material used is large, dry cane leaves.

Stoddard, in his unpublished manuscript on the birds of Grady County, says that the Indigo Bunting, like the Blue Grosbeak, has radically changed its breeding habits in recent years:

> This species has during recent years "taken over" the tung groves on Sherwood for breeding (although the "natural" location is shrubby growth on field edges and in the open piney woods). When the leaves drop in the fall, we find two or three to a half a dozen of the characteristic nests in each grove. This, coupled with the observation of the singing males, is the basis of our estimate of a maximum nesting population of one breeding pair to each two or three acres of grove. As

there are thirteen of the groves totaling some 125 acres, a considerable breeding population is indicated. Very few pairs, however, continue to nest in the open piney woods of the place, to which they were largely confined as breeders before the tung groves were planted. On July 20, 1940, a nest with three eggs was noted near the end of a tung branch not over eighteen inches above ground. The more usual situation in tung trees is from five to fifteen feet up.

Eastern Painted Bunting
Passerina ciris ciris   (Linnaeus)

GENERAL DISTRIBUTION: Breeds from southern Kansas, central Arkansas, northern Mississippi, and southeastern North Carolina south to southeastern Texas, southern Louisiana, southern Georgia, and northern Florida. Winters in the Bahamas and Cuba, and from central Florida, central Mexico, and Yucatán to Panama.

STATUS IN GEORGIA: A common summer resident on the coast and along the Savannah River as far north as Augusta. Largely of accidental occurrence in the interior of the state.

The Painted Bunting has been reported as breeding at Savannah, Hinesville, Allenhurst (Liberty County), Darien, Brunswick, Woodbine (Camden County), and St. Marys; and it unquestionably nests elsewhere on the coast where conditions are suitable. Little information is available concerning its status between Savannah and Augusta, but as it is a common summer resident at Augusta, it probably occurs along the Savannah River wherever there is suitable habitat. Denton [1950] reports three singing males at Waynesboro, Burke County, on May 28, 1950, and suggests that it possibly breeds also at Sardis, Hilltonia, Sylvania, and Millen. As Waynesboro is approximately seventeen miles from the Savannah River, this indicates a more extensive breeding range than has been recognized.

At Savannah, the average date of arrival in the spring is April 14, the earliest record being that of a single bird seen April 7 (1925). It was reported at Hinesville, April 20 (1944); on Cumberland Island, April 14 (1902); and on Sea Island, April 16 (1947). At Augusta, extreme dates of occurrence are April 29 (1945) and October 21 (1944).

Away from the coast it is rarely observed. Stoddard has four records for Grady County: April 27, 1926, May, 1935, May 5, 1940, and April 16, 1952; and there is one record for Fitzgerald, a male having been collected there, April 29, 1940 [Norris, 1940].

Definite breeding records are limited to Augusta, three half-incubated eggs, June 1, 1924 (Burleigh); and Savannah, nesting extremes

617

(forty nests, four fresh eggs, May 17 (1908); three slightly incubated eggs, July 15 (1908) (Rossignol).

HABITS AND RECOGNITION: A description of the male Painted Bunting gives the impression of a rather gaudy bird, for the head and nape are dark violet-blue, the back yellow-green, the rump red, and the underparts scarlet. But while it is admittedly highly plumaged, its colors are far from gaudy and blend so well that this little bunting is an unusually handsome and attractive bird. Its common name of Nonpareil is an indication of the high esteem in which it is held by those familiar with its beauty; and so far as appearance goes, it is certainly "of unequaled excellence." The female is less apt to attract attention, but is unique in its own right, its bright green back giving it the distinction of being the only finch of that color in Georgia.

In common with the other buntings, the Painted Bunting is a bird of hedgerows, thickets, and underbrush at the sides of roads and in abandoned and partially overgrown fields. Drainage ditches bordered by a thick growth of bushes are favored spots during the summer months, as are myrtle thickets in and at the edge of groves of live oaks. Here the female leads an inconspicuous existence in the underbrush, while the male spends much of each day singing from an elevated perch near by. When it is seen with the sky as a background, there is little to suggest the brilliance of its plumage, and only when it is approached and dives precipitately into the nearest thicket, does the flash of blue and scarlet betray its bright colors. Normally shy, it disappears from sight if undue interest is shown in its activities, and it is rarely possible then to catch more than an occasional distant glimpse of it.

The song, heard from the time the first males appear in April until early July, suggests that of the Indigo Bunting, but it is not as spirited, nor does it have nearly the volume of that of its near relative. The Painted Bunting is by no means so persistent a singer as the Indigo, and as the long hot days of midsummer approach, it gradually becomes quiet.

As fresh eggs can be found in May and again in July, it is probable that at least two broods are reared in Georgia each year. The nest is built in a bush or sapling, usually within three or four feet of the ground, and is compactly constructed of weed stems, fragments of dead leaves, and grasses, lined with fine grasses and, where available, horsehair. Four eggs are normally laid, but not infrequently three comprise the complete clutch.

Dickcissel
Spiza americana　(Gmelin)

GENERAL DISTRIBUTION: Breeds from northeastern Wyoming, northwestern North Dakota, northwestern Minnesota, southern Michigan, and southeastern Ontario south to southern Texas, central Mississippi, central Alabama, and northern Georgia (casually). Winters from Guatemala to Colombia, Venezuela, and Trinidad.

STATUS IN GEORGIA: A fairly common summer resident at Augusta, otherwise a local and rather erratic summer resident in the northern part of the state, and an extremely scarce transient south of its breeding range.

The Dickcissel was first recorded in Georgia in June, 1847, by Joseph LeConte, who collected a pair, apparently breeding, at Indian Springs, Butts County. Both these specimens are now in the U. S. National Museum, Washington, D. C. It was reported as breeding in 1885 at Rising Fawn, Dade County, by J. T. Park [Howell, 1909], but in subsequent years has not been found nesting again in this locality.

At Augusta, it was at one time a common breeding bird [Murphey, 1937], but it has decreased noticeably in numbers in recent years. Denton [1947] states that in 1946 only two breeding pairs could be located, but that in 1947 an encouraging increase was noted, four singing males, several females, and at least one brood of fully grown young being seen on June 15.

At Athens [Burleigh, 1938], it proved to be extremely erratic in occurrence. There were years when none were seen and an occasional year when it was a fairly common spring transient. In 1925, it was present in unusual numbers, and two pairs remained to breed, one nest being found on May 29 that held four fresh eggs. Otherwise, it was recorded at irregular intervals in late April and throughout May. In 1923, a single bird, a male, was seen May 4; in 1928, it was noted almost daily from May 3 through May 29; in 1929, two males, both singing, were seen April 29 and May 7. It was not until 1947 that the Dickcissel was again reported at Athens, three singing males and two females being found on May 18 in grain fields north of the city [Odum, 1947]. As the birds were still present on May 31, although no nests were actually located, there is little question that they nested that year. Three years later, on May 8, 1950, two pairs were again found at this same spot, and on May 16 a female was flushed from a nest that held four eggs [Johnston, 1950].

About Atlanta, the Dickcissel had never been recorded even as a transient until 1947 when a pair was found in a vetch field in the South River area near Constitution, in DeKalb County, and the female flushed from a nest that on May 25 held four well-incubated eggs [Griffin, 1947]. Four years later, in 1951, a small breeding colony was found on the U. S. Prison Honor Farm at Panthersville, DeKalb County, five singing males and three females being seen on May 26, and a nest located there on June 9 containing four eggs [Parks, 1951]. In 1953, this species was found nesting for the first time near Chickamauga, Walker County, a nest being located on May 26 by Mrs. G. L. Hight, Jr., that held five young birds two or three days old. Two birds were seen that year at Rome from February 8 through March 8 and, considering the unusually early date, had possibly wintered there [Dorsey, letter].

As a transient south of its breeding range, this species has been noted on but few occasions. There are three records for Macon, April 30, 1921 (Mounts), and June 7, 1953, and October 8, 1954 (Johnston); two for Milledgeville, May 11, 1926, and March 16, 1945 (Tait); one for Grady County, April 29, 1947 (Stoddard); and one for Houston County, May 11, 1952 (Whitney). The earliest date on which it has been seen in the spring at Augusta is April 19 (1953); the latest it has been noted in the fall, September 9 (1945) (Denton).

HABITS AND RECOGNITION: The history of the Dickcissel is both interesting and unusual. Prior to 1880 it was a common breeding bird on the Atlantic coastal plain, occurring as far north as Massachusetts. Suddenly, and for no obvious reason, it disappeared almost completely from this part of its breeding range, and up to the present time is still, with a few exceptions, rare and irregular in its appearance anywhere east of the Alleghenies. The fact that in recent years it has been found nesting for the first time near Atlanta and is apparently becoming established as a breeding bird at Athens, would indicate that it is possibly attempting to establish itself again in territory from which it has long been absent. If such is the case, it is to be hoped that the efforts will meet with success.

At Augusta, its decrease is attributed by Murphey [1937] to a changed environment:

> Like several of the species enumerated herein, this was a valley bird, hemmed in by dense swamps on either side and by the fall line at the upper extremity of its range. It inhabited the flat hay-fields on either side of the Savannah River and was rather a conspicuous bird because of its habit of choosing the telegraph wires or some dead limb of a tree from which to sound its characteristic "rusty" song. Many of the fields where it formerly ranged have been transformed into ponds of open water, since the soft alluvial clay is extensively used in the making of brick and ponds are formed where the excavation has been done.

In 1945, Denton [letter] succeeded in finding seven occupied nests in Richmond County; the earliest held three fresh eggs on May 16, the latest three fresh eggs on June 27. They varied in height from nine inches to two and one-half feet from the ground, and were located in trumpet vines on the levees and, in two instances, in briar thickets. The single nest found at Athens in 1925 was somewhat similarly situated, being two and one-half feet from the ground in a thick vine growing on the side of a ditch. Griffin [1947] describes the nest he found near Atlanta as but six inches from the ground in a thick clump of vetch.

In appearance, the male Dickcissel has been aptly compared to a miniature Meadowlark, the breast being yellow and marked with a conspicuous black patch. The female looks very much like a female House Sparrow, but a close glance will reveal a trace of yellow on the underparts.

Eastern Evening Grosbeak
Hesperiphóna vespertína vespertína   (Cooper)

GENERAL DISTRIBUTION: Breeds in western Alberta east to northern Michigan, and once at Woodstock, Vermont. Winters in the interior of North America, south of the Saskatchewan and east of the Rocky Mountains, and more or less irregularly to Quebec, New England, New York, and Pennsylvania, and south sporadically to Missouri, Kentucky, Ohio, Maryland, the District of Columbia, Delaware, and New Jersey.

STATUS IN GEORGIA: Unrecorded in the state until 1955, when an unexpected invasion of this boreal species resulted in small flocks being seen as far south as Macon. At Rome, Floyd County, Gordon L. Hight, Jr. [letter], observed a flock of five "on the Berry Schools campus" on February 18, another flock of "about ten" at the same spot on February 21, and an even larger flock of twenty-seven (eleven males and sixteen females) on February 28. A male was collected on February 21, and was identified by John W. Aldrich, of the Fish and Wildlife Service, as *vespertína*. At Atlanta, a flock of six was seen February 5 [Mrs. Sam Anderson, fide Griffin and Parks], and another flock of thirteen on April 4 [Marene Snow et al, fide Griffin and Parks]. David W. Johnston [letter] reports the latest record for the state, two birds seen on the campus of Mercer University, at Macon, on April 7.

HABITS AND RECOGNITION: South of the New England states the Evening Grosbeak is extremely erratic in its appearance during the winter months, and its occurrence then is always worthy of comment. Its movements are probably influenced less by weather conditions than by an available food supply, for while it is normally seldom seen over much of the eastern United States, there are occasional years when small flocks are reported by many observers. In recent years it has appeared with increasing regularity in the Southern states, but so unpredictable are its movements that its actual status will always be a matter of uncertainty.

Usually tame and unsuspicious, small flocks encountered can be approached with little difficulty, and the appearance of both males and females is so distinctive that there will never be any doubt about their identity. The unusually large yellowish-green bill, rather short tail, and conspicuous white wing-patch are the most noticeable characters where both sexes are concerned, and once the short metallic alarm note is heard, it will never be confused with any other species. Favorite foods are the seeds of the box elder, the privet, and the yellow poplar, and to a lesser extent such fleshy fruits as the dogwood, hawthorn, red cedar, and poison ivy are also eaten.

Eastern Purple Finch
Carpodacus purpureus purpureus (Gmelin)

GENERAL DISTRIBUTION: Breeds from northwestern British Columbia, northeastern Alberta, northern Ontario, and southern Quebec south to southern Alberta, North Dakota, central Minnesota, northern Illinois, Pennsylvania, northern New Jersey, and Long Island. Winters from considerably north of the southern boundary of its breeding range to the Gulf Coast from Texas to Florida.

STATUS IN GEORGIA: A fairly common winter resident over most of the state, although less frequently observed south of the fall line.

In fall, small flocks of Purple Finches appear in Georgia the latter part of October or early November, and are present where there is an available food supply until the following April.

Extreme dates of occurrence are at Atlanta, October 21 (1945) and April 26 (1929); Athens, October 23 (1925) and April 24 (1926); Macon, November 16 (1952) and April 11 (1955); Fitzgerald, December 22 (1939) and March 21 (1940); and Grady County, November 24 (1949) and March 1 (1946). The latest in the spring were noted at Sea Island, March 17 (1947); Savannah, March 16 (1927); Milledgeville, April 15 (1941); and Dalton, April 21 (1944). Hebard [1941] reports this species seen in the Okefenokee Swamp by Francis Harper from December 27, 1916, through January 12, 1917, and by himself in western Camden County, November 22, 1936.

Specimens representing this race have been examined from Center, Jackson County (January 14, 1946); Athens (between the dates of November 18 [1945] and January 3 [1946]; Lawrenceville (February 28, 1946); Stone Mountain (April 2, 1947); Atlanta (between the dates of October 21 [1945] and April 13 [1940]); and Riverdale, Clayton County (December 23, 1949).

HABITS AND RECOGNITION: Unlike other northern finches, the Purple Finch appears regularly each fall in Georgia, and can be seen throughout the winter where its favorite foods, the seeds of ash, box elder, and yellow poplar, can be found. It also feeds at times on the fleshy fruit of the dogwood and the black gum, but apparently not to any great extent. Quiet and rather deliberate in its movements, it can be easily overlooked and consequently is not generally known. A small flock will fly into the top of an ash or box elder, each bird will pick out a spot where the seed is hanging in thick clusters, and then for a long interval there will be little movement to reveal their presence as the birds satisfy their appetites. The fact that such flocks consist largely of dull-plumaged females and immature males aids in making them an inconspicuous part of the winter bird life. Adult males apparently require several years to attain their rosy-red dress, and rarely will more than one or two be seen in the usual flocks. In early spring, this finch finds the swelling buds of such trees as the elms and maples much to its liking, and at that season it frequently comes into the towns and feeds in the shade trees on the lawns and streets. It sometimes attracts attention then. Murphey [1937] makes an interesting comment in this connection in discussing the bird life in and about Augusta:

> More abundant above the fall line than below, but comes down into the valley in March and early in April to feed upon the buds of shade trees. The high winds of March frequently blow these flower-buds off the trees, particularly from the elms, and the Purple Finch along with the Goldfinch comes to the ground after them. On several such occasions I have had excited citizens to come in and inform me that they had seen "pink English Sparrows" feeding in the streets.

On Sherwood Plantation in Grady County, Stoddard [MS] found the Purple Finch very fond of the berries of the Privet (*Ligustrum sinense*), and he also was able to attract this species to his feeding tray, where it fed regularly on pecan bits.

The song of the Purple Finch, a rich, melodious warble, can frequently be heard in late March and April before the birds depart for their northern breeding grounds.

Newfoundland Purple Finch
Carpodacus purpureus nesophilus Burleigh and Peters

GENERAL DISTRIBUTION: Breeds in Newfoundland. Winters south to Georgia and probably to the Gulf Coast, although at present little is known of its winter range.

STATUS IN GEORGIA: An uncommon winter resident over the entire state.

Four specimens of this recently described race from Newfoundland have been taken in Georgia, males at Austell, Cobb County, March 11, 1946 (Burleigh); Smyrna, Cobb County, January 21, 1949 (Griffin); and Grady County, February 4, 1951 (Stoddard); and a female at Athens, Clarke County, March 23, 1946 (Burleigh).

HABITS AND RECOGNITION: Like so many Newfoundland races, the Purple Finch of this fog-enshrouded Maritime Province is characterized by being distinctly darker in both sexes. In general appearance and actions, however, there is little to distinguish it.

Northern Pine Siskin
Spinus pinus pinus   (Wilson)

GENERAL DISTRIBUTION: Breeds from central Manitoba, central Quebec, and Newfoundland south to southeastern Nebraska, northern Minnesota, northern Michigan, New Brunswick, and Nova Scotia, and in the mountains from the New England states to North Carolina. Winters over most of the United States south to northern Mexico and southern Florida.

STATUS IN GEORGIA: An erratic winter resident over the entire state, abundant some years, scarce or absent others.

The appearance of the Pine Siskin in Georgia during the winter is unpredictable. On a few occasions, it has been noted as early as late October, but it is usually the middle of November or later before the first small flocks are seen, and there have been winters when it has not appeared at all. If they were present during the winter, in spring, small flocks linger throughout April and not infrequently through the first week in May.

Summarized briefly, the following dates show the irregularity with which this little finch has been recorded in the state: Dalton, noted from April 8 through May 7, 1944 [Hamilton, et al, 1944]; Rome, seen from April 1 through April 9, 1949, March 22 and December 21, 1952, February 8 through April 22, 1953 [Dorsey, letter]; Atlanta, an irregular winter resident, with extreme dates of occurrence, October 31 (1954) and May 13 (1947) [Griffin and Parks, MS].

At Athens, in the winters of 1921–22 and 1922–23, small flocks were numerous, the following year few were seen, and in the winter of 1924–25, despite a careful search, none were noted. The next winter, 1925–26, they were again abundant, but were absent during the winter of 1926–27, and were scarce the following two years. During the entire period, extreme dates for arrival in the fall and departure in the spring were October 20

(1925) and May 6 (1923) [Burleigh, 1938]. In 1942 this species was noted as late as May 7 [Odum, 1942].

Concerning appearance of this bird at Augusta, Murphey [1937] comments as follows: "Most irregular in its visitations. There have been some years when it could properly be designated as abundant, others when it was scarce, and still others when no Siskin could be found in spite of diligent search. The winters of 1890 and of 1898–99 were periods of great local abundance. While observed throughout the winter, it was most plentiful in late March and early April." Denton [1944] reports it at Augusta, March 9 and 11, 1944. For Milledgeville, there are two records: April 6, 1939, and March 6, 1943 [Tait, 1946]. At Macon, extreme dates of occurrence are December 26 (1952) and May 15 (1955) [Johnston, MS].

In Grady County, Stoddard [MS] writes: "A very erratic winter visitant, usually in small numbers and at rather long intervals. During the winter of 1946–47, however, they appeared in the region in great numbers. . . . Two were first noted with a small flock of Goldfinches on December 1, 1946. By the first of the year they were becoming numerous, and seen and heard almost daily. Their numbers gradually declined during March, and by the last of the month only a few of the horde remained." Small flocks were observed at intervals throughout April, and on May 7 the siskin was noted for the last time that spring in Grady County.

In the Okefenokee Swamp, small numbers were seen by Francis Harper, December 22, 1916, through January 8, 1917; and Hebard [1941] reports small flocks there, December 29, 1929, and January 3 and 10, 1930. Hebard also saw small flocks at Coleraine, November 28 and December 3, 1940, and a single individual in eastern Charlton County, December 5, 1940. Johnston [1947] reports three birds seen in the Swamp, April 27, 1947.

At Statesboro, two birds were reported on the extremely late date of May 23 (1947); flocks of seventy or more individuals were observed here that year by Miss Malvina Trussell, from February until early May [Johnston, 1948].

About Savannah, these birds were observed in small numbers, April 25, 1926, and November 18, 1928 (Burleigh), and from January 2 through February 20, 1944 [Tomkins, 1944].

HABITS AND RECOGNITION: If one is interested in finding the Pine Siskin in Georgia during the late fall and early winter months, it is only necessary to watch the sweet gums that have produced a good seed crop. Here, in their years of appearance, the scattered flocks will be sure to be found in the upper limbs of the larger trees, busily engaged in extracting the small seeds from the hard, sharp-pointed pods. Frequently flying from one branch to another and uttering their characteristic wheezy call notes as

EASTERN PAINTED BUNTINGS

Passerina ciris ciris

This remarkably colored bird I did not see in southwestern Georgia,
but it was fairly common, locally, near Savannah. It seemed to be especially
fond of the plant shown in the painting, a shrub known as the
yaupon, a sort of holly. The two bright birds are adult males,
the dull one an adult female.

they move about, a flock of Pine Siskins is not easily overlooked. Seen from the ground, their small size and stout appearance remind one of the Goldfinch, but an occasional bird will come close enough to reveal its heavily streaked plumage and conspicuous yellow spots in the wings and tail. Observed for any length of time, the flock will suddenly, and for no obvious reason, leave the tree in which it has been feeding, and either circle overhead and return to the spot just left, or depart noisily and soon be out of sight. In late winter, possibly because this source of food has been largely depleted, the siskins desert the sweet gums and can be found in alder thickets bordering the streams. Here the many small cones furnish an abundant food supply, and the birds, displaying the same restlessness, will cling to the outer twigs for a short time as they satisfy their appetites and then be gone. While seeds of one kind or another are generally eaten, this little finch apparently occasionally varies its diet with insects, and I once witnessed an interesting example of this departure from its normal habits. At Athens, on February 17, 1923, small flocks were noted in several stretches of open pine woods, and the birds were found to be devouring in large numbers a minute brown aphid with which the smaller twigs of many of the trees were badly infested.

Normally peaceful and well behaved, the Pine Siskin, under certain circumstances, can be rather quarrelsome. Such at least was Stoddard's experience at his feeding station on the Sherwood Plantation in Grady County. He says [MS]:

> These little creatures were extraordinarily pugnacious at the feeders, where they were thrown in close contact with both their own kind and the (nearly) equally pugnacious Goldfinches, which they greatly resemble in both build and behavior. They are fearless of other birds regardless of size or usual position in the "peck order," which all other birds coming to the feeders observed. The fluttering, biting, and fighting Siskins seemed to confuse the other birds, and when feeding, the Siskins and Goldfinches usually had things pretty much to themselves.

Western Pine Siskin
Spinus pinus vagans Aldrich

GENERAL DISTRIBUTION: British Columbia coast region north to southern Alaska and south to northern Lower California, eastward normally to the Rocky Mountains from Canada to northern Mexico. Apparently breeds farther east during years of excessive wandering to Ontario, Wisconsin, Michigan, and Ohio.

STATUS IN GEORGIA: Known from a single specimen taken at Statham, Barrow County, March 7, 1946 (Burleigh).

HABITS AND RECOGNITION: It is possible that this recently described race occurs oftener in Georgia than this one record would indicate, but further collecting will be necessary to determine this fact. It is described as differing from the nominate race, *pinus,* by being lighter and less heavily streaked with black both above and below.

Eastern American Goldfinch
Spinus tristis tristis (Linnaeus)

GENERAL DISTRIBUTION: Breeds from southern Manitoba and southern Quebec south to eastern Colorado, southern Oklahoma, central Arkansas, northern Alabama, northern Georgia, and northwestern South Carolina. Winters over most of its breeding range and southward to the Gulf Coast.

STATUS IN GEORGIA: A fairly common summer resident in the northern part of the state, and locally along the western edge as far south as Edison, Calhoun County; a common winter resident from the mountains to the coast.

In northern Georgia the Goldfinch is known to breed only as far south as Athens and Atlanta, but its presence during the summer months as far south as Augusta, Milledgeville, and Macon indicates that it nests to the fall line in this part of the state. South and west of Fulton County it has been found in recent years occurring in small numbers during the summer months at least to Fort Gaines, Clay County, and Edison, Calhoun County. Dreyfoos [1946] noted a few birds at this season of the year at Columbus, apparently breeding, although no nests were found; and Norris [1948] reports summering individuals seen in 1947 at Richland, Webster County, July 30, Ft. Gaines, August 2 and 19, and Edison, August 5. Norris [1951] also states that a single bird was seen in the summer of 1948 near Lumpkin, Stewart County, by R. F. Thorne.

Although reported as breeding at numerous localities in the upper Piedmont and in the mountain counties, definite breeding records for the Goldfinch in the state are limited at present to Athens: five fresh eggs, July 30, 1921; four well-incubated eggs, July 31, 1922; three fresh eggs, July 24, 1924; three slightly incubated eggs, July 29, 1931 (Burleigh); and Atlanta: nesting extremes, two eggs, June 19 (1939); and four young, August 27 (1937) [Griffin, 1940].

During the winter, this little finch is common over all of Georgia, numerous flocks being present then from the lower slopes of the moun-

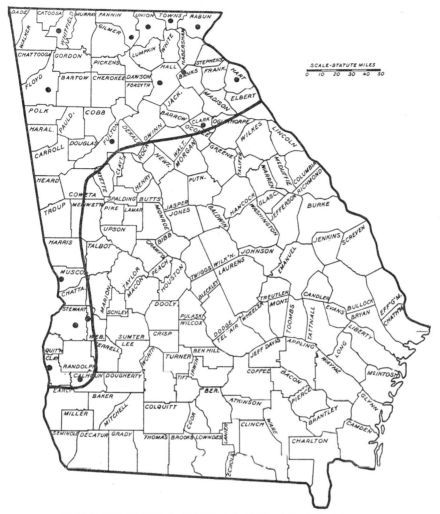

BREEDING DISTRIBUTION OF THE GOLDFINCH

tains to the cypress and tupelo swamps of the coastal plain. There is probably no county in the state where, a suitable food supply being available, it is not found at this time of the year. South of its breeding range, extreme dates of occurrence have been reported as follows: Hinesville, November 21 (1943) to April 25 (1944); Grady County, October 26 (1925) to May 7 (1939); and Americus, November 13 (1941) to May 6 (1942). At Fitzgerald the earliest date of arrival in the fall is October 15 (1939), while at Tifton the latest departure date in the spring is May 7 (1952).

HABITS AND RECOGNITION: From November until late April the Goldfinch is abundant in Georgia. The numerous flocks seen then feed, much as the Pine Siskins do, first in the sweet gums and later in the alders. At this time of the year both sexes are much alike in appearance, and are rather drab looking, the back being olive-brown, the underparts dull white. Restless and seldom quiet for any length of time, a flock feeding in the top of a sweet gum presents a picture of great animation, one or another of the birds continually flying to another branch or, with fluttering wings, shifting position to one of greater comfort or convenience. As they satisfy their hunger, they frequently utter their plaintive call note, which, lacking the wheezy quality of that of the siskin, at once identifies them as goldfinches.

As spring approaches, they appear in the maples and in the elms, feeding on the flower buds and, as it ripens, the seed of the elms. It is then that the males gradually acquire their handsome golden-yellow and jet-black dress. It is then, too, that the males can be heard uttering their spirited, ecstatic song that increases in ardor as the days pass. By late April, the flocks that were for a brief interval so much in evidence have disappeared, and until late fall only scattered pairs or single birds will be seen in the limited portion of the state where this species nests.

In the northern part of its range, it is usually late July or early August before nests of the Goldfinch with fresh eggs can be found. In Georgia, apparently unaffected by the earlier arrival of spring and the longer interval of warm weather, this species also delays nesting, while apparently awaiting the ripening of seeds on which the young are fed, until early summer. Its choice of a nesting site in the Piedmont of Georgia, however, so far as my limited experience goes, is radically different. As relatively little is known of its breeding habits this far south, it may be of interest to give in some detail my original impressions [Burleigh, 1925]:

As a general rule, where a species has a wide breeding range, there is little actual difference in the manner in which it nests in widely separated localities. A Catbird in Pennsylvania or Ohio, or Montana, or a Cedar Waxwing in New York, or Washington, remains true to its inherited tendencies and nests as one familiar with its breeding habits would expect. The Goldfinch, however, seemingly prefers to be original in this respect, and in the Piedmont region of Georgia, the farthest south that it breeds in the East, it has departed quite radically from the habits of its Yankee brothers and sisters farther north. Such at least has been my experience about Athens.

Here the original forest was probably entirely coniferous, with the loblolly pine (*Pinus taeda*) and the shortleaf pine (*Pinus echinata*) covering large areas with practically pure stands. Gradually, with the encroachment of civilization, this virgin forest was cut out and replaced with scattered stands of mixed hardwoods, the pine timber remaining being largely second growth, even-aged, and in comparatively short stretches. Through this section the Goldfinch breeds in small numbers, and while by no means common, it can still be found during the summer months quite regularly in certain spots.

I felt that I was reasonably familiar with its breeding habits and as the middle of July approached, during my first year in Georgia, I made an attempt to locate a nest, feeling confident that I would have little difficulty in doing so. I made the error, however, of confining myself to the scattered stretches of hardwoods, spots such as, in Pennsylvania, these birds would unquestionably have chosen, and it was only by accident that I finally found my first nest.

I was passing through a short stretch of open pine woods when a male Goldfinch flew by overhead, circled, calling, and was answered almost immediately by another bird in a tree near me. A short search revealed the nest in a large shortleaf pine, sixty feet from the ground and six feet out at the outer end of one of the upper limbs. This was the 30th of July, 1921, and the nest on that date held five fresh eggs. It was typical of this species, being compactly built of weed stems, grasses, shreds of bark and numerous small dried flowers, well lined with thistledown, and covered somewhat on the outside with spiders' webs.

It was not until the following year that I was able to devote more time to these birds, but with this one experience as a clue to where and when to look, I had little trouble in verifying the data already at hand. On the 31st of July, 1922, I found a nest that held four well-incubated eggs that was thirty feet from the ground at the extreme outer end of a limb of a shortleaf pine at the edge of a short stretch of open pine woods. Like the last, it was compactly built of weed stems, grasses, shreds of bark, and plant down, deeply cupped and well lined with thistle down. Almost two months later, in another stretch of open pine woods, I found a nest that on the 23rd of September held either eggs or young, and was forty-five feet from the ground at the outer end of an upper limb of a shortleaf pine. Attracted by the very evident distress of both the birds, I looked about for the cause and was just in time to see a Blue Jay fly from the nest to an adjoining tree and calmly wipe its bill. The nest proved to be empty, but it unquestionably had held either eggs or young earlier in the day and was probably the second brood of this pair of birds.

Eastern Red Crossbill
Loxia curvirostra minor   (Brehm)

GENERAL DISTRIBUTION: Breeds from northern Minnesota, central Ontario, Quebec and Nova Scotia south to Michigan and locally in the Alleghenies to western North Carolina (also casually in Massachusetts,

Maryland, and Virginia). Winters irregularly south to northern Texas, Louisiana, and Florida.

STATUS IN GEORGIA: A scarce and irregular winter visitant over the entire state, and apparently of accidental occurrence during the summer in the mountains.

On the basis of specimens, identified by Ludlow Griscom, the Eastern Red Crossbill has been recorded in Georgia but three times. There are three specimens in the U. S. National Museum taken at Midway, Liberty County, by Joseph LeConte in 1850 [Griscom, 1937]; a specimen taken at St. Marys by Arnow in November, 1906; and one in the Emory University Museum collected by Luther R. Smith in Fulton County, December 31, 1908 [Greene, 1933].

Although sight records may refer to any of the other races, for convenience the following additional instances of the occurrence of the Red Crossbill in Georgia are listed here under the race that possibly can be expected to occur most frequently in the state. In 1887 and again in 1899, small flocks were seen in Richmond County [Murphey, 1937]; in 1914, three birds were reported by Hoxie as being seen on February 28 at Savannah; in 1917, Mrs. S. E. Woodbury reported three birds seen at Vinings on February 20; in 1936, a flock of seven birds, five males and two females, was seen on Levelland Mountain, Lumpkin County (near Neel's Gap), January 9 [Dorsey, 1936]; in 1953, a flock of about twenty-five birds was reported by Dr. Fred Crenshaw as being seen almost daily at his feeding station at the Battey State Hospital, Rome, from January 25 through February 14 [Dorsey, letter].

The only record for the summer months is that of a flock of approximately thirty birds observed near the top of Brasstown Bald, Towns County, on June 25, 1923 [Burleigh, 1927].

HABITS AND RECOGNITION: In many respects the Red Crossbill is a unique bird. Its food is largely seeds extracted from the cones of such coniferous trees as the pines, spruces, and firs; and where such a food supply is available in quantity, there the crossbill is apt to be found. At intervals there will be years when in certain localities these conifers fail to produce a seed crop, and then the crossbill will disappear completely and not reappear, perhaps, for several years. On such occasions it may, in its search for the food it prefers, cross half the continent and appear unexpectedly in areas where it has rarely, or never, before been recorded. Taking advantage of an abundant food supply, it will even nest far south of its normal breeding range, and rear its young irrespective of season or weather conditions. It is probable that the average pair nests in the spring or early summer, but as there are breeding records for midwinter as well as early fall, it would

632

seem that, unlike other birds, this erratic species frequently nests when it pleases and with more or less disregard of the calendar.

Normally unsuspicious and easily approached, the individuals comprising a flock feeding overhead can usually be watched from the ground without distracting their attention, except momentarily, from the task of extracting the seeds from the cones. Their crossed bills are admirably suited to this purpose, even the hardest and toughest pine cones being opened without much difficulty. Clinging parrot-like and at every conceivable angle to the cones, they pry the scales open and, if they are dry and brittle, often break them off as the seeds are exposed and eaten. The plumage of the males is dull red, that of the females dull olive-gray, while the young of the year are heavily streaked and quite unlike their parents. However, their actions and especially the crossed bill will readily identify this species wherever seen, regardless of plumage.

That food other than the seeds of conifers is eaten on occasion was demonstrated by the flock seen near the top of Brasstown Bald on June 25, 1923. At the spot where these birds were found, the trees were entirely deciduous hardwoods, chestnut, and chestnut oak predominating, and in the outer branches of these trees the crossbills were assiduously searching the twigs and foliage for insects. To me they seemed strangely out of place, for until that day I had invariably found this species feeding in conifers. Characteristically restless, they continually moved from one tree to another, and it was not long before they flew to an adjoining ridge and were not seen again.

Newfoundland Red Crossbill
Loxia curvirostra pusilla Gloger

GENERAL DISTRIBUTION: Breeds in Newfoundland. Winters south to Georgia.

STATUS IN GEORGIA: Recorded on only two occasions in the state, but possibly of more frequent occurrence than these records indicate.

Ludlow Griscom [1937] states that "according to Mr. van Rossem the type of *pusilla* Gloger is supposed to have come from Georgia." Otherwise it was only in 1951 that the Newfoundland Red Crossbill was recorded in the state, being observed at Stone Mountain, DeKalb County, from February 11 through May 30 [Sciple, 1952].

HABITS AND RECOGNITION: In view of the infrequent occurrence of the crossbill in Georgia it is of interest to quote in some detail the circumstances connected with the appearance of the Newfoundland race on Stone Mountain in 1951. Sciple [1952] states:

633

In February, 1951, a flock of Red Crossbills (*Loxia curvirostra*) was located at Stone Mountain, DeKalb County, Georgia, by Mr. and Mrs. Norman Descoteaux. The birds were first seen by them on February 11. A flock, or flocks, remained in the vicinity of this 700 foot high granite monadnock at least through May 30, 1951, and the birds were observed by the Descoteaux and members of the Atlanta Bird Club on numerous occasions.

On February 24, 1951, the author, accompanied by Richard A. Parks, arrived slightly before sunrise in the immediate area where the birds previously had been reported. After several hours of search, a flock of seven or eight Crossbills was located.

On March 3, a flock of 15 birds was observed in four locations over a period of several hours. A striking behavior in the flock was seen during this time. All the birds in the flock perched in the lower branches of small leafless persimmon trees less than 25 feet in height. Individuals repeatedly fluttered down to the ground, and were seen to be scratching about in the dry vegetation littering the surface. These individuals would then fly back up to their original perches, or to others in immediate proximity. Often they carried with them in their mandibles small bits of unidentified material. While holding this material in their bills, they several times sat quietly in the trees for periods of many seconds to one or two minutes. It was at first thought that this behavior represented a feeding or grit-collecting activity engaged in by several members of the flock, while other members remained quiescent. A quite different interpretation was apparent as their activity increased in tempo. It was seen that the birds dropping to the ground were usually males, while the females stayed in the trees. Finally a male picked from the ground a long frayed strand of vegetation and flew with it to a perch near a female. The male went through a series of rapid, jerky head and body movements before the female. He "presented" the trailing straw to the female. There was little apparent response on the part of the female; she did not accept the straw, and after the lapse of a few seconds the male flew away. The entire performance was accomplished in silence.

On April 8, Mr. and Mrs. Descoteaux and Hugh Moore, Jr., observed a pair of Crossbills building a nest in a pine tree about halfway up the mountain. On May 1, a male was seen in the vicinity of the nesting tree by Descoteaux, Moore, and Dr. E. P. Odum. However, the nest appeared to be unfinished and was never used.

Sciple and Parks took six specimens on Stone Mountain, three on February 24, two on March 10, and one on March 17, and these have been identified by Allen J. Duvall as the Newfoundland Crossbill, *Loxia curvi-rostra pusilla.*

Green-tailed Towhee
Chlorura chlorura   (Audubon)

GENERAL DISTRIBUTION: Breeds from central Oregon and south central Montana to southern California, southeastern New Mexico, and central western Texas. Winters from southern California and western Texas to Cape San Lucas and Guanajuato, Mexico.

STATUS IN GEORGIA: Of accidental occurrence.

The only record of this species in Georgia is that of a specimen taken at Rome, Floyd County, on April 27, 1953, by Gordon L. Hight, Jr., and George A. Dorsey [Dorsey, 1953]. The skin was sent to the U. S. National Museum, and the identification confirmed by John W. Aldrich, of the Fish and Wildlife Service.

HABITS AND RECOGNITION: Anyone seeing a Green-tailed Towhee for the first time will wonder why it was ever called a towhee, for it bears no resemblance to its namesake of the eastern United States. Both sexes are alike in appearance and so distinctive that, seen at reasonably close range, they can be confused with no other species. A glimpse of the underparts will reveal a gray breast and a conspicuous white throat patch, while the upperparts include a reddish-brown crown, olive-gray back, and bright green wings and tail. An inhabitant of thickets and underbrush, this towhee is normally shy and difficult to become acquainted with, its characteristic mewing notes usually being the first indication of its presence. Occurring as it does in the Far West, it is, of course, largely an accident when it is found in the East, and it will be interesting to see if in future years it will again be recorded in Georgia.

Red-eyed Rufous-sided Towhee
Pipilo erythrophthalmus erythrophthalmus   (Linnaeus)

GENERAL DISTRIBUTION: Breeds from southeastern Saskatchewan, southern Manitoba, southern Ontario, and southern Maine south to central Kansas and northern Georgia. Winters from southeastern Nebraska, Wisconsin, and the Ohio and Potomac valleys (casually New England) to central Texas, the Gulf Coast, and central Florida.

STATUS IN GEORGIA: A fairly common summer resident in the northeast-

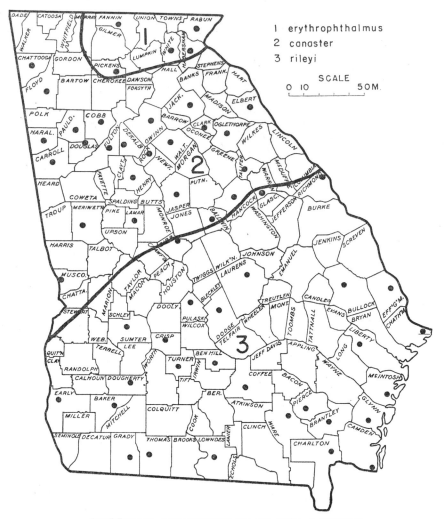

1 erythrophthalmus
2 canaster
3 rileyi

BREEDING DISTRIBUTION OF THE TOWHEE

ern corner of the state and a common winter resident south of its breeding range.

Specimens representing the breeding population and found to be typical of *erythrophthalmus* have been taken in 1945 in Pickens County (a male at Jasper on May 28); and in 1946 in Habersham County (a male and a female at Clarksville on May 28); in White County (a male and a female on Yonah Mountain on June 28); and in Rabun County (a male at Tiger on June 25 and a male on Chestnut Mountain on June 26). Another male of this northern race, taken near Blue Ridge, in Fannin County, on April 17, 1945, was singing, and showing a decided interest in a female towhee, so it, too, very probably represented the breeding population of this region of the state [Burleigh, 1947].

At Athens, this race of the towhee was found to be a common winter resident, extreme dates of occurrence, based on specimens taken, being October 27 (1929) and April 10 (1935). Stoddard [MS] states that in Grady County it is an abundant winter resident, appearing in October and disappearing in April. Grimm [1946] considers it a common winter resident at Hinesville (Liberty County), occurring between the dates of October 10 (1943) and April 2 (1944). Specimens typical of this race were taken on Blackbeard Island, January 25, 1931 (Burleigh), and in the Okefenokee Swamp, December 22, 1916, April 22, 1933, and November 7, 1935 (Harper), and December 30, 1945 (Burleigh).

There is but a single definite breeding record for the state, a nest found at Margret, Fannin County, on June 24, 1921, that held three incubated eggs (Burleigh).

HABITS AND RECOGNITION: During its winter sojourn in Georgia, the Redeyed Eastern Towhee frequents thickets and underbrush in and at the edges of wooded areas, and is a bird easy to see and become acquainted with. Invade its haunts, and one will be greeted with a vigorous "tow-hee," and first one and then another of the birds feeding on the ground in the vicinity will fly up into the nearest bush and nervously inspect the intruder. It is an active, energetic bird, and as it scratches for food in the dead leaves, it scatters them in all directions in a manner anything but furtive. While not shy, it apparently can see no good reason to seek the proximity of man, and only rarely will it be found in shrubbery about houses. Throughout the winter, it can usually be found in small flocks that include both sexes, and with its wide distribution and inquisitive disposition it is a familiar and far from inconspicuous part of the bird life at that season.

The single nest found in Fannin County on June 24, 1921, was three feet from the ground in a thick laurel bush in scrubby underbrush on a wooded ridge, and was substantially built of dead leaves, weed stems, and grasses, lined with fine weed stems.

Alabama Rufous-sided Towhee
Pipilo erythrophthalmus canaster Howell

GENERAL DISTRIBUTION: Breeds and is largely resident from Tennessee and southwestern North Carolina south to the Gulf Coast.

STATUS IN GEORGIA: A common summer resident south of the mountains and north of the coastal plain. A scarce winter resident within its breeding range, but fairly common during the winter months in the southern part of the state.

Breeding specimens of this race have been examined from many localities throughout the northern part of the state, including Summerville, Rome, Atlanta, Athens, McDonough, Crawfordville, Monticello, Milledgeville, Barnesville, Greenville, and Columbus.

Canaster has always been considered resident throughout its range in Georgia, but on the basis of specimens taken during the winter months in the northern part of the state, this is apparently not the case. From the latter part of October, 1946, until the following April, towhees were closely scrutinized, and an occasional specimen taken, but only *erythrophthalmus* was recorded from late October until after the middle of February. The first specimen of *canaster,* a male, was taken at Decatur on February 16, and it was the first of March before the breeding population was apparently present in any numbers. It is probable that an occasional individual of *canaster* winters in the northern part of the state, but it would appear now that the breeding birds, to a very large extent, winter farther south, and are replaced at this season of the year by the northern race. [Burleigh, 1948.]

In further confirmation of this assumption, wintering individuals of *canaster* have been examined from Valdosta and from Savannah, where the breeding race is *rileyi.*

Although the Alabama Eastern Towhee unquestionably nests wherever seen during the summer months, definite breeding records are limited to the following localities: Rome, fledglings, May 29, 1936; three eggs, April 15, 1942; four young, just hatched, April 25, 1942 [Jones, 1947]; three eggs, March 25, 1953 [Dorsey, letter]; Atlanta, nesting extremes, three eggs, April 5 (1932) (Greene); three young, September 5 (1939) (Griffin) [Griffin, 1940]; Athens, nesting extremes, two young just out of the nest, April 25 (1928); three slightly incubated eggs July 18 (1925) [Burleigh, 1938].

HABITS AND RECOGNITION: The Alabama Eastern Towhee is larger than its more northern relative, its flanks are paler, and the white markings on the wings are less extensive, but characters such as these are not detectable in the field. In general appearance and actions it is like the Red-eyed Eastern Towhee.

At Athens, the few nests I succeeded in finding were with one exception in bushes or small saplings, varying in height from a foot and a half to three feet from the ground, and were well hidden in thickets or stretches of underbrush. The only exception was a nest found on May 15, 1925, that was sunken flush with the ground at the base of, and well concealed by, a small persimmon sprout growing at the edge of a stretch of open pine woods. The female was incubating three eggs and did not flush until almost stepped on, when she fluttered along the ground for fully thirty feet, feigning a broken wing. At least two broods are reared each year, as fresh eggs can be found as early as the first week in April and as late as the middle of July.

Riley's Rufous-sided Towhee
Pipilo erythrophthalmus rileyi Koelz

GENERAL DISTRIBUTION: Resident on the Atlantic Coast from North Carolina south to northern Florida, west through the southern part of Georgia to extreme southeastern Alabama.

STATUS IN GEORGIA: Resident and common over the larger part of the coastal plain.

Although doubt has been expressed concerning the validity of *rileyi*, it would appear now on the basis of a small series of both breeding and winter specimens from southeastern Georgia that it is a race worthy of recognition. In measurements it is definitely larger than typical *alleni*, approaching *canaster* in this respect, and the females are easily recognized by their lighter brown coloration both above and on the throat. In the amount of white on the tail and in the wing, *rileyi* is intermediate in its characters, having less than *canaster* and more than *alleni*, but its darker red flanks readily separate it from typical *canaster*. Specimens representing this recently described race were taken in 1945 in the Okefenokee Swamp (males, December 29 and 30, and a female, December 30) and in 1946 in Chatham County (two males on Tybee Island on January 27 and May 1), in Liberty County (males at Hinesville on January 23, April 17 and April 26, and at Allenhurst on April 10, and a female at Hinesville on January 26), in Pierce County (a male at Blackshear on May 3), in Long County (a male at Ludowici on April 4), in Bacon County (a female at Alma on May 4), in Tattnal County (a male at Glennville on April 5), in Evans County (a male at Claxton on April 28), in Telfair County (a male at McRae on April 27), and in Treutlen County (a male at Soperton on April 14) [Burleigh, 1947].

Since the above report was published, a detailed taxonomic study of this species by Dickinson [1952] has shown that the breeding range of *rileyi* is far more extensive than was originally supposed, and includes the larger part of the state south of the fall line.

Breeding records are not numerous, and are limited to the following localities:

639

Augusta: Nest with two young about five days old, July 20, 1947 (Denton).

Fitzgerald: One fresh egg, July 11, 1941 (Hopkins).

Baker County: Nest with one egg, May 24, 1950 (Hopkins).

Grady County: Three eggs, May 5, 1940; three eggs, July 4, 1940; three eggs, April 30, 1946 (Stoddard).

Chatham County: Nesting extremes, three fresh eggs, May 9 (1908), and three slightly incubated eggs, July 15 (1908) (Rossignol).

HABITS AND RECOGNITION: Unlike most subspecies, the white-eyed race, *rileyi,* differs noticeably in its appearance and actions from the other races occurring in the state. Its haunts are to a large extent the palmetto thickets in the open pine woods, where, somewhat shy and prone to keep out of sight, it is more often heard than seen. Its ordinary call note can be recognized at once as that of a towhee, but is higher pitched and has a questioning up-slurring to it that is quite distinctive. When the bird is seen at reasonably close range, the creamy white iris characteristic of this race is at once apparent.

A nest that I found at Savannah on June 16, 1923, held four slightly incubated eggs and was three feet from the ground in a small, bushy live oak sapling in a field overgrown with scrubby underbrush. It was bulky but compact, and was constructed of dry fern leaves, weed stems, coarse grasses, and dead leaves, deeply cupped and well lined with fine grasses.

Norris [1942] made a careful study of a breeding pair of these towhees at Tifton, and as very little information is available concerning the nesting habits of this species in Georgia, his comments are quoted:

> The nest site was selected close to our house, some three feet up in the yellow jasmine (cultivated shrub). All the building was done by the female towhee. On each trip to the nest she would carefully round out the interior, arranging the materials. In both approach and departure she followed a definite pattern. Each was from the same side of the shrub, but one differed from the other in that separate configurations of the branches were invariably followed. She remained generally quiet during the work time, in contrast to the male, who sang frequently from a near-by water oak, the shrubbery, and the house top. His three main song variations were thus syllabified: *chuk-see-he-he-he-he-he, we-e-e-e-e-e,* and *chu-ke-e-e-e-e-e.* Their common call was the quaint *ch, reek* which seemed to be used also as a note of alarm. The only other call was a sibilant *tsee-a-wee-e* given once by the female on the nest. The male bird was not seen to accompany her on trips to and from the nest, showing little interest in the actual building operations.
>
> Construction of the nest was observed on May 31 and June 1 in the early morning only, although observation was not continuous

through the day. No building took place on June 2, when the nest apparently was complete.

The completed nest was a substantial cup of rather heavy construction, built with small pliable twigs, leaves, and whitish weed tops, being lined with fine grasses. A scrap of pasteboard was used in the bottom portion. The female towhee disregarded an offering of possible nest substances—string, cloth, and paper strips, placed on the lawn.

The first egg was laid sometime between mid-afternoon and 7:30 P.M. on June 3. Next day the second egg was found about 9 A.M., and the third on the following day at 8:15 A.M.

Only the female towhee was observed incubating; the male in this period was never seen closer than fifteen feet to the nest. Incubation began gradually. There were half-hearted sittings or at least visits on the day of the first egg, and time on the nest increased with each egg. Only one egg, the third laid, hatched on June 17 about noon, making the incubation period (time from laying of last egg to hatching of that egg) a little more than twelve days. The two unhatched eggs were addled.

Upon egg-hatching, the behavior of the male towhee abruptly changed, and he became very attentive, feeding his mate both on and off the nest and feeding the young bird. The male's manner of nest approach, unlike his mate's, was from the ground under the nest upward.

Lark Bunting
Calamospiza melanocorys   Stejneger

GENERAL DISTRIBUTION: Breeds from southern Alberta, southern Saskatchewan, and southwestern Manitoba south to southeastern New Mexico and northwestern Texas, and east to eastern Nebraska and west central Minnesota. Winters from southern Texas and southern Arizona to southern Mexico.

STATUS IN GEORGIA: Of accidental occurrence.

The single record for Georgia is that of an adult male collected by Herbert L. Stoddard at the north end of Tybee Island on June 27, 1952.

HABITS AND RECOGNITION: The Lark Bunting is one of the characteristic birds of the western plains, and its presence in Georgia at any time is, of course, accidental. Its appearance on Tybee Island in late June was decidedly unexpected, and it will probably be many years, if ever, before this species is again reported in the state.

RILEY'S RUFOUS-SIDED TOWHEES
Pipilo erythrophthalmus rileyi

This was the first of my paintings. I made it in an opening in the brush not
far from a woods road. While I was at work one of my free wild models
gave voice to its annoyance, coming closer and closer, until my companion
Rip, a fine setter, unable to endure the scolding longer, gave me a look
of profound understanding, rose, and chased the towhee out of sight
and hearing. Rip died a week or so later. In his own loyal way he helped
me to paint the picture, hence his name as part of the signature.
The flowers are those of the yellow jessamine; the male bird
of the pair is above.

Ipswich Sparrow
Passerculus princeps   Maynard

GENERAL DISTRIBUTION: Breeds on Sable Island, Nova Scotia. Winters from Sable Island, south on the Atlantic Coast to Georgia.

STATUS IN GEORGIA: A scarce winter resident on the coast.

The Ipswich Sparrow was first recorded in Georgia in 1890 by W. W. Worthington, who took two specimens on Jacks Bank, at the mouth of the Altamaha River (Glynn County) on January 8 and 15; and saw a third bird at this same spot on January 27 [Worthington, 1890]. It was next reported by A. H. Helme, who collected a specimen on Cumberland Island (Camden County) on April 14, 1903 [Helme, 1904]. Tomkins [1935] collected a specimen on Oysterbed Island (Chatham County) on January 23, 1931, and observed single birds there on December 30, 1934, and January 13, 1935. The most recent record is of a specimen collected by Tomkins, again on Oysterbed Island, on February 22, 1953 [Tomkins, letter].

HABITS AND RECOGNITION: In view of its extremely limited breeding range—a single small island off the coast of Nova Scotia—and the fact that it winters along the entire stretch of coast from Nova Scotia to Georgia, it is doubtful that the Ipswich Sparrow will ever be of more than casual occurrence in the state. Few birds are more restricted in their distribution during the winter months. Sand dunes within sound of the surf seem essential for this inconspicuous little sparrow, and there in the patches of tall beachgrass it spends its days. If approached, it prefers to seek safety by running rapidly through the sparse vegetation, and only when alarmed will it fly. Then it is apt to go some distance, and when it drops to the ground again, it is extremely difficult to find a second time. In appearance it resembles a Savannah Sparrow, but it is larger and noticeably paler than even the palest race of that species.

Eastern Savannah Sparrow
Passerculus sandwichensis savanna   (Wilson)

GENERAL DISTRIBUTION: Breeds, so far as is now known, in Nova Scotia and the Magdalen Islands. Winters southward in the Atlantic Coast states.

STATUS IN GEORGIA: A common winter resident throughout the state.

The Savannah Sparrow usually appears in Georgia in the fall in the latter part of September or early October, and in the spring frequently lingers until the latter part of May. Small flocks are most frequently observed, however, in the open fields and pastures from the latter part of October until the middle of April.

Records of occurrence, based largely on sight identification, may refer to any of the races found in the state during the winter months, but as there is no way of knowing to which they actually refer, they are, for convenience, here placed under the Eastern Savannah Sparrow.

Extreme dates of occurrence are as follows:

Augusta: October 1 (1944) and May 10 (1953).

Athens: September 19 (1925) and May 19 (1927).

Atlanta: October 1 (1938) and May 19 (1951).

Macon: October 8 (1954) and May 15 (1931).

Fitzgerald: October 11 (1941) and May 10 (1941).

Grady County: September 30 (1949) and May 7 (1949).

Savannah: October 22 (1909) and May 28 (1910).

Numerous specimens of the subspecies, *savanna,* have been taken in Georgia between the dates of September 24 (1930) (Athens) and May 10 (1933) (Savannah); and represent the following localities: Richmond County (Augusta), Oconee County (Bogart and Watkinsville), Franklin County (Lavonia), Walton County (Loganville), DeKalb County (Decatur), Fulton County (Atlanta), Rockdale County (Magnet), Spalding County (Sunny Side and Griffin), Sumter County (Americus), and Grady County (Beachton).

HABITS AND RECOGNITION: Although common and widely distributed throughout the state during the winter, the Savannah Sparrow is not a well-known bird. This is due not only to its small size and modest coloration, but also to the nature of its haunts, for it occurs in open fields and pastures, preferably where the grass is long, and usually it must be searched for to be seen. Should one walk through a field frequented by these inconspicuous little birds, the first intimation of their presence will be the sight of one flushing almost under foot, flying a short distance, and dropping out of sight again in the thick grass. Pursue it with the object of getting a satisfactory view of it, and the usual reward will be another brief glimpse of a small, brown sparrow flushing unexpectedly from a spot some distance away from where it was last seen. Fortunately, an occasional bird will be found perching on a fence post or in the top of a bush or sapling, when it is possible to identify it satisfactorily. In appearance, the Savannah Sparrow is a small, grayish-brown sparrow with a short, slightly notched tail, streaked underparts, and a line through the eye that is more or less tinged with yellow, characters at once apparent if it is seen under favorable conditions. The Eastern Savannah Sparrow as distinct from other subspecies is relatively pale and brownish in coloration. It has never been known to sing during its winter sojourn in Georgia, the only note heard being a weak "chip" that is uttered when the bird is alarmed.

The Savannah Sparrow is so called because it was originally described by Alexander Wilson in 1811 from a specimen collected at Savannah, Georgia; it is, thus, an object of special interest to those interested in the bird life of the state.

Labrador Savannah Sparrow
Passerculus sandwichensis labradorius   Howe

GENERAL DISTRIBUTION: Breeds in Labrador and Newfoundland. Winters south to the Gulf Coast and southern Georgia.

STATUS IN GEORGIA: A regular and not uncommon winter resident throughout the state.

That this far northern race has a wide distribution in Georgia is shown by the following records of specimens taken:

Athens: Nine specimens collected between the dates of November 24 (1932) and May 20 (1928) (Burleigh).

Lavonia (Franklin County): One female, March 6, 1946 (Burleigh).

Constitution (DeKalb County): Females, October 25, 1947, and November 6, 1948 (Griffin).

Atlanta: One male, March 29, 1947 (Burleigh).

Americus: A female, March 12, 1942 (Denton).

Fitzgerald: One specimen, May 10, 1941 (Norris).

Grady County: Females, April 11 and May 2, 1948 (Stoddard).

Savannah: A male, February 26, 1933 (Burleigh), and females, May 14, 1933, October 7, 1934, and May 1, 1952 (Tomkins).

Hinesville (Liberty County): A female, May 2, 1946 (Burleigh).

HABITS AND RECOGNITION: The characters separating this race of the Savannah Sparrow are its dark, almost chocolate-brown, coloration above and heavier brown streaking below. Specimens are necessary for positive identification.

Churchill Savannah Sparrow
Passerculus sandwichensis oblitus   Peters and Griscom

GENERAL DISTRIBUTION: Breeds on the western side of Hudson Bay south to northern Minnesota, western Ontario, and western Quebec. Winters south to the Gulf Coast and southern Georgia.

STATUS IN GEORGIA: Of casual occurrence during the winter.

Specimens of this race have been taken in Georgia as follows:

Elba Island (Chatham County): February 17, 1936 (Tomkins).

Fitzgerald: January 19, 1940 and May 10, 1941 (Norris).

Donalsonville (Seminole County): December 30, 1941 (Norris).

Athens: January 13, 1946.

Bogart (Oconee County): February 7, 1946.

Decatur: December 3, 1946.

Atlanta: February 18, 1947 (Burleigh).

Grady County: April 10, 1949, and March 25, 1951 (Stoddard).

Savannah: March 29, 1953 (Tomkins).

HABITS AND RECOGNITION: The Churchill Savannah Sparrow is the darkest of the Savannah Sparrows occurring in the state and gives the impression of being a blackish bird. It is darker gray above and more heavily streaked with black below than are the other races. It is possibly commoner and more widely distributed in Georgia during the winter than the few records indicate, but further collecting will be necessary to determine this point, for only on the basis of actual specimens can it be satisfactorily identified.

Nevada Savannah Sparrow
Passerculus sandwichensis nevadensis   Grinnell

GENERAL DISTRIBUTION: Breeds from southern British Columbia, eastern Oregon, and northeastern California east to northern Colorado, Montana, and North Dakota and south to southern Nevada and northern New Mexico. Winters south to northern Mexico.

STATUS IN GEORGIA: As yet recorded but twice in the state, males having been taken by Stoddard in Grady County on December 5, 1948, and January 28, 1951.

HABITS AND RECOGNITION: The Nevada Savannah Sparrow is characterized by being paler above and less heavily streaked below than any of the race of this species occurring in the state, but as with most subspecies, this difference is not noticeable in the field.

Southeastern Savannah Sparrow
Passerculus sandwichensis mediogriseus   Aldrich

GENERAL DISTRIBUTION: Breeds from the Gaspé Peninsula south (excepting Nova Scotia) to New England and New Jersey, and west to Minnesota and Iowa.

STATUS IN GEORGIA: A common winter resident throughout the state.

On the basis of actual specimens, this race is the most common of the five subspecies of the Savannah Sparrow known to occur in Georgia during

646

Family Fringillidae: GROSBEAKS, FINCHES, SPARROWS, & BUNTINGS

the winter. It has been taken on numerous occasions in various parts of the state, as follows:

Athens: Sixteen specimens between the dates of November 5 (1945) and April 4 (1935).

Washington (Wilkes County): December 21, 1945.

Decatur: Six specimens between the dates of January 10 and February 15, 1946.

Constitution (DeKalb County): December 26, 1947.

Atlanta: November 9, 1946, and January 15, 1949.

Sharpsburg (Coweta County): March 10, 1947.

Milledgeville: March 19, 1947.

Tifton: February 15, 1943.

Blakely: December 30, 1933.

Grady County: April 4 and 11 and November 26, 1948, and March 25, 1951.

Savannah: February 26, 1933.

HABITS AND RECOGNITION: The Southeastern Savannah Sparrow is characterized by being darker and less rufescent than typical *savanna*. In general appearance and actions it has nothing to distinguish it in the field.

Eastern Grasshopper Sparrow
Ammodramus savannarum pratensis (Vieillot)

GENERAL DISTRIBUTION: Breeds from southern Wisconsin, southern Ontario, and southern New Hampshire south to central Alabama, central Georgia, and northern South Carolina. Winters from southern Illinois and North Carolina south to the Bahamas, Cuba, Yucatán, and Guatemala.

STATUS IN GEORGIA: A fairly common but local summer resident in the northern half of the state and an uncommon winter resident north at least to Atlanta and Athens.

Because it can be so easily overlooked and must be searched for to be seen, the exact status of the Eastern Grasshopper Sparrow in Georgia is difficult to assess with any degree of accuracy. Singing males in early April possibly indicate the arrival of this species in the spring, although individuals noted in March, silent then and inconspicuous, may be actual first arrivals. Again in fall, this obscure little sparrow is only infrequently seen after the last of September, and whether an occasional bird recorded in October and November is a belated transient or will remain throughout the winter is open to question. Since, with few exceptions, specimens of wintering individuals taken represent the western race, it is not improbable that *pratensis* winters very sparingly, and that Grasshopper Sparrows seen from late October until March are to a large extent *perpallidus*.

Extreme dates of occurrence (excluding obvious winter records) in the northern part of the state, where this species breeds are Augusta, March 27 (1945) and October 29 (1944); Athens, March 16 (1923) and November 9 (1946); Atlanta, March 19 (1916) and November 21 (1936);

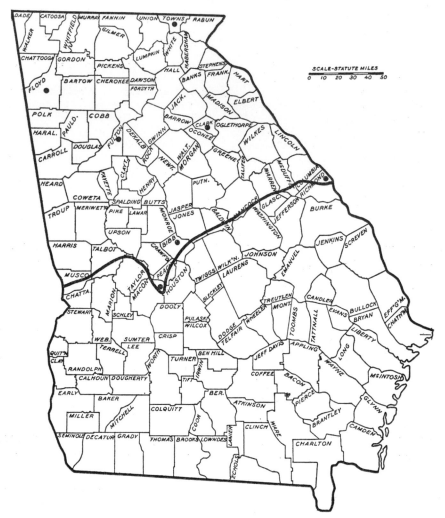

BREEDING DISTRIBUTION OF THE GRASSHOPPER SPARROW

and Macon, March 24 (1934) and November 11 (1931). It has also been reported from Milledgeville (February 11, 1941, March 14, 1942); Tifton (October 20, 1941); Irwin County (May 6, 1952); and Grady County (October 1 [1950] through April 13 [1937]). At Augusta, a single bird was seen on December 3, 1944. Since in many cases sight records are involved, this migration data may apply to either race. Specimens representing the form breeding in the state have been taken at Athens (May 28, 1928; June 25, 1929; November 9, 1946); Tucker, DeKalb County (November 21, 1936); Constitution, DeKalb County (October 12, 1947; May 23, 1948); Atlanta (February 8 and March 13, 1948); and Grady County (February 4, 1940 and October 1, 1950).

Although long known to nest locally in the northern part of the state

(Rome, Young Harris, Atlanta, Athens, Augusta, and Macon), only in recent years has the Grasshopper Sparrow been found as a breeding bird south of the fall line. Norris and Odum [letter] report five singing males seen July 26, 1947, in fields three miles east of Marshallville, Macon County, and a male in breeding condition was collected that day. This is the farthest south in Georgia that this species is now known to occur during the summer months.

Definite breeding records for the state are not numerous. At Athens, I succeeded in finding but two nests, one with two partially incubated eggs on June 13, 1925, the other with four fresh eggs on June 23, 1929. Johnston [letter] has in recent years made a detailed study of the breeding population of this species in Clarke County and reports a large increase in its numbers during the summer months, unquestionably prompted by the development of permanent pastures. In 1950, he succeeded in locating twenty-two breeding pairs and found three occupied nests, one with five eggs on May 16, another with four eggs on May 23, and the third with four eggs on May 31. At Atlanta, Greene [1933] reports a nest with four young on June 8, 1931. Denton [letter] reports a nest at Augusta that held four fresh eggs on May 28, 1945.

HABITS AND RECOGNITION: It is doubtful that any other bird is more easily overlooked than is the Grasshopper Sparrow. Shy and secretive at all times, with a weak, insect-like song which only under exceptional circumstances attracts any attention, its presence in the fields could easily go undetected year after year. Its chosen haunts are open fields where the grass is thick enough to afford concealment, and here its days are spent out of sight of the casual observer. If approached as it feeds on the ground, it will not fly until almost walked on, and then, with a noticeably weak and indirect flight, it will go a short distance, drop into the grass, and not be seen again. During the breeding season, the males utter their strange little song from the top of a tall weed or even a fence post, but as it is inaudible at any distance, one must usually have this inconspicuous little sparrow in mind to realize its presence. Only under such circumstances is it possible to get a good view of it and note its distinguishing characteristics—the short tail, black and russet back, and unstreaked buffy breast.

The nest is sunken flush with the ground, and being in thick grass and arched over, is exceedingly difficult to find. If the female is incubating, she will not flush until practically stepped on, and her actions then will usually reveal the site of the nest. It is a simple structure of fragments of weed stems and grasses, lined with fine grasses and horsehair. In Georgia, apparently two broods are reared each year, for at Athens I have on several occasions seen fully fledged young already out of the nest in late May and have found nests with fresh eggs in late June.

Western Grasshopper Sparrow
Ammodramus savannarum perpallidus (Coues)

GENERAL DISTRIBUTION: Breeds from southeastern British Columbia, northwestern Montana, North Dakota, and southern Minnesota south to southern California and southern Texas. Winters from central California and southern Texas south to Guatemala and Costa Rica, and casually to the Gulf Coast and Georgia.

STATUS IN GEORGIA: A scarce but apparently regular winter resident throughout the state.

Although apparently uncommon during the winter months in the northern part of the state, the Grasshopper Sparrow can be found there at this season of the year in many of the fields that are overgrown with broom sedge. Being shy and rather secretive, it must almost be stepped on before it makes its presence known and, consequently, is so easily overlooked that it may be commoner than is generally supposed. The birds that nest in Georgia appear to winter rarely, if at all, within their breeding range, for three specimens taken in 1946 that represented wintering individuals are all referable to *perpallidus*. All are males, and were collected in Troup County (LaGrange) on January 15, in Clarke County (Athens) on February 22, and in Oconee County (Watkinsville) on March 29. [Burleigh, 1947.]

Specimens of this western race have been taken also at Newton (Baker County) on January 27, 1936 [Burleigh, 1941]; in Grady County on March 2, 1947, October 31, 1948, and February 13, 1949 (Stoddard); and at Atlanta on April 17, 1948 (Griffin).

HABITS AND RECOGNITION: During the winter months the Grasshopper Sparrow appears partial to fields overgrown with broom sedge, and is only infrequently seen elsewhere. In general appearance and actions there is little to distinguish this western race; it differs only in being paler both above and below.

Leconte's Sparrow
Passerherbulus caudacutus (Latham)

GENERAL DISTRIBUTION: Breeds from Great Slave Lake, Mackenzie, southern Saskatchewan, and Manitoba south to North Dakota and southern Minnesota. Winters from southern Kansas, southern Missouri, and western Tennessee to Texas, Florida, and the coast of South Carolina.

STATUS IN GEORGIA: A scarce winter resident throughout the state.

The type locality for the Leconte's Sparrow is the "interior of Georgia" [Latham, *Index Orn.* 1, 1790, 459], but despite this fact, it is one of the least-known birds in the state. W. W. Worthington took specimens on Sapelo Island, February 22, 1888 [Worthington, 1888], and in McIntosh County, January 8, 1897; otherwise, the only specimens collected in Georgia are a male at Athens, April 6, 1937 [Burleigh, 1941]; a female at Tifton February 13, 1943 [Norris and Hopkins, 1953]; a female at Constitution, DeKalb County, November 23, 1946 [Major, 1947]; and a male at Atlanta, January 1, 1953 [Griffin, 1953].

Hebard [1941] reports single birds seen in Camden County, November 22, 1936, and in Charlton County, November 22, 1937.

HABITS AND RECOGNITION: Few small birds are as secretive and difficult to see as is the Leconte's Sparrow. In Georgia, it seems to prefer old fields overgrown with broom sedge in which to spend the winter months, and to find one in such a spot requires both perseverance and a certain amount of luck. Reluctant at all times to fly, it will, if alarmed, seek safety by running swiftly along the ground, and only when hard pressed will it flush and remain briefly in view. Its flight then appears slow and feeble, and it will go but a short distance before dropping into the concealing vegetation. Instant pursuit may or may not result in another glimpse of this elusive little sparrow, depending largely on whether one has guessed correctly in which direction it ran on reaching the ground again. Considering these circumstances, it is not surprising that it has been so seldom reported in the state, and it is not improbable that it is much more common during the winter than the few records would indicate. In appearance, Leconte's Sparrow is smaller than the Grasshopper Sparrow, and its buffy underparts are noticeably streaked on the sides. Like the Grasshopper Sparrow, its tail is rather short, but differs in being pointed at the end.

Eastern Henslow's Sparrow
Passerherbulus henslowii susurrans   Brewster

GENERAL DISTRIBUTION: Breeds from New York and southern New Hampshire south to northern Virginia. Winters in the southeastern states to Florida.

STATUS IN GEORGIA: A scarce and local transient and winter resident in the northern part of the state, and an uncommon winter resident south of the fall line.

The Henslow's Sparrow appears in Georgia in the fall late in October and is present in spring until after the middle of April. Being shy and secretive in its habits, it must be searched for to be seen, and doubtless is more abundant than the infrequent records would indicate. Two races occur in the state, but on the basis of specimens critically examined, *susur-*

rans is the one most commonly seen, and for this reason all available sight records are cited under this race. It is realized, of course, that some of these records refer to the race *henslowii:*

1848: Two specimens in the United States National Museum collected in Liberty County in December.

1888: Found by W. W. Worthington to be common on Sapelo Island in January and February, and specimens taken then.

1905: Five specimens collected by Helme at St. Marys on January 27.

1909: One specimen (now at Emory University) taken in Camden County, January 19.

1911: One specimen taken by Hoxie at Savannah, February 10.

1926: One bird seen in Grady County, March 5 (Stoddard).

1933: A specimen taken at Athens, April 19 [Burleigh, 1938].

1936: Specimens collected at Folkston, January 16 (Harper), in Camden County, February 24 (Hebard), and in Charlton County, December 4 (Hebard).

1939: Three seen at Fitzgerald, October 21 [Norris, 1939].

1940: Noted at Fitzgerald, November 22 [Norris, 1940]; one bird seen at Atlanta, December 22 [Griffin, 1941].

1943: One bird seen at Atlanta, March 13 [Johnston, 1943].

1945: A specimen taken at Augusta, April 8 [Denton, 1945a]; one bird noted at Athens, April 22 [Denton, 1945b].

1946: Three collected at Tifton, December 26 (Gaulding and Norris).

1948: A specimen taken at Constitution, DeKalb County, October 30 [Sciple, 1949].

1949: A specimen taken at Statesboro, Bullock County, April 3 (Sciple).

1952: One seen, April 9, at Tifton (Norris); one trapped, October 25, at Rome by Dr. Fred Crenshaw and banded by G. L. Hight, Jr. [Dorsey, letter].

HABITS AND RECOGNITION: The Henslow's Sparrow is another shy and secretive little sparrow that will run rather than fly when approached, and consequently is extremely difficult to see. Like the Leconte's Sparrow, it can be found during the winter in fields overgrown with broom sedge or in stretches of wiregrass in open pine woods, but it appears partial to damp situations, and often will be flushed in wet meadows where the grass is high enough to afford concealment. Only when alarmed can it be forced to fly, and when vigorously pursued, it will, oddly enough, sooner or later take refuge in the top of a bush or small sapling. Here it will remain motionless until almost touched, making it possible for one to study it at leisure. Seen thus, its distinguishing characteristics—short tail, streaked sides, and greenish nape—can be noted to advantage. On its northern breeding grounds, it has a curious little song that suggests the syllables "chis-lick," uttered as the male perches on the top of a tall weed or clump of grass, and audible only for a short distance.

Western Henslow's Sparrow
Passerherbulus henslowii henslowii (Audubon)

GENERAL DISTRIBUTION: Breeds from South Dakota and Ontario to northern Texas and Ohio. Winters from southeastern Texas to northwestern Florida.

Family Fringillidae: GROSBEAKS, FINCHES, SPARROWS, & BUNTINGS

STATUS IN GEORGIA: A scarce and local winter resident in the southern part of the state.

Specimens representing this western race have been taken by Francis Harper at Folkston (December 27, 1935); and by Robert Norris in western Camden County (November 27, 1940), Fitzgerald (November 2 and 8, 1940, and January 8, 1941), and Tifton (February 10, 1943 and March 6 and 27, 1952). It probably occurs regularly in southern Georgia during the winter.

HABITS AND RECOGNITION: In general appearance and actions there is nothing to distinguish the Western Henslow's Sparrow from its more eastern relative. It differs in having a stouter bill and in being more rufous above.

Intermediate Sharp-tailed Sparrow
Ammospiza caudacuta caudacuta   (Gmelin)

GENERAL DISTRIBUTION: Breeds on the Atlantic Coast from New Hampshire to Virginia. Winters on the coast from New Jersey (casually Massachusetts) to Florida.

STATUS IN GEORGIA: A common winter resident on the coast.

This nominate race of the Sharp-tailed Sparrow was reported by Worthington as common in winter at the mouth of the Altamaha River, and by Helme on Cumberland Island in March and early April, 1902. Specimens have been taken on Cumberland Island, January 1 and April 25, 1903; St. Marys, January 29 and February 1, 1903; Chatham County, May 2, 1907; and Savannah, October 22, 1915; November 18, 1928; October 20, 1931; December 15, 1933; and October 10, 1937. Since one bird, identified as of this race, struck the Tybee Light on September 29, 1930, apparently the southward movement in the fall is well under way by the latter part of that month.

HABITS AND RECOGNITION: Sharp-tailed Sparrows are familiar only to those who seek them in the extensive stretches of salt marsh along the coast. Here they are numerous and well distributed during the winter, but as they stay where the vegetation is relatively thick and high, it is easy to overlook them. Invade their haunts, however, and, their curiosity aroused, first one and then another will appear in the tops of the reeds to inspect the intruder. If approached, they at once drop out of sight, and will then be glimpsed only momentarily as long as one remains in their vicinity. Loath to fly, they will, if alarmed, seek safety by running along the ground, and only if hard pressed will they leave the concealment of the salt-marsh

653

vegetation in which they have been feeding. Seen at reasonably close range, Sharp-tailed Sparrows can be recognized by their small size, approximately that of the Savannah Sparrow, and by their narrow, pointed tails which give them the name by which they are commonly called.

Acadian Sharp-tailed Sparrow
Ammospiza caudacuta subvirgata (Dwight)

GENERAL DISTRIBUTION: Breeds on the Atlantic Coast from southeastern Quebec, Prince Edward Island, and Cape Breton Island south to Penobscot Bay, Maine. Winters on the coasts of South Carolina, Georgia, and northern Florida.

STATUS IN GEORGIA: A locally common winter resident on the coast.

The first specimen of this race taken in the state was a female collected in Camden County on April 4, 1877 [Peters, 1942]. Some years later, in March, 1902, A. H. Helme considered it a common winter resident on Cumberland Island and took specimens there [Cooke, 1908]. Other specimens have since been collected on Cumberland Island, January 16, 1903; at St. Marys, January 29, 1903; Liberty County, February 18, 1907; St. Simons Island, January 1, 1941 [Norris, 1941]; and at Savannah (Tomkins).

HABITS AND RECOGNITION: It is only in the salt-water marshes on the coast that the Acadian Sharp-tailed Sparrow can be found during the winter in Georgia. Here its days are spent in the reeds and thicker stretches of marshgrass, where, quiet and inconspicuous, it must be searched for to be seen. It is the palest of the five races of the Sharp-tailed Sparrow now known from the state, but this difference is not apparent in the field, and specimens are necessary to confirm identification.

Nelson's Sharp-tailed Sparrow
Ammospiza caudacuta nelsoni (Allen)

GENERAL DISTRIBUTION: Breeds from Great Slave Lake and west central Alberta to southwestern Manitoba, Minnesota, and northeastern South Dakota. Winters on the Atlantic and Gulf coasts from North Carolina to Florida and Texas.

STATUS IN GEORGIA: A common winter resident on the coast and an uncommon transient in the interior of the state.

Cooke [1908] first recorded this race in the state, his record based on specimens taken on Cumberland Island by A. H. Helme in 1902. Additional specimens have since been examined from the coast region as follows:

St. Marys: October 22, 1902, and February 24, 1903.

McIntosh County: January 23 and 25 and February 13 and 14, 1890.

Sapelo Island: December 14, 1887.

Cumberland Island: January 11, 1905.

Wilmington Island (near Savannah): May 2, 1907.

Chatham County: October 20, 1907, and November 26, 1908.

Cockspur Island (near the mouth of the Savannah River): October 20, 1931.

In the interior of the state, there are four records of this sparrow. At Athens, two specimens were taken in the Sandy Creek bottoms, October 19, 1925, and May 27, 1928 (Burleigh). Greene [1933] reports a single bird seen at Atlanta on October 5, 1930, and Denton, one at Macon on May 14, 1932.

HABITS AND RECOGNITION: In contrast to the other members of this genus, Nelson's Sharp-tailed Sparrow occurs during the summer months in fresh-water marshes in the interior of the country; therefore, it is not surprising that it can be found in migration away from the coast. It is probably more common then than the few records indicate, as it frequents wet meadows, where it remains concealed in the thick grass and must be almost walked on before it will reveal its presence by flying. Thus, it is largely by accident that one will be seen, and many doubtless escape observation by running when approached—normal behavior on the part of all the Sharp-tailed Sparrows. At Athens, I noted this elusive little sparrow but twice in more than ten years, both times in the open Sandy Creek bottoms, and on each occasion the bird flushed unexpectedly from under my feet, flew for a short distance, and then abruptly dropped to the ground again. On the coast, it associates with others of its kind and, being very similar in appearance and actions, can be identified satisfactorily only on the basis of actual specimens.

Bishop's Sharp-tailed Sparrow
Ammospiza caudacuta diversa (Bishop)

GENERAL DISTRIBUTION: Breeds on the Atlantic Coast from southern Delaware to North Carolina. Winters south to southern Florida.

STATUS IN GEORGIA: Apparently a fairly common winter resident on the coast.

The first specimen of this race, for Georgia, identified by Peters [1942], was taken by W. W. Worthington in McIntosh County on February 22, 1890. Tomkins has nine specimens taken in recent years near Savannah and identified as *diversa* by A. H. Howell; and a single specimen was collected by Norris on St. Simons Island, in Glynn County, on November 8, 1941.

HABITS AND RECOGNITION: Except for its darker coloration, this race differs in no way, either in general appearance or actions, from the other Sharp-tailed Sparrows.

James Bay Sharp-tailed Sparrow
Ammospiza caudacuta altera Todd

GENERAL DISTRIBUTION: Breeds in central western Quebec. Winters on the Atlantic and Gulf coasts from South Carolina to northern Florida and Louisiana.

STATUS IN GEORGIA: Possibly of regular occurrence on the coast during the winter months, but now known from but three specimens. J. L. Peters [1942] lists a specimen taken on Sapelo Island, December 14, 1887, that he identified as *altera*. Two specimens have also been taken at Savannah, November 18, 1928, and October 20, 1931.

HABITS AND RECOGNITION: This race closely resembles Nelson's Sharp-tailed Sparrow, but differs in being paler above and in having the white streaks of the back narrower and less noticeable. In general appearance and actions it is similar in every respect to the other Sharp-tailed Sparrows.

Northern Seaside Sparrow
Ammospiza maritima maritima (Wilson)

GENERAL DISTRIBUTION: Breeds on the Atlantic Coast from southern Massachusetts to Virginia. Winters from Virginia to northern Florida (rarely in Massachusetts, Connecticut, and New Jersey).

STATUS IN GEORGIA: Apparently a fairly common winter resident on the coast.

A. H. Helme found Seaside Sparrows numerous on Cumberland Island in March and April, 1902, and again from January to April, 1903; specimens collected then by him were identified as of this northern race. Other specimens of *maritima* have been examined also from McIntosh County (January 5, 1897); Liberty County (February 18, 1907); Savannah (November 18, 1928, October 20, 1931, October 10, 1937); and Blackbeard Island (January 22, 1932).

HABITS AND RECOGNITION: The Seaside Sparrow is well named, for it is only within sight and sound of the ocean that this large, drab-colored sparrow can be found. During the winter, it frequents the extensive stretches of salt marsh fringing the coast, and here in the dense vegetation it leads a quiet and inconspicuous existence. If its haunts are invaded, its curiosity will usually cause it to appear in the tops of the reeds or thick marshgrass, but it will soon slip out of sight and not be seen again. At all times, it shows a noticeable reluctance to fly, and if forced to do so, will go but a short distance before again seeking the concealment afforded by the dense marsh vegetation.

Macgillivray's Seaside Sparrow
Ammospiza maritima macgillivraii   (Audubon)

GENERAL DISTRIBUTION: Resident on the Atlantic Coast from North Carolina to Georgia.

STATUS IN GEORGIA: Apparently resident on the coast, where, locally, it is a fairly common breeding bird.

Breeding specimens of this race have been examined from Cabbage Island, Chatham County, taken May 2, 1907 (Rossignol), and May 10, 1933 (Howell and Burleigh); and from Brunswick, Glynn County, taken May 30, 1929 (Burleigh). It is also known to nest on Raccoon Keys, Chatham County; and doubtless occurs elsewhere on the coast during the summer under suitable conditions.

Definite breeding records are, with two exceptions, limited to Cabbage Island, where Rossignol, from 1907 through 1933, succeeded in finding thirty-nine occupied nests. The earliest held four incubated eggs on April 27 (1914), the latest, three fresh eggs on June 6 (1915). The majority held eggs, fresh to well incubated, between the dates of May 10 and May 30. A single nest was found by Rossignol on Raccoon Keys, May 10, 1915, with four slightly incubated eggs. Norris [letter] reports a nest along the causeway between Brunswick and St. Simons Island, Glynn County, that held three eggs on June 19, 1939.

Specimens of wintering individuals were taken by Helme at St. Marys, December 12, 1902, February 24, 1903, and January 23, 1905; and by Hoxie near Savannah, October 22, 1915.

HABITS AND RECOGNITION: Ivan Tomkins [1941] has published a detailed account of the life history of the Seaside Sparrow that breeds in Georgia, and as his paper comprises to a large extent our present knowledge of this interesting bird, it is quoted in some detail:

657

Macgillivray's Seaside Sparrows

Ammospiza maritima macgillivraii

This species lived in the salt marshgrass. We found it common near the
city of Brunswick. If we wished to see it clearly, all we had to do was step
into mud or water up to our knees, hide in the grass, and make squeaking
sounds. All the birds, adult and young alike, were curious. Some flew
in for a close look. Others climbed up the grass blades.
Several of my living models straddled blades. In the painting the adult
is to the left, a bird in juvenal plumage to the right.

Of the many things necessary to provide suitable habitat, but two are plainly enough marked to be set down here. First, an adequate feeding ground is necessary, and second, suitable nesting cover must be had within easy flight of the feeding grounds.

Many, perhaps most, of the *Fringillidae* (the sparrows, towhees, *etc.*) find these two major requirements of habitat implanted on each other or mixed together in the same area. Under such conditions has developed the now well-known territory-holding behavior, of some generality among the group, though not as yet well charted for other than a few species.

The Seaside Sparrows of this locality often live where the two requirements are not always together or even meeting, but also where the feeding grounds and the nesting place are separated by a short distance. This way of living is of importance, and has introduced differences of behavior which will be set down later on.

The food requirements are far stronger than nesting needs in determining habitat limitations. For nests may be built in many situations, may be composed of such material as is at hand, and vary from eight inches above the marsh mud in *Sporobolus-Paspalum* to three feet in *Spartina* or *Juncus*, and up to five feet in *Baccharis*. But because suitable food is not near by, these birds have not been found nesting beyond commuting distance from the wet banks of the salt creeks (where *S. alterniflora* grows ranker), the ponds that head the creeks in the salt meadows, and the grass patches (*S. alterniflora*) of the outer beaches that are flowed by each tide.

In a number of places under observation over several seasons, changes of terrain due to the erosion of tides and storms have brought coincident shifting of the Seaside Sparrow populations according to the feeding-ground limitations outlined above.

The nests are built of the softer grass blades of the vicinity, and when not covered by the natural foliage, are canopied. This canopy was more nearly complete where there were heavily incubated sets of eggs, so probably it is added to as incubation progresses. The growing grasses are woven into the canopy if available. Those nests naturally sheltered by the foliage in the tops of *Baccharis* are without canopy.

None but the females have been found showing incubation patches, and some things seem to indicate a partial dissociation of the sexes during incubation, but it is extremely difficult to observe well the life of a species that spends so much of its time below decks, so to speak, in the thick cover it inhabits. The birds pop up at the least disturbance to see what it is all about, the males do their singing well out in sight, and both sexes come out into the open to fly directly to some desired point, yet much of their time is spent either directly on the marsh mud, or in the lower part of the grasses above it.

The nesting season here is very long. Incomplete sets of eggs have been found in late April, and young birds partly fledged have been seen in late August. The greatest number of nests has been found in June and nearly as many in May, but not so many visits have been made in July and August. The natural supposition would be that two or more broods are raised each year. But lacking further proof, it is uncertain that this is always the case with a long nesting season. With favorable conditions of food and temperature over a long portion of the year, and with a species whose comparatively short migrations indicate that it has nearly optimum conditions for year-round residence, the long-drawn-out nesting season might be expected to approach that of some of the resident tropical species.

My observations all point to a lack of territorial jealousy in the species. Territory is here considered to mean a behavior involving a nesting and feeding area, which is defended by one or both parents against others of their own, or of a highly competitive, species.

"Territory cannot mean just the nest spot when the adults feed in common; this may be 'nest territory,' but it is a very different matter from a territory in its strict sense to which parents confine themselves during the breeding season. Again, the very essence of a territory lies in its exclusiveness; if a bird's range is not defended, it is not a territory." [Nice, 1933.]

It seems that Seaside Sparrows do feed in common, sometimes in pairs, sometimes singly, just prior to the egg-laying time, and most probably at other times also. I have seen five pairs in a sparse patch of *Juncus* some fifty feet across, and could follow their course underneath by the notes, yet failed to notice any particular disagreement.

Neither does the song appear to be a declaration warning other birds away. The singing is done from a grass stalk well out in sight, and it is usual to see a bird leave its perch, fly a couple of hundred yards away over other singing males, there to alight and resume song. The singing is done close to the nest location and also on the feeding grounds. On one occasion two birds sang about fifty feet apart. There was no appearance of competition about it, and the songs were timed quite independently of each other. Then one bird went below in the grass, and after a minute the other flew over, perched nearby, sang for a minute, then went below too, and there was no evidence of other than tolerance for each other. Sometimes a bird is halfheartedly chased by another as it flies over, but there is no determination in it.

It is not to be expected that colony-nesting birds have a territory in the strict sense, and the Seaside Sparrows have developed a semicolonial nesting habit with feeding grounds within commuting distance, where enough food is available so that no jealousy is necessary. This seems a good explanation for the lack of territory holding.

Smyrna Seaside Sparrow
Ammospiza maritima pelonota (Oberholser)

GENERAL DISTRIBUTION: Resident on the Atlantic Coast from St. Marys, Georgia, to New Smyrna, Florida.

STATUS IN GEORGIA: Breeds, and is probably resident, in the salt marshes at St. Marys, Camden County, but not known to occur farther north.

On May 13, 1933, eight breeding specimens of the Seaside Sparrow were taken by Arthur H. Howell and myself in the salt marshes of St. Marys, and on being critically examined, were found to represent this race. Another specimen was collected here by John W. Aldrich on April 7, 1946, that has also been identified as *pelonota*.

HABITS AND RECOGNITION: In general appearance and actions there is nothing to distinguish this race from the other Seaside Sparrows. It closely resembles *macgillivraii*, but it is smaller and the upperparts are not as dark.

Because of its limited breeding range, it is not a well-known bird; therefore, it is of interest to quote the comments of William Brewster, as contained in his Journal, April 11, 1877, concerning its breeding habits in the salt marsh at St. Marys:

Most of the marsh was open with short grass springing up, but interspersed through it were beds of tall reeds some five feet high, each blade ending in a point as sharp and hard as a needle. In the reeds, besides the rails, were innumerable Seaside Sparrows and a few Long-billed Marsh Wrens. The sparrows were in full song, the males uttering their notes usually while perched on the tops of the reeds. Their song is simple, consisting of only two notes but quite musical. Every now and then one would mount up into the air to the height of a few rods and sing continuously as he descended, commencing as usual and ending in a fine liquid warble. When approached they hid in the reeds and flushed only when nearly trodden on. Their flight was exactly like that of a Sharp-tailed Sparrow. The females were incubating. The nest was woven prettily in between the upright reeds about twelve inches above the ground and containing four eggs. In the next clump I came to I found three nests with four-three-three eggs, all within a few rods of each other. I afterwards found two more with three eggs. All these nests were built within a few feet of open spaces—not in the ranker growth. With the exception of the first, the birds left them before I came to the spot. Those with four eggs were all incubated four or five days. Those with three were fresh. The birds showed not the slightest solicitude.

Eastern Vesper Sparrow
Pooecetes gramineus gramineus (Gmelin)

GENERAL DISTRIBUTION: Breeds from southern Michigan, southern Quebec, and Cape Breton Island south to eastern Nebraska, central Missouri, Kentucky, and North Carolina. Winters from the southern part of its breeding range to eastern Texas, the Gulf Coast, and southern Florida.

STATUS IN GEORGIA: A fairly common winter resident throughout the state.

In fall, the Vesper Sparrow usually appears in Georgia the latter part of October, and in spring, lingers until late April or early May. In the northern part of the state, it is of irregular occurrence during the winter, and while small flocks are observed at infrequent intervals, it is only in November and again in March that it is at all common. South of the fall line it is common throughout the winter.

Extreme dates of occurrence in various parts of the state are:

Atlanta: October 19 (1938) and May 5 (1939).

Athens: October 18 (1927) and April 23 (1926).

Macon: October 2 (1949) and April 29 (1952).

Americus: November 13 (1941) and April 25 (1942).

Fitzgerald: October 1 (1940) and May 2 (1940).

Grady County: October 8 (1924) and April 7 (1943).

Savannah: October 23 (1910) and April 13 (1912).

Hinesville: November 3 (1943) and March 16 (1945).

It has been reported also at St. Marys, October 31, 1905, and at Milledgeville as late in the spring as April 21 (1944).

Numerous specimens of this southeastern race have been examined from Georgia, including those from Atlanta (eighteen specimens between the dates of October 30 [1948] and April 10 [1949]); Athens (four specimens between the dates of January 1 [1929] and March 28 [1946]); Blakely (December 31, 1933); Grady County (eight specimens); and Hinesville (January 23, 1946).

HABITS AND RECOGNITION: Despite its rather plain attire, the Vesper Sparrow is an easy bird to recognize. The small flocks that are seen in Georgia during the winter frequent open fields and pastures where the

662

grass is short, offering little or no concealment, and roadsides are also favored spots at this season of the year. Approached on the ground, the individuals comprising the flock will at first run ahead of the intruder, then fly, when their white outer tail feathers will reveal their identity.

The Vesper Sparrow is far less shy and secretive than the other sparrows found in the open fields, commonly alighting in the top of a bush or on a fence post, if disturbed while feeding. Thus seen, it appears perceptibly larger and grayer than the Savannah Sparrow and has a longer tail, which, even when the bird is perching quietly, shows traces of white on the sides. It is possible at times to note the reddish-brown patch at the bend of the wing, but to do so requires a closer approach than the average bird will usually permit.

Quiet and inconspicuous during the winter months, flocks of Vesper Sparrows suddenly become a noticeable part of the landscape after the middle of March, as the males can then frequently be heard singing. The song is loud and clear and, uttered from the upper branches of a bush or sapling or from the top of a fence post, cannot fail to attract attention.

Western Vesper Sparrow
Pooecetes gramineus confinis Baird

GENERAL DISTRIBUTION: Breeds from British Columbia, Alberta, and southern Saskatchewan south to eastern California, Arizona, New Mexico, and Texas; and east to the middle of the Great Plains. Winters from southern California and central Texas to southern Lower California and southern Mexico (casually, Louisiana).

STATUS IN GEORGIA: Of accidental occurrence.
The only record for this western race in Georgia is that of a specimen taken by Herbert L. Stoddard on Sherwood Plantation, in Grady County, on January 31, 1943.

HABITS AND RECOGNITION: The Vesper Sparrow of the western United States resembles the nominate race, *gramineus,* but is paler and grayer. There is nothing distinctive about its general appearance or actions, and only by means of specimens can it be satisfactorily identified.

Northern Vesper Sparrow
Pooecetes gramineus polius Braund and Aldrich

GENERAL DISTRIBUTION: Breeds in east central Ontario and northern Michigan. Winters south to the Gulf Coast and Georgia.

STATUS IN GEORGIA: A transient and possible winter resident throughout the state.

"This dark race of the Vesper Sparrow, heretofore unrecorded in the state, is apparently not uncommon in migration, and doubtless occurs during the winter months as well. It can now be placed on the accredited state list on the basis of four specimens taken both in the spring and in the fall, as follows: males, Athens, March 23, 1946, Decatur, November 28, 1946; females, Athens, October 21, 1945, Bogart (Oconee County), November 16, 1945" [Burleigh, 1948]. Since the above was written, another specimen of *polius* has been taken by Ira N. Gabrielson in Grady County, March 28, 1952.

HABITS AND RECOGNITION: There is nothing about the general appearance or actions of this race of the Vesper Sparrow to distinguish it in the field. It resembles typical *gramineus*, but the upperparts are darker and grayer.

Eastern Lark Sparrow
Chondestes grammacus grammacus   (Say)

GENERAL DISTRIBUTION: Breeds from eastern Nebraska, Minnesota, central Wisconsin, and southern Ontario, south to southern Louisiana and central Alabama, east to western Pennsylvania, Maryland, and West Virginia. Winters in southeastern Texas and eastern Mexico.

STATUS IN GEORGIA: Of accidental occurrence.

A specimen was taken by Arnow at St. Marys, Camden County, on August 11, 1908 [Arnow, 1908]; and Pindar [1926] reports "a few noted May 1 to 10" (1919) at Chickamauga Park. There are no other records.

HABITS AND RECOGNITION: The Lark Sparrow frequents much the same kind of country as does the Vesper Sparrow, being found in open fields and pastures where the grass is both short and sparse. Since it also shows a definite partiality for roadsides, it cannot be easily overlooked. If approached, it will at once fly, its rounded tail, showing conspicuous white patches on either side, readily identifying it, even at a distance. At closer range, its striped crown and white underparts marked in the center with a single dark spot will also distinguish it.

Eastern Bachman's Sparrow
Aimophila aestivalis bachmanii   (Audubon)

GENERAL DISTRIBUTION: Breeds from southern Ohio, southwestern Pennsylvania, and central Virginia south to the Gulf Coast from Alabama to northwestern Florida. Winters from Georgia and southern North Carolina to the Gulf Coast and central Florida.

STATUS IN GEORGIA: A fairly common summer resident over all of the state south of the mountains except the extreme southern part. Winters commonly in the coastal plain and locally and in small numbers north of the fall line.

Although an occasional bird remains throughout the winter in the northern part of the state, it is usually early March before the Bachman's Sparrow is seen in the Piedmont of Georgia in spring. Earliest transients were noted at Macon, February 29 (1904); Athens, March 8 (1921); Atlanta, February 28 (1945); Canton, March 14 (1905); and Dalton, March 24 (1944). Winter records, not numerous, are as follows: Athens, January 15, 1922 [Burleigh, 1938]; Augusta, December 20, 1944, and February 3, 1945 [Denton, 1945]; White Hall, Clarke County, December 5, 1945 (Burleigh); and Stone Mountain, DeKalb County, November 11, 1946 [Burleigh, 1947]. Tait [1946] reports single birds seen at Milledgeville, February 11, 1939, and October 13, 1943; and it is probable that these were wintering individuals. The same may be true of a single bird seen at Athens, October 19, 1948 [Johnston, letter].

The farthest north in the state that this species has been found during the summer is Pinelog Mountain, in Cherokee County, where a pair, apparently breeding, were seen at an altitude of 2,000 feet on July 29, 1945 [Denton and Odum, 1945]. At Athens, it was rather local in distribution and by no means common during the summer months. No nests were found there, but on July 4, 1922, three fully fledged young of the year were seen. Griffin [1940] gives as nesting extremes for the Atlanta area, four young, May 8 (1903) (Mills), and four fresh eggs, June 25 (1920) (Hembree). Breeding specimens of this more northern race have been examined from Stone Mountain (March 15, 1929, April 15 and 20, 1945), Athens (March 25 and 28, 1929), Hephzibah, Burke County (May 8, 1933); Fayette County (August 4, 1946), Blakely (May 20, 1933), and Newton (July 13, 1929, May 10, 1931). Other specimens, transients south of the breeding range, have been taken in Grady County, November 25, 1937, October 1, 1940, September 27, 1941, February 13, 1943; Thomasville, February 14, 1924; Waycross, May 14, 1933; and Statenville, Echols County, March 22, 1947.

HABITS AND RECOGNITION: Being a shy bird and rather secretive, Bachman's Sparrow could be easily overlooked were it not for the clear, sweet song the male utters from an elevated perch during the spring. During much of the year, this inconspicuous sparrow remains on the ground where weeds or patches of thick grass offer concealment, and being reluctant to

665

fly, it usually must be looked for to be seen. In March, however, and generally throughout April and May, the male will seek the top of a bush or sapling or the lower limb of a larger tree, if one is available, and its presence is then revealed, as, motionless, it sings for long intervals. Approached under such circumstances, it will suddenly dive precipitately to the ground, and it is doubtful that it will be seen again, so adept is it in taking advantage of what cover there is. Its secretive nature is well shown by the fact that after the breeding season it is rarely observed, and departure dates in the fall can only be guessed.

It doubtless lingers in the northern part of its breeding range through September, and possibly into October, but both at Athens and Atlanta there are very few fall records later than the end of August. In the Piedmont of Georgia, the Bachman's Sparrow can be found in abandoned fields and slashings partially overgrown with young pines and thickets of deciduous undergrowth, the open spots covered with broom sedge and other grasses. Farther south, in the coastal plain, it is one of the characteristic birds of the open pine woods, although it likewise frequents old fields and cut-over areas. It is much more common in the southern part of the state than north of the fall line, possibly because conditions are more to its liking.

The nest is placed flush with the ground, is normally arched over with dry grasses, and is so well concealed that it is extremely hard to find. When the female is incubating, she will run from the nest if disturbed; and if eventually seen, she will usually be some distance from the nest. In appearance, Bachman's Sparrow is a plain-colored, medium-sized sparrow, the upperparts being reddish-brown streaked with black and gray; the underparts dull white with the breast and flanks tinged with brown.

Florida Bachman's Sparrow
Aimophila aestivalis aestivalis (Lichtenstein)

GENERAL DISTRIBUTION: Largely resident from southeastern South Carolina to southern Florida.

STATUS IN GEORGIA: A common breeding bird in the extreme southern part of the state. There are few records for the winter months, but it doubtless winters regularly.

Breeding specimens of this race have been examined from Waycross (May 14, 1933), Folkston (April 25, 1938), Blackshear (May 3, 1946), Hinesville (April 3 and 23, 1946), Darien (May 24, 1931 and May 11, 1933), and Woodbine, Camden County (May 13, 1933). Males taken at Waynesboro, Burke County, May 9, 1933, and at Eastman, Dodge County, June 13, 1947, approached *aestivalis* in their characters, but were closer to *bachmanii.* Grady County is apparently the farthest west in the state where *aestivalis* occurs, and here also there is noticeable intergradation with *bachmanii.* Specimens examined have in some instances been typical of *aestivalis,* but others approached *bachmanii* in the lighter color of the upperparts. However, the characters of *aestivalis* are constant enough to justify including **Grady County** in the range of this race. Norris [letter] states that similar intergraduation occurs in Ben Hill County and that, on the basis of specimens taken at Fitzgerald, *aestivalis* is the breeding race there.

Definite breeding records are limited at present to three localities. At Savannah, Rossignol [letter] succeeded in finding five occupied nests, the earliest on April 21 (1913) with three fresh eggs, the latest on May 22 (1909) with four fresh eggs. Stoddard [MS] noted that this sparrow reared two and possibly three broods each year in Grady County, his extreme dates being a nest with three eggs found April 28 (1935) and one that held three fresh eggs on August 31 (1948). Hebard [letter] reports several nests found in western Charlton County, among them one with three eggs on May 11, 1942, another with young on June 16, 1942, and a third with three young about five days old on July 22, 1951.

HABITS AND RECOGNITION: Stoddard's unpublished manuscript on the birds of Grady County gives us all the information now available on the life history of Bachman's Sparrow in southern Georgia:

> Our only *native* resident sparrow and one of the most charming songsters of the South. Under primitive conditions this attractive bird was a characteristic species of the open parklike piney woods, building its well-roofed nest (like a Bobwhite nest in miniature) of the materials of the forest floor, rearing its young within striking distance of little "refuges" of shrubby growth in these same wooded areas, and spending its life in this type of surroundings. It is a highly adaptable species, however, and finds life more attractive in present day tung-oil groves or around borders of cultivated fields.
>
> This sparrow has a very long nesting season. A nest with three eggs was found on Sherwood, April 28, 1935; "Nest in a little tuft of grass which escaped spring fire on edge of small open field surrounded by piney woods. Nest well roofed. . . ." A nest with four slightly incubated eggs was found on the same place, May 9, 1924, and another was incubating four eggs in a little pasture near by: "Nest of grasses in a little hole, and backed into a grass clump. Bird in plain sight (once the exact location of the nest is known), but as she faces north, is never in direct sunlight." Sherwood, July 16, 1935: "Nest with three young well over half-grown . . . in very open stand

of old broom sedge about forty feet in two directions from pine woods." The above nests are typical. Sometimes there are five eggs (Thomas County, on May 8, 1944. This nest was peculiar in being without the usual sheltering roof, though the eggs were well concealed by sprout growths of Runner Oak, New Jersey Tea, etc.).

The length of the nesting season is shown by a nest found in Thomas County on August 21, 1944, with four fresh eggs, and another with three fresh eggs on Susina Plantation, Grady County, August 31, 1948.

This species seems to be forever in moult, bob-tailed ragged adults and young being the rule throughout the summer and fall months, while they seem to be replacing lost feathers much of the time during the winter months. During the late summer and fall, the family groups have begun to frequent the writer's tung groves, feeding in the lush growths of Crimson Clover and other legumes used as "cover crops" and full of insect life. Here the young birds sit in the dense vegetation of the tung trees, where the adult birds feed them for a considerable period.

The extremely attractive song, to be heard at all hours of the day, but very characteristic of the quiet hours of early morning and late evening, first becomes prominent in the piney woods in early March (March 8, 1925) and continues into September (September 7, 1939). It has a sweet, slightly plaintive, and haunting quality, hungered for by those whose youth was spent in the virgin open pinelands of the original unmodified coastal plain of the deep Southeast. It was as much a part of the southeastern "flatwoods" as the aged longleaf pines themselves, or the songs of the Pine Warblers, and the queer notes of the Red-cockaded Woodpeckers and the Brown-headed Nuthatches. Like the longleaf pines and the Red-cockaded Woodpeckers, it was dependent through the ages on the frequent grass fires that kept the "flatwoods" open and parklike, with the characteristic prairie-type flora. As man changed the ecology of vast areas with his plowing, livestock grazing, fire exclusion, and other activities in line with his requirements, some creatures, like the Red-cockaded Woodpecker, have declined to a remnant with the virgin pines. Others, like the sparrow under discussion, have modified their habits and prospered.

During some winters, few Pines-woods Sparrows are to be found in the county; during others, many may be found in the short herbaceous vegetation of the open woodlands, fields, or even in the fence rows with other sparrows. To me they always seem to be out of character in the latter situations. A charming, harmless denizen of the piney woods; long may its tribe survive!

668

Northern Slate-colored Junco
Junco hyemalis hyemalis   (Linnaeus)

GENERAL DISTRIBUTION: Breeds from northwestern Alaska (Point Barrow), northern Mackenzie, northern Manitoba, central Quebec, and Newfoundland south to southern Yukon, central Alberta, northern Minnesota, central Michigan, Ontario, and Nova Scotia, and in the mountains to Pennsylvania, New York, and Massachusetts. Winters from southern Ontario south through the eastern United States to the Gulf Coast and northern Florida.

STATUS IN GEORGIA: A common winter resident throughout the state.

Small flocks of Slate-colored Juncos normally appear in Georgia the latter part of October or the first of November, and are present over much of the state from then until the middle of the following April.

Extreme dates of occurrence are:

Athens: October 26 (1927) and April 22 (1926).

Atlanta: October 17 (1942) and April 24 (1949).

Milledgeville: November 13 (1943) and April 10 (1938).

Macon: November 6 (1926) and April 17 (1943).

Americus: November 10 (1941) and March 14 (1942).

Fitzgerald: November 29 (1940) and April 5 (1941).

Grady County: October 27 (1949) and March 29 (1951).

Hinesville: November 24 (1944) and March 1 (1944).

At Savannah, this species was noted as late in the spring as May 3 (1909); at Columbus, March 24 (1946); and at Dalton, April 15 (1944).

During the winter, juncos are less numerous in the southern part of the state than north of the fall line, and their relative abundance is apparently governed to some extent by the severity of the weather. This was noted by Herbert L. Stoddard in Grady County, who [MS] says, "That they may at times be forced southward by cold and storm is indicated by their numbers during the record-breaking cold of 1940, when my notes read, 'Most continuous cold on record in January, and the most juncos I have ever seen here.' The same was true of the very cold weather of 1950–51." I observed a similar fluctuation in numbers at Newton, in Baker County, where in December, 1929, juncos were scarce and rarely seen, but found to be fairly plentiful in January, 1932. Hebard [1941] reports but a single record for the Okefenokee Swamp, February 27, 1936, and three for Coleraine, November 22, and December 6 and 12, 1940.

Specimens representing this northern race have been examined from many parts of the state, including the following localities:

Trenton, Dade County: December 16, 1946.

Blairsville, Union County: November 23, 1945.

Lula, Banks County: March 25, 1947.

Athens: Twelve specimens between the dates of November 30 (1933) and April 11 (1935).

Decatur, DeKalb County: Ten specimens between the dates of November 25 (1946) and March 28 (1947).

Blakely: February 4, 1937.

Newton, Baker County: December 1, 1929.

Grady County: Five specimens between the dates of November 22 (1939) and February 22 (1948).

Charlton County: December 20, 1952.

HABITS AND RECOGNITION: According to common usage, the Slate-colored Junco is known as the Snowbird, and it must be admitted that this is much the better name. It is in the late fall when the familiar summer birds are gone and the days are growing short and the first heavy frosts are whitening the ground that small flocks of these slate-gray sparrows appear. Not infrequently their appearance coincides with the first snowfall, and as, throughout much of the United States, such flocks are a familiar sight during the bleak, cold days of winter, the appropriateness of the name Snowbird can be appreciated. Sociable by nature, a single junco is seldom found feeding alone, and even small flocks are often associated with other sparrows. Its food, almost entirely small seeds at this time of year, is picked up on or near the ground, the individuals comprising a flock scattering out in all directions as they energetically search their immediate vicinity for whatever fare is available. On occasion they may be found at the edges of open fields, but their preference is for wooded areas where there are thickets and stretches of underbrush. If alarmed by too close an approach, one bird and then another will fly into the tops of the bushes near by, the flash of white on their outer tail feathers being rather noticeable. While not especially timid, they are restless during the winter months, and a flock that is disturbed while feeding will usually seek another spot rather than return to the same ground.

In flight, a distinctive, rapidly repeated note is uttered that will aid in recognizing the junco even when seen at a distance. The song, commonly heard in Georgia in late February and March, is a simple little trill suggestive of that of the Chipping Sparrow, but more musical.

Cassiar Slate-colored Junco
Junco hyemalis cismontanus Dwight

GENERAL DISTRIBUTION: Breeds from extreme south central Yukon Territory south through interior British Columbia east of the coast ranges into the interior Stikine River basin. Winters south to California and casually east to the Atlantic seaboard.

STATUS IN GEORGIA: Apparently of rare occurrence in the state during the winter.

There are at present three specimens of this far northwestern junco that have been taken in Georgia, all females: one from Athens (November 14, 1945) (Burleigh), another from Decatur (February 13, 1947) (Burleigh), and the third from Chatham County (November 27, 1952) (Tomkins).

HABITS AND RECOGNITION: In general appearance and actions there is little to distinguish this race of junco in the field. In the male the color of the head is darker in contrast to the back than in *hyemalis,* and the edge of the slate color on the chest is convex rather than concave. In the female the sides are washed with brown rather than gray.

Carolina Slate-colored Junco
Junco hyemalis carolinensis Brewster

GENERAL DISTRIBUTION: Breeds in the mountains from western Maryland, Virginia, and West Virginia south to northern Georgia. Winters in the adjacent lowlands.

STATUS IN GEORGIA: Resident and common in the mountains in the northeastern corner of the state. Of accidental occurrence during the winter months south of the mountain counties.

The Carolina Junco has been reported as breeding in Rabun County (Rabun Bald and Chestnut Mountains), Towns County (Brasstown Bald), Union County (Blood Mountain and Slaughter Mountain), Gilmer County (Rich Mountain), and White County (Tray Mountain); and doubtless can be found during the summer on other high ridges where conditions are suitable.

Definite breeding records are at present limited to Brasstown Bald, where in 1922 [Burleigh, 1925] three nests were found, one on June 27 with three slightly incubated eggs, another the same day with two half-grown young, and the third on July 16 with three well-incubated eggs; and to Tray Mountain, where adults were seen feeding young out of the nest on June 17, 1949 [Denton and Neal, 1951].

During the winter, this junco leaves the higher ridges to a large extent and can be found on the lower slopes and in the valleys. While at Young Harris on January 4, 1934, I spent part of the day on Brasstown Bald, and while no juncos were seen at the top of the mountain, where they nest, small flocks were noted in the valley and, infrequently, to an altitude of approximately 3,000 feet. The only definite record for this race south of the mountains is that of a male taken at Lithonia, DeKalb County, on February 26, 1947. Specimens previously identified as *carolinensis,* collected at Augusta, Athens, and Fitzgerald, have been re-examined and, while approaching *carolinensis* in their characters, were found to be closer to *hyemalis,* and are apparently from the extreme southern part of the breeding range of this more northern subspecies, where it begins to intergrade with the Appalachian Mountain race.

Breeding specimens of *carolinensis* have been taken on Brasstown Bald (June 19, 1928, June 23, 1932, May 29, 1933), Blood Mountain (May 30, 1933), Slaughter Mountain (July 21, 1939), and Chestnut Mountain (June 26, 1946).

HABITS AND RECOGNITION: Because of its rather limited range in the state, the Carolina Slate-colored Junco is not familiar to the average bird student in Georgia, and little information is available on its occurrence and nesting activities. Therefore, I am quoting from short accounts I wrote some years ago, covering my all too brief acquaintance with this interesting species on Brasstown Bald:

The top of Brasstown Bald is one of the few spots in the state where this species breeds, and here none were seen during the summer below an elevation of 4,000 feet. The birds find a congenial summer home among the rhododendron thickets that dot the northern slope of this rugged mountainside and are fairly plentiful over this limited area. The first nest was found June 27 and held on that date three slightly incubated eggs. It was sunken flush with the ground in thick green moss and was protected and concealed from above by a protruding root, and was on a steep slope practically at the top of the mountain. It was compactly built of rootlets, grasses, and green moss, thickly lined with rabbit fur. Another nest found the same day held two half-grown young and was sunken in the moss and ferns covering a ledge of a large boulder. These were without doubt second sets, for on June 20, a young bird, out of the nest several days, was seen being fed by both adult birds. A third nest found July 16, that held three well-incubated eggs, was to me remarkably interesting for it differed radically from any of this species (*hyemalis*) or any of its subspecies that I had ever seen. It was fully eight feet from the ground in a red maple sapling and partially concealed by a grape vine, and was a large, rather loose ball of green moss intermixed with a few dead leaves and rootlets, well cupped and lined with black rootlets and, at the bottom, fine grasses and a few horsehairs. I later realized that this method of nesting was seemingly by no means uncommon here, for two other nests were found during the summer in situations very similar to this. These are to the best of my knowledge the first authentic breeding records for the state, although this species has been known to occur here during the summer months. [Burleigh, 1925.]

So little is known concerning the nesting habits of this species in the state that I was glad of the further opportunity to add to the little knowledge I had already acquired. Seemingly a second brood is almost invariably raised during the latter part of June, and in 1923 two nests were found that helped verify this assumption. On June 27, as I was following a narrow ledge that crossed a wide sheet of rock on a very steep slope near the top of the mountain, a bird flushed from almost beneath my feet and revealed a nest that held three very slightly incubated eggs. The rock was carpeted with a thick layer of green moss, and the nest was sunken in this and very well concealed. Apparently the moss here had merely been hollowed out and the cavity well lined with grasses, fine weed stems, and a little 'possum hair. The second nest was found three days later, on the 30th, and likewise held three slightly incubated eggs. It was up four feet from the ground on a narrow ledge of a low cliff in open woods almost at the top of the mountain and was sunken in the green moss covering the rocks, and well concealed by a clump of weeds growing at the front and to one side of it. In construction it differed but little, the cavity in the moss being well cupped and lined with fine rootlets, grasses, and cow hair. In 1925, but one nest was found, the bird flushing from four practically fresh eggs as I passed within two feet of her while following the trail to the top of the mountain. The nest was sunken in the ground at the base of and well in under a chestnut sapling on a steep slope at an elevation of approximately 4,200 feet, and because of the scant undergrowth was afforded little concealment. This was on May 26, and, as indicated by the number of eggs, was unquestionably a first brood. The nest was compact and fairly substantial, and was built of weed stems, rootlets, bits of dead leaves, shreds of bark, and a little green moss, lined with fine moss stems. [Burleigh, 1927.]

The Carolina Slate-colored Junco is larger and grayer than typical *hyemalis,* with a grayish rather than pinkish bill, which at reasonably close range is easily noticeable.

Eastern Chipping Sparrow
Spizella passerina passerina (Bechstein)

GENERAL DISTRIBUTION: Breeds from Yukon, Mackenzie, northern British Columbia, Saskatchewan, central Manitoba, northern Ontario, southern Quebec, and Newfoundland south to central Texas, southern Mississippi, southern Alabama, and southern Georgia. Winters chiefly in the Southern states, occasionally as far north as Oklahoma and southern New Jersey.

Florida Bachman's Sparrow

Aimophila aestivalis aestivalis

When the spring sun warms and brightens the pinelands, this quietly
colored little bird flies to a leafless branch fifteen or twenty feet from the
ground, lifts its head, and sings almost as if knowing that it has found a voice
for all the silent things about it—the carpet of brown needles and leaf mold,
the burgeoning dogwood buds, the canopy of pine tops, the sky. No scientist
can have thoughts of this sort, of course, but an ordinary bird artist can.

GEORGE
MIKSCH
SUTTON
1952

Family Fringillidae: GROSBEAKS, FINCHES, SPARROWS, & BUNTINGS

STATUS IN GEORGIA: Resident over much of the state, breeding commonly north of the fall line and locally and in relatively small numbers in the coastal plain. Winters from the mountains to the coast, but is less numerous at this time of the year in the northern part of the state than south of the fall line.

As far south as Augusta and Macon, the Chipping Sparrow is common during the summer, but throughout the rest of the state it has been reported as breeding in but a few widely separated areas. Further field work may prove it to be more common than present records indicate, but for the time being it must be considered an uncommon breeding bird in the coastal plain. In the eastern part of the state, there are breeding records for Millen, Jenkins County; and Hinesville, Liberty County; while farther west it has been reported as breeding at Americus, Sumter County; Lumpkin, Stewart County; Ft. Gaines, Clay County; and Blakely, Early County.

Definite breeding records are not numerous, and are limited to the following localities:

Dalton: Nest with three half-grown young, August 28, 1940 [Hamilton, 1940].

Rome: Nest with four eggs, May 10, 1937 [Jones, 1947].

Young Harris: Nest with three incubated eggs, June 15, 1922 (Burleigh).

Athens: Nesting extremes, twelve nests, four half-incubated eggs, April 29 (1925); two slightly incubated eggs, August 21 (1928) [Burleigh, 1938].

Atlanta: Nesting extremes, small young, May 6 (1932) (Greene); four eggs August 24 (1939) (Griffin) [Griffin, 1940].

Millen: One young bird just out of the nest, May 21, 1949 [Denton, 1950].

Hinesville: Adult feeding a young bird, July 1, 1943; adult feeding two fledglings, June 7, 1945 [Grimm, 1946].

In Grady County, where it is not known to nest, the Chipping Sparrow is reported to be a common winter resident, occurring between the dates of October 20 (1944) and May 4 (1926). A specimen taken at Thomasville on July 31, 1921, would indicate the possibility that this species breeds at least sparingly in this part of the state. However, at Tifton, it has not been noted in the spring later than May 1 (1952), nor, at Fitzgerald, earlier in the fall than November 1 (1941). At Savannah, where it is also a common winter resident, it has been noted between the dates of October 22 (1909) and April 15 (1910), and on Cumberland Island as late as April 17 (1902). Both Harper and Hebard consider it common during the winter in the Okefenokee Swamp.

HABITS AND RECOGNITION: In Georgia, it is probable that the Chipping Sparrow was originally found to a large extent in the open pine woods that covered much of the state. It is still a common bird in that habitat, but as settlements replaced the wooded areas, this little sparrow adapted itself to the changing environment, and it is now a familiar sight in or-

chards, about farmhouses, and even in the shade trees in the towns. It is a
gentle, confiding bird that has readily accepted the advantages man has
to offer, and only during the winter is it briefly absent from the farmyards
and from the gardens in the residential sections of the towns. Then, gathered in loose flocks that forage in the fields and pastures and the more open
stretches of woods, frequently in the company of Field Sparrows, it leads
a nomadic existence until spring approaches.

In late March, the males appear at the spots where broods of young
will later be reared, and their simple little song, a rather unmusical series
of "chips," uttered with varying degrees of rapidity, can be heard throughout much of the day. Pairs frequenting the open pine woods almost invariably build their nests at the outer end of a limb of one of the larger
pines, the height varying from ten to, not infrequently, thirty or forty feet
from the ground. Elsewhere, nests have been found in apple trees in orchards, in shade trees about houses, and on a few occasions in bushes at
the sides of roads. Nests vary little in construction, being compactly constructed of weed stems, rootlets, and grasses, well lined with horsehair. In
Georgia, two or possibly three are reared each year, as fresh eggs, usually
four but often three to a clutch, can be found as early as the latter part of
April and, rarely, as late as the middle of August. It is in May and June,
however, that the bulk of the birds are busily engaged in nesting.

No difficulty should be experienced in recognizing the Chipping
Sparrow. It will usually permit a reasonably close approach before becoming alarmed and flying away, and its small size, bright rufous crown,
black-bordered white line over the eye, and dull white, unstreaked underparts will readily identify it.

Stoddard, in his manuscript on the bird life of Grady County, tells us
that, during the late winter and early spring months from 1924 to 1930,
many Chipping Sparrows were caught and banded that had entered the
quail traps operated by the Co-operative Quail Investigation. "A considerable percentage of those handled at this season had swollen and sore feet
and toes, being afflicted with 'bird pox' of varying severity. Often toes or
toenails were missing from previous cases of this disease, though all evidence of soreness had long since disappeared. At least one of the Chipping Sparrows banded during this period lived to a ripe old age, eight
years having elapsed from the time of banding until it was recaptured on
a local feeding tray."

Eastern Field Sparrow
Spizella pusilla pusilla (Wilson)

GENERAL DISTRIBUTION: Breeds from southern Minnesota, southern
Michigan, southern Quebec, and southern Maine south to central Texas,

central Louisiana, southern Alabama, and northwestern Florida. Winters from Missouri, Illinois, southern Pennsylvania, and New Jersey to the Gulf Coast.

STATUS IN GEORGIA: Resident over the entire state, although occurring only locally and in small numbers in summer south of the fall line.

North of Augusta and Macon, the Field Sparrow breeds commonly wherever there is suitable habitat, but on the coastal plain it is somewhat scarce and of local occurrence during the summer. There is evidence, however, that in recent years it has increased in numbers and become more widely distributed as a breeding bird in the southern half of the state, and it is possible that in time it may nest commonly there. In the course of field work carried on at Newton, Baker County, in 1929 and again in 1931, I found this species extremely scarce. A singing male was seen there on July 14, 1929, and another on May 10, 1931, but otherwise it was not noted, despite careful search in areas affording suitable habitat. Some years later, an intensive study of the summer bird life of the southwestern corner of Georgia in 1947 and 1948 by Robert Norris [Norris, 1951] brought out the fact that the Field Sparrow had increased perceptibly in numbers in this part of the state, and now nested as far south as Seminole County. Stoddard [MS] also comments on the fact that "Field Sparrows have, during the past two or three years, begun to summer in increasing numbers in the region. During the summer of 1951, Leon Neel, who is now the writer's 'ears,' pointed out three or four singing males in adjoining Thomas County, Georgia, and Leon County, Florida. This year (1952) a singing male has been located in typical nesting cover on Sherwood Plantation. We can predict with confidence that nests will be located within a year or two, and that soon the species will breed with us with more or less regularity."

Actual breeding records are at present limited to the following localities, although the Field Sparrow unquestionably nests commonly over much of the state:

Rome: Nest with four young, May 8, 1941 [Jones, 1947].

Margret, Fannin County: Four incubated eggs, June 21, 1921; three slightly incubated eggs, July 6, 1921 (Burleigh).

Young Harris: Three well-incubated eggs, June 22, 1922 (Burleigh).

Augusta: Nesting extremes, twelve nests, four eggs, April 29 (1945); two young, August 1 (1952) (Denton).

Athens: Nesting extremes, fourteen nests, four fresh eggs, April 7 (1927); three slightly incubated eggs, August 1 (1925) [Burleigh, 1938].

Atlanta: Nesting extremes, four incubated eggs, April 22 (1919) (Arpal); three fresh eggs, August 12 (1918) (Harris) [Griffin, 1940].

Newton, Baker County: Three eggs, June 26, 1950 [Hopkins, 1951].

Savannah: Two eggs, May 23, 1942 (Tomkins).

During the winter, the Field Sparrow is an abundant bird over the entire state, its numbers being increased by numerous flocks of transients from farther north. At Fitzgerald (Norris and Hopkins), it is a common winter resident, extreme dates of occurrence being October 6 (1939) and April 30 (1941). In Grady County, Stoddard also reports it a common winter resident, occurring between the dates of October 25 (1940) and April 18 (1943). At Hinesville, Grimm [1946] noted it from November 21, 1943, to April 2, 1944. On Sea Island [Woodward, 1949], it was seen as late as March 24, 1947.

HABITS AND RECOGNITION: The Field Sparrow is a small sparrow, approximately the same size as the Chipping Sparrow, but in every other way it differs radically from its near relative. As its name implies, it is a bird of fields and pastures overgrown with briar thickets and deciduous underbrush. Open pine woods are avoided unless changed into open slashings by logging operations, but when this happens, the Field Sparrow soon takes advantage of the new, favorable environment. It is noticeably more retiring than the Chipping Sparrow, and rarely if ever will be seen far from the brushy fields that it prefers. Here it can be found in small flocks during the winter, and here it nests during the summer.

The Field Sparrow is a persistent singer, rivaling the Indigo Bunting in this respect, its clear, rather pensive little song being one of the characteristic sounds of midsummer, when the long, hot days have silenced most of the other birds. In Georgia, it is in the first warm days of February that the song is first heard, and it continues unabated until the middle of August, when the long nesting season is finally over.

The nest is placed in a thick bush or clump of weeds, in, or at the edge of, a thicket or stretch of underbrush, and is usually within a foot or two of the ground. It varies little in construction, being built of weed stems and grasses and lined with horsehair. Two, and possibly three, broods are reared each year, for fresh eggs can be found from the middle of April until early August.

Although resembling the Chipping Sparrow somewhat in appearance and actions, the Field Sparrow can be recognized by its longer tail, more reddish-brown upperparts, and pink, rather than black, bill.

Harris's Sparrow
Zonotrichia querula (Nuttall)

GENERAL DISTRIBUTION: Breeds at Fort Churchill, Hudson Bay; Artillery Lake, Mackenzie; and probably at Great Bear Lake and in the district just south of the Barren Grounds. Winters from northern Kansas, southern Nebraska, and western Missouri south to southern Texas.

Family Fringillidae: GROSBEAKS, FINCHES, SPARROWS, & BUNTINGS

STATUS IN GEORGIA: Of accidental occurrence in the northern part of the state.

There are two records for the occurrence of the Harris's Sparrow in Georgia. A specimen was taken by J. Fred Denton at Athens on April 23, 1937 [Denton, 1937]; and another by William W. Griffin near Atlanta on January 18, 1953 [Griffin, 1953].

HABITS AND RECOGNITION: As Georgia is far east of the normal winter range of this large, handsome sparrow, it is doubtful that it will ever be other than of casual occurrence in the state. Stragglers seen elsewhere in the eastern United States have almost without exception been with flocks of White-throated or White-crowned Sparrows, and it is in such situations that it may possibly be found in Georgia. Like these species, it frequents thickets and stretches of underbrush, in or at the edges of which it feeds on the ground, scratching in the dead leaves for what insects or weed seeds it can find. It is one of the less timid of the sparrows, showing little concern unless too closely approached, when it will fly into the nearest bush and calmly watch the intruder until its curiosity is satisfied. Being easily observed, it is just as easily identified, its large size and black markings on the crown and throat readily distinguishing it.

Eastern White-crowned Sparrow
Zonotrichia leucophrys leucophrys   (Forster)

GENERAL DISTRIBUTION: Breeds from northern Manitoba, northern Quebec, and Newfoundland to central Manitoba, southern Quebec, and southern Greenland. Winters from southern Kansas and the Ohio Valley south to Florida, Louisiana, and southern Mexico.

STATUS IN GEORGIA: An irregular transient and winter resident throughout the state.

In fall, the White-crowned Sparrow appears in Georgia at infrequent intervals in late October, and in spring lingers until the middle of May. In recent years, it has been noted in increasing numbers, and it is possible that, to some extent, its former apparent scarcity may have been due to its having been overlooked.

Records of its occurrence to date include the following localities:

Chickamauga Park: A few noted in April, 1919 [Pindar, 1926].

Dalton: One bird seen, April 22 and 24, 1940, and another in late October, 1940; a single bird seen, April 30, 1941 [Hamilton, 1941].

Union County: A flock of five birds seen, April 26 and 27, 1940 [Bell, 1940].

Atlanta: Single birds seen, April 11, 1936 [Griffin, 1941], March 18, 1944 [Johnston, 1944], November 6, 1946 [Burleigh, 1947], and November 30 and December 22, 1946 (Johnston); also a flock of eight or ten from January 1 to May 3, 1953 [Griffin, 1953].

Athens: Single birds seen, May 3 and October 25 and 27, 1925, November 28 and December 3, 1926, and May 13, 1928 [Burleigh, 1938]; one bird trapped, April 23, 1937 [Denton, 1937]; reported on November 13, 1942 [Odum, 1943]; a flock of eleven birds noted at a feeding station from November 15, 1943, through May 7, 1944 [Petrides, 1944]; two birds collected from a flock of four, December 27 and 28, 1949 (Johnston).

Rome: Thirteen birds, possibly more, noted from January 25 through May 1, 1953 [Dorsey, letter].

Augusta: One bird seen, April 27, 1934 [Murphey, 1937].

Macon: One bird seen, February 8–May 5, 1935 [Mounts, 1936].

Tifton: Single birds collected, January 4, 1943 [Norris, 1944], and October 28, 1944 [Gaulding, 1945]; two birds collected, February 25, 1946 [Norris, 1946]; thirteen birds collected between the end of February and April 24, 1952 (Norris).

Savannah: One bird collected, November 23, 1939 [Tomkins, 1940].

HABITS AND RECOGNITION: The one adjective most commonly applied to the White-crowned Sparrow is aristocratic, and it is well deserved. Lacking the nervous mannerisms displayed by the other sparrows with which it at times associates, it has a dignified bearing, which at once sets it apart, and this impression is emphasized by the striking crown pattern that gives the adult bird a truly distinguished appearance. Other sparrows characteristically skulk in thickets and underbrush, but the White-crown prefers to remain in the open and, only when danger threatens, seeks temporary concealment. It has no liking for thick woods, and when seen in Georgia will be feeding at the edge of thickets in open fields or at the sides of country roads. In its migrations, it shows a definite tendency to remain west of the Alleghenies, and nowhere in the southeastern United States, east of these mountains, is it at any time common. Young of the year, seen in the fall and winter, have reddish-brown instead of black stripes on the crown, with the white obscured by a buffy wash, but they are sufficiently like the adults in appearance and actions to be identified without much difficulty.

Gambel's White-crowned Sparrow
Zonotrichia leucophrys gambelii (Nuttall)

GENERAL DISTRIBUTION: Breeds in northwestern Alaska and northern Mackenzie south to central Montana and west to southeastern British Columbia. Winters from northern California and Utah south to northern Mexico, and casually east to the Atlantic Coast.

STATUS IN GEORGIA: Recorded once in the southern part of the state.

Gambel's White-crowned Sparrow has been taken in Georgia by Robert A. Norris, who collected an immature female at Tifton, March 1, 1952.

680

The identification was confirmed by Allen J. Duvall, of the Fish and Wild-life Service.

HABITS AND RECOGNITION: This western race of the White-crowned Sparrow differs from typical *leucophrys* in that the white superciliary stripe is continuous beyond the eye and the black spot in front of the eye characteristic of *leucophrys* is lacking. Otherwise, in its appearance and actions there is nothing to distinguish it, and specimens are necessary for satisfactory identification.

White-throated Sparrow
Zonotrichia albicollis   (Gmelin)

GENERAL DISTRIBUTION: Breeds from northern Mackenzie, northern Manitoba, central Quebec, and Newfoundland south to central Alberta, southern Montana, central Minnesota, central Wisconsin, southern Ontario, northern New England, Nova Scotia, and the mountains of northeastern Pennsylvania, New York, and Massachusetts. Winters from Missouri, the Ohio Valley, southern Pennsylvania, Connecticut, and Massachusetts south to northeastern Mexico and Florida.

STATUS IN GEORGIA: A common winter resident throughout the state.

In fall, the first White-throated Sparrows appear in Georgia in early October; small flocks are soon common, and are present until the latter part of the following April. After the first of May, there is a perceptible decrease in both number and size of the flocks seen, and after the middle of that month only an occasional belated individual will be seen.

Extreme dates of occurrence over the state are as follows:

Dalton: October 15 (1944) and May 13 (1944).

Atlanta: October 5 (1943) and May 29 (1903).

Athens: October 6 (1925) and May 18 (1922).

Macon: October 12 (1955) and May 16 (1931).

Americus: October 25 (1941) and May 6 (1942).

Fitzgerald: October 15 (1939) and May 13 (1939).

Grady County: October 10 (1944) and May 17 (1951).

Savannah: October 22 (1909) and May 25 (1919).

Hinesville: October 24 (1943) and April 28 (1943).

At Milledgeville, the earliest arrival date reported in the fall is October 12 (1938). The latest spring record at Augusta is May 26 (1953). An unusually late date for the state is that of a single bird seen at Blairsville, June 11, 1936 [Denton, 1936].

HABITS AND RECOGNITION: In wooded areas, the White-throated Sparrow is the common winter sparrow of Georgia. It has little liking for the more open country, and only occasionally will one find flocks about thickets or underbrush in fields and along roadsides. In this respect, it is just the opposite of the White-crowned Sparrow which, in size and general appearance, it somewhat resembles. Dense undergrowth in and at the edges of thick woods is its preferred habitat, and it is there that flocks of varying size can be seen during the winter. Such flocks are not easily overlooked, for the White-throated Sparrow is an energetic and far from inconspicuous bird, with little of either shyness or secretiveness about it. Approach a flock as the birds are scratching vigorously in the dead leaves covering the ground, and first one bird and then another will fly into the nearest bush, uttering a distinctive, metallic "chink," and remaining quietly in full view as the source of their disturbance is inspected. If the birds are not alarmed and the observer stands motionless, it is not uncommon to have one or more give their clear, plaintive song before returning to the ground and resuming their search for food. Few birds in Georgia sing as freely during the winter as this species. Within a few weeks after their arrival in fall, the first individuals can be heard singing on cloudy, cool days, and until their departure in the spring there are few days when the sweet refrain of this familiar sparrow cannot be listened to and enjoyed.

Stoddard, in his unpublished manuscript of the birds of Grady County, has given us an account of the actions of the White-throated Sparrow on Sherwood Plantation sufficiently interesting to justify quoting here:

> Several of these birds bathing in the early morning dew of a grass-clover lawn makes a charming sight seldom mentioned in the literature. Plants such as clover and the Bermuda grasses hold much water when the dews of winter are heavy. As the White-throats work over the lawns, they frequently squat in the wetter spots, quiver their wings, and fluff and shake their plumage, just as they do in the bird baths. Several were enjoying grass bathing on the fine bright and warm morning of January 25, 1950. One spent fully three minutes in the aggregate hopping from one clover spot to another, bathing with ecstasy in each.

He comments further on the fact that banding operations have revealed that "the same little groups may return to the same identical thickets year after year from their far northern summer homes."

This opinion was earlier advanced by Baldwin [1922], who, while carrying on banding operations at Thomasville, banded a White-throated Sparrow on March 5, 1916, and caught the same individual at the same spot at intervals through March 27, 1921.

The White-throated Sparrow is one of the larger sparrows, with a white throat that stands out in contrast to the gray breast. The pattern of the head suggests that of the White-crowned Sparrow, but lacks the grayish tone of that species, particularly on the neck; in both sexes there is a distinct yellow spot between the eye and the bill.

Eastern Fox Sparrow
Passerella iliaca iliaca (Merrem)

GENERAL DISTRIBUTION: Breeds from northern Quebec and Labrador south to southeastern Quebec and Newfoundland. Winters from the lower Ohio and Potomac valleys to central Texas, the Gulf Coast (casually), and central Florida.

STATUS IN GEORGIA: A fairly common winter resident over the greater part of the state, being scarce and irregular in occurrence only in the more southern counties.

In northern Georgia, the Fox Sparrow winters regularly, usually appearing in the fall in early November and being only infrequently seen in the spring after the middle of March. Extreme dates of occurrence are, for Athens, October 22 (1927) and April 1 (1929); Atlanta, November 11 (1923) and April 2 (1950); Milledgeville, October 25 (1937) and March 17 (1941); and Macon, October 24 (1923) and March 25 (1945).

Over much of the coastal plain, this large sparrow is usually rather scarce, its presence during the winter months being apparently governed to a great extent by the severity of the weather farther north. At Fitzgerald, Norris and Hopkins [MS] report it between the dates of November 17 (1938) and February 18 (1939). In the course of field work in Baker County in 1929, I noted this species but once, two birds being seen on December 1. In 1950, however, small flocks were observed in this same area by Hopkins [1951] on January 9 and 23 and February 2. At Blakely, Early County, one small flock was seen on February 11, 1936. Stoddard [MS] states that it winters sparingly in Grady County, the few individuals recorded each year being found only by diligent search. His extreme dates of occurrence are November 24 (1938) and March 6 (1949). While on Blackbeard Island, a short distance off the coast from Darien, on January 25, 1931, I was interested to find the Fox Sparrow fairly plentiful, single birds, occasionally two or three together, being seen at intervals during the day feeding with flocks of White-throated Sparrows. Specimens now in the United States National Museum were taken on Sapelo Island March 15, 1888, and on Egg Island, near Darien, January 13, 1890.

Since it is not possible to identify races of the Fox Sparrow in the field, the migration data cited above obviously include the two races known to occur in Georgia, and should not be considered as applying sole-ly to *iliaca.*

Specimens typical of the eastern race have been examined from the following localities:

Hartwell, Hart County: December 13, 1945.

Hull, Madison County: March 5, 1946.

Athens, Clarke County: December 6, 1928, April 1, 1929, January 1, 1934, December 15, 1942, January 7, 1946.

Bogart, Oconee County: February 7, 1946.

Stone Mountain, DeKalb County: April 2, 1947.

Atlanta, Fulton County: December 30, 1946.

Monroe, Walton County: December 20, 1945.

Blakely, Early County: February 11, 1936.

Blackbeard Island, McIntosh County: January 25, 1931.

HABITS AND RECOGNITION: The Fox Sparrow is one of the hardiest of the sparrows, spending the summer in the far north, and in late fall coming south just far enough to escape the deep snows and low temperatures normal to the Northern states during most winters. In northern Georgia, it occurs regularly during the winter, but only during years of heavy snows in the southern part of its winter range does it appear in any numbers south of the fall line. During its winter sojourn in Georgia, it is largely limited in its distribution to stretches of thick, swampy woods bordering the larger streams; and being shy and difficult to approach, must usually be sought to be seen.

Its food, which consists mostly of weed seeds and small fleshy fruits, is picked from the ground; vigorous scratching in the dead leaves often attracts one's attention when the bird itself is well concealed in the dense underbrush. Arouse its curiosity, and an occasional bird will appear in the top of a bush or sapling to see what is going on, but its inherent shyness soon causes it to disappear abruptly, not to be seen again. The first small flocks observed in the fall are quiet and inconspicuous, but their presence is sooner or later revealed by their characteristic note of alarm, loud and emphatic and somewhat suggestive of that of the Brown Thrasher. By the latter part of November, however, especially if the weather is cloudy and rainy, many of the birds begin to sing, and until early spring the rich, clear song of this shy recluse of the thickets can be heard in the wooded bottom-lands. In migration, single birds, and often small flocks, can be found feeding with other sparrows in thickets and underbrush at the edges of open fields and pastures, and it is then that this species can be observed to best advantage. Little difficulty should be experienced in recognizing it, its large size and bright reddish-brown plumage being very distinctive.

Family Fringillidae: GROSBEAKS, FINCHES, SPARROWS, & BUNTINGS

Yukon Fox Sparrow
Passerella iliaca zaboria   Oberholser

GENERAL DISTRIBUTION: Breeds from Alaska, Mackenzie, and Hudson Bay south to Alberta and Manitoba. Winters south to Texas, Louisiana, and Florida.

STATUS IN GEORGIA: A fairly common winter resident in the northern part of the state and at least of casual occurrence during the winter months in the coastal plain.

"This recently described race is apparently as common in Georgia during the winter months as is *iliaca*, for out of a series of thirty Fox Sparrows taken in the northern part of the state, fourteen, or almost 50 per cent, were found referable to *zaboria*. These were taken as follows: Madison County (Pocatelago), male, February 14, 1946; Jackson County (Center), male, December 3, 1945; Clarke County (Athens), male, February 2, 1946, female, January 13, 1946; DeKalb County (Stone Mountain), male, December 10, 1944, female, December 24, 1946; (Decatur), males, February 22 and March 6, 1947, female, March 8, 1947; Fulton County (Atlanta), males, February 24 and March 11, 1947, females, January 6, March 4 and 7, 1947." [Burleigh, 1948.] The only record for the southern part of the state is that of a female taken by Francis Harper in the Okefenokee Swamp on February 7, 1936.

HABITS AND RECOGNITION: This western race resembles the Eastern Fox Sparrow, *iliaca*, but it is paler both above and below, being noticeably grayer on the back. There is nothing in its general appearance and actions to distinguish it in the field.

Northern Lincoln's Sparrow
Melospiza lincolnii lincolnii   (Audubon)

GENERAL DISTRIBUTION: Breeds from the Kowak and Yukon valleys, Alaska, southern Mackenzie, northern Manitoba, northern Quebec, and Newfoundland south to northern Minnesota, central Ontario, northern New York, New Brunswick, and Nova Scotia. Winters from southern Oklahoma, northern Mississippi, and Georgia south to southern Mexico and central Guatemala.

STATUS IN GEORGIA: A scarce transient and winter resident throughout the state.

In its long journeys to and from its summer home in the far north, the Lincoln's Sparrow follows a route that lies mainly west of the Allegheny

685

Mountains, and in the southeastern United States occurs to a large extent merely as a straggler. In Georgia, an occasional bird has been noted from early October until the following May, but at such infrequent intervals that the appearance of one is a noteworthy event.

The following records summarize the records of this species in the state up to the present time:

1900: One collected at Atlanta, January 24 [Smith, 1903].

1924: Single birds trapped in Grady County, April 7, 11, and 24 (Stoddard).

1928: One collected at Athens, May 13 [Burleigh, 1938].

1929: One collected at Athens, April 28, and another seen there, October 6 [Burleigh, 1938].

1940: Three seen on the Piedmont National Wildlife Refuge, near Round Oak, April 28 [Fleetwood, 1941]; one collected five miles south of Fitzgerald, December 19 (Norris).

1941: One bird seen at Atlanta, April 20 [Griffin, 1941]; single birds seen at Tifton, December 19 and 20, and one collected [Norris, 1942].

1943: One bird seen at Augusta, March 15 (L. Johnson); one bird seen at Macon, December 5 (Meanley).

1944: Single birds seen at Macon, March 27 and April 21 [Meanley, 1944]; one bird seen at Augusta, October 22 [Denton, 1944].

1946: One bird collected at Decatur, October 24 [Burleigh, 1947]; one bird seen at Atlanta, November 4 [Burleigh, 1947].

1948: One bird collected at Plainsville, Gordon County, October 21 [Autry, 1949].

1949: One bird seen in Charlton County, December 8–12 (Hebard).

1952: One bird seen near Tifton, April 22, and one (apparently the same individual) collected there, April 28 (Norris).

1953: One bird seen at Atlanta, April 8 (Parks).

HABITS AND RECOGNITION: In Georgia, few birds are harder to see and know than is the Lincoln's Sparrow. Its outstanding characteristic is extreme shyness, for it consistently remains concealed in the densest thickets and underbrush, and seeing one is more a matter of luck than anything else. In its summer home, its presence is soon revealed by the bubbling, wren-like song that the male frequently utters during much of the day, but even there it is difficult to become acquainted with, for the same reluctance is shown to appear in the open. Its retiring disposition makes it a hard bird to identify satisfactorily, for although its tail is shorter, it bears a close resemblance to the Song Sparrow, and the brief glimpse one usually gets leaves much to be desired in visualizing the appearance of the bird. Seen at reasonably close range, the buffy band across the breast and and the finer streaking of the underparts will distinguish it, but too often one merely sees a medium-sized sparrow skulking in a thicket, only to have it disappear when approached. In migration, it seems to prefer the vicinity of water, for at Athens, the few which I was fortunate enough to see were in each case in underbrush in the Sandy Creek bottoms.

Southern Swamp Sparrow
Melospiza georgiana georgiana (Latham)

GENERAL DISTRIBUTION: Breeds from Minnesota east to Nova Scotia and south to northern Nebraska, northern Missouri, northern Illinois, and West Virginia. Winters from Nebraska, the Ohio Valley, and New Jersey south to southern Florida, the Gulf Coast, and northern Mexico.

STATUS IN GEORGIA: A common winter resident throughout the state.

In fall, the Swamp Sparrow appears in Georgia in early October, is soon common, and remains so until the latter part of the following April. The small flocks so numerous during the winter are gone by early May, but an occasional belated individual can usually be seen until the middle of that month.

Extreme dates of occurrence over the state are as follows:

Dalton: October 11 (1941) and May 6 (1942).

Americus: October 11 (1941) and May 6 (1942).

Atlanta: October 6 (1946) and May 13 (1939).

Fitzgerald: October 9 (1940) and May 8 (1941).

Athens: October 2 (1925) and May 20 (1928).

Grady County: October 14 (1942) and May 7 (1940).

Macon: October 6 (1945) and May 7 (1932).

Savannah: October 18 (1910) and May 10 (1910).

At St. Marys, the earliest arrival date in the fall is October 19 (1905). At Augusta, the latest date of departure in the spring is May 9 (1943).

As the two races of the Swamp Sparrow found in Georgia are almost equally common, the migration data cited above, based largely on sight records, obviously cover both of them and are included under the present race merely for convenience. Many specimens typical of *georgiana* have been examined from various localities in the state, including the following:

Blairsville, Union County: November 23, 1945.

Bethlehem, Barrow County: December 24, 1945.

Toccoa, Stephens County: March 13, 1946.

Monroe, Walton County: December 20, 1945.

Lavonia, Franklin County: March 6, 1946.

Decatur, DeKalb County: December 10, 1946, April 22, 1947.

Danielsville, Madison County: March 8, 1946.

Atlanta, Fulton County: December 6, 1945, March 26, 1946.

Hull, Madison County: March 5, 1946.

Griffin, Spalding County: November 26, 1946.

Jefferson, Jackson County: December 19, 1945.

Zebulon, Pike County: December 31, 1946.

Athens, Clarke County: Fourteen specimens between the dates of November 3 (1945) and April 23 (1945).

LaGrange, Troupe County: December 2, 1937.

Winterville, Clarke County: November 30, 1945.

Hinesville, Liberty County: April 17, 1946.

Crawford, Oglethorpe County: November 7, 1945.

HABITS AND RECOGNITION: The Swamp Sparrow is one of the more common winter sparrows of Georgia. Its preference for the vicinity of open marshes and streams, however, limits its distribution, for rarely, if ever, will it be found in thickets or underbrush far from water. Cattail marshes are favored spots, and here its numbers during the winter months are limited only by the size of the area covered by the cattails. Bottomland fields overgrown with broom sedge likewise have their winter quota of Swamp Sparrows, provided a stream is close by and the ground is damp.

While not especially timid, this rather drab sparrow spends its days in the concealment of the vegetation in which it feeds, and were it not for its inquisitive disposition, could be easily overlooked. However, any disturbance will bring those birds within hearing distance to the top of the reeds or cattails in which they were lurking, and there they will remain until their curiosity is satisfied. On such occasions, they utter a sharp alarm note very much like that of the White-throated Sparrow. At a distance, the Swamp Sparrow resembles the Song Sparrow in both appearance and actions, but seen at reasonably close range, as is usually possible, its darker back and gray, unstreaked underparts will readily identify it. Before their departure in spring, males can frequently be heard singing, the song being a simple trill like that of the Chipping Sparrow, but more musical.

Northern Swamp Sparrow
Melospiza georgiana ericrypta   Oberholser

GENERAL DISTRIBUTION: Breeds in Alberta, Mackenzie, Manitoba, southern Quebec, and Newfoundland, and as far south as North Dakota. Winters south to Florida, the Gulf Coast, and northern Mexico.

STATUS IN GEORGIA: A fairly common winter resident throughout the state.

In a series of forty-two Swamp Sparrows taken in the northern half of the state from October 10, 1945, through April 23, 1946, sixteen, or a little over one-third, were found to represent *ericrypta*. As they came from ten counties, as far apart as Talbot County on the Alabama line and Hart County on the South Carolina line, this race can be considered as fairly common and of general distribution in northern Georgia during the winter months. Actual localities where these specimens were collected were Hart County (Hartwell), Clarke County (Athens), Oglethorpe County (Crawford), Jackson County (Commerce), Oconee County (Bogart and Watkinsville), Gwinnett County (Dacula), DeKalb County (Decatur and Lithonia), Fulton County (Atlanta), Wilkinson County (Irwinton), and Talbot County (Talbotton).

A single specimen from the coast, a female taken on Tybee Island, in

Chatham County, on January 27, 1946, is also referable to *ericrypta.* [Burleigh, 1947.]

That this race is equally common in southern Georgia is shown by a series of thirteen Swamp Sparrows collected by Herbert L. Stoddard in Grady County, seven of which were found to be typical of *ericrypta.* These were taken on December 6, 1943; January 2, 1944; and March 14 and 28, April 18, and November 7, 1948. Norris [Greene, et al., 1945] has taken specimens of this race at Tifton, January 1 and 3, 1943.

HABITS AND RECOGNITION: This race is distinguished by its smaller size and lighter upperparts. In general appearance and actions it is not different from other races of the Swamp Sparrow.

Coastal Plain Swamp Sparrow
Melospiza georgiana nigrescens Bond and Stewart

GENERAL DISTRIBUTION: Breeds in the Nanticoke River marshes, Wicomico County, Maryland, and probably also at other known breeding areas for the species on the Eastern Shore of Chesapeake Bay, in Maryland and Delaware, and northward near the coast to southwestern New York. Largely resident within its breeding range, but occurring in small numbers south at least to northern Georgia.

STATUS IN GEORGIA: Probably of casual occurrence in the state during the winter.

There is at present a single record of *nigrescens* in the state, a male taken at Decatur, February 14, 1947 (Burleigh).

HABITS AND RECOGNITION: Unlike the other races of the Swamp Sparrow, this dark form is found during the breeding season in the brackish tidal marshes on the coast. Within its rather limited range it is a common bird and apparently of almost equal abundance throughout the year. In contrast to *georgiana,* the upperparts are darker and more extensively black, a character readily apparent from specimens in hand.

Eastern Song Sparrow
Melospiza melodia melodia (Wilson)

GENERAL DISTRIBUTION: Breeds from central Ontario, southern Quebec, and Newfoundland southward east of the Appalachians and Piedmont to the coastal plain of Virginia. Winters from Massachusetts and New Jersey south to southern Florida and the Gulf Coast.

STATUS IN GEORGIA: A winter resident throughout the state, but apparently of casual occurrence except on the coast, where it is probably common during the winter.

Typical *melodia* are possibly largely confined to the coast region during the winter months, for but six specimens taken in the northern part of the state were found to represent this race. They were males taken at Princeton (Clarke County) on November 19, 1945, at Comer (Madison County) on January 11, 1946, and at Athens (Clarke County) on February 22 and March 10, 1946; and females taken at Talbotton (Talbot County) on November 1, 1945, and at Crawford (Oglethorpe County) on November 7, 1945 [Burleigh, 1947].

Additional specimens from the interior of the state have been examined from Flowery Branch, Hall County (November 18, 1946); Stone Mountain, DeKalb County (October 28, November 11, and December 24, 1946); Atlanta, Fulton County (October 21, 1946, and March 26 and 29, 1947); and Sharpsburg, Coweta County (March 10, 1947). Stoddard considers this race common in Grady County during the winter months, having taken specimens there on January 1, 1938, January 17 and 31, and December 6, 1943, and January 2, 1949.

In the coast region, specimens of this race have been collected at Savannah (February 26, 1933) and Hinesville (January 28, 1946).

HABITS AND RECOGNITION: During the winter months the Song Sparrow shows the same preference for the vicinity of water as the Swamp Sparrow, and can commonly be found in close association with that species. However, since thickets and underbrush bordering fields and pastures, roadsides, and wooded areas are seemingly almost as acceptable, this familiar and well-known sparrow has a wide distribution in Georgia during its winter sojourn in the state. The various races are indistinguishable in the field.

Appalachian Song Sparrow
Melospiza melodia euphonia Wetmore

GENERAL DISTRIBUTION: Breeds north to Michigan, southern Ontario, and northern Pennsylvania south to Indiana, Ohio, and Virginia, and in the Appalachians to Georgia and northwestern South Carolina. Winters south to the Gulf Coast and Florida.

STATUS IN GEORGIA: A common breeding bird in the mountain counties, where it is probably resident; south of its breeding range, a common winter resident throughout the state.

The Song Sparrow is another species which in recent years has been extending its breeding range southward into the southeastern United States. Less than fifty years ago, it was not known to breed in Georgia, but today it is fairly common in the mountains during the summer, and is beginning to invade the Piedmont. W. H. LaPrade first reported it as breeding in Union County in 1913, and that is possibly the first time that it nested in the state, as a few years earlier, in July, 1908, none were seen by A. H. Howell during ten days spent in the field at Young Harris, Towns County [Howell, 1909].

In 1922, I spent all of July at Young Harris and was interested to find the Song Sparrow fairly common there. A nest found on July 10 with three slightly incubated eggs was apparently the first verified nesting record for the state [Burleigh, 1925]. The following year I was again at Young Harris from the latter part of June until the end of July, and noted a perceptible increase in the number of Song Sparrows nesting there, scattered pairs being found in the thickets and stretches of underbrush about the town. With little difficulty, five nests were located that summer that held either eggs or young [Burleigh, 1927].

In late May, 1945, Eugene P. Odum and I "made a special effort to find out if the species had actually reached the Piedmont. Driving north from Atlanta, we first encountered Song Sparrows at Ellijay, Gilmer County, and collected a juvenile not long out of the nest. Farther east the species was singing and evidently breeding at Cleveland, White County. Finally Mr. Glenn Bell has reported a nest from Lakemont. A line drawn connecting these points approximately represents the present 'front.' All three of these localities are south of the Blue Ridge and have altitudes of less than 1,600 feet. Therefore, the Song Sparrow has actually gotten out of the mountain valleys and become established on the northern edge of the Piedmont." [Odum and Burleigh, 1946.]

The following year this species was noted breeding for the first time at Dalton, in Whitfield County, a nest being found there on June 3, 1946, that held two young [Hamiltons, 1946]. In 1949, further extension of range in the eastern part of the state was noted, Song Sparrows being found breeding at three widely separated localities in Habersham County, Clarkesville, Demorest, and Cornelia [Neal and Denton, 1950]. Finally, and rather surprisingly, the Song Sparrow was reported as nesting in 1950 at Milledgeville, Baldwin County, at the lower edge of the Piedmont [Dorris, et al., 1951]. Two pairs were present there throughout the spring and summer, and both succeeded in rearing two broods. So far as is known, it does not now nest anywhere between Cornelia and Milledgeville, and it will be interesting to see if, and when, this intervening territory is occupied by breeding Song Sparrows.

South of its breeding range, this species is a common winter resident, appearing in the fall in early October and lingering in the spring until late

April or early May. Extreme dates of occurrence in various parts of the state are as follows:

Athens: October 2 (1921) and April 22 (1928).

Atlanta: October 6 (1898) and May 9 (1939).

Macon: October 10 (1930) and May 3 (1924).

Americus: October 19 (1941) and April 25 (1942).

Fitzgerald: October 18 (1940) and March 16 (1941).

Savannah: October 12 (1910) and May 10 (1913).

Hinesville: October 31 (1943) and April 23 (1944).

These migration records are based to a large extent on sight records, and obviously involve the different geographic races known to occur in the state. However, as *euphonia* is without any question the commonest and has the widest distribution in Georgia during the winter, it seems desirable to cite all migration data under this form.

In a large series of specimens examined critically, taken during the winter months and representing practically all parts of the state, almost two-thirds were found referable to *euphonia*. Localities involved are too many to list with any degree of completeness, but include the following: Blairsville, Hartwell, Athens, Monroe, Canton, Atlanta, Griffin, LaGrange, Blakely, Grady County, Savannah, and Hinesville.

Breeding specimens typical of this Appalachian race were collected at Young Harris (Towns County), June 18 and 20, 1928 and June 19, 1929; Dillard (Rabun County), June 26, 1930; Hiawassee (Towns County), May 27, 1933; Ellijay (Gilmer County), May 29, 1945; and Helen (White County), June 27, 1946.

HABITS AND RECOGNITION: In the mountains of Georgia, where it is a common bird during the summer months, the Appalachian Song Sparrow frequents thickets and underbrush in the valleys. It has no liking for thick woods, and will never be seen on mountainsides or in wooded ravines. It is a confiding, social bird and seems to prefer the vicinity of man, as its appearance in or at the edge of a town in localities where it had not been previously observed attests. This was the case at Young Harris, and only as it increased in numbers was it gradually found at any distance from the town itself. The pair that nested at Cornelia in 1949 had selected an overgrown lot opposite the Grand Theatre, while at Milledgeville, one pair nested on the campus of the Georgia State College for Women and another on the front lawn of an apartment house close by. This characteristic lack of timidity makes the Song Sparrow an easy bird to become acquainted with, and consequently it is familiar to the average person.

In other parts of its breeding range, two or three broods are reared each year, so nests found at Young Harris in July were very probably those for second broods. The first nest found there in 1923, on July 4, held two eggs and two newly hatched young, while another examined on July 23 held four fresh eggs. These and four others that were found at Young Harris were in briar thickets, varying in height from one to four feet from the ground, and were well built of weed stems, rootlets, and grasses, lined with fine grasses and horsehair. At Milledgeville, barberry bushes were utilized as nesting sites. The single nest found there held one young bird a day or two old on June 27, but young of later broods were seen in late July and early August.

Atlantic Song Sparrow
Melospiza melodia atlantica Todd

GENERAL DISTRIBUTION: Largely resident on the Atlantic Coast from Rhode Island to North Carolina.

STATUS IN GEORGIA: Of casual occurrence on the coast during the winter.

This race of the Song Sparrow has been recorded in the state only twice, specimens having been taken by Tomkins in Chatham County on January 15, 1935 [Tomkins, 1935], and February 8, 1936.

HABITS AND RECOGNITION: Unlike the other Song Sparrows, *atlantica* is a bird of the ocean beaches, being rarely, if ever, found far from salt water. It nests in myrtle thickets and in willows at the edge of the salt marsh, obtaining much of its food in the marsh itself, somewhat in the manner of the Seaside Sparrow. Being largely resident wherever it occurs, it will probably never be of more than casual occurrence in Georgia. In appearance it is perceptibly grayer above and less heavily streaked below than the other races found in the state, but specimens are necessary to determine these characters.

Dakota Song Sparrow
Melospiza melodia juddi Bishop

GENERAL DISTRIBUTION: Breeds from Saskatchewan and eastern Montana to the Turtle Mountains, North Dakota. Winters south to Texas and New Mexico and casually east to the Gulf Coast and Georgia.

STATUS IN GEORGIA: An uncommon winter resident.

Specimens of this western race have been taken in the state as follows:

1942: Tifton, January 5 (Norris).
1946: Irwinton, January 29; Dacula (Gwinnett County), February 12; Ila (Madison County), February 13;

Decatur, February 15 and 25; Athens, February 19 and March 9; Lithonia (DeKalb County), February 25 [Burleigh, 1947].

1948: Grady County, November 7 (Stoddard).

1949: Grady County, February 6 (Stoddard).

HABITS AND RECOGNITION: In neither general appearance nor actions does this Song Sparrow differ from the others; it is merely a pale, buffy race from the relatively arid northern plains country.

Mississippi Song Sparrow
Melospiza meloda beata   Bangs

GENERAL DISTRIBUTION: Breeds in the upper Mississippi Valley region; winters south to Georgia and northern Florida.

STATUS IN GEORGIA: Of at least casual occurrence in the state during the winter months.

Specimens representing this race have been taken at Washington, Wilkes County, December 21, 1945 (Burleigh); and in Grady County, January 6, 1951 (Stoddard). Further collecting during the winter will doubtless reveal its presence elsewhere in the state.

HABITS AND RECOGNITION: Recent studies have shown that the Song Sparrows of the prairie country of the upper Mississippi Valley region are distinct from other breeding populations and that *beata* is a valid race. In appearance it is pale like *juddi*, but the upperparts are grayer, less buffy, and the dark streaks on the back are more rufescent.

Common Lapland Longspur
Calcarius lapponicus lapponicus   (Linnaeus)

GENERAL DISTRIBUTION: In North America breeds on Arctic islands and in Greenland south to Mackenzie, northern Manitoba, and northern Quebec. Winters from southern Quebec and north central United States irregularly south to the middle states and Texas.

STATUS IN GEORGIA: Largely of accidental occurrence in the state.

There are at present only a few records of the Lapland Longspur in Georgia. It was first recorded for the state by Tomkins, who saw two birds on Oysterbed Island, at the mouth of the Savannah River, on March 24, 1935, and collected one of them to verify the identification [Tomkins, 1935]. Some years later, Denton [letter] noted three birds on the airport at Augusta, January 11 to 13 and February 15, 1953, and a single bird at this same spot, January 1, 1954.

Family Fringillidae: GROSBEAKS, FINCHES, SPARROWS, & BUNTINGS

HABITS AND RECOGNITION: The Lapland Longspur is a hardy bird that rarely comes very far south, and then only during winters characterized by unusually deep snows and low temperatures. Consequently it will probably never be of more than casual occurrence in Georgia. In the interior of the state it should be looked for in open, exposed fields, since, like the Horned Lark, it seems to delight in the most barren, inhospitable sites. It is not an easy bird to see, for if approached, it will crouch motionless on the ground, taking advantage of such objects as rocks or lumps of dirt that never fail to afford it concealment. It is said to associate commonly with flocks of Horned Larks during the winter months, and this fact should be borne in mind by those in the field in late December and January.

Eastern Snow Bunting
Plectrophenax nivalis nivalis (Linnaeus)

GENERAL DISTRIBUTION: In North America, breeds in the Arctic Zone from at least latitude 83 degrees north (including Greenland) to the northern parts of the mainland from Alaska to northern Quebec. Winters from Unalaska, southern Alberta, Manitoba, and Quebec south to the northern United States, and irregularly to eastern Oregon, Colorado, Kansas, Indiana, Ohio, Virginia, Georgia, and Florida.

STATUS IN GEORGIA: Of casual occurrence during the winter months in the eastern part of the state.

What is apparently the first record of the Snow Bunting in Georgia is a specimen recorded in the catalog of the United States National Museum as taken in Liberty County and presented to the Museum by Joseph Le-Conte in 1864. This specimen is doubtless the basis for the mention of "Georgia" in the winter range of the species as given in Baird, Brewer, and Ridgway [1874], but it cannot now be found. Murphey [1937] states that a specimen was taken in Columbia County by Henry Hillyer in February, 1891. It was later destroyed by a fire, with the rest of his collection, at the University of Georgia. Wayne [1927] reports three birds seen by Mrs. L. J. Dodge at Grovetown, Columbia County, on January 28, 1927. Tomkins [1933] took a specimen on Oysterbed Island, near the mouth of the Savannah River, on December 24, 1932. Murphey [1938b] reports a specimen taken near Blythe, Richmond County, on November 10, 1937. The most recent record is that of two specimens taken by Tomkins on Tybee Island, Chatham County, December 28, 1952.

HABITS AND RECOGNITION: Nesting as it does in the far north, the Snow Bunting is a hardy bird, and only under exceptional circumstances comes as far south as Georgia during the winter. It should be looked for in those winters when the Northern states are experiencing unusually severe weather, as it is doubtful that the average winter there inconveniences to any extent a species whose summer home is well within the Arctic Circle. Like the Horned Lark and the Longspur, it feeds by preference in the most open, exposed fields, and will never be found where the grass is long enough to conceal it even partially. Flocks encountered during the winter months are characterized by their restlessness, and soon attract attention wherever they occur, for at a distance, and especially when in the air, the birds appear wholly white. Seen at reasonably close range, however, which is frequently possible since the birds are not timid, the brown of the back and crown is at once noticeable. Essentially a ground-loving species, the Snow Bunting rarely alights in a tree or even on the top of a fence post, but when one pictures the openness of the Arctic tundra in which the summer months are spent, this preference is easily understood.

HYPOTHETICAL LIST

In preparing the list of birds accredited to Georgia, an occasional species was found recorded for the state on evidence that was considered questionable or inconclusive. Consequently the decision was reached that only those species whose presence in Georgia has been verified by a specimen taken in the state and examined by a competent ornithologist would be placed on the accredited list. While certain sight records are probably correct, in view of the difficulty of choosing among such records, it seems desirable to consider all of them hypothetical until specimens are actually taken.

Pacific Loon
Gavia arctica pacifica (Lawrence)

This species was credited to the state by John LeConte, who prepared a list of the birds of Georgia published in 1849 in the appendix of *Statistics of the State of Georgia*, by George White. The list was not annotated, and in view of the lack of any actual data this record is considered extremely doubtful.

Audubon's Shearwater
Puffinus lherminieri lherminieri Lesson

Mentioned by Audubon [1840–44] as occurring in Georgia, but without further evidence this species must be placed in the hypothetical list.

Northern White-tailed Tropic-bird
Phaethon lepturus catesbyi Brandt

William W. Griffin [1940] reports this species at Atlanta on August 15, 1940, one bird being seen that day on one of the waterworks lakes. He was doubtless correct in his identification, but until a specimen has been taken in Georgia, it seems desirable to place this tropic-bird in the hypothetical list.

White-bellied Booby
Sula leucogaster leucogaster (Boddaert)

Audubon [1840–44] states that this species occurs off the coast of Georgia, but this evidence is too inconclusive to warrant placing the White-bellied Booby on the accredited state list.

Cattle Egret
Ardeola ibis   (Linnaeus)

In view of the recent appearance and almost immediate increase of this Old World species in Florida, it was not unexpected that it should be reported in 1954 in Georgia. On July 27 a single bird was seen by Herbert L. Stoddard in McIntosh County (letter), "flying down the Altamaha River, beating his way slowly against a head wind." While there can be no question of the identification of this bird, the Cattle Egret should remain on the hypothetical list until a specimen is taken in the state.

Scarlet Ibis
Endocimus ruber   (Linnaeus)

Walter Faxon [1896] included this species in his list of water-color paintings of the birds of Georgia made by John Abbot from about 1800 to 1810. Latham, in his *General History of Birds* [1X:145, 1824], also recorded it on Abbot's authority. In view of the fact that the normal range of this ibis is in tropical South America, these old records must be left in question.

Flamingo
Phoenicopterus ruber   Linnaeus

The Flamingo was included on the list of Georgia birds prepared by John LeConte [White, 1849], but no evidence was given for the inclusion of this species so far north of its normal range.

Trumpeter Swan
Olor buccinator   Richardson

The Trumpeter Swan is another species that John LeConte included in his list of the birds of Georgia [White, 1849]. It is not improbable that at one time, when this swan existed in far greater numbers than it does now, it occurred in the state, but as there are no definite records, it seems advisable to keep it on the hypothetical list.

White-winged Scoter
Melanitta deglándi   (Bonaparte)

J. Fred Denton reports (letter) that "On January 23, 1954, Saturday P.M., the Schwalbes located an adult male [of this species] on the river about ¾ of a mile above the pumping station [at Augusta]. They studied it carefully and were sure of its identification so telephoned me when they got in that night. Schwalbe and I went out early the next morning and found the bird feeding in the same spot. I had excellent views of it sitting on the water, raising its wings, and in short flight." There is no reason to question this identification, but until a specimen is taken in the state, it seems desirable that the White-winged Scoter remain on the hypothetical list.

698

White-tailed Kite
Elanus leucurus majusculus   Bangs and Penard

This is still another species included by John LeConte in his list of the birds of Georgia [White, 1849]. It has been recorded both in Florida and in South Carolina, but more definite evidence seems desirable before it can be accepted in Georgia.

Florida Bobwhite
Colinus virginianus floridanus   (Coues)

Hebard [1941] states that Dr. E. W. Nelson identified specimens of the Bobwhite from St. Marys, in southeastern Camden County, as typical of *floridanus*. However, recent taxonomic studies by Aldrich [1946a] show that even in northern Florida this species is intermediate in its characters between *floridanus* and *virginianus*. Hence, this subspecies is put in the hypothetical list.

Eskimo Curlew
Numenius borealis   (Forster)

This is another species included by John LeConte in his list of the birds of Georgia [White, 1849]. Even in the days when it was common in migration on the Atlantic Coast, it was never recorded south of New Jersey, and definite evidence would be required to include it in the Georgia list.

Hudsonian Godwit
Limosa haemastica   (Linnaeus)

This is still another species included by John LeConte in his list of the birds of Georgia [White, 1849]. Although it would not be surprising if this species occurred occasionally, it must be considered hypothetical until a specimen is actually taken.

Black-legged Kittiwake
Rissa tridactyla tridactyla   (Linnaeus)

Tomkins [1940] reports seeing a Kittiwake near Savannah on April 6, 1937 under circumstances that left little doubt in his mind as to identification of this far northern gull. However, since the appearance of a species such as this can only be accidental in Georgia, it seems desirable to place it on the hypothetical list until a specimen is taken.

Roseate Tern
Sterna dougalli dougalli   Montagu

Hebard [1940] states that on November 5, 1940, a young Roseate Tern that had just died was picked up by John Burch on Mill Creek in western Camden County. The skin was sent to the Academy of Natural Sciences at Philadelphia, Pennsylvania, but it has since been misplaced and cannot now be found. Some doubt has developed concerning the identification of this specimen, and thus it seems desirable to place this species in the hypothetical list.

Atlantic Puffin
Fratercula arctica arctica (Linnaeus)
Audubon [1840–44] mentions this species as occurring off the Georgia coast, but as there are no definite records, the Puffin must remain on the hypothetical list.

Burrowing Owl
Speotyto cunicularia Bonaparte
On January 9, 1941, a Burrowing Owl was seen on Sea Island, McIntosh County, by Mr. and Mrs. Athos Menaboni [Menaboni, 1941], but it was not possible at the time to collect it. There are no other records for the state, so until a specimen is actually taken, this species must remain on the hypothetical list.

Florida Jay
Aphelocoma coerulescens coerulescens (Bosc)
Thompson [1896] reports seeing two jays at the edge of the Okefenokee Swamp which impressed him as being distinct from the Blue Jay. He succeeded in killing one with an arrow, and found that it was a Florida Jay. Unfortunately the specimen was not saved, and while his identification was probably correct, southern Georgia is so far north of the accepted range of this species that it seems advisable, pending further confirmation, to place it in the hypothetical list.

Eastern Warbling Vireo
Vireo gilvus gilvus (Vieillot)
The Warbling Vireo has been reported in the state on two occasions. W. W. Worthington saw a bird which he identified as this species at the mouth of the Altamaha River on April 28, 1890; and Dr. Eugene E. Murphey [1937] has another sight record for Augusta, October 15, 1935. While both identifications may be correct, there is always the possibility of error where such an obscure species as this vireo is concerned, so until a specimen is taken it seems desirable to place it on the hypothetical list.

Brewster's Warbler
Vermivora leucobronchialis (Brewster)
Brewster's Warbler is a hybrid between the Golden-winged Warbler (*Vermivora chrysoptera*) and the Blue-winged Warbler (*Vermivora*

pinus). There are records for both Atlanta and Augusta, the most recent being a male taken by Richard A. Parks at Atlanta on April 30, 1949 [Parks, 1950].

Audubon's Warbler
Dendroica auduboni (Townsend)

Dr. Thomas W. Simpson, of Winston-Salem, N. C., writes [letter] that on February 17, 1936, a dead warbler was picked up in the school yard of the high school at Brunswick that closely resembled a Myrtle Warbler, but differed in having "a bright yellow throat." The specimen was not preserved, but a detailed description was sent to Dr. Alexander Wetmore, who agreed that there was little question that it was an Audubon's Warbler. It is unfortunate that the bird was not saved, as under the circumstances this species must be placed in the hypothetical list until its occurrence in the state is further verified.

Sutton's Warbler
Dendroica potomac Haller

The exact status of Sutton's Warbler is in doubt, but it seems probable that it is a hybrid between the Parula Warbler (*Parula americana*) and the Yellow-throated Warbler (*Dendroica dominica*). It has been reported from the state but once, a male being seen at Demorest by Mrs. Dorothy P. Neal on May 10, 1949 [Neal, 1949].

Ridgway's Grackle
Quiscalus quiscula ridgwayi Oberholser

This grackle is now considered a hybrid between the Bronzed Grackle (*Quiscalus quiscula versicolor*) and the Purple Grackle (*Quiscalus quiscula stonei*) [Chapman, 1940]. A typical male was taken by William W. Griffin in Fulton County on September 21, 1939.

Common Redpoll
Acanthis flammea flammea (Linnaeus)

This little finch was first reported for the state by Earle R. Greene [1933], who saw several at Atlanta on February 5 and 11, 1922. Farrar [1952] reports a single individual seen at Macon during January, 1951. As no specimens were taken and it is easy to confuse this species with the Pine Siskin, it seems desirable that the Redpoll be placed on the hypothetical list until more conclusive evidence verifies its occurrence in the state.

White-winged Crossbill
Loxia leucoptera leucoptera Gmelin

John Abbot included this species in his series of water-color paintings of the birds of Georgia listed by Walter Faxon [Faxon, 1896], and Latham, *General History of Birds* [V:210, 1822] listed it from the same authority. Modern collected specimens are desirable.

Tree Sparrow
Spizella arborea   (Wilson)
There is a single sight record of the Tree Sparrow in Georgia, three birds being seen by Aaron C. Bagg on February 25, 1921, feeding on a lawn within the city limits of Augusta [Bagg, 1922]. He was probably correct in his identification, but in the case of a species such as this which could be confused with other common species, a specimen should be taken before it is placed on the accredited list.

Clay-colored Sparrow
Spizella pallida   (Swainson)
Alexander Sprunt [1936b] reports seeing a Clay-colored Sparrow on Cumberland Island, Camden County, on April 15, 1932, but did not collect it. Another bird was observed by Richard Kuerzi on his front lawn at St. Marys, April 22, 1950 [Denton, letter]. A species such as this is difficult to identify in the field; therefore, while the identification in each case may be correct, the Clay-colored Sparrow should remain on the hypothetical list until a specimen is actually taken in the state.

LIST OF BIRDS ORIGINALLY

DESCRIBED FROM GEORGIA

SPECIES	TYPE LOCALITY	PRESENT STATUS OF NAME
Rallus longirostris waynei Brewster Proc. New Engl. Zool. Club, 1, 50 (June 9, 1899).	St. Marys, Camden County	In use
Arenaria interpres morinella (Linnaeus) *Tringa Morinella* Linnaeus, *Syst. Nat.*, ed. 12, 1 (1766), 249. Based mainly on "The Turn-Stone," *Morinellus marinus* Catesby, *Carolina*, 1, 72.	Coast of Georgia	In use
Dendrocopos villosus audubonii (Swainson) *Picus Audubonii* Swainson, in Swainson and Richardson, *Fauna Bor.-Am.*, 11 (1831) [1832], 306.	Georgia	In use
Thryothorus ludovicianus alleghani Bailey Bailey, *Mus. Nat. Hist.*, Bull. No. 2 (1924).	Cobb County	Synonym of *ludovicianus*
Telmatodytes palustris griseus (Brewster) *Cistothorus palustris griseus* Brewster, *Auk*, X, No. 3 (July, 1893), 216.	Sapelo Island	In use
Cistothorus platensis stellaris (Naumann) *Troglodytes stellaris* "(Lichst.)" Naumann, *Naturg. Vogel Deutschl.*, 111 (1823), table to p. 724 (see Stresemann, *Auk*, 70 [1953], 113–17).	Vicinity of Georgia	In use
Regulus satrapa satrapa Lichtenstein *Regulus satrapa* Lichtenstein, *Verz. Doubl.* (1823), 35. Am. sept. = vicinity of Savannah (see Stresemann, *Auk*, 70 [1953], 113–17).	Savannah	In use
Dendroica pinus pinus (Wilson) *Sylvia pinus* Wilson, *Am. Orn.*, 111 (1811), 25 (pl. 19, fig. 4).	Georgia	In use

Seiurus aurocapillus canivirens
  Burleigh and Duvall
    Wilson Bull., 64, No. 1 (March,
    1952), 39–42.

Margret, Fannin
County

In use

Geothlypis trichas typhicola
  Burleigh
    Proc. Biol. Soc. Wash., 47 (Feb. 9,
    1934), 21–22.

Athens

In use

Loxia curvirostra pusilla Gloger
    Loxia pusilla Gloger, *Vollst. Handb.*
    Nat. Vögel Europa's (1834), 356.

Georgia

In use

Pipilo alleni rileyi Koelz
    Proc. Biol. Soc. Wash., 52 (July 22,
    1939), 121–22.

Brunswick

In use

Passerculus sandwichensis savanna
  (Wilson)
    Fringilla Savanna Wilson, *Am. Orn.*,
    111 (1811), 55 (pl. 22, fig. 3).

Savannah

In use

Passerherbulus caudacutus
  (Latham)
    Fringilla caudacuta Latham, *Index*
    Orn., 1 (1790), 459.

Interior of Georgia

In use

Ammospiza maritima waynei
  (Oberholser)
    Thryospiza maritima waynei (Ober-
    holser), *Proc. Biol. Soc. Wash.*, 44,
    123–28.

Cabbage Island,
Chatham County

Synonym of
macgillivraii

Aimophila aestivalis aestivalis
  (Lichtenstein)
    Fringilla aestavalis Lichtenstein,
    Verz. Doubl. (1823), 25.

Georgia

In use

Melospiza georgiana georgiana
  (Latham)
    Fringilla georgiana Latham, *Index*
    Orn., 1 (1790), 460.

Georgia

In use

BIBLIOGRAPHY

OF GEORGIA ORNITHOLOGY

Abbott, Gerald Alan
  1915. Abbott's collection of North American Warbler's eggs. Oologist, 32:129–30.
Aldrich, John Warren
  1944. Geographic variation of Bewick Wrens in the eastern United States. Occas. Papers Mus. Zool., La. State Univ., 18:305–309.
  1946a. The United States Races of the Bob-white. Auk, 63:493–508.
  1946b. New subspecies of birds from western North America. Proc. Biol. Soc. Wash., 59:129–36.
———, and Thomas D. Burleigh
  1946. Coastal pine forest. Audubon Mag., sec. II (Aud. field notes), 10th breeding-bird census, Nov.–Dec.: 145.
Aldrich, John W., and Herbert Friedmann
  1943. A Revision of the Ruffed Grouse. Condor, 45:85–103.
Allen, Elsa Guerdrum
  1942. A third set of John Abbot bird drawings. Auk, 59:563–71.
  1948. A résumé of John Abbot's "Notes on my life." Oriole, 13:31–32.
  1951. The history of American ornithology before Audubon. Trans. Am. Philos. Soc. 41 (new ser.): 387–591. 53 figs.
Allen, Joel Asoph
  1888. Further Notes on Seaside Sparrows. Auk, 5:246.
Amadon, Dean
  1949. Purple sandpiper in Georgia—A correction. Oriole, 14:20.
Ambrosen, Donald R.
  1950. Blue Goose and Sandhill Crane in Jones County, Georgia. Oriole, 15:8.
American Ornithologists' Union
  1931. Check-List of North American birds, 4th ed. Prepared by an A.O.U. committee, Witmer Stone, chairman.

Arnow, Isaac F.
  1904a. Holboell's Grebe and the White Pelican at St. Mary's, Georgia. Auk, 21:277.
  1904b. Capture of Krider's Hawk at St. Mary's, Georgia. Auk, 21:277–78.
  1906. The Seaside Sparrow nesting in bushes. Auk, 23:226.
  1907a. The American Crossbill in Camden County, Georgia. Auk, 24:439–40.
  1907b. Large set of Brown-headed Nuthatch's eggs. Auk, 24:447.
  1908a. American Woodcock breeding at Saint Mary's, Georgia. Auk, 25:220.
  1908b. Masked Duck (Nomonyx dominicus) in Chatham County, Georgia. Auk, 25:472.
  1908c. American Avocet (Recurvirostra americana) in Camden County, Georgia. Auk, 25:473.
  1908d. Lark Sparrow (Chondestes grammacus) in Camden County, Georgia. Auk, 25:476.
  1908e. Bachman's Warbler in Camden County and breeding in Chatham County, Georgia. Auk, 25:479.
  1908f. Cape May Warbler in Camden County, Georgia. Auk, 25:479.
  1909. The Masked Duck—A Correction. (Specimen reported as this species found to be a Lesser Scaup). Auk, 26:189.
Audubon, John James
  1831–39. Ornithological biography, or an account of the habits of the birds of the United States of America, with descriptions of the American birds and delineations of American scenery and manners. Edinburgh, Adam Black. Vols. I–V.
  1840–44. The Birds of America, from drawings made in the United States and their territories. 7 vols. New

York, J. J. Audubon; Philadelphia, J. B. Chevalier. 500 pl.

Autry, H. V.
1949. Lincoln's Sparrow in northwest Georgia. Oriole, 14:10.

Bagg, Aaron Clark
1922. Tree Sparrow (*Spizella monticola monticola*) in Georgia. Auk, 39:263–264.

Bailey, Harold Harris
1924. A wren from the Southern Alleghenies, *Thryothorus ludovicianus alleghani*. Bailey Mus. Nat. Hist., Bull. No. 2.

Bailey, Harry Balch
1883. Memoranda of a collection of eggs from Georgia. Bull. Nuttall Orn. Club, 8:37–43.

Baird, Spencer Fullerton
1858. *Helmitherus swainsoni*, Bonap. Swainson's Warbler. Rep. Pacific R.R. Survey, 9:253.
———, T. M. Brewer, and Robert Ridgway
1874. A history of North American birds: Land birds. Vol. I, xxviii, 596 pp.; vol. II, 590 pp.; vol. III, xxviii, 560 pp. 64 pl.

Baldwin, Samuel Prentiss
1919. Bird banding by means of systematic trapping. Abs. Proc. Linnean Soc. of N. Y., 1918–19, 31 (Dec. 23, 1919): 23–56.
1921. Recent returns from trapping and banding birds. Auk, 38:228–37.
1922. Adventures in bird banding in 1921. Auk, 39:210–24.
1925. History of the quail investigation. Wilson Bull., 37:98–100.
1931. Bird banding by systematic trapping. Sci. Pub. Cleveland Mus. Nat. Hist., 1 (No. 5):125–68.

Bangs, Outram
1898a. Some new races of birds from eastern North America. Auk, 15:173–83.
1898b. Cairn's Warbler (*Dedroica caerulescens cairnsi*) in Georgia on migration. Auk, 15:192.
1902. A new Long-billed Marsh Wren from eastern North America. Auk, 19:349–53.
1930. The Screech Owls of Eastern North America. Auk, 47:403–404.

Barkalow, Fred Schenck
1936. Unusual nesting records of the Mourning Dove from Cobb County, Georgia. Oriole, 1:26.
1940. Additional notes on nesting extremes for birds breeding in the Atlanta region. Oriole, 5:53–54.

Barton, Benjamin Smith
1817. Some account of the *Tantalus ephouskyca*, a rare American bird. Trans. Linnean Soc., London, 12 (Pt. I):24–27, pl. 1.

Bartram, William
1791. Travels through North and South Carolina, Georgia, East and West Florida, the Cherokee Country, etc. Philadelphia. xxiv, 522 pp., 9 pl.

Bassett, Anna Stowell (Mrs. V. H.)
1927. Prothonotary Warbler breeding in Chatham County, Georgia. Auk, 44:425.
1928. Yellow-headed Blackbird and Baltimore Oriole in Georgia. Auk, 45:221.
1930. Notes from Georgia. Bird-Lore, 32:125.
1933a. Starling nests in Georgia. Bird-Lore, 35:210.
1933b. Anhinga nesting in Liberty Co., Ga. Auk, 50:427.
1937. Notes on Anhingas seen at King's Pond. Oriole, 2:4–5.
1938. Some Georgia records of John Abbot, naturalist. Auk, 55:244–54.
1939. Orphans of the Tillandsia. Oriole, 4:13–15.
1941. A late specimen of Bachman's Warbler from Georgia. Oriole, 6:38.

Belger, Clarence Albert
1950a. Whistling Swan and Red-backed Sandpiper again at Augusta, Georgia. Oriole, 15:9.
1950b. Northern Phalarope in Augusta. Oriole, 15:41.

Bell, Glenn W.
1938. Some nesting data on north Georgia birds. Oriole, 3:21–22.
1939. Notes of interest from Morgan County. Oriole, 4:64.
1940a. Black-billed Cuckoo nesting in Fulton County. Oriole, 5:34.
1940b. Random notes from about state. Oriole, 5:34.
1941. The Least Flycatcher breeding in northeast Georgia. Oriole, 6:36–37.
1942. Correction: on article, "The Least Flycatcher breeding in north-

706

east Georgia." (Record considered hypothetical pending further evidence). Oriole, 7:9.

1944. The Golden Eagle in northeast Georgia. Oriole, 9:37.

1952. Whistling Swans in Floyd County. Oriole, 17:28.

———, and Ray C. Werner

1947. King Rail nesting in DeKalb County near Atlanta. Oriole, 12:36-37.

Bendire, Charles Emil

1893. The Cowbirds. Rep. U. S. Nat. Mus., 1893 (1895):589-624.

Bent, Arthur Cleveland

1921. Life histories of North American gulls and terns. Order *Longipennes*. U. S. Nat. Mus., Bull. 113 (Aug. 27, 1921). x, 345 pp., 93 pl.

1926. Life histories of North American marsh birds. Orders *Odontoglossae*, *Herodiones* and *Paludicolae*. U. S. Nat. Mus., Bull. 135 (March 11, 1927). xii, 490 pp., 98 pl.

1927. Life histories of North American shore birds. Order *Limicolae*. U. S. Nat. Mus., Bull. 142 (Dec. 31, 1927), Pt. I. ix, 420 pp., 55 pl.

1929. Life histories of North American shore birds. Order *Limicolae*. U. S. Nat. Mus., Bull. 146 (March 24, 1929), Pt. II. ix, 412 pp., 66 pl.

1932. Life histories of North American gallinaceous birds. Orders *Galliformes* and *Columbiformes*. U. S. Nat. Mus., Bull. 162 (May 25, 1932). xi, 490 pp., 93 pl.

1937. Life histories of North American birds of prey. Order *Falconiformes*. U. S. Nat. Mus., Bull. 167 (May 3, 1937), Pt. I. viii, 409 pp., 102 pl.

1938. Life histories of North American birds of prey. Orders *Falconiformes* and *Strigiformes*. U. S. Nat. Mus., Bull. 170 (Aug. 8, 1938), Pt. II. viii, 482 pp., 92 pl.

1939. Life histories of North American woodpeckers. U. S. Nat. Mus., Bull. 174 (May 23, 1939). viii, 334 pp., 39 pl.

1940. Life histories of North American cuckoos, goatsuckers, hummingbirds, and their allies. Orders *Psittaciformes, Cuculiformes, Trogoniformes, Coraciiformes, Caprimulgiformes* and *Micropodiiformes*. U. S. Nat. Mus.,

Bull. 176 (July 20, 1940). viii, 506 pp., 73 pl.

1942. Life histories of North American flycatchers, larks, swallows, and their allies. U. S. Nat. Mus., Bull. 179 (May 8, 1942). xi, 555 pp., 70 pl.

1946. Life histories of North American jays, crows, and titmice. Order *Passeriformes*. U. S. Nat. Mus., Bull. 191 (Jan. 27, 1947). xi, 495 pp., 68 pl.

1948. Life histories of North American nuthatches, wrens, thrashers, and their allies. Order *Passeriformes*. U. S. Nat. Mus., Bull. 195 (July 7, 1948). xi, 475 pp., 90 pl.

1949. Life histories of North American thrushes, kinglets, and their allies. Order *Passeriformes*. U. S. Nat. Mus., Bull. 196 (June 28, 1949). viii, 454 pp., 51 pl.

1950. Life histories of North American wagtails, shrikes, vireos, and their allies. Order *Passeriformes*. U. S. Nat. Mus., Bull. 197. vii, 411 pp., 48 pl.

Berry, H. A.

1882. Monkey-headed Owl. Orn. and Ool., 7:111-12.

Brannon, Peter A.

1920. The Purple Grackle at Albany, Georgia. Auk, 37:454.

Braun, Emma Lucy

1950. Deciduous forests of eastern North America. Philadelphia and Toronto, the Blakiston Co. xiv, 596 pp.

Brewer, Thomas Mayo

1878. (A note on measurements of eggs of *Peucaea arizonae* and *Peucaea aestivalis*). Proc. U. S. Nat. Mus., 1:127.

1879. Notes on the nests and eggs of the eight N. A. species of *Empidonaces*. Proc. U. S. Nat. Mus., 2:1-10.

Brewster, William

1877. The Yellow-throated Warbler (in Georgia). Bull. Nuttall Orn. Club, 2:102.

1880. Nesting of the Blue Yellow-backed Warbler in Southern Georgia. Bull. Nuttall Orn. Club, 5:48.

1882. Impressions of some southern birds. Bull. Nuttall Orn. Club, 7:94-104.

1883. Lists of birds observed in the vicinity of Colorado Springs, Colorado, during March, April, and May, 1882. Comment made on a specimen of *Helminthophila celata obscura* Ridgway taken at St. Mary's, Ga., in the spring. Bull. Nuttall Orn. Club, 8:151–61.

1885. Swainson's Warbler. Auk, 2:65–80.

1887. Three new forms of North American birds. Auk, 4:145–49.

1888. *Cistothorus palustris marianae* on the coast of Georgia. Auk, 5:432.

1889. Krider's Hawk (*Buteo borealis kriderii*) on the coast of Georgia. Auk, 6:70.

1890. The Acadian Sharp-tailed Sparrow and Scott's Seaside Sparrow on the coast of South Carolina. Comment made on specimens taken at St. Mary's Ga. Auk, 7:212.

1893a. Description of a new Marsh Wren, with critical notes on *Cistothorus marianae* Scott. Auk, 10:215–19.

1893b. The Ipswich Sparrow (*Ammodramus princeps*) on the coast of Georgia. Auk, 10:302.

1893c. Two corrections. Comment on Ipswich Sparrow taken in Georgia. Auk, 10:365.

1899. An undescribed Clapper Rail from Georgia and east Florida. Proc. New Eng. Zool. Club, 1:49–51.

1950. St. Mary's, Georgia: 1877. From the journal of William Brewster. Ed. by Frederick V. Hebard. Oriole, 15: 1–6, 25–30.

Brodkorb, Pierce

1950. Geographical variation in the Gray Kingbird, *Tyrannus dominicensis*. Auk, 67:333–44.

Broley, Charles Lavelle

1947. Migration and nesting of Florida Bald Eagles. Wilson Bull., 59:3–20.

Brooks, Maurice

1940. The breeding Warblers of the central Allegheny Mountain region. Wilson Bull., 52:249–66.

Burleigh, Thomas Dearborn

1923. In the haunts of Swainson's Warbler. Murrelet, 4 (No. 1):5–7.

1925a. Notes on the breeding birds of Northeastern Georgia. Auk, 42:70–74.

1925b. Notes on the breeding habits of some Georgia birds. Auk, 42:396–401.

1927a. High lights of the past nesting season in Georgia. Murrelet, 8 (No. 1).

1927b. Three interesting breeding records for 1925 from the Piedmont region of northeastern Georgia. Wilson Bull., 39:15–19.

1927c. Further notes on the breeding birds of northeastern Georgia. Auk, 44:229–34.

1927d. Effect of an early spring on the resident breeding birds of Athens, Clarke Co., Georgia. Auk, 44:429–31.

1927e. A preliminary list of the birds of the campus of the Georgia State College of Agriculture, Athens, Clarke County, Georgia. Cypress Knee, 1927:29–45.

1928a. Occurrence of the Old Squaw (*Clangula hyemalis*) at Athens, Clarke Co., Georgia. Auk, 45:92–93.

1928b. Occurrence of the Connecticut Warbler (*Oporornis agilis*) at Athens, Clarke Co., Georgia. Auk, 45: 102–103.

1933. The present status of Brewer's Blackbird in the Southeast. Wilson Bull., 45:111–13.

1934a. Description of a new subspecies of Yellow-throat, *Geothlypis trichas*, from Georgia. Proc. Biol. Soc. Wash., 47:21–22.

1934b. A critical study of the distribution and abundance of *Dendroica castanea* and *Dendroica striata* in the southeastern states during the spring and fall migrations. Wilson Bull., 46:142–47.

1935a. The Brewer's Blackbird at Athens, Clarke County, Georgia. Wilson Bull., 47:236–37.

1935b. Two new birds from the southern Appalachians. Proc. Biol. Soc. Wash., 48:61–62.

1936. Egg laying by the Cowbird during migration. Wilson Bull., 48:13–16.

1937. The Yellowthroats of Georgia. Oriole, 2:32–33.

1938. The birds of Athens, Clarke County, Georgia. Occas. Paper No. 1, Ga. Orn. Soc. (February):1–35.

1941a. Further notes on the birds of Athens, Clarke County, Georgia. Oriole, 6:5–7.

1941b. Occurrence of the Western Grasshopper Sparrow in Georgia. Oriole, 6:11–12.

1941c. Probable breeding of the Eastern Nighthawk in Clarke County. Oriole, 6:38.

1942. The Arkansas Kingbird (*Tyrannus verticalis*) in Georgia. Oriole, 7:6.

1943. Recent notes from Athens, Clarke County, Georgia. Oriole, 8:17–18.

1944. The bird life of the Gulf Coast region of Mississippi. Occas. Papers Mus. Zool., La. State Univ., 20:329–490. 1 fig.

1946. Notes on the fall migration of 1945 in northeastern Georgia. Oriole, 11:11–14.

1947a. Notes on the fall migration of 1946 in the Atlanta, Georgia, area. Oriole, 12:13–15.

1947b. Notes on birds of Georgia based on recent collections made in the state. Oriole, 12:25–32.

1948a. Notes on the birds of Georgia based on recent collections made in the state, Part II. Oriole, 13:2–8.

1948b. An early summer record for the American Egret at Athens. Oriole, 13:10.

1948c. A Georgia record for the Mexican Ground Dove. Oriole, 13:26.

1948d. A further extension of the breeding range of the Mountain Vireo in the lower Piedmont plateau of Georgia. Oriole, 13:34.

———, and Allen Joseph Duvall

1952. A new Ovenbird from the southeastern United States. Wilson Bull., 64:39–42.

———, and George H. Lowery, Jr.

1944. Geographical variation in the Red-bellied Woodpecker in the southeastern United States. Occas. Papers Mus. Zool., La. State Univ., 17:293–301. 2 figs.

1945. Races of *Vireo griseus* in eastern United States. Am. Mid. Nat., 34 (No. 2): 526–30.

———, and Harold S. Peters

1948. Geographic variation in Newfoundland birds. Proc. Biol. Soc. Wash., 61:111–24.

Burns, Franklin Lorenzo

1908. Alexander Wilson IV, the making of the American ornithology. Wilson Bull., 20:165–85.

Burns, Mary

1943. Blue-gray Gnatcatcher at Milledgeville in winter. Oriole, 8:21.

Campbell, Marius R.

1925. *See* LaForge, *et al.*

Cantrell, Horace B.

1947. How I became interested in bird photography. Oriole, 12:18–20.

Carver, Gail Luke

1944. Economic value of birds. Oriole, 9:3.

Cassin, John

1863. Notes on the *Picidea*, with descriptions of new and little known species. Proc. Acad. Nat. Sci. Phila., 15:194–204, 322–28.

Catesby, Mark

1731–71. The natural history of Carolina, Florida, and the Bahama Islands. London, 1st ed., 1731–45; 2nd ed., 1754; 3rd ed., 2 vols., 1771.

Chapman, Frank Michler

1899. The distribution and relationships of *Ammodramus maritimus* and its allies. Auk, 16:12.

1907. The eastern forms of *Geothlypis trichas*. Auk, 24:30–34.

1940. Further studies of the genus *Quiscalus*. Auk, 57:225–33.

Cleckley, M. T.

1897. List of birds of Georgia. Nat. Sci. Journ. (New Bedford, Conn.): 45–46.

1903. Nest and eggs of the Swainson's Warbler. Auk, 20:438–39.

1904. Nest and eggs of Swainson's Warbler. Oologist, 21:26–27.

1907. In the haunts of Swainson's Warbler. Privately printed pamphlet (7 pp.) with photographs by the author. July 1.

Clements, Frederick Edward, and Victor Ernest Shelford

1939. Bio-ecology. New York, John Wiley and Sons, Inc.

Cole, Leon Jacob, Herbert Lee Stoddard, and Edwin Vaclar Komarek

1949. Red Bob-white—A report and correction. Auk, 66:28–35.

Colston, J. Willard

1950. Duck Hawk in Habersham County, Georgia. Oriole, 15:23.

Cooke, Wells Woodbridge
1908a. The Horned Lark in Georgia.
Auk, 25:318.
1908b. The Acadian Sharp-tailed Sparrow in Georgia and Florida. Auk, 25:319.
1908c. The Nelson Sparrow in Georgia and Florida. Auk, 25:318–19.
1911. Our Greatest Travelers. Nat. Geo. Mag., 22:346–65.
Cooke, Wythe
1925. *See* LaForge *et al.*
Cottam, Clarence
1951. Snow Goose near Richmond Hill, Georgia. Oriole, 16:23.
Coues, Elliott
1875. Fasti ornithologiae redivivi.—No. 1, Bartram's "Travels." Proc. Acad. Nat. Sci. Phila., 27:338–58.
Davis, T. F., and David W. Johnston
1947. Summer occurrence of the Black Duck in Georgia. Oriole, 12:47.
Delacour, Jean
1951. Preliminary note on the taxonomy of Canada geese, *Branta canadensis*. Am. Mus. Novitates, 1537:1–10.
DeLoach, R. J. H.
1940. Birds in relation to the 1940 hurricane. Oriole, 5:28.
Denton, James Fred
1936a. Wood Ibis and American Egret at Macon, Bibb County, Georgia. Oriole, 1:8–9.
1936b. Does the Cerulean Warbler nest in Georgia? Oriole, 1:10.
1936c. The Florida Gallinule at Athens, Clarke County, Georgia. Oriole, 1:26.
1936d. The White-throated Sparrow in Georgia in June. Oriole, 1:27.
1937. Harris's Sparrow in Georgia. Oriole, 2:19.
1942a. The Carolina Junco at Athens, Clarke County, Georgia. Oriole, 7:19–20.
1942b. The Red-backed Sandpiper at Augusta. Oriole, 7:34–35.
1942c. The Redstart breeding at Americus, Sumter County, Georgia. Oriole, 7:35.
1942–43. Notes on the birds of Americus, Sumter County, Georgia. Oriole, 7:29–31; 8:3–5.
1943a. A fall specimen of the Black-

polled Warbler from Augusta. Oriole, 8:20–21.
1943b. Ring-billed Gull at Augusta. Oriole, 8:22.
1943c. A probable record of the Sage Thrasher in Georgia. Oriole, 8:22.
1943d. A Nighthawk-Kingbird incident. Oriole, 8:23.
1944a. Correction (*re* Sage Thrasher record). Oriole, 9:17.
1944b. Records with comments on the status of certain warblers in Richmond County, Georgia. Oriole, 9:30–31.
1944c. The Stilt Sandpiper at Augusta. Oriole, 9:35–36.
1944d. Royal Tern at Augusta. Oriole, 9:36–37.
1944e. The Mississippi Kite at Macon. Oriole, 9:37.
1944f. The Lincoln's Sparrow at Augusta. Oriole, 9:37–38.
1944g. Chimney Swift banded in Georgia recovered in Peru. Oriole, 9:38.
1944h. The 1944 fall season at Augusta. Oriole, 9:39–40.
1945a. Partial albinism in a White-throated Sparrow. Oriole, 10:10–11.
1945b. Winter and early spring records from Augusta. Oriole, 10:12.
1945c. Notes on some birds of Cochran, Bleckley County, Georgia. Oriole, 10:24–25.
1945d. The Yellow Warbler breeding at Augusta, Georgia. Oriole, 10:30–31.
1945e. Early arrival of Purple Martin in Jones County, Georgia. Oriole, 10:32.
1945f. Henslow's Sparrow at Augusta, Georgia. Oriole, 10:33.
1945g. Henslow's Sparrow at Athens, Georgia. Oriole, 10:33.
1945h. The 1945 spring season at Augusta. Oriole, 10:34–35.
1946a. The breeding status of the Cowbird in Georgia. Oriole, 11:24–27.
1946b. Grinnell's Water-thrush in Georgia in winter. Oriole, 11:43.
1946c. White-eyed Vireo at Augusta in winter. Oriole, 11:43–44.
1946d. Red-breasted Nuthatch at Augusta. Oriole, 11:52–53.
1946e. Winter roosting site of Phoebe. Oriole, 11:53–54.

1946f. White-rumped Sandpiper at Augusta in fall. Oriole, 11:65.

1946g. Georgia Roseate Spoonbill records—Corrections. Oriole, 11:66–67.

1947a. A note on the summer birds of Yonah Mountain, White County, Georgia. Oriole, 12:9.

1947b. Red-wings feeding on seeds of long-leafed pine. Oriole, 12:10.

1947c. Editor's note. Oriole, 12:35.

1947d. A note on the occurrence and habits of the Cerulean Warbler at Augusta. Oriole, 12:37–38.

1948. First record of Swainson's Warbler in the Georgia mountains in summer. Oriole, 13:24–25.

1950a. Forster's Tern at Augusta, Richmond County, Georgia. Oriole, 15:9.

1950b. The Robin breeding at Thomson, McDuffie County, Georgia. Oriole, 15:21.

1950c. A case of multiple nests of the Carolina Wren. Oriole, 15:31–32.

1950d. The Fish Crow breeding in McDuffie County, Georgia, a further extension of its range. Oriole, 15:33.

1950e. The Painted Bunting summering at Waynesboro, Georgia. Oriole, 15:40.

1950f. Blue Grosbeak breeding at Helen, White County, Georgia. Oriole, 15:41.

1950g. The Chipping Sparrow breeding in Jenkins County, Georgia. Oriole, 15: 41–42.

1950h. The occurrence of the Pine Warbler in a cypress swamp. Oriole, 15:42.

1951a. The probable breeding of the Prothonotary Warbler in Lincoln County, Georgia. Oriole, 16:10–11.

1951b. The Yellow Warbler breeding at Macon, Bibb County, Georgia. Oriole, 16:12.

1951c. Is the Phoebe attempting to extend its range southward in Georgia? Oriole, 16:18–19.

1951d. A note on the summer range of the Prairie Warbler in the coastal plain of Georgia. Oriole, 16:20–21.

1951e. The Mountain Vireo breeding in southern Wilkes County, Georgia, a further extension of its range in the lower Piedmont. Oriole, 16:30–31.

1952. In memoriam: Eugene Edmund Murphey. Oriole, 17:15-16.

1953. The summer birds of Lookout Mountain, Georgia–Alabama. Oriole, 18:25–31.

———, and E. E. Byrd

1935. The Water-turkey (*Anhinga anhinga*) in Clarke County, Georgia. Auk, 52:300.

———, and Tom Hall

1943. Warbler caught in a spider's web. Oriole, 8:23.

———, and Dorothy Neal

1951. The abundance and distribution of some summer birds of Tray Mountain, Georgia. Oriole, 16:25–30.

———, and Eugene P. Odum

1945. Bachman's Sparrow and Black-throated Green Warbler summering on Pinelog Mountain, Cherokee County. Oriole, 10:53–55.

Dice, Lee Raymond

1943. The biotic provinces of North America. Ann Arbor, Univ. of Mich. Press. viii, 78 pp.

Dickinson, Joshua Clifton, Jr.

1952. Geographic variation in the Red-eyed Towhee of the eastern United States. Bull. Mus. Com. Zool., 107: 273–352. 3 maps.

Dorris, Fern E., Blanche Tait, and Katherine Weaver

1951. The Song Sparrow breeding at Milledgeville in middle Georgia in 1950. Oriole, 16:17.

Dorsey, George A.

1936a. Duck Hawk at Atlanta airport. Oriole, 1:34.

1936b. Red Crossbill at Neel Gap, Georgia, Oriole, 1:34–35.

1939. The Olive-sided Flycatcher in Lumpkin County. Oriole, 4:59.

1953. Green-tailed Towhee at Rome, Georgia. Oriole, 18:18.

Dreyfoos, Wallace D.

1946. Notes on birds of Fort Benning and Columbus, Georgia. Oriole, 11: 14–18.

Duncan, Wilbur Howard

1941. Guide to Georgia Trees. Athens, Univ. Ga. Press. 63 pp.

1950. Preliminary reports on the flora of Georgia. 2. Distribution of 87 trees. Am. Mid. Nat., 43 (No. 3): 742–61. 87 range maps.

Dutcher, William

1891. (Marsh wrens from Georgia).

Abs. Proc. Linnean Soc. of N. Y., 3:2.

Dwight, Jonathan, Jr.
1900. Remarks upon some of the April birds of Georgia. Abs. Proc. Linnean Soc. of N. Y., 12:2–3.

Edwards, J. Lee
1889. Birds of Macon County, Georgia. Oölogist, 6:51.

Elliott, Charles Newton
1932. Feathers of the Okefenokee. Am. For., 38:202–206, 253. 8 figs.
1934. Deep South Ravens. Am. For., 40:348–49, 384. 4 figs.
1946. Georgia's native pheasant, the Ruffed Grouse. Oriole, 11:47–48.

Erichsen, W. J.
1919a. Some summer birds of Liberty County, Georgia. Auk, 36:380–93.
1919b. Additions to the "Birds of Liberty County, Georgia." Auk, 36:590–91.
1920. Observations on the habits of some breeding birds of Chatham County, Georgia. Wilson Bull., 32:133–39.
1921. Notes on the habits of the breeding water birds of Chatham County, Georgia. Wilson Bull., 33:16–28; 33:69–82.
1922. Notable increase of Egrets in Chatham County, Georgia. Auk, 39:251–52.
1926. Gull-billed Tern (*Gelochelidon nilotica*) breeding on the coast of Georgia. Auk, 43:533–34.
1935a. European Starling nesting at Savannah, Ga. Auk. 52:313.
1935b. Scarlet Tanager on the coast of Georgia. Auk, 52:314.

Eyles, Don Edgar
1936a. Two January Woodcock nesting records from Marietta, Georgia. Oriole, 1:9.
1936b. Nesting data from the Atlanta area. Oriole, 1:11.
1936c. Ground Dove in middle-western Georgia. Oriole, 1:19.
1936d. White-crowned Sparrow and Ring-billed Gull in Atlanta, Ga. Oriole, 1:19.
1936e. Does the Duck Hawk nest in Georgia? Oriole, 1:25–26.
1936f. Woodcock nesting in Coweta County, Georgia. Oriole, 1:34.

1936g. Winter record of the Grasshopper Sparrow near Atlanta, Ga. Oriole, 1:35.
1937a. Migration extremes from the Atlanta area. Oriole, 2:5–6.
1937b. Double-crested Cormorant near Atlanta. Oriole, 2:7.
1937c. Florida Gallinule near Atlanta, Georgia. Oriole, 2:19.
1938a. A nesting study of the Tybee Island heronry. Oriole, 3:1–4.
1938b. White Pelican at the mouth of the Savannah River. Oriole, 3:17.
1938c. Gray Kingbird nesting in Georgia. Oriole, 3:24–25.
1938d. Georgia wildlife areas. Oriole, 3:29–33.
1938e. Wilson's Petrel in Georgia. Oriole, 3:35–36.
1941. Status of the Gray Kingbird in Georgia. Oriole, 6:1–5.
———, and Norman Giles, Jr.
1935. Notes of interest from Georgia. Auk, 52:461–62.

Fargo, William Gilbert
1934. Walter John Hoxie. Wilson Bull., 46:169–96.

Farrar, Edmund, Jr.
1951a. White Ibis and Wood Ibis at Macon. Oriole, 16:17–18.
1951b. An instance of dominance at a bird bath. Oriole, 16:19.
1952. Notes from the Macon area. Oriole, 17:8–9.
———, and Nathaniel R. Whitney, Jr.
1952. Deciduous flood-plain forest. Aud. field notes, 16th breeding-bird census, 6:310.

Faxon, Walter
1896. John Abbot's drawings of the birds of Georgia. Auk, 13:204–15.
1897. What is *Fringilla macgillivraii* Aud.? Auk, 14:321–22.

Fenneman, Nevin M.
1938. Physiography of eastern United States. New York, McGraw-Hill Book Co., Inc. xiii, 714 pp.

Fitch, Frank, Thomas Hall, and Thomas Bivens
1942. Swallow-tailed Kite at Milledgeville. Oriole, 7:19.

Flagg, Homer H.
1937. Southern Robin nesting at Waycross, Ware County, Georgia. Oriole, 2:27.

Fleetwood, Raymond Judy
1940. Birds of the Piedmont National Wildlife Refuge. Oriole, 5:25–28.
1941a. Bluebird nesting in ground. Oriole, 6:12–13.
1941b. Lincoln's Sparrow in Jones County, Georgia. Oriole, 6:13.
1942. Sandhill Cranes in Jones County, Georgia. Oriole, 7:34.
1945a. Cooper's Hawk breeding in Jones County, Georgia. Oriole, 10:56.
1945b. Prairie Warbler nesting in Jones County, Georgia. Oriole. 10:56.
1946a. Arrival dates of Purple Martin in Jones County, Georgia. Oriole, 11:18–19.
1946b. Chimney Swifts roosting in a water tank. Oriole, 11:19.
1946c. Bluebird nest containing six eggs. Oriole, 11:19.
1946d. Slate-colored Junco with a split lower mandible. Oriole, 11:19.
1946e. Catbird wintering in Jones County, Georgia. Oriole, 11:45.
1946f. The Florida Nuthatch in Jones County, Georgia. Oriole, 11:66.
1947a. Horned Grebe in the Okefenokee Swamp. Oriole, 12:21–22.
1947b. Red-wings feeding on the seeds of loblolly and slash pine. Oriole, 12:39–40.
1947c. The Mountain Vireo nesting for the first time in the lower Piedmont plateau of Georgia. Auk, 64:462–63.
1947d. Longleaf-slash pine, palmetto flatwoods. Aud. field notes, 11th breeding bird census, 1:197.
1947e. Mature, understocked longleaf pine and palmetto flatwoods. Aud. field notes, 11th breeding-bird census, 1:197.
1948a. Partial albino Newfoundland Robin in Charlton County, Georgia. Oriole, 13:10.
1948b. Longleaf pine and palmetto flatwoods. Aud. field notes, 12th breeding-bird census, 2:238–39.
1949. Unusual nesting site of the Purple Martin. Oriole, 14:18–19.
Fletcher, Orlin K.
1946. Sight record of a White Pelican at Cordele. Oriole, 11:44.
Folk, G. Edgar, Jr.
1939. Easter on Wassaw Island. Oriole, 4:21–23.

Fox, Henry (W. H.)
1882. Stray notes from Lookout Mountain, Tenn. Bull. Nuttall Orn. Club, 7:191–92.
1926. Georgia. In Naturalist's Guide to the Americas, ed. by V. E. Shelford, et al. Baltimore, Williams and Wilkins Co. xv, 761 pp.
Gambel, William
1847. (Observations on a species of Picus from Georgia). Proc. Acad. Nat. Sci. Phila., p. 278.
Ganier, Albert Franklin
1934. The status of the Duck Hawk in the Southeast. Auk, 51:371–73.
1954. A new race of the Yellow-bellied Sapsucker. Migrant, 25:37–41.
———, and George R. Mayfield
1933. Translation, from the German, of Gerhardt's papers on the birds of northwest Georgia, 1855–56. Nashville, Tenn. Mimeographed.
Gaulding, Willard, Jr.
1944a. Crested Flycatcher nesting in gourds. Oriole, 9:13.
1944b. Unusual number of Cape May Warblers at Tifton. Oriole, 9:13.
1944c. Carolina Wren roosting in mail box. Oriole, 9:13–14.
1944d. Odd mannerism of Indigo Bunting. Oriole, 9:38.
1945a. Another White-crowned Sparrow at Tifton. Oriole, 10:8.
1945b. Florida Gallinule and Bewick's Wren at Tifton. Oriole, 10:32.
1945c. The Barn and Long-eared Owls at Tifton, Georgia. Oriole, 10:57.
Gaylord, Anne Hall
1922. Everyday birds about an Atlanta (Ga.) suburban home. Bird-Lore, 24:133–35.
Gerhardt, Alexander
1855–56. Ueber die Lebenweise der Vogel Nordamerikas welche in Staate Georgia vorkommen. Naumannia, 5:380–97, 458–69; 6:1–18.
Giffen, Mrs. T. T.
1953. Avocet and Brown Pelican at Albany. Oriole, 18:11.
Giles, Norman Henry, Jr.
1936a. White Ibis at Atlanta. Oriole, 1:9.
1936b. Seasonal notes from Atlanta. Oriole, 1:11.
1936c. The Roseate Spoonbill in Georgia. Oriole, 1:25.

1936d. Pine Siskin near Atlanta, Georgia. Oriole, 1:35.

1937. Yellow-crowned Night Herons in Atlanta in July. Oriole, 2:25–26.

1940. Records from Lake Rabun. Oriole, 5:15.

Godfrey, William Earl

1946. A new Carolina Wren. Auk, 63: 564–68.

1951. A new Northwestern Olive-backed Thrush. Can. Field Nat., 65: 173.

———, and Albert Lawrence Wilk

1948. Birds of the Lake St. John region, Quebec. Nat. Mus. Can., Bull. 110: 1–32.

Gordon, Claire M.

1949. Arkansas Kingbird at Atlanta, Georgia. Oriole, 14:22.

Gorman, W. R.

1895. Extinction of the Bluebird. Forest and Stream, 45:315.

Greene, Earle Rosenbury

1922. Redpoll in Georgia. Bird-Lore, 24:96.

1923. Bay-breasted Warbler, Atlanta. Auk, 40:543.

1927. Connecticut Warbler, Atlanta. Auk, 44:426.

1928. Starling finally reaches Atlanta. Auk, 45:101.

1929. The Atlanta Bird Club. Fla. Nat., 3:25–26.

1930a. Unusual winter records from southern Georgia. Auk, 47:266.

1930b. Holboell's Grebe in Georgia. Auk, 47:412.

1930c. White Pelican in Georgia. Auk, 47:415–16.

1930d. Duck Hawk wintering in Atlanta. Auk, 47:418.

1931a. Golden Eagle captured in Georgia. Auk, 48:118.

1931b. A late spring record of Lesser Scaup Duck (*Nyroca affinis*) in Georgia. Auk, 48:256–57.

1931c. Snowy Owl in Georgia. Auk, 48:268.

1931d. A Herring Gull takes up golf. Bird-Lore, 33:186.

1931e. Bird Life on Brasstown Bald, Ga. Auk, 48:616.

1932a. Another Golden Eagle captured in Georgia. Auk, 49:217.

1932b. List of birds found about At-

lanta. Elementary Science Helps for Teachers.

1933. Birds of the Atlanta, Georgia, area. Ga. Soc. Nat., Bull. No. 2. 46 pp., 5 pl., 2 maps.

1934a. Brewer's Blackbird (*Euphagus cyanocephalus*) in Georgia. Auk, 51: 91.

1934b. Florida Grackle (*Quiscalus quiscula aglaeus*) in northern Georgia. Auk, 51:91.

1934c. Bicknell's Thrush (*Hylocichla minima minima*) in Georgia. Auk, 51:241.

1935. Two rare birds in Georgia. Auk, 52:98–99.

1936. A natural wildlife refuge, the Okefenokee Swamp. Oriole, 1:13–14.

1944. Georgia's first bird club. Oriole, 9:23–24.

1951. A Georgia record for the Arctic Tern. Oriole, 16:39.

———, William W. Griffin, Eugene P. Odum, Herbert L. Stoddard, and Ivan R. Tomkins

1945. Birds of Georgia. Occas. Pub. No. 2, Ga. Orn. Soc.:1–111. 2 pls.

Griffin, William Welcome

1939a. The winter season in Atlanta. Oriole, 4:8.

1939b. The spring season in the Atlanta area. Oriole, 4:19.

1939c. Seasonal notes from Atlanta. Oriole, 4:29–30.

1939d. Some recent winter records from Atlanta. Oriole, 4:30.

1939e. Blue-winged Warbler nesting in Atlanta. Oriole, 4:32.

1939f. Seasonal notes from Atlanta. Oriole, 4:66.

1940a. Nesting extremes for birds breeding in the Atlanta region. Oriole, 5:1–6.

1940b. Saw-whet Owl from Atlanta. Oriole, 5:8.

1940c. Seasonal notes from Atlanta. Oriole, 5:9–10.

1940d. A Purple Gallinule record from Northern Georgia. Oriole, 5:14–15.

1940e. Seasonal notes from Atlanta. Oriole, 5:17–18.

1940f. Seasonal notes from Atlanta. Oriole, 5:31–32.

1940g. Crested Flycatcher catches sparrow. Oriole, 5:32.

1940h. Sight record of a Yellow-billed Tropic Bird in Atlanta. Oriole, 5:32.

1940i. Notes from Lake Rutledge, Morgan County. Oriole, 5:54.

1940j. Seasonal notes from Atlanta. Oriole, 5:54–55.

1941a. Four unpublished Golden Eagle records from Georgia. Oriole, 6:12.

1941b. Seasonal notes from Atlanta. Oriole, 6:14.

1941c. Migration of birds in the Atlanta region. Oriole, 6:17–23.

1941d. Seasonal notes from Atlanta. Oriole, 6:27–28.

1941e. A Gannet on St. Simons Island. Oriole, 6:49.

1942a. An invasion of the Red-breasted Nuthatch in Georgia. Oriole, 7:7.

1942b. Seasonal notes from Atlanta. Oriole, 7:7.

1947a. The Dickcissel breeding near Atlanta. Oriole, 12:34.

1947b. The Willow Thrush in Georgia. Oriole, 12:46.

1947c. An old record of the Scarlet Tanager nesting in Fulton County, Georgia. Oriole, 12:46–47.

1948a. A Woodcock nest near Atlanta. Oriole, 13:9.

1948b. Wintering Yellow-throats in the Atlanta region. Oriole, 13:13–16.

1948c. Henslow's Sparrow near Atlanta. Oriole, 13:25.

1948d. A Purple Gallinule in the Atlanta region. Oriole, 13:26.

1948e. Swainson's Warbler in Atlanta. Oriole, 13:26.

1949. Pigeon Hawk in Atlanta. Oriole, 14:21–22.

1950a. Notes from Floyd County, Georgia. Oriole, 15:10–11.

1950b. Bay-breasted Warbler near Atlanta in winter. Oriole, 15:32.

1951a. Shorebirds in man-made habitats near Atlanta. Oriole, 16:1–5.

1951b. Horned Lark nesting in Georgia. Oriole, 16:8–10.

1952a. A new breeding species for Georgia: the Spotted Sandpiper. Oriole, 17:27–28.

1952b. Connecticut Warbler in Atlanta. Oriole, 17:29.

1952c. White-rumped Sandpiper at Atlanta. Oriole, 17:29.

1953. Notes on the occurrence of three uncommon species of sparrows near Atlanta. Oriole, 18:18–19.

———, and James C. Major

1947. Notes on interesting nests near Atlanta in 1946. Oriole, 12:35–36.

———, and Eugene Odum

1946. Black-throated Green Warbler definitely breeding on Pinelog Mountain. Oriole, 11:51–52.

———, and George W. Sciple, Jr.

1938. Arkansas Kingbird in Georgia. Oriole, 3:25.

Grimes, Samuel Andrew

1944. An early nest of the Florida Nuthatch. Oriole, 9:13.

Grimm, William Carey

1946. Bird life of the Camp Stewart, Georgia, region. Oriole, 11:27–42.

Griscom, Ludlow

1937. A monographic study of the Red Crossbill. Proc. Boston Soc. Nat. Hist., 41 (No. 5):77–210.

1944. A second revision of the Seaside Sparrows. Occas. Papers Mus. Zool., La. State Univ., 19:313–28.

Hall, J. A., and Wallace Rogers

1928. Some useful Georgia birds. Issued by the State Board of Game and Fish. March 8. Bulletin prepared for Loyal Legion of Nature Guardians.

Hall, Thomas M.

1949. Wood Ibis in southeastern Georgia. Oriole, 14:23.

Hamilton, Anne Pfeiffer (Mrs. R. E.)

1940a. White-crowned Sparrow in Northwest Georgia. Oriole, 5:18.

1940b. Chipping Sparrow's nest. Oriole, 5:34.

1941. Report of spring migration in the Dalton area. Oriole, 6:26–27.

1944. Red-breasted Nuthatch at Cloudland, Georgia. Oriole, 9:14.

1945. The Yellow Rail in Whitfield County. Oriole, 10:8–9.

(MS) Birds observed on Fort and Grassy Mountains.

Hamilton, R. E. and Anne

1946. Song Sparrow breeding at Dalton, Whitfield County, Georgia. Oriole, 11:51.

Hamilton, Mr. and Mrs. R. E., and Fannie McLellan

1940. Spring notes from Dalton. Oriole, 5:21–22.

Hamilton, Mr. and Mrs. R. E., Billy

Mitchell, Warren Herron, and Warren Sims

1944a. Spring notes from Dalton and Whitfield County, 1944. Oriole, 9: 14–15.

1944b. Summer and Fall (1944) notes from Dalton and Whitfield County. Oriole, 9:40.

Hanson, Harold Carsten, and Robert H. Smith

1950. Canada Geese of the Mississippi flyway. Bull. Ill. Nat. Hist. Sur., vol. 25, art. 3:59–210. 82 figs., 47 tables.

Harper, Francis

1912. Report of expedition into Oke-fenokee Swamp, Georgia. Bird-Lore, 14:402–407. 1 fig.

1914. "A fortnight in the Okefenokee." Abs. Proc. Linnean Soc. of N. Y., for years ending March 12, 1912, and March 11, 1913, 1913 (April 15, 1914):35.

1915. A sojourn in the primeval Oke-fenokee. Brooklyn Mus. Quarterly, 2:226–44. 7 figs.

1918. The White-winged Dove (*Melopelia asiatica asiatica*) in Georgia. Auk, 35:76–77.

1920. Okefenokee Swamp as a reservation. Nat. Hist., 20:28–41. 11 figs., 1 map.

1929. Spring bird notes from Randolph County, Georgia. Wilson Bull., 41:235–40.

1934a. The Boat-tailed Grackle of the Atlantic Coast. Proc. Acad. Nat. Sci. Phila., 86:1–2.

1934b. The Okefenokee wilderness. Nat. Geo. Mag., 61 (May):597–624.

1936a. The distribution of the Limpkin and its staple food, *Pomacea*. Nautilus, 50:37–40.

1936b. The distribution of the Limpkin and its staple food. Oriole, 1:21–23. 1 fig.

1938. The Chuck-will's-widow in the Okefenokee region. Oriole, 3:9–14.

1943. Travels in Georgia and Florida, 1773–74. A report to Dr. John Fothergill, by William Bartram, annotated by Francis Harper. Trans. Amer. Philos. Soc., 33 (No. 2):123–242. 24 pl.

Harper, Roland McMillan

1930. The natural resources of Geor-gia. Univ. Ga., Bull. 30 (No. 3). xi, 105 pp.

Harris, Lucien, Jr.

1927. An unusual nest of the White-breasted Nuthatch. Wilson Bull., 39:41–42.

1936. A day with the birds in south Georgia. Oriole, 1:16–17.

Hasbrouck, Edwin Marble

1891a. The present status of the Ivory-billed Woodpecker (*Campephilus principalis*). Auk, 8:174–86.

1891b. The Carolina Paroquet (*Conurus carolinensis*). Auk, 8:369–379.

1893. The geographical distribution of the genus *Megacops* in North America. Auk, 10:250–64.

1944. Apparent status of the European Widgeon in North America. Auk, 61:93–104.

Head, J. F.

1878. Breeding of the Woodcock in Georgia. Bull. Nuttall Orn. Club, 3: 151.

Hebard, Frederick Vanuxem

1936. The Limpkin in southeastern Georgia. Oriole, 1:18.

1938a. Limpkin in Charlton County, Georgia. Oriole, 3:17.

1938b. The Duck Hawk in the Oke-fenokee Swamp. Oriole, 3:17–18.

1938c. Golden Eagle in Georgia. Oriole, 3:18.

1940. Roseate Tern in western Camden County. Oriole, 5:48, 53.

1941a. Winter birds of the Okefenokee and Coleraine. Ga. Soc. Nat., Bull. No. 3. x, 88 pp., 3 maps.

1941b. Harlan's Hawk in Georgia. Oriole, 6:24.

1942a. Yellow-throated Vireo (*Vireo flavifrons*) in winter. Oriole, 7:6.

1942b. The winter of 1941–1942 in interior southeastern Georgia. Oriole, 7:8.

1942c. Correction: "Harlan's Hawk in Georgia." Oriole, 7:9.

1943. The Southern Pileated Woodpecker in southeastern Georgia. Oriole, 8:1–3.

1945a. Recent new or interesting winter records from interior southeastern Georgia. Oriole, 10:4–6.

1945b. Weights of Ring-necked and other ducks. Oriole, 10:11.

1945c. The Parula Warbler in southeastern Georgia. Oriole, 10:22–24.

1945d. Bird notes from southeastern Georgia. Oriole, 10:26–28.

1945e. Spring and summer notes from southeastern Georgia. Oriole, 10:57–58.

1946a. Winter status of House Wrens in southern Georgia. Oriole, 11:21.

1946b. The Starling at Folkston, Georgia. Oriole, 11:53.

1946c. Red-bellied Woodpecker and Red-tailed Hawk nesting in same tree. Oriole, 11:53.

1947. Belligerency in Tree Swallows. Oriole, 12:21.

1948a. The Yellow-billed Cuckoo in southeastern Georgia. Oriole, 13:21–23.

1948b. Bald Eagle eating shoat on highway. Wilson Bull., 60:53.

1949a. Reddish Egret in Georgia. Oriole, 14:12.

1949b. Lesser Loon in Georgia. Oriole, 14:23.

1949c. Duck Hawk in Camden County, Georgia. Oriole, 14:23–24.

1949d. Sexual selection in woodpeckers. Auk, 66:91–92.

1950a. Glossy Ibis breeding in Georgia. Oriole, 15:9–10.

1950b. Diversionary behavior of Red-cockaded Woodpecker. Wilson Bull., 62:38.

1952a. Recent range extensions and sub-specific problems in Georgia. Oriole, 17:35–38.

1952b. Blue geese in Glynn County. Oriole, 17:39.

1953. The Sandhill Crane in Georgia. Oriole, 18:10–11.

———, and David W. Johnston

1951. Additional subspecies for Georgia from Camden County. Oriole, 16:11–12.

Helme, Arthur Hudson

1904a. The western Meadowlark (*Sturnella magna neglecta*) in southern Georgia. Auk, 21:280.

1904b. The Ipswich Sparrow, Kirtland's Warbler, and Sprague's Pipit in Georgia. Auk, 21:291.

Helmuth, William Todd

1920. Extracts from notes made while in naval service. Auk, 37:255–61.

Hembree, D. V.

1914. From Georgia. Oologist, 31:136–38.

Henderson, Daniel W.

1936a. Mississippi Kite in Richmond County. Oriole, 1:25.

1936b. Swainson's Warbler in Richmond County. Oriole, 1:26–27.

1941a. The Mississippi Kite (*Ictinia misisippiensis*) in Richmond County. Oriole, 6:24.

1941b. On the food of the Southern Crow. Oriole, 6:25.

1945. The value of Bob-white propagation. Oriole, 10:42–44.

Herbert, Richard, Roger Tory Peterson, and Walter Richardson Spofford

1943. Duck Hawk eyries in southern states. Auk, 60:274.

Hinton, W. B.

1887. The Purple Martin in the south. Orn. and Ool., 12:77–78.

Hopkins, John M.

1947. Forty-five years with the Okefenokee Swamp, 1900–1945. Ga. Soc. Nat., Bull. No. 4. 70 pp., illus.

Hopkins, Milton Newton, Jr.

1942a. Little Blue Heron rookery near Fitzgerald, Ga. Oriole, 7:34.

1942b. Two additional species from the Fitzgerald region. Oriole, 7:25–36.

1949. An unusual nesting site of the Brown-headed Nuthatch. Oriole, 14:18.

1951. Observations of the bird life of southwest Georgia during 1950. Oriole, 16:13–16.

1953a. Breeding of the grackle at Athens, Clarke County, Georgia. Oriole, 18:10.

1953b. Another occurrence of the Red-breasted Nuthatch in southern Georgia. Oriole, 18:11.

1953c. The Black Vulture as a predator in southern Georgia. Oriole, 18:15–17.

1953d. Feeding methods of the shrike. Oriole, 18:19.

(MS) (On the breeding ecology of mourning doves in southwestern Georgia).

Howe, Henry Branch, Jr.

1943. Spring occurrence of the Red Head Duck at Decatur. Oriole, 8:9.

1944. A review of Christmas bird counts in Georgia. Oriole, 9:26–29.

1947. The White Pelican at Tybee Island, Georgia. Oriole, 12:11.

1948. Unusual species observed at Atlanta during Christmas bird count. Oriole, 13:8.

Howe, Reginald Heber, Jr.

1901. A new subspecies of *Passerculus sandwichensis*. Contrib. N. Am. Orn., 1:1–2.

1902. "Notes on various Florida birds." Contrib. N. Am. Orn., 1:25–32.

Howell, Arthur Holmes

1909. Notes on the summer birds of northern Georgia. Auk, 26:129–37.

1928. A study of the Red-winged Blackbirds of the southeastern United States. Auk, 45:155–63.

1936. A reconnaissance of the summer bird life of Georgia. Oriole, 1:29–32.

———, and Adriaan Joseph Van Rossem

1928. A study of the Red-winged Blackbirds of southeastern United States. Auk, 45:155–63.

Howell, Thelma, and Suzanne Davis

1944. Bird study at Wesleyan College. Oriole, 9:5–6.

Hoxie, Walter John

1910a. Notes on the Bald Eagle in Georgia. Auk, 27:454.

1910b. Supposed nesting of the Pine-woods and Bachman's sparrows in Chatham County, Georgia. Auk, 27:457–58.

1910c. The Bank Swallows at Savannah, Georgia. Auk, 27:460.

1911a. Birds of Chatham County, Georgia. Savannah Morning News. 8 installments, beginning April 30, 1911.

1911b. The Saw-whet Owl in Georgia. Auk, 28:265–66.

1911c. The Greater Shearwater on the coast of Georgia. Auk, 28:481–82.

1914. Bird census in the Bona Bella tract. Savannah Morning News, May 25, 1914, p. 7.

Huber, Wharton

1931. European Widgeon in Georgia. Auk, 48:256.

Hudson, Ben

1892. Buzzard Island. Oölogist, 9:240–42.

Huey, Laurence Markham

1927. A Pacific coast race of the Yel-low-crowned Night Heron. Condor, 29:167–68.

Hunter, Earle Bee, Jr., James Hobart Jenkins, and Dan Quillian

1949. The Barn Owl nesting at Bogart, Georgia. Oriole, 14:17.

Hyde, Arthur Sidney

1939. The life history of Henslow's Sparrow, *Passerherbulus henslowi* (Audubon). Univ. Mich. Mus. Zool., Misc. Pub. No. 41:1–72. 4 pl.

Jarrard, Berma

1936. Two late breeding records for the Mourning Dove. Oriole, 1:9–10.

Jenkins, James Hobart

1948a. Pine Siskins in south Georgia near Waycross. Oriole, 13:27.

1948b. On the occurrence of an albino Field Sparrow at Blackbeard Island. Oriole, 13:28.

1949a. The occurrence of the Chachalaca on Sapelo Island, Georgia. Oriole, 14:11–12.

1949b. Marbled Godwit on the Georgia coast in summer. Oriole, 14:22.

1950. A comparison of the food habits of the Barn Owl in the Piedmont and lower coastal plain of Georgia. Wilson Bull., 62:149, abstract.

1953. Wildlife resources of Georgia. Georgia Game and Fish Comm., Game Mgmt. Div. Atlanta. 114 pp.

Johnston, David Ware

1943a. Henslow Sparrow in the Atlanta region. Oriole, 8:10.

1943b. The Wilson Warbler at Atlanta. Oriole, 8:21.

1943c. Fall notes from Atlanta. Oriole, 8:24.

1944a. Green-winged Teal and White-crowned Sparrow in Atlanta. Oriole, 9:11.

1944b. Spring notes from Atlanta, 1944. Oriole, 9:14.

1945. Recent migration extremes at Atlanta. Oriole, 10:6–8.

1947a. Interesting records from Rabun County, Georgia. Oriole, 12:32–33.

1947b. Fish Crow and Tennessee Warbler at Athens. Oriole, 12:33–34.

1947c. Birds observed on a three-day field trip into coastal Georgia. Oriole, 12:49–50.

1948a. The 1946–47 Pine Siskin invasion of Georgia. Oriole, 13:1–2.

1948b. Unusual wintering Grasshopper Sparrow at Athens. Oriole, 13:9–10.

1948c. First occurrence of the Florida Cormorant in Georgia. Oriole, 13: 33.

1949a. Surf Scoter records from Georgia. Auk, 66:81.

1949b. Yellow-bellied Flycatcher again at Athens, Georgia. Oriole, 14:11.

1949c. Winter specimen of the Broadwinged Hawk from St. Mary's, Georgia. Oriole, 14:13.

1949d. Notes on the food of certain birds in the Athens, Georgia, area. Oriole, 14:19.

1950a. Spring notes from the Athens area. Oriole, 15:34–36.

1950b. Further breeding of the Blackthroated Green Warbler in Georgia. Oriole, 15:40–41.

1951. An aberrantly colored Summer Tanager. Wilson Bull., 63:116–17.

1952. An analysis of the distribution of Dowitchers in Georgia. Oriole, 17: 21–27.

1954. Supplemental notes on birds of the Athens area. Oriole, 19:1–3.

1955. Mass bird mortality in Georgia, October, 1954. Oriole, 20:17–26.

———, and Jimmy (James Calder) Major
1947. Virginia Rail in Atlanta. Oriole, 12:10.

1950. Bird observations from coastal McIntosh County, Georgia. Oriole, 15:37–39.

———, and Eugene P. Odum
(MS) Breeding bird populations in relation to plant succession on the Piedmont of Georgia.

Jones, Harold Charles
1942–44. The status of water-birds at Mount Berry, Georgia. Oriole, 7:1–5; 9:1–2.

1947. Breeding birds of the Rome, Georgia, area. Oriole, 12:15–17.

Jones, William L.
1848. Description of a new species of Woodpecker. Ann. Lyc. Nat. Hist., N. Y., 4:489–90. 1 pl.

Keith, Arthur
1925. See LaForge, et al.

Kelso, Leon Hugh
1933. The forgotten Georgian owl. Auk, 50:106–107.

Kendeigh, Samuel Charles
1952. Parental care and its evolution in birds. Ill. Biol. Mono., 22 (Nos. 1–3):1–356.

Koelz, Walter
1939. Three new sub-species. Proc. Biol. Soc. Wash., 52:121–22.

Kroeber, Alfred L.
1939. Cultural and natural areas of North America. Univ. Calif. Pub. Am. Arch. and Ethnol., 38. xii, 242 pp.

LaForge, Laurence, Wythe Cooke, Arthur Keith, and Marius R. Campbell, with an introduction by S. W. McCallie
1925. Physical geography of Georgia. Geol. Surv. Ga., Bull. No. 42. ix, 189 pp.

Land, Manilla B.
1949. Sight record of a Snow Goose at Marietta, Georgia. Oriole, 14:10.

LaPrade, William H., Jr.
1922a. Breeding warblers around Atlanta, Georgia. Wilson Bull., 34:80–83.

1922b. Nesting of Swainson's Warbler in Atlanta. Oologist, 39:88–89.

Latham, John
1781–1801. A general synopsis of birds. 3 vols., each of 2 parts and 2 supplements. London.

1821–24. A general history of birds. 10 vols. Winchester, England.

LeConte, John
1849. A list of the birds of Georgia. Included in the appendix of *Statistics of the State of Georgia, 1849*, by George White, appendix, under the title "Catalogue of the Fauna and Flora of the State of Georgia, prepared for this work by eminent naturalists."

LeConte, Joseph
1903 The autobiography of Joseph LeConte. Ed. by William Dallas Ames. New York, D. Appleton, 1903.

Lincoln, Frederick Charles
1933. State distribution of returns from banded ducks. Second paper—British Columbia, California, Connecticut, Georgia, Illinois, Iowa, and Kansas. Bird-Banding, 4:19–32.

1944. Chimney Swift's winter home discovered. Auk, 61:604–609.

Lovell, H. B.
1952. Black Vulture depredations at Kentucky woodlands. Wilson Bull., 64:48–49.

Lowery, George Hines, Jr.

1940. Geographical variation in the Carolina Wren. Auk, 57:95–104.

1945. Trans-Gulf migration of birds and the coastal hiatus. Wilson Bull., 57:92–121.

1951. A quantitative study of the nocturnal migration of birds. Univ. Kan. Pub. Mus. Nat. Hist., 3 (No. 2): 361–472.

Lunk, William A.

1952. Notes on variation in the Carolina Chickadee. Wilson Bull., 64:7–21.

McAtee, Waldo Lee

1911. Local names of waterfowl and other birds. Forest and Stream, 77: 172–74, 196–97.

1913. An item for bibliographers. Auk, 30:117.

1941. Unidentified bird names. Auk, 58:134.

1946. Georgian records in John Latham's "General History of Birds," 1821–1824. Oriole, 11:1–11.

———, Thomas D. Burleigh, George H. Lowery, Jr., and Herbert L. Stoddard

1944. Eastward migration through the Gulf states. Wilson Bull., 56:152–60.

———, and Herbert L. Stoddard

1930. American raptores and the study of their economic status. Condor, 32:15–19.

McCallie, S. W.

1925. *See* LaForge, *et al.*

McQueen, A. S.

1932. History of Charlton County. Atlanta, Stein Printing Co.

———, and Hamp Mizell

1926. History of the Okefenokee Swamp. Clinton, S. C., Press of Jacobs and Co. 191 pp., 27 pl.

Major, Jimmy (James Calder)

1945a. Spring (1945) notes from Atlanta. Oriole, 10:33.

1945b. Additional records of mountain warblers. Oriole, 10:55–56.

1945c. Notes on a Least Bittern's nest at Atlanta. Oriole, 10:56.

1947. Leconte's Sparrow near Atlanta. Oriole, 12:10.

———, and Dave (David Ware) Johnston

1944. Least Bittern breeding near Atlanta. Oriole, 9:36.

May, John Bichard

1924a. Bird banding at Thomasville, Ga. 1924. Auk, 41:451–62.

1924b. Pegleg and his friends. Bird-Lore, 26:317–21.

Mayfield, George Radford

1944. D. C. Peacock—pioneer in field work for G.O.S.—an appreciation. Oriole, 9:24–26.

Meanley, M. Brooke

1944a. Notes on some birds of Bibb County, Georgia. Oriole, 9:3–5.

1944b. Albino Crows in Monroe County. Oriole, 9:13.

1944c. Spring notes from Macon. Oriole, 9:15–16.

1944d. The Golden-winged Warbler in Ocmulgee River bottom. Oriole, 9:39.

1945a. First winter specimen of Ovenbird from Georgia. Oriole, 10:9.

1945b. Yellow-throated Warbler at Fitzgerald in winter. Oriole, 10:9–10.

1945c. Bobolink in central Georgia in winter. Oriole, 10:10.

1945d. Prairie Horned Lark at Macon in winter. Oriole, 10:10.

1945e. Bewick's Wren at Bowen's Mill, Ben Hill County, Georgia. Oriole, 10:11.

1945f. Lingering of migrants. Oriole, 10:28–29.

1945g. Wild Turkey in the Ocmulgee River bottom. Oriole, 10:32.

1945h. The 1945 spring migration at Macon. Oriole, 10:33–34.

1945i. Notes on Swainson's Warbler in central Georgia. Auk, 62:395–401.

1946a. Notes from the Ocmulgee River bottom, Wilcox County, Georgia. Oriole, 11:44.

1946b. Upland Plover over Atlanta. Oriole, 11:52.

———, and Gorman Morton Bond

1950. A new race of Swainson's Warbler from the Appalachian Mountains. Proc. Biol. Soc. Wash., 63: 191–94.

Menaboni, Sara (Mrs. Athos)

1941. Coastal observations from McIntosh County, Georgia. Oriole, 8:13–14.

1943. Valley of the birds. Audubon Mag., 45:209–14.

1946a. Fun with birds, then what? Oriole, 11:63–65.

1946b. Albinism in the offspring of a pair of Bluebirds. Oriole, 11:66.

1947. Albino Bluebirds. Auk, 64:629.

Merriam, Clinton Hart

1894. Laws of temperature control of geographic distribution of terrestrial animals and plants. Natl. Geo. Mag., 6:229–38.

Miller, Alden Holmes

1951. An analysis of the distribution of the birds of California. Univ. Calif. Pub. Zool., 50 (No. 6):531–644.

Mills, William

1902. My summer boarders. Wilson Bull., 14:124–25.

1905. Some breeding records from East Point, Georgia. Wilson Bull., 17:115–16.

Mindling, G. W. (compiler)

1941. Climate of Georgia. In *Climate and Man,* Yearbook of Agriculture, pp. 819–28. Tables, figs. Washington, D. C., Govt. Printing Office.

Mitchell, Billy, Warren Sims, and Warren Herron

1944. Red-breasted Nuthatch and Prairie Horned Lark at Dalton. Oriole, 9:12.

Mounts, Beryl T.

1922. A Blue-gray Gnatcatcher's nest (at Macon). Wilson Bull., 34:116–17.

1925. Further notes on the food of the Loggerhead Shrike. Wilson Bull., 37:222.

1926. Behavior of birds at a Georgia feeding tray. Wilson Bull., 38:42.

1927. Birds excited by a snake. Wilson Bull., 39:108–109.

1928. A Brown Thrasher feeds a snake to its young. Wilson Bull., 40:202.

1930. Some unusual records from Bibb County, Georgia. Wilson Bull., 42:61–62.

1936. White-crowned Sparrow in Bibb County. Oriole, 1:10.

Murphey, Eugene Edmund

1890. Junco; Field Sparrow. Oologist, 7:108.

1937a. The influence of the fall line on habitat zones along the Savannah River. Oriole, 2:9–11.

1937b. Observations on the bird life of the middle Savannah valley, 1890–

1937. Contrib. Charleston (S. C.) Mus., No. IX.

1938a. Ring-billed Gull. *Larus delawarensis* (ord.). Oriole, 3:18.

1938b. Eastern Snow Bunting. *Plectrophenax nivalis nivalis* (Linnaeus). Oriole, 3:18.

1938c. The Swallow-tailed Kite in Richmond County. Oriole, 3:36.

1944a. Notes from Richmond County, Georgia. Oriole, 9:38–39.

1944b. Correction (*re:* a misidentified specimen of a Red-tailed Hawk). Oriole, 9:41.

1945a. Whistling Swan in Columbia County, Georgia. Oriole, 10:12.

1945b. In memoriam—William Henry LaPrade. Oriole, 10:41–42.

Murphy, Robert Cushman, and William Vogt.

1933. The Dovekie influx of 1932. Auk, 50:325–49.

Musselman, Thomas Edgar

1923. Bird banding at Thomasville, Ga., 1923. Auk, 40:442–52.

1928. Foot disease of Chipping Sparrow (*Spizella passerina*). Auk, 45:137–47.

Neal, Dorothy P. (Mrs. Charles)

1947. Yellow-bellied Sapsucker breeding in Georgia. Oriole, 12:45–46.

1948. Common Loon and Bonaparte's Gull in Demorest, Georgia. Oriole, 13:34

1949a. Blue Goose at Demorest, Habersham County, Georgia. Oriole, 14:10.

1949b. Double-crested Cormorant and Nashville Warbler at Demorest, Georgia. Oriole, 14:20.

1949c. Sutton's Warbler seen in Demorest, Georgia. Oriole, 14:20–21.

1950. Scarlet Tanager nesting in Demorest. Oriole, 15:21.

———, and J. Fred Denton

1950. A further extension of the breeding range of the Song Sparrow in Georgia. Oriole, 15:33–34.

Neill, Wilfred T.

1949a. Summer records of the Black Duck in the coastal plain of Georgia. Oriole, 14:11.

1949b. Little Blue Herons breeding in the juvenile plumage. Oriole, 14:17–18.

Nelson, Dan
 1952. The Mourning Dove study in Georgia. Final report 17-R, Ga. Game and Fish Comm. Mimeo., 98 pp.
Nichols, John Treadwell
 1913. Notes on offshore birds. Auk, 30:505–11.
Noble, G.
 1885. Destructive electric light towers. Forest and Stream, 25:305.
Norris, Joseph Parker
 1888. A series of eggs of Swainson's Warbler. Orn. and Ool., 13:185–86.
 1889. A series of eggs of the Chuck-will-widow. Orn. and Ool., 14:116.
Norris, Robert Allen
 1939a. Gray Kingbird on St. Simons Island. Oriole, 4:30.
 1939b. Ring-billed Gulls at St. Simons Island during June. Oriole, 4:31.
 1939c. Early occurrence of Pintail in Fitzgerald region. Oriole, 4:63.
 1939d. Eastern Henslow's Sparrow near Fitzgerald. Oriole, 4:63–64.
 1940a. Some recent winter records from the Fitzgerald region. Oriole, 5:8–9.
 1940b. Spring notes from the Fitzgerald region. Oriole, 5:15–17.
 1940c. Mourning Dove breeds in old heron nest. Oriole, 5:19.
 1940d. Summer notes from the Fitzgerald region. Oriole, 5:32–34.
 1940e. Whistling Swan in the Fitzgerald area. Oriole, 5:53.
 1940f. Fall notes from the Fitzgerald region. Oriole, 5:55.
 1941a. New Year's notes from St. Simons. Oriole, 6:24–25.
 1941b. Winter notes from the Fitzgerald region. Oriole, 6:25–26.
 1941c. Spring notes from the Fitzgerald region. Oriole, 6:26.
 1941d. "Whisper song" of a Pine Warbler. Migrant, 12:40–41.
 1941e. Hooded Warbler flying backward. Auk, 58:101.
 1941f. Fall season in Tift County. Oriole, 6:49.
 1941g. Philadelphia Vireo in south Georgia. Oriole, 6:50.
 1941h. Some nesting data on the Acadian Flycatcher. Oriole, 6:51–52.
 1941i. Indigo Bunting sings at night. Migrant, 12:74–75.
 1942a. Winter notes from Tift County. Oriole, 7:8.
 1942b. Notes on the nesting of a pair of Alabama Towhees. Oriole, 7:14–17.
 1942c. Partial albinism in three bird species. Oriole, 7:20–21.
 1942d. Notes on "whisper singing" of a Yellow-throated Vireo. Migrant, 13:49–50.
 1942e. Giant Red-wing in south Georgia. Oriole, 7:35.
 1943a. Churchill Savannah Sparrow at Florida line. Auk, 60:103.
 1943b. Diving by a Long-billed Marsh Wren. Wilson Bull., 55:132.
 1943c. Arkansas Kingbird at Waycross, Ga. Oriole, 8:9.
 1944a. Specimen of the Gray Kingbird from St. Simon's Island. Oriole, 9:9.
 1944b. White-crowned and Leconte's Sparrows in South Georgia. Oriole, 9:10.
 1946a. White-crowned Sparrow again at Tifton. Oriole, 11:44–45.
 1946b. Aggressiveness of Painted Bunting. Oriole, 11:65.
 1947. Georgia record of the Newfoundland Crossbill found to be erroneous. Oriole, 12:20–21.
 1948a. Summer records of the Goldfinch in south Georgia. Oriole, 13:27.
 1948b. Anatomical abnormality of an Eastern Kingbird. Oriole, 13:28.
 1950. Does the Gray-headed Nuthatch occupy southwestern Georgia? Oriole, 15:22.
 1951a. Relative frequency of shore and water birds at the Tifton Experiment Station pond, January, 1932–March, 1934. Oriole, 16:5–8.
 1951b. Remarks on Georgia records of Sharp-tailed Sparrows and their relation to our need for quantitative data. Oriole, 16:31–32.
 1951c. Distribution and population of summer birds in southwestern Georgia. Occas. Pub. No. 3, Ga. Orn. Soc. vi, 67 pp., 16 figs.
 1952a. Cerulean Warblers in fall on the upper coastal plain of Georgia. Oriole, 17:1–5.
 1952b. The British Columbia Waterthrush in southern Georgia. Oriole, 17:17–18.

1952c. Postjuvenal molt of tail feathers in the Pine Warbler. Oriole, 17:29–31.

1952d. Immature longleaf pineland with small clearings. Aud. field notes, 16th breeding-bird census, 6:321–22.

———, and Willard Gaulding, Jr.

1944. Another Scissor-tailed Flycatcher in Georgia. Oriole, 9:9.

———, and Milton Newton Hopkins, Jr.

1947. The breeding of Swainson's Warbler near Tifton, Georgia. Oriole, 12:7–9.

1953. Migration of birds in Ben Hill, Tift, and Irwin Counties, Georgia. Oriole, 18:1–9.

Norton, Arthur Herbert

1902. The Boat-tailed Grackle as a stowaway. Auk, 19:289–90.

Oberholser, Harry Church

1896. Descriptions of two new subspecies of the Downy Woodpecker, *Dryobates pubescens* (Linnaeus). Proc. U. S. Nat. Mus., 18:547–50.

1898. A revision of the wrens of the genus *Thryomanes*, Sclater. Proc. U. S. Nat. Mus., 21:421–50.

1905. The forms of *Vermivora celata* (Say). Auk, 22:242–47.

1911. A revision of the forms of the Hairy Woodpecker, *Dryobates villosus* (Linnaeus). Proc. U. S. Nat. Mus., 40:595–621.

1917. Critical notes on the eastern subspecies of *Sitta carolinensis* Latham. Auk, 34:181–87.

1918a. Notes on the subspecies of *Numenius americanus* Bechstein. Auk, 35:188–95.

1918b. The common raven of North Carolina. Ohio Journ. Sci., 18:213–25.

1919. *Passerherbulus lecontei* (Audubon) becomes *Passerherbulus caudacutus* (Latham). Proc. Biol. Soc. Wash., 32:47.

1921. The geographic races of *Cyanocitta cristata*. Auk, 38:83–89.

1931. The Atlantic coast races of *Thryospiza maritima* (Wilson). Proc. Biol. Soc. Wash., 44:123–28.

1936. Ornithological problems and opportunities in Georgia. Oriole, 1:7–8.

1946. Three new North American birds. Journ. Wash. Acad. Sci., 36:388–89.

Odum, Eugene Pleasants

1941. Technics in life history study. Oriole, 6:29–35.

1942a. Long incubation by a Carolina Chickadee. Auk, 59:430–31.

1942b. Notes from Athens. Oriole, 7:20.

1943a. Some possible range extensions in north Georgia. Oriole, 8:6–8.

1943b. Long-eared Owl, White-crowned Sparrows, and Prairie Horned Larks at Athens. Oriole, 8:20.

1944a. What do we know about Georgia birds? Oriole, 9:6–8.

1944b. What do we know about Georgia birds? Oriole, 9:33–35.

1944c. Summer occurrence of the Oven-bird at Athens. Oriole, 9:35.

1945a. In quest of Georgia mountain warblers. Oriole, 10:15–19.

1945b. Northern species summering at the edge of the Blue Ridge. Oriole, 10:48–52.

1945c. A nest of the Blackburnian Warbler in Pickens County, Georgia. Oriole, 10:53.

1945d. Chuck-will's-widow and Whip-poor-will in Dade County. Oriole, 10:55.

1945e. The concept of the biome as applied to the distribution of North American birds. Wilson Bull., 57:191–201.

1947a. The breeding of the Least Flycatcher in Rabun County, Georgia. Oriole, 12:5–7.

1947b. Owls new to the Athens list. Oriole, 12:33.

1947c. Dickcissel at Athens. Oriole, 12:34–35.

1947d. Marsh Hawks responding to peak abundance of cotton rats. Oriole, 12:48–49.

1947e. Young southern loblolly-shortleaf pine. Aud. field notes, 11th breeding-bird census, 1:197–98.

1947f. Climax southern oak-hickory forest. Aud. field notes, 11th breeding-bird census, 1:213–14.

1948. Nesting of the Mountain Vireo at Athens, Georgia, conclusive evidence of a southward invasion. Oriole, 13:17–20.

1949. Weight variations in wintering White-throated Sparrows in relation to temperature and migration. Wilson Bull., 61:3–14.

1950. The Vermilion Flycatcher in Georgia. Oriole, 15:13–14.

1952. House Wren nesting at Athens for the second season. Oriole, 17:8.

———, and Thomas D. Burleigh

1946. Southward invasion in Georgia. Auk, 63:388–401.

———, and David W. Johnston

1951. The House Wren breeding in Georgia: an analysis of a range extension. Auk, 68:357–66.

———, and Robert A. Norris

1949. Effect of DDT on birds in Georgia pecan orchards with a note on late summer census methods. Journ. Wildlife Mgmt., 13:415–17.

Ogilvie-Grant, William Robert

1912. Catalogue of the collection of birds' eggs in the British Museum (Natural History), vol. V. London. xxiii, 547 pp., 22 pl.

Oliver, James H., Jr.

1952. Unusual nesting behavior of the Brown-headed Nuthatch. Oriole, 17:17.

Oosting, Henry John

1942. An ecological analysis of the plant communities of Piedmont, North Carolina. Am. Mid. Nat., 28:1–126.

1948. The study of plant communities. San Francisco, W. H. Freeman and Company, 389 pp.

Palmer, Theodore Sherman

1912. The Man-o-war bird (*Fregata aquila*) on the coast of Georgia. Auk, 29:531–32.

Parks, Richard Anthony

1947. Late spring occurrence of the Cowbird at Atlanta. Oriole, 12:47–48.

1948a. Another Swainson's Warbler collected at Atlanta. Oriole, 13:9.

1948b. Male Bluebird antagonistic to nest building. Oriole, 13:9.

1948c. Another Saw-whet Owl in Atlanta, Georgia. Oriole, 13:26.

1949. The Philadelphia Vireo at Atlanta, Georgia. Oriole, 14:10.

1950a. Cowbird breeding in Atlanta. Oriole, 15:8–9.

1950b. Cowbird breeding at Atlanta again. Oriole, 15:32.

1950c. Brewster's Warbler at Atlanta. Oriole, 15:36.

1951a. Virginia Rail at Atlanta. Oriole, 16:20.

1951b. The Dickcissel nesting near Atlanta. Oriole, 16:39–40.

1952a. A summer record of the Blue-winged Teal near Atlanta. Oriole, 17:8.

1952b. Philadelphia Vireo at Atlanta. Oriole, 17:18.

1954. Notes from Atlanta. Oriole, 19:46.

Pearson, Thomas Gilbert

1911. The new Georgia law. Bird-Lore, 13:273.

1922. Notes on the birds of Cumberland Island, Georgia. Wilson Bull., 34:84–90.

1926. The killing of Purple Martins in Atlanta. Bird-Lore, 28:375–77.

1929. Birds of an old rice field. North Am. Review, 227:321–24.

Peet, Max Minor

1947. The Florida form of the Brown-headed Nuthatch in southwestern Georgia. Wilson Bull., 59:37.

Pennock, Charles John

1890a. Nesting site of the Brown-headed Nuthatch. Orn. and Ool., 15:11–12.

1890b. Notes on breeding habits of Brown-headed Nuthatch at Thomasville, Ga. Orn. and Ool. (Semi-annual), 2:29–31.

Perry, Troup Douglas

1884a. Ground Dove. Young Oologist, 1:10.

1884b. Painted Bunting or Nonpareil. Young Oologist, 1:21.

1884c. Cardinal Grosbeak (*Cardinalis virginianus*). Young Oologist, 1:57.

1884d. (Several nests of Bachman's Finch found in Georgia). Young Oologist, 1:72.

1884e. Bachman's Finch. Young Oologist, 1:83.

1884f. Blue Grosbeak. Young Oologist, 1:107.

1884g. Summer Redbird. Young Oologist, 1:116–17.

1885a. Yellow-breasted Chat. Young Oologist, 1:155–56.

1885b. From Georgia. Young Oologist, 2:16.

1885c. Pigmy Nuthatch. Young Oologist, 2:44.

1886. Nesting of Swainson's Warbler. Orn and Ool., 11:188.

1887a. Jottings. Oologist, 4:90.

1887b. Nesting of the Ground Dove. Orn and Ool., 12:102, 168.

1887c. Some additional notes on Swainson's Warbler. Orn. and Ool., 12:141.

1887d. Spotted eggs of the Blue Grosbeak. Orn. and Ool., 12:153–54.

1887e. Additional notes on the nesting of the Ground Dove. Orn. and Ool., 12:168.

1892. (Early Woodcock eggs, a set taken at Savannah, Feb. 22, 1892). Orn. and Ool., 17:63.

1910. Swainson's Warbler (*Helinaia swainsoni*). Oologist, 27:54–56.

1911. An oölogical paradise. Oologist, 28:176–77.

1917. A day and night on Buck Hummock. Oologist, 34:72–74.

1918. Spotted eggs of the Blue Grosbeak. Oologist, 35:148–49.

Peters, Harold Seymour
1952. Sandhill Crane taken in Fulton County, Oriole, 17:31.

Peters, James Lee
1942. Records of James Bay Sparrow taken in Camden County, April 4, 1877. Ann. Carnegie Mus., 29:205.

———, and Ludlow Griscom
1938. Geographical variation in the Savannah Sparrow. Bull. Mus. Comp. Zool., 80 (No. 13):445–77. 1 pl.

Petrides, George Athan and Miriam P.
1944. White-crowned Sparrows wintering at Athens. Oriole, 9:10–11.

Pettingill, Olin Sewall, Jr.
1951. A guide to bird finding east of the Mississippi. New York, Oxford Univ. Press. xvii, 659 pp.

Phillips, John Charles
1915. The old New England Bobwhite. Auk, 32:204–207.

1928. Wild birds introduced or transplanted in North America. U. S. Dept. Agr., Tech. Bull. 61:1–64.

Pindar, L. Otley
1926. Birds of Chickamauga Park, Georgia. Oologist, 43:86–93.

Pitelka, Frank Alois
1941. Distribution of birds in relation to major biotic communities. Am. Mid. Nat., 25:113–37.

1950. Geographic variation and the species problem in the shore-bird genus *Limnodromus*. Univ. Calif. Pub. Zool., 50:1–108. 10 pl., 9 figs.

Porter, John B.
1895. Fluctuations of the Bluebird stock. Forest and Stream, 45:356.

Ramsey, Ralph, Jr.
1941. A Red-breasted Nuthatch in Atlanta. Oriole, 6:50.

Read, A. C.
1913. Birds seen on a long journey. Oologist, 30:264–68.

Rhoads, Samuel Nicholson
1918. Georgia's rarities further discovered in a second American portfolio of John Abbot's bird plates. Auk, 35:271–86.

Ridgeway, Robert
1873. Catalogue of the ornithological collection of the Boston Society of Natural History. Part 2, *Falconidae*. Proc. Boston Soc. Nat. Hist., 16:43–72.

1876. On geographical variation in *Dendroica palmarum*. Bull. Nuttall Orn. Club, 1:81–87.

1910. Concerning three alleged "erroneous Georgia records." Auk, 27:88.

Rogers, Mabel T.
1937. Notes from Milledgeville. Oriole, 2:6–7.

1940a. Bird banding at Milledgeville. Oriole, 5:7.

1940b. Bird-banding in Milledgeville—1940. Oriole, 5:45–46.

1944. A specimen of the Golden Eagle from Milledgeville. Oriole, 9:12.

1947. The lining of Hummingbirds' nests. Oriole, 12:49.

Rogers, Wallace
1922. A plea for bird photography (with illustrations by the author). Camera Craft, 29:165–69.

Romanes, R. A.
1932. Flickerings. Nature Mag., 19:87–91.

Rossignol, Gilbert R., Jr.
1911. Rare swallows in Georgia. Auk, 30:106.

1912. An albino egg of Wilson's Plover. Auk, 29:392.

1913. White Pelican at Savannah, Ga. Auk, 30:106.

1915. Rossignol on subspecies. Oologist, 32:34–35.

Rotchford, Lucille C.

1952. A Glynn County sight record of the Avocet. Oriole, 17:17.

1953. Sight record of Blue Goose in Baldwin County, Georgia. Oriole, 18:9–10.

Salyer, J. Clark, II, and Frank Dufresne

1948. Okefenokee A national wildlife refuge. Conservation in Action, No. 6:1–9. Fish and Wildlife Service, U. S. Dept. of the Interior.

"Sayville"

1897. Georgia quail and turkeys. Forest and Stream, 48:209.

Saunders, William Edwin

1896. Ornithology — Blue Bird — Dickcissel. Ottawa Nat., 9:212–14.

Sciple, George Washington, Jr.

1939. Wilson's Petrel near Brunswick. Oriole, 4:31.

1949a. A specimen of Wilson's Warbler from Union County, Georgia. Oriole, 14:9.

1949b. Another winter record of the occurrence of the Spotted Sandpiper in Georgia. Oriole, 14:21.

1949c. Another Henslow's Sparrow near Atlanta. Oriole, 14:22.

1950a. A second Georgia specimen of Cabot's Tern. Oriole, 15:8.

1950b. American Brant, *Branta b. hrota*, in Georgia. Auk, 67:383.

1951a. Several recent occurrences of Ring-billed Gulls in Bartow County, Georgia. Oriole, 16:19–20.

1951b. An occurrence of Brewer's Blackbird near Cartersville, Georgia. Oriole, 16:31.

1951c. Observations and comments upon waterfowl present in Bartow County, northwest Georgia. Oriole, 16:33–38.

1951d. Mandibular abnormalities in a Chimney Swift specimen. Oriole, 16:40.

1952. The collection of a series of Newfoundland Crossbills at Stone Mountain, Georgia. Oriole, 17:6–7.

———, and William W. Griffin

1939. Golden Eagle in Georgia in summer. Oriole, 4:31.

1941. Another winter Spotted Sandpiper in Georgia. Oriole, 6:12.

1951. Parula Warbler breeding in the Georgia Piedmont. Oriole, 16:22–23.

Sennett, George Burritt

1889. The Clapper Rails of the U. S. and West Indies compared with *Rallus longirostris* of South America. Auk, 6:161–66.

Shelford, Victor Ernest

1945. The relative merits of the life zone and biome concepts. Wilson Bull., 51:248–52.

Short, Ernest H.

1909. (An egg of a mockingbird taken near Augusta, Georgia). Oologist, 26:128.

Skutch, Alexander Frank

1950. Outline for an ecological life history of a bird. Ecology, 31 (3): 464–69.

Small, John Kunkel

1933. Manual of the southeastern flora. New York, pub. by the author. xxii, 1554 pp.

Smith, Parker B.

1945a. Ruffed Grouse breeding near Toccoa, Stephens County. Oriole, 10:55.

1945b. Two additional records of the Whistling Swan in Georgia. Oriole, 10:56–57.

1946. Old-squaw Duck in Elbert County. Oriole, 11:18.

Smith, Robert Windsor

1901a. Bachman's Sparrow in DeKalb County, Georgia. Wilson Bull., 13: 3–5.

1901b. Food and gravel. Wilson Bull., 13:16–17.

1901c. The cold wave of February 1899 in DeKalb County, Georgia. Wilson Bull., 13:32–36.

1901d. An albino Towhee (*Pipilo erythrophthalmus*). Wilson Bull., 13: 47.

1901e. The passing of the bird. Wilson Bull., 13:61–65.

1901f. Blue-gray Gnatcatcher (*Polioptila caerulea*). Wilson Bull., 13: 71–72.

1903a. New Year's Day bird census (Kirkwood, Ga.). Wilson Bull., 15: 27–28.

1903b. Birds of Kirkwood, DeKalb County, Georgia. Wilson Bull., 15: 49–59.

1905. Bird migration at Kirkwood, Georgia. Wilson Bull., 17:130–31.

Spratt, Nelson

1936. White Pelican in Atlanta, Georgia. Oriole, 1:8.

Sprunt, Alexander, Jr.

1930. White Pelican (*Pelecanus erythrorhynchos*) in Georgia. Auk, 47: 242.

1932a. Further notes on the iris of the Boat-tailed Grackle. Auk, 49:227–28.

1932b. Some notes from Cumberland Island, Ga. Auk, 49:364.

1933. The Glossy Ibis in Georgia. Auk, 50:352.

1934. A new grackle from Florida. Charleston (S. C.) Mus. Leaflet, 6: 1–5.

1936a. The Roseate Spoonbill in Georgia. Auk, 53:203–204.

1936b. Some observations on the bird life of Cumberland Island, Ga. Oriole, 1:1–6.

1945. Summer birds of a coastal plantation. Oriole, 10:45–48.

1946. Northward extension of the summer range of the Limpkin. Auk, 63: 101.

———, and Edward Burnham Chamberlain

1931. Second supplement to Arthur T. Wayne's *Birds of South Carolina.* Contrib. Charleston (S. C.) Mus., No. VI. 37 pp.

St. Clair, J. W.

1877. Some southern wood notes. Forest and Stream, 8:240.

1879. St. Clair on the Robin. Forest and Stream, 13:765.

1880. Southern wood notes. Forest and Stream, 14:123.

Stevenson, Henry Bernard

1932. Early nesting of the Bluebird and Mockingbird. Auk, 49:353.

1934. Wilson's Warbler in Georgia. Auk, 51:383.

1936a. Golden Eagle captured in Burke County, Georgia. Oriole 1:18–19.

1936b. A Black Tern in Waynesboro, Georgia. Oriole, 1:19.

1940. Anhingas breeding in Waynesboro, Georgia. Oriole, 5:56–57.

Stevenson, Henry Miller, Jr.

1944a. Southeastern limits of the Spotted Sandpiper's breeding range. Auk, 61:247–51.

1944b. A summer bird count from Lookout Mountain. Oriole, 9:16–17.

1948. Comments on the distribution of certain Georgia birds. Oriole, 13:32–33.

Stewart, Robert Earl

1951. Clapper rail populations of the middle Atlantic states. Trans. 16th N. Am. Wildlife Conf.: 421–30.

Stoddard, Herbert Lee

1926. Methods of banding Chimney Swifts in the south. Wilson Bull., 38:122–23.

1928. The Rough-legged Hawk in southern Georgia and the Goshawk in Florida. Auk, 45:211–12.

1931. The Bobwhite Quail: Its habits, preservation, and increase. New York, Scribner's. xxix, 559 pp., 69 pl. (5 col.), 32 figs.

1936. Management of wild turkey. Proc. N. Am. Wildlife Conf.: 352–56.

1937. A late spring record of the Loon. Oriole, 2:25.

1938. The place of scientific collecting in Georgia ornithology. Oriole, 3:4–5.

1939a. Northern Phalarope in Grady County, Georgia. Auk, 56:77–78.

1939b. Bobwhite Quail, Wild Turkey, Rose-breasted Grosbeak, Blue Grosbeak, Indigo Bunting, Ruby-crowned Kinglet. Oriole, 4:64–65.

1940. The Golden Eagle in southwest Georgia. Oriole, 5:8.

1941. Predator control in southeastern quail lands. Trans. 6th N. Am. Wildlife Conf.: 288–93.

1942. The Blue Goose and the Lesser Snow Goose as migrants in Georgia. Oriole, 7:18–19.

1946a. Cooper's Hawk attacking a Sparrow Hawk. Oriole, 11:19 20.

1946b. "Shadow-boxing" of a Ruby-crowned Kinglet. Oriole, 11:20.

1947. Pied-billed Grebes and Purple Gallinules nesting abundantly in Baker and Dougherty counties, Georgia. Oriole, 12:38–39.

1951. Bullock's and Baltimore Orioles, *Icterus bullockii* and *galbula*, in southwest Georgia. Auk, 68:108–10.

(MS) Birds of Grady County, Georgia.

———, and Earle R. Greene
1937. White Ibis nesting abundantly in Camden County, Georgia. Oriole, 2:26–27.

———, and Edwin Vaclar Komarek
1941. The carrying capacity of southeastern quail lands. Trans. 6th N. Am. Wildlife Conf.: 148–55.

Straw, Richard Myron
1947. Notes on the bird life at Fort Benning, Georgia. Oriole, 12:41–45.

Stresemann, Erwin
1953. On a collection of birds from Georgia and Carolina made about 1810 by John Abbot. Auk, 70:113–17.

Sutton, George Miksch, and Josselyn Van Tyne.
1935. A new Red-tailed Hawk from Texas. Occas. Papers Mus. Zool., U. Mich., 321:1–6.

Swainson, William
1840. Taxidermy, with the biography of zoologists and notices of their works. 8 vols. London. 392 pp., 2 pl.

Taber, William Brewster, Jr.
1930. The fall migration of Mourning Doves. Wilson Bull., 42:17–28.

Tait, Blanche
1946. Migration of birds in the Milledgeville region. Oriole, 11:48–51.
1947. Black and White Warbler at Milledgeville in winter. Oriole, 12:22.

Talbot, Lester Raymond
1922. Bird banding at Thomasville, Ga., in 1922. Auk, 39:334–50.

Tanner, James Taylor
1942. The Ivory-billed Woodpecker. Nat. Aud. Soc., Research Report No. 1 (October, 1942). xii, 111 pp., 20 pl., 22 figs.
1946. Long-billed Curlew and Marbled Godwit at Sea Island, Georgia. Oriole, 11:21.

Taylor, Boyd
1915. Bird notes. Oologist, 32:55.

Taylor, Lynn
1915a. Just from Georgia. Oologist, 32:86.
1915b. From Georgia again. Oologist, 32:141.
1917. From Georgia. Oologist, 34:55.

Taylor, Warner
1926. Status of the Yellow-headed Blackbird (*Xanthocephalus xanthocephalus*) on the Atlantic seaboard. Auk, 43:241–42.

Thayer, John Elliott, and Outram Bangs
1909. Description of a new subspecies of Snowy Heron. Proc. New Eng. Zool. Club, 4:39–41.

Thomas, William Wayt, Jr.
1943. The Mississippi Kite in Richmond County during 1943. Oriole, 8:21–22.
1945. Some additional Georgia records of interest. Oriole, 10:25–26.

———, and J. Fred Denton
1943. The Swallow-tailed Kite at Augusta. Oriole, 8:22.

Thompson, James Maurice
1885. By-ways and bird notes. New York, U. S. Book Co. 179 pp.
1896. An archer's sojourn in the Okefenokee. Atlantic Monthly, 77:486–91.

Thompson, Will Henry
1915. Deep in the Okefenokee Swamp. Forest and Stream, 85:298–302, 337–39.

Thorne, Robert F.
1949. Inland plants on the Gulf coastal plain of Georgia. Castanea, 14:88–97.
(MS) Plant associations in southwestern Georgia.

Todd, Walter Edmund Clyde
1913. A revision of the genus *Chaemepelia*. Ann. Car. Mus., 8:507–603.

Tomkins, Ivan Rexford
1929a. The Avocet in Georgia. Auk, 46:383–84.
1929b. The Barn Owl nesting on the lower Savannah River. Auk, 46:387.
1930. Some records from the Savannah River entrance during 1929. Auk, 47:577.
1931a. A Snowy Owl from coastal Georgia. Auk, 48:268.
1931b. Further notes from the Savannah River entrance. Auk, 48:279–82.
1931c. Additional species for the Georgia list. Auk, 48:435–36.
1932a. The Black Skimmer a permanent resident in Georgia. Auk, 49:85–86.
1932b. Worthington's Marsh Wren in

the vicinity of Savannah, Ga. Wilson Bull., 44:40.

1932c. Some observations on the Eastern Willet at nesting time. Wilson Bull., 44:46–47.

1932d. A Greater Snow Goose from Georgia. Auk, 49:213–14.

1932e. A Sooty Tern from Georgia. Auk, 49:219.

1932f. Yellow-eyed Boat-tailed Grackles again. Auk, 49:227.

1933a. The Western Willet in winter in Georgia and South Carolina. Auk, 50:102.

1933b. Ring-billed and Herring Gulls at the Savannah River mouth in July and August. Auk, 50:103.

1933c. An Eastern Snow Bunting from Georgia. Auk, 50:227.

1933d. Ways of the Black Skimmer. Wilson Bull., 45:147–51.

1933e. Upward currents not required for soaring flight. Wilson Bull., 45:200.

1934a. Notes from Chatham County, Georgia. Auk, 51:252–53.

1934b. A curious Tern accident. Wilson Bull., 46:128.

1934c. Hurricanes and subspecific variations. Wilson Bull., 238–40.

1935a. A Blue Goose from Georgia. Auk, 52:78.

1935b. Another Ipswich Sparrow from Georgia. Auk, 52:194.

1935c. Another Blue Goose from Georgia. Auk, 52:302.

1935d. An Atlantic Song Sparrow from Georgia. Auk, 52:315.

1935e. The Lapland Longspur (*Calcarius l. lapponicus*); a South Carolina specimen, and a Georgia sight record. Auk, 52:315.

1936a. The Red-tailed Hawk breeding on the Georgia coast. Oriole, 1:9.

1936b. Southern Sharp-tailed Sparrow in Georgia and South Carolina. Auk, 53:335–36.

1936c. The Ring-billed Gull summering again in Georgia. Oriole, 1:9.

1936d. Nesting records of a Catbird in Chatham County. Oriole, 1:10.

1936e. The Bank Swallow, a fall migrant in coastal Georgia. Oriole, 1:10.

1936f. Miscellany. Oriole, 1:15–16.

1936g. Hovering of the Red-tailed Hawk. Oriole, 1:18.

1936h. Partial albinism in two species of birds. Oriole, 1:19.

1936i. Notes on the winter food of the Short-eared Owl. Wilson Bull., 48:77–79.

1936j. The Stilt Sandpiper again on the lower Savannah River. Auk, 53:329.

1936k. An eleven-year list of the shore birds of the Savannah River entrance. Oriole, 1:32–34.

1936l. A Georgia specimen of Wayne's Marsh Wren. Auk, 53:339–40.

1937a. The status of Macgillivray's Seaside Sparrow. Auk, 54:185–88.

1937b. Wayne's Clapper Rail carries its young. Wilson Bull., 49:296–97.

1937c. Marsh Hens of the Georgia coast. Oriole, 2:29–31.

1938. Geese in the Savannah area. Oriole, 3:24.

1939. Eastern Nighthawks from the Savannah area. Oriole, 4:30–31.

1940a. Sight record of a Kittiwake from the Savannah River. Oriole, 5:8.

1940b. White-crowned Sparrow from coastal Georgia. Oriole, 5:9.

1940c. Whistling Swan from the Savannah area. Oriole, 5:17.

1941a. Notes on Macgillivray's Seaside Sparrow. Auk, 58:38–51.

1941b. Broken-wing performance by the Eastern Willet. Auk, 58–95.

1941c. Foot-washing by the Black Skimmer. Auk, 58:96.

1941d. A Georgia specimen of the Iceland Gull. Oriole, 6:49–50.

1941e. Snow Goose from the Savannah area. Oriole, 6:49–50.

1941f. The Stilt Sandpiper in Georgia. Oriole, 6:50–51.

1941g. Sight record of European Cormorant in Georgia. Oriole, 6:51.

1942a. The "injury-feigning" behavior of the Florida Nighthawk. Wilson Bull., 54:43–49.

1942b. Osprey occurrence in January. Oriole, 7:6.

1942c. The range of the Little Sparrow Hawk in Georgia and South Carolina. Oriole, 7:13–14.

1942d. A Blue Goose on Blackbeard Island, Georgia. Oriole, 7:17–18.

1944a. Pine Siskins at Savannah. Oriole, 9:8.

1944b. Gannets at sea off the Georgia coast. Oriole, 9:9–10.

1944c. Wilson's Plover in its summer home. Auk, 61:259–69.

1946a. Georgia Swan records—A correction. Oriole, 11:20–21.

1946b. Duck Hawk wintering at Savannah. Oriole, 11:21.

1946c. Nesting of the Barn Owl on the lower Savannah River. Oriole, 11:59–63.

1947. The Oyster-catcher of the Atlantic coast of North America and its relation to oysters. Wilson Bull., 59:204–208.

1948. More notes on the two races of Sparrow Hawk inhabiting Georgia. Oriole, 13:23–24.

1949a. The Mississippi Kite along the Savannah River in Georgia and South Carolina. Auk, 66:82.

1949b. Orchard Oriole feeding on nectar. Oriole, 14:19–20.

1949c. Stilt and White-rumped Sandpipers in the Savannah, Georgia, area. Oriole, 14:22–23.

1950a. Purple Sandpipers wintering in Georgia. Oriole, 15:7.

1950b. A Georgia breeding record of the Black-necked Stilt. Oriole, 15:30–31.

1950c. Unusual bird records after the Labor Day storm. Oriole, 15:39–40.

1950d. Notes on wing-flashing in the Mockingbird. Wilson Bull., 62:41–42.

1951a. Method of feeding of the Black Skimmer, *Rynchops nigra*. Auk, 68:236–39.

1951b. Notes from the Savannah area. Oriole, 16:39.

1952a. The Purple Sandpiper as a regular winter visitor on Tybee Beach. Oriole, 17:28–29.

1952b. More about the Buff-breasted Sandpiper in the Savannah area. Oriole, 17:38–39.

1954. Golden Plover and Arkansas Kingbird in Chatham County. Oriole, 19:18.

Townsend, Charles Wendell
1926. Thrills of an eastern ornithologist in the south. Bird-Lore, 28:319.

Upton, Lucy H.
1918. Migrating Bobolinks in Atlanta. Bird-Lore, 20:181.

W., J. M.
1887a. The weight of quail in the south. Forest and Stream, 28:66.

1887b. Weight of quail. Forest and Stream, 28:226.

Walcott, Frederick Collin, *et al.*
1932. Okefenokee Swamp. 72 Cong., 1 sess., Sen. Report, pp. 1–15.

Walkinshaw, Lawrence Harvey
1947. A week in the Okefenokee. Oriole, 12:1–5.

1949. The Sandhill Crane. Bloomfield Hills, Mich., Cranbrook Inst. Sci.

1953. The Greater Sandhill Crane in Georgia. Oriole, 18:13–15.

Wayne, Arthur Trezevant
1906. A contribution to the ornithology of South Carolina, chiefly the coast region. Auk, 23:56–68.

1907a. The Yellow-headed Blackbird (*Xanthocephalus xanthocephalus*) in Georgia. Auk, 24:100–101.

1907b. The Philadelphia Vireo (*Vireo philadelphicus*) in Georgia. Auk, 24:104.

1908. Three erroneous Georgia records. Auk, 25:229–30.

1910a. Birds of South Carolina. Contrib. Charleston (S. C.) Mus., No. I. 243 pp.

1910b. Concerning three erroneous Georgia records. Auk, 27:213–14.

1911. The Black-billed Cuckoo (*Coccyzus erythropthalmus*) breeding on the coast of South Carolina. Auk, 28:485.

1912a. The Seaside Sparrow (*Passerherbulus maritimus maritimus*) breeding on the coast of Georgia near Savannah. Auk, 29:103–104.

1912b. Bachman's Warbler in Camden County and breeding in Chatham County, Georgia. Auk, 29:105.

1918. Notes on six birds from Georgia. Auk, 35:485–86.

1925. A late autumnal record for the Bachman's Warbler. Wilson Bull., 37:41.

1927a. The Snow Bunting (*Plectrophenax n. nivalis*) in Georgia. Auk, 44:423.

1927b. Snow Bunting in Georgia — A correction. Auk, 44:568.

Werner, Ray Cowles
  1940. Coot on top of skyscraper. Oriole, 5:21.
  1941. Canada Geese in the Atlanta area. Oriole, 6:49.
  1942. Veery in song in Atlanta. Oriole, 7:19.
  1943. One of Jack Miner's geese reaches Georgia. Oriole, 8:10.
  1944a. Short-eared Owl at Atlanta. Oriole, 9:11–12.
  1944b. A specimen of the Florida Barred Owl from Atlanta. Oriole, 9:12.
  1944c. Observations at a Red-bellied Woodpecker's nest. Oriole, 9:32–33.
  1945a. Whistling Swans in the Atlanta area. Oriole, 10:29.
  1945b. A large "blackbird" roost at Atlanta. Oriole, 10:29.
  1945c. Baltimore Oriole (*Icterus galbula*) in Atlanta. Oriole, 10:30.
  1945d. Kentucky Warbler (*Oporornis formosus*) nest in Atlanta. Oriole, 10:31.
  1945e. Florida Nuthatch (*Sitta carolinensis atkinsi*) nesting in Atlanta. Oriole, 10:31–32.
  1946. Abnormal albino White-throated Sparrow taken at Atlanta. Oriole, 11:54–55.
  1947a. Cape May Warblers numerous in spring migration. Oriole, 12:37.
  1947b. The Barred Owl in Atlanta. Oriole, 12:48.
  1948a. The Horned Grebe in Atlanta. Oriole, 13:8.
  1948b. Canvas-back Duck in Atlanta. Oriole, 13:26.
  1949. Sora Rail near Atlanta, Georgia. Oriole, 14:10–11.
Westbrook, D. C.
  1913. Large set of Mourning Dove. Oologist, 30:51.
Wharton, Charles H.
  1940. Sandhill Cranes at Jackson Lake. Oriole, 5:18–19.
  1941. A Swallow-tailed Kite from the Atlanta area. Oriole, 6:50.
White, George
  1849. Statistics of the State of Georgia. Savannah. (Contains the bird list by John LeConte).

Whiteman, Grace M.
  1952. The Oven-bird at West Point, Georgia, in winter. Oriole, 17:9–10.
Whitney, Nathaniel Ruggles, Jr.
  1953. A Dickcissel record for Houston County. Oriole, 18:9.
———, and Mary S. Whitney
  1952. Upland abandoned field and hedge. Aud. field notes, 16th breeding-bird census, 6:321.
Whittaker, Carter Reade
  1925. Brewster's Warbler in Georgia. Bird-Lore, 27:251.
Whittle, Charles Livy
  1922. A Myrtle Warbler invasion. Auk, 39:23–31.
Wickersham, Cornelius Wendell
  1902. Sickle-billed Curlew. Auk, 19:353–56.
Wilson, Alexander
  1808–14. American ornithology, or the natural history of the birds of the United States. 9 vols. Philadelphia.
Wood, William
  1868. The Mottled Owl. Am. Nat., 2:370–75.
Woodward, Barbara
  1949. Birds of the Sea Island, Georgia, region. Oriole, 14:1–9.
Worthington, Willis Woodford
  1888. (Leconte's Sparrow in Georgia). Orn. and Ool., 13:128.
  1890a. The Ipswich Sparrow in Georgia. Auk, 7:211–12.
  1890b. The King Eider (*Somateria spectabilis*) at Brunswick, Ga. Auk, 7:284.
Wright, Albert Hazen
  1911. Other early records of the Passenger Pigeon. Auk, 28:427–49.
  1912. Early records of the Carolina Paroquet. Auk, 29:343–63.
  1914. Early records of the Wild Turkey. Auk, 31:334–58.
  1926. The vertebrate life of Okefenokee Swamp in relation to the Atlantic coastal plain. Ecology, 7:77–95.
———, and Francis Harper
  1913. A biological reconnaissance of the Okefenokee Swamp: the birds. Auk, 30:477–505.
Wynn, Glenn B.
  1892. (Nest of Mourning Dove). Orn. and Ool., 17:10.

THE SUBSCRIBERS

The following organizations, plantation people, and other individuals interested in birds have donated $39,437.50 toward the publication of this book in the interest of the Herbert L. Stoddard and George M. Sutton Ornithological Scholarships, established at the University of Georgia and the University of Oklahoma, respectively:

Mrs. George F. Baker
Horseshoe Plantation
Tallahassee, Florida

Mr. H. Beadel
Tall Timber Plantation
Tallahassee, Florida

Mrs. Julian C. Bolton
Melrose Plantation
Thomasville, Georgia

Mrs. Warren Bicknell, Jr.
Sinkola Plantation
Thomasville, Georgia

Mr. C. Merrill Chapin, Jr.
Elsoma Plantation
Thomasville, Georgia

Mr. Hendon Chubb
Springwood Plantation
Thomasville, Georgia

Mr. Charles G. Cushing
New York, New York

Mr. Walter E. Edge
Sunnyhill Plantation
Thomasville, Georgia

Mrs. Royal Firman, Jr.
2740 Chesterton Road
Cincinnati, Ohio

Mrs. J. K. Fleishman
Welaunee Plantation
Tallahassee, Florida

Mrs. A. Gurnee Gallien
Mistletoe Plantation
Thomasville, Georgia

Georgia-Florida Field Trial Club
Thomasville, Georgia

Miss Frances C. Griscom
Water Oak Plantation
Tallahassee, Florida

Mr. James G. Hanes
Senah Plantation
Albany, Georgia

Mr. Hal Price Headley
Pinebloom Plantation
Albany, Georgia

Mrs. Howard M. Hanna
Santa Barbara, California

George M. & Pamela E. Humphrey
Fund
Cleveland, Ohio

Mrs. Mary H. Hunter
Tarva Plantation
Albany, Georgia

Mr. & Mrs. R. L. Ireland
Forshalee Plantation
Tallahassee, Florida

Mr. Alfred W. Jones
Sea Island, Georgia

Mr. C. Mahlon Kline
Tallassee Plantation
Albany, Georgia

Mr. E. V. Komarek
Birdsong Plantation
Thomasville, Georgia

Dr. Shepard Krech
Elsoma Plantation
Thomasville, Georgia

Mrs. Shepard Krech
Elsoma Plantation
Thomasville, Georgia

Mr. Shelby Langston
Miami, Florida

Mrs. George H. Love
Loveridge Plantation
Lloyd, Florida

Richard King Mellon Foundation
Pittsburgh, Pennsylvania

The Nichols Foundation
Cincinnati, Ohio

Mr. John M. Olin
Nilo Plantation
Albany, Georgia

Mrs. Katherine Perkins
Springhill Plantation
Thomasville, Georgia

Miss Leigh Perkins
Springhill Plantation
Thomasville, Georgia

Mr. Ralph Perkins
Springhill Plantation
Thomasville, Georgia

Mr. G. R. Pirrung
Aragon Farms
Bainbridge, Georgia

Mrs. Elizabeth Ireland Poe
Pebble Hill Plantation
Thomasville, Georgia

Mr. William C. Potter
Blue Spring Plantation
Albany, Georgia

Mrs. Philip G. Rust
Winnstead Plantation
Thomasville, Georgia

Mr. R. B. Shepard
St. Paul, Minnesota

Mr. Herbert L. Stoddard, Sr.
Sherwood Plantation
Thomasville, Georgia

Mr. Walter C. Teagle
Norias Plantation
Thomasville, Georgia

Mr. Joseph H. Thompson
Cleveland, Ohio

Mr. L. S. Thompson
Gillionville Plantation
Albany, Georgia

Mr. Richard Tift
The Oaks
Albany, Georgia

Mr. G. G. Wade
Mill Pond Plantation
Thomasville, Georgia

Mr. John Hay Whitney
Greenwood Plantation
Thomasville, Georgia

Mr. R. W. Woodruff
Ichauway Plantation
Newton, Georgia

INDEX

(Names of ornithologists and other researchers who have been cited in this volume are not included in this index. The bibliography on pages 705–31 contains full information on all sources consulted.)

GEORGIA BIRDS

was set on the Linotype in 10-point Caledonia, with 3 points of space allowed between the lines to assure easy readability.

Caledonia was designed by the distinguished contemporary American typographer, lettering artist, and book designer, the late William Addison Dwiggins, who based his drawings for this type on Scotch Roman, popular in Britain around the beginning of the nineteenth century. His slight but important deviations from the original letters embody the Dwiggins touch and inject a nobility of form and "liveliness of action" that the prototypes lack.

The headings of the bird orders were set by hand in Baskerville capitals. The Baskerville types preceded Scotch Roman by about fifty years.

For the title page, the words "Georgia Birds" have been hand lettered, care being taken to shape the serifs, or terminal strokes, with incisive sharpness to accompany the lines set in Baskerville.

Thus Caledonia, Baskerville, and hand lettering have been used together to create a suitable, homogeneous typographic effect.